Geometry

ISIDORE DRESSLER

AMSCO

When ordering this book, please specify
either **R 146 P** or GEOMETRY PAPERBACK EDITION

AMSCO SCHOOL PUBLICATIONS, INC.
315 Hudson Street   New York, N.Y. 10013

ISBN 0-87720-234-6

Printed in the United States of America

PREFACE

Geometry was written to provide appropriate materials to help both teacher and student achieve the following objectives of a modern geometry course:

1. To develop an understanding of geometric relationships in a plane and in space.
2. To develop an understanding of the meaning and nature of proof.
3. To teach the method of deductive proof in both mathematical and nonmathematical situations.
4. To develop the ability to think creatively, and critically, in both mathematical and nonmathematical situations.
5. To integrate geometry with arithmetic, algebra, and numerical trigonometry.

In the preparation of this book, the author has kept in mind the recommendations made by the Commission on Mathematics of the College Entrance Examination Board, the School Mathematics Study Group, and the Bureau of Mathematics Education of the New York State Education Department, but he has avoided the use of undue rigor which is beyond the comprehension and sophistication of the average geometry student.

In this text geometry is developed as a postulational system of reasoning. Clearly marked definitions, postulates, theorems, and corollaries will help give students an understanding of the structure of geometry and the meaning and nature of mathematical proof. The student is taught the use of postulates in deductive proofs involving arithmetic, algebraic, and geometric settings. At first the proofs require the use of only one postulate. Later the proofs require the use of several postulates. Finally, the student is taught how to use definitions and theorems as well as postulates in the development of formal proofs of a more challenging nature.

An unusual feature of this book is its method of organization. Each chapter contains a series of learning units which, with proper application, the student can master for himself. Definitions, postulates, theorems, and corollaries are stated concisely and precisely. They are then explained by specific examples stated in simple language and illustrated by clearly and accurately drawn geometric figures. Model problems, whose solutions are preceded by analyses and plans of attack, teach the student how to apply the new geometric principles. The student can complete his mastery of the unit by solving a set of carefully graded and varied problems. The most challenging problems appear at the end of each set.

The author hopes that the reader will be well served by the book's thorough and modern treatment of congruence, parallelism, quadrilaterals, circles, similarity, areas, regular polygons, inequalities, coordinate geometry, locus treated from geometric, algebraic, and graphic points of view, and the improvement of reasoning.

The modern trend in a geometry course is to include a study of space geometry. Chapter XVII, "Solid Geometry," will provide appropriate materials for those teachers who desire this study. Included in this chapter are units dealing with properties of planes, parallelism and perpendicularity of lines and planes, polyhedrons, locus, measuring surface areas of solid figures, and measuring volumes of solid figures.

Because of the lack of time in the school year, it may not be possible to consider the proofs of all theorems that may be needed in a well-rounded course in geometry. In this book not all theorems are proved. Chapter XIII contains the proofs of those theorems which the Bureau of Mathematics Education of New York State indicates should be required in a geometry course. With each synthetic proof is given a plan of attack which will crystallize for the student the most important aspects of the proof.

A cross section of important construction exercises is presented in Chapter XIV. Each construction is accompanied by a detailed description of the steps to be followed as well as by a plan of proof of the construction. Asterisks mark those constructions which the Bureau of Mathematics Education of New York State indicates should be required.

Throughout the book, in the model problems and in formal and informal proofs, the author illustrates the solution of geometric problems through the effective use of algebraic techniques. Chapter XVIII, "Review of Algebra," will help the student recall and fortify those concepts and skills usually taught in an algebra course which are necessary tools in a modern geometry course.

The inclusion of modern materials will in no way interfere with the effective use of the book by those teachers who for one reason or another wish to restrict the course to topics dealing with synthetic plane geometry and exclude such topics as coordinate geometry and solid geometry.

For their many valuable criticisms and suggestions, the author is very grateful to Mr. Arthur Meyer, Chairman of the Mathematics Department of Midwood High School, New York City, and Dr. Robert E. Dressler, Associate Professor of Mathematics at Kansas State University.

Isidore Dressler

CONTENTS

Contents

CHAPTER I

Lines and Angles

The History of Geometry

For thousands of years, civilized man has needed to know how to work with the size, shape, or position of things. To help him solve many of the practical problems of his day, he devised methods of measuring line segments, angles, and surfaces. For example, when the Nile River overflowed its banks each year in ancient Egypt, landmarks and boundaries were wiped out. The Egyptians therefore had to develop methods of measuring line segments, angles, and land surfaces to help restore lost landmarks and boundaries. In this way, the branch of mathematics known as *geometry* came into being.

Although the ancient Egyptians evidently used geometry only for practical daily problems, the ancient Greeks became interested in organizing this branch of mathematics. In fact, the word *geometry* is derived from the Greek words *gē,* meaning "earth," and *metron,* meaning "measure." Beginning about 600 B.C., the Greeks sought explanations for the geometric facts that had become known, and they discovered important relationships among these facts. Furthermore, Greek scholars organized geometry into a *logical system.*

Among the Greeks who contributed to geometry were Thales, Pythagoras, Plato, Aristotle, and Euclid. About 300 B.C., Euclid, in his work called *Elements,* collected and organized the geometry of his day into a single logical system. Euclid's system became the basis for the study of geometry for the next 2000 years—the geometry you are about to study.

1. Defining Terms

Importance of Defining Terms

In every discussion, it is of fundamental importance that all persons give the same meaning to the same word. Misunderstandings frequently arise when different meanings are given to the same word. It is therefore of the greatest importance to define carefully all key words about whose meaning there might be a difference of opinion. If we are to learn how to think clearly and how to express our thoughts accurately, both in geometry and in everyday situations, we must learn how to define key words or terms clearly and precisely.

Undefined Terms

We ordinarily define a term by using a simpler term. The simpler term is then defined by using a still simpler term. But this process cannot go on endlessly. There comes a time when the definition must use a term whose meaning is assumed to be clear. Because its meaning is accepted without definition, such a term is called an *undefined term*.

In geometry, we are concerned with such ideas as *set, point, line,* and *plane.* Since we cannot give a satisfactory definition of these words using simpler defined words, we will consider them as *undefined terms.*

Although the words *set, point, line,* and *plane* are undefined terms, we still must make clear the properties and characteristics they possess.

A *set* refers to a collection or group of objects with some common characteristic. Each of the following is an example of a set:

1. the set of all girls in the U.S.A. who are 16 years old
2. the set of vowels in the English language
3. the set of all odd integers

A *point* may be represented as a dot on a piece of paper, and is usually named by a capital letter. The point shown in Fig. 1–1, for example, is called "point *P.*" Since a geometric point has no length, width, or thickness, the smaller the dot that is used, the better it represents such a point. In geometry, a point has no size; it only indicates position.

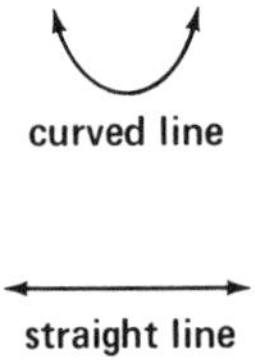

.P

Fig. 1–1

A *line* may be considered as a set of points. The set of points that is chosen may form a curved line or it may form a straight line as shown in Fig. 1–2. If the set of points can be arranged along the edge of a ruler, the points form a straight line. Unless it is otherwise stated, the term *line* will mean *straight line.*

curved line

straight line

Fig. 1–2

We can also think of a line as a string of points which extends endlessly in both directions. With this in mind, we will assume that a line extends indefinitely in two opposite directions.

Arrowheads are sometimes used in a geometric drawing which represents a line to emphasize the fact that there are no endpoints. A line has no width. It can be thought of as being an infinite set of points.

A line may be named by naming two points on it and placing a double-headed arrow over them. In Fig. 1–3, the line which contains points A and B is named "line AB," which is represented by $\overleftrightarrow{AB}$. A line may also be named by placing a lowercase (non-capital) letter next to it. Fig. 1–4 shows "line m."

A B	m
Fig. 1–3	Fig. 1–4

A *plane* may be considered as a set of points that form a completely flat surface extending indefinitely in all directions. To help you visualize a plane, think of the flat floor of a room. Although a plane extends infinitely far in all directions, it has no thickness. A plane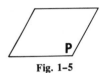

Fig. 1–5

is often represented in a diagram by means of a four-sided figure like the one shown in Fig. 1–5. A plane may be named by a single capital letter. The plane shown in Fig. 1–5 is named "plane P."

Defined Terms

Since good definitions are a fundamental necessity if terms used in a discussion are to have the same meaning for all persons, let us learn the properties of a good definition.

REQUIREMENTS OF A GOOD DEFINITION:

1. A definition should name the term that is being defined.

   For example, the definition "A pencil is a writing instrument that uses lead" names the pencil as the term that is being defined.

2. A definition should be expressed in words which have already been defined or words which have been accepted as undefined.

   For example, in the definition of a pencil, the words *writing instrument* and *lead* should have been defined previously.

3. A definition should place the term that is being defined in the smallest or nearest set to which it belongs.

   For example, in defining a pencil, we placed the term *pencil* in the set of *writing instruments*. We did not place it in the larger or more inclusive set of "instruments."

4. A definition should state the characteristics of the defined term which distinguish it from all other members of the set.

   For example, when the definition of a pencil states that it uses lead, this characteristic distinguishes it from all other writing instruments.

5. A definition should state the least amount of information. It should not include unnecessary information.

For example, we do not include in the definition of a pencil the kind of material used to make the writing instrument, or the color of the lead that is in the writing instrument.

6. A definition should always be reversible; that is, when the subject and predicate of the definition are interchanged, the resulting statement should also be true.

For example, when the form of the definition "A pencil is a writing instrument that uses lead" is reversed, the resulting statement, "A writing instrument that uses lead is a pencil," is also true.

NOTE. For additional work on the topic of "Definitions," see pages 565–568.

EXERCISES

In 1–4, tell whether the geometric figure represents a point, a line, or a plane; and name the figure.

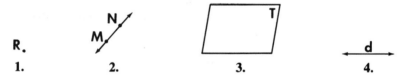

R.   N   T   d

1.   2.   3.   4.

In 5–7, tell whether a point, a line, or a plane is illustrated by the expression.

5. the top of a table
6. the edge of the page of a book
7. the tip of a pencil

In 8–11, in order to answer the question, it is essential to define a key word or phrase. Select the word or phrase.

8. Was Franklin D. Roosevelt a great President?
9. If Mr. Roberts paid $18.00 for a pair of shoes, did he buy an expensive pair of shoes?
10. If Tom walked a mile, did he walk a long distance?
11. If 500 people attended a high school football game, was the game well attended?

In 12–14, select from the given sets the smallest or nearest set to which the given term belongs.

12. A violin belongs to the set of   (*a*) musical instruments   (*b*) instruments   (*c*) stringed instruments.

13. A boy belongs to the set of   (*a*) living things   (*b*) mammals   (*c*) animals.

14. George Washington belongs to the set of   (*a*) Presidents of the United States   (*b*) citizens of the United States   (*c*) officeholders of the United States.

In 15–18, tell why the statement is *not* an example of a good definition.

15. It is a place where football games are played.

16. A longshoreman is a laborer.

17. A father is a male parent of a child and one who loves and protects the child.

18. An island is a body of land.

In 19–22, reverse the definition.

19. A girl is a young female person.

20. A caddie is a person who carries the clubs for golf players.

21. A mathematician is one who is versed in the science of mathematics.

22. A peninsula is a piece of land almost surrounded by water and connected with the mainland by a neck called an isthmus.

2. Definitions Involving Sets

The Elements of a Set

When a collection of distinct objects is so clearly described that we can always tell whether or not an object belongs to it, we call the collection a *well-defined collection,* or more simply a *set.* For example, the odd counting numbers less than 10 form a well-defined collection, or set. The numbers 1, 3, 5, 7, and 9 belong to this set. These numbers are called the *members,* or *elements,* of the set. The number 2 does not belong to this set and is therefore not an element of this set.

One way of indicating a set is to list the names of its elements within braces, { }. For example, to indicate the set whose elements are 1, 3, 5, 7, 9 we can write {1, 3, 5, 7, 9}. It does not matter in which order the elements are listed.

By using a capital letter such as A to represent the set, we can write $A = \{1, 3, 5, 7, 9\}$. This is read "A is the set whose elements are 1, 3, 5, 7, and 9." To indicate that the number 3 is an element of set A, or is contained in set A, we use the symbol $\in$ and write $3 \in A$. To indicate that the number 2 is not an element of set A, or is not contained in set A, we use the symbol $\notin$ and write $2 \notin A$.

Another way of describing a set is to state a rule for selecting the elements of the set.

For example, $A = \{$all odd counting numbers less than ten$\}$ is read "A is the set of all odd counting numbers less than ten." Observe that this is another way of describing the set $A = \{1, 3, 5, 7, 9\}$.

To represent the set of counting numbers from 1 through 500, we may write $\{1, 2, 3, 4, \ldots, 500\}$. The three dots indicate that additional counting numbers 5, 6, 7, and so on up to 500 are to be included.

To represent the set of counting numbers, also called the set of natural numbers, we may write $\{1, 2, 3, 4, \ldots\}$. The three dots indicate that additional counting numbers 5, 6, 7, and so on indefinitely are to be included.

Kinds of Sets

A *finite set* is a set whose elements can be counted, and in which the counting process comes to an end.

Some examples of finite sets are:

1. the set of all pupils in your mathematics class
2. the set of all counting numbers less than one billion

An *infinite set* is a set whose elements cannot be counted, and in which the counting process does not come to an end.

Some examples of infinite sets are:

1. the set of counting numbers
2. the set of points that are on a straight line

The *empty set,* or *null set,* is the set that has no elements. Since the empty set does not have an infinite number of elements, it is a finite set.

Some descriptions of the empty set are:

1. the set of months that begin with the letter Q
2. the set of odd numbers exactly divisible by 2

The empty set may be represented by the symbol $\varnothing$ or by a pair of empty braces, $\{\ \ \}$.

Note that the set which has as its only element the number 0, represented by $\{0\}$, is *not* the empty set, because it does contain an element.

EXERCISES

In 1–3, list the elements of the set that is described.

1. {days of the week that begin with the letter T}

2. {even integers greater than 3 and less than 12}

3. {natural numbers less than 100 that are the squares of natural numbers}

In 4 and 5, tabulate the elements of the set that is described. Use three dots when convenient or necessary.

4. the set of all even counting numbers

5. the set of all integers greater than 10 and less than 1000

In 6–8, state whether the set is a finite non-empty set, an infinite set, or the empty set.

6. the set of all the people who live in the United States today

7. the set of all women who are 12 feet tall

8. the set of natural numbers greater than 1 billion

In 9–11, give a description of the given set.

9. {January, June, July}

10. {2, 4, 6, 8, 10, . . .}

11. {3, 6, 9, 12, . . . , 999}

Relationships Between Sets

Set A is equal to set B if every element of A is an element of B and every element of B is an element of A. In other words, set A and set B contain exactly the same elements.

For example, if $A = \{1, 3, 5, 7, 9\}$ and $B = \{$all odd counting numbers less than ten$\}$, then set A is equal to set B, denoted by $A = B$, because both A and B contain exactly the same elements, namely, 1, 3, 5, 7, and 9.

To indicate that set C is not equal to set D, we write $C \neq D$.

For example, if $C = \{1, 2\}$ and $D = \{2, 3\}$, then $C \neq D$.

Set A and set B are *matching sets,* or *equivalent sets,* denoted by $A \sim B$, if each element of set A can be matched with (or corresponded with) exactly one element of set B, and each element of set B can be matched with exactly one element of set A. When two sets can be matched in this way, we say that there is a *one-to-one correspondence* between the two sets.

For example, the two sets $A = \{1, 3, 5\}$ and $B = \{2, 4, 6\}$ are equivalent sets because the elements of set A can be matched with the elements of set B in any of the following ways:

$$A = \{1, 3, 5\} \quad\quad A = \{1, 3, 5\} \quad\quad A = \{1, 3, 5\}$$

$$\text{or} \quad\quad\quad \text{or} \quad\quad\quad \text{or}$$

$$B = \{2, 4, 6\} \quad\quad B = \{2, 4, 6\} \quad\quad B = \{2, 4, 6\}$$

$$A = \{1, 3, 5\} \quad\quad A = \{1, 3, 5\} \quad\quad A = \{1, 3, 5\}$$

$$\text{or} \quad\quad\quad \text{or}$$

$$B = \{2, 4, 6\} \quad\quad B = \{2, 4, 6\} \quad\quad B = \{2, 4, 6\}$$

Each of these matchings is called a *one-to-one correspondence*. Because of the manner in which set A and set B can be matched, we say that there is a one-to-one correspondence between set A and set B.

In each of the previous matchings, the double-headed arrow indicates that the matching holds in both directions. For example, when the arrow joins the element 1 in set A with the element 2 in set B, this implies that 1 in set A is being matched with 2 in set B, and 2 in set B is being matched with 1 in set A.

Notice that if two sets are equal sets, they are also equivalent sets. However, if two sets are equivalent sets, they are not necessarily equal sets.

The **universal set,** or the **universe,** is the entire set of elements under consideration in a given situation and is usually denoted by the letter U. For example:

1. In algebra, the universal set in a given situation may be the set of all real numbers.
2. In geometry, the universal set in a given situation may be the set of all points in a plane.

Subsets

Set A is a **subset** of set B, denoted by $A \subset B$, if every element of set A is an element of set B.

For example:

1. The set $A = \{$Harry, Paul$\}$ is a subset of the set $B = \{$Sue, Harry, Mary, Paul$\}$.
2. The set of odd positive integers is a subset of the set of all integers.

Since a subset of a set may contain all the elements of the set itself, a subset can have the very same elements as the set itself. When this is true, the two sets are equal. We see, therefore, that every set is a subset of itself.

Mathematicians can show that the empty set $\varnothing$ is a subset of every set.

Intersection of Sets

Set A and set B are said to *intersect* if there is at least one element common to both A and B.

For example, if $A = \{1, 2, 3, 4, 5\}$ and $B = \{2, 4, 6, 8, 10\}$, then set A and set B intersect because they have the elements 2 and 4 in common.

Two sets, C and D, are *disjoint sets* if set C and set D do not intersect.

For example, the sets $\{1, 3, 5, 7\}$ and $\{2, 4, 6, 8\}$ are disjoint sets because they do not have a common element.

The *intersection of two sets*, A and B, denoted by $A \cap B$, is the set of all elements that belong to both sets, A and B.

For example:

Fig. 1–6

1. If $A = \{1, 2, 3, 4, 5\}$ and $B = \{2, 4, 6, 8, 10\}$, then the intersection of A and B, written $A \cap B$, is $\{2, 4\}$.
2. In Fig. 1–6, the intersection of the set of points contained in line $\overleftrightarrow{AB}$ and the set of points in line $\overleftrightarrow{CD}$ is the set which has one element, point E.

Like a line or a plane, any geometric figure can be considered as a set of points. The intersection of any two geometric figures consists of the set of points common to both figures. Hence, point E is the intersection of line $\overleftrightarrow{AB}$ and line $\overleftrightarrow{CD}$.

If two sets, C and D, are disjoint sets, then their intersection set, which has no elements, is the empty set. We can, therefore, write $C \cap D = \varnothing$.

For example, if $C = \{1, 3, 5, 7\}$ and $D = \{2, 4, 6, 8\}$, then $C \cap D = \varnothing$.

Union of Sets

The *union* of two sets, A and B, denoted by $A \cup B$, is the set of all elements that belong to set A or to set B, or to both set A and set B.

For example:

1. If $A = \{1, 2, 3, 4, 5\}$ and $B = \{2, 4, 6, 8\}$, then the union of A and B, written $A \cup B$, is $\{1, 2, 3, 4, 5, 6, 8\}$.

Note that an element is not repeated in the union of two sets if it is an element of each set.

2. In Fig. 1–7, both region R (vertical shading) and region S (horizontal shading) represent sets of points. The shaded parts of both regions represent $R \cup S$, and the cross-hatched part where both regions overlap represents $R \cap S$.

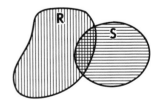

Fig. 1–7

EXERCISES

In 1–3, use the symbol $=$ or $\neq$ to write a true sentence about the two sets.

1. $A = \{5, 10, 15, 20\}$ and $B = \{20, 15, 10, 5\}$
2. $C = \{1, 3, 5\}$ and $D = \{1, 3, 5, 7\}$
3. $K = \{0\}$ and $L = \varnothing$

In 4–6, (*a*) tell whether or not there is a one-to-one correspondence between the two sets and (*b*) state whether the two sets are equivalent.

4. $\{6, 7, 8, 9\}$ and $\{1, 2, 3, 4\}$
5. $\{a, b, c, d\}$ and $\{x, y, z\}$
6. $\{$Tom, Dick, Harry$\}$ and $\{$Sally, Mary, Sue$\}$

In 7 and 8, show all the ways in which the elements of set A can be matched in one-to-one correspondence with the elements of set B.

7. $A = \{$Tom, Dick, Harry$\}$ and $B = \{$Sally, Mary, Sue$\}$
8. $A = \{R, S, T\}$ and $B = \{D, E, F\}$
9. *a.* If set A has three elements and set B has four elements, can set A and set B be put into one-to-one correspondence?
   b. Explain the answer given in part *a.*

In 10–14, tell whether the sentence is true or false. Justify the answer.

10. $\{$Sam, Bill$\}$ is a subset of $\{$Jim, Bill, Sam$\}$
11. $\{6, 7, 8, 9\}$ is a subset of $\{6, 7, 8\}$
12. $\varnothing$ is a subset of $\{10, 11, 12\}$
13. $\{2, 4, 6\} \subset \{1, 2, 3, 4, 5, 6\}$
14. $\{$odd natural numbers$\} \subset \{$odd natural numbers$\}$

In 15–18, $A = \{13, 14, 15\}$. Write all the subsets of A that meet the indicated condition.

15. contain one element   **16.** contain two elements
17. contain three elements   **18.** contain no elements

In 19–26, $A = \{1, 2, 3\}$, $B = \{3, 4, 5, 6\}$, $C = \{1, 3, 4, 6\}$. List the elements of the given sets.

19. $A \cap B$ **20.** $A \cup B$ **21.** $C \cap B$ **22.** $C \cup A$
23. $C \cap A$ **24.** $C \cup B$ **25.** $B \cap \varnothing$ **26.** $A \cup \varnothing$

In 27–29, write a symbol, a word, or a phrase which will make the resulting sentence a true statement.

27. The intersection of set C and set D is the set of all elements that belong to _____ .

28. The union of set C and set D is the set of all elements that belong to _____ .

29. If two sets are disjoint, their intersection set is _____ .

30. Suppose set A has two elements and set B has three elements.
   a. What is the greatest number of elements that $A \cup B$ can have?
   b. What is the least number of elements that $A \cup B$ can have?
   c. What is the greatest number of elements that $A \cap B$ can have?
   d. What is the least number of elements that $A \cap B$ can have?

In 31–33, the straight lines and curves represent sets of points. Draw diagrams similar to the ones shown. Then mark, in color, and name with a letter or letters the point or points that represent the element or elements of the intersection of the two given sets of points.

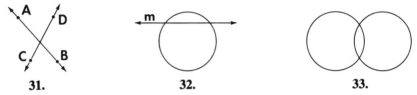

31.   **32.**   **33.**

In 34–36, each geometric figure represents sets of points. Draw diagrams similar to the ones shown. Then mark, in color, the points that represent the elements of the union of the two given sets of points.

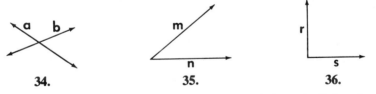

34.   **35.**   **36.**

In 37–39, each diagram pictures region A (shaded vertically) and region B (shaded horizontally), which represent sets of points. (*a*) Draw diagrams similar to the ones shown. Then mark, in color, thé part that represents the union of set A and set B, $A \cup B$. (*b*) Draw diagrams similar to the ones shown. Then mark, in color, the part that represents the intersection of set A and set B, $A \cap B$.

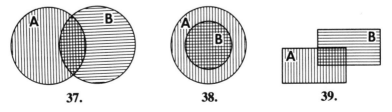

37.   **38.**   **39.**

3. Definitions Involving Lines and Line Segments

The Number Line

In your study of algebra, you learned that the set of real numbers can be associated with the set of points on the **number line.**

To construct the number line, we select two points on a line; we make the one on the left correspond to 0 and the one on the right correspond to 1, as shown in Fig. 1–8. The point corresponding to 0 is called the **origin.** Using the distance between the origin and the point associated with the number 1 as the unit distance, we mark off additional points to the right and to the left of the origin. For example, the point that is two units to the right of the origin corresponds to the number 2, which is an integer; the point that is one unit to the left of the origin corresponds to the number −1, which also is an integer.

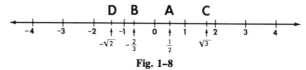

Fig. 1–8

Some points on the number line correspond to rational numbers. For example, point A corresponds to $\frac{1}{2}$, and point B corresponds to $-\frac{2}{3}$. Still other points correspond to irrational numbers. For example, C corresponds to $\sqrt{3}$, and D corresponds to $-\sqrt{2}$. The number associated with a point on the number line is called the **coordinate** of the point. The point associated with a number is called the **graph** of the number.

We will assume that every real number is associated with a point on the number line, which is also called the **real number line.** The real number line is an infinite set of points having the following two characteristics:

1. To every real number, there corresponds exactly one point on the line.
2. To every point on the line, there corresponds exactly one real number.

Since the set of real numbers and the set of points on the real number line can be matched or made to correspond in this manner, we say that there is a *one-to-one correspondence* between the set of points on a line and the set of real numbers. Such a correspondence is called a *coordinate system* on a line.

The Distance Between Two Points

To find the distance between two points, C and D, we can use a ruler, as is shown in Fig. 1–9. We place the zero end of the ruler at C and then read the number that corresponds to point D. Thus, the distance from C to D, denoted by CD, is 2. If we are using a ruler with the inch as the unit, the distance between C and D is 2 inches.

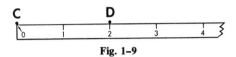

Fig. 1–9

Naturally, if we were to use a ruler with a different unit of measure, for example, the centimeter, to find the distance between C and D, we would obtain a different number of units. Hence, when we talk about the distance between two points, we mean the distance between the two points in terms of a given unit of measure.

No matter what type of ruler we use to measure the distance between C and D in the previous example, we always obtain a positive real number as the answer unless C and D are the same point, in which case the answer is 0. Also, if we measure the distance from D to C, we obtain the same result as we do when we measure the distance from C to D.

In future discussions, we will assume that a unit has been chosen and that this unit is used throughout the discussion.

Observe that if, in measuring the distance between points C and D, we had moved the ruler to the left (see Fig. 1–10), the distance between these two points would not have changed. Although C would now correspond to the number 1 and D would now correspond to the number 3, the distance between C and D would still be the positive number 2.

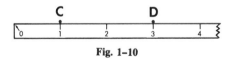

Fig. 1–10

In this case, the distance between C and D could be determined by finding the difference between the two coordinates corresponding to points C and D. Hence, $CD = 3 - 1$, or $CD = 2$.

Observe that if we had reversed the order in which the coordinates of C and D were subtracted, we would have found that $CD = 1 - 3$, or -2, which is a negative number. This would create a problem because we want the distance between points C and D to be the positive number 2. We can resolve this problem by making use of the idea of *absolute value*. Recall the fact that the absolute value of a negative number n is $-n$. In this case, the absolute value of -2 is $-(-2)$, or 2, symbolized by $|-2| = 2$, which is the same value that we obtained previously. Recall also:

1. The absolute value of a positive number p is p. For example, $|6| = 6$.
2. The absolute value of 0 is 0. Hence, $|0| = 0$.

Additional illustrations of absolute value follow:

Column A Column B

1. $|9 - 3| = |6| = 6$ 1. $|3 - 9| = |-6| = 6$
2. $|7 - (-2)| = |9| = 9$ 2. $|(-2) - 7| = |-9| = 9$
3. $|(-3) - (-8)| = |5| = 5$ 3. $|(-8) - (-3)| = |-5| = 5$

Observe that in examples 1, 2, and 3, the same numbers appear in both column A and column B. However, the order of subtraction in column B is the reverse of the order of subtraction in column A. Nevertheless, this does not affect the final result. If in each example the numbers are associated with points on a number line, the result represents the distance between the two points. Once again, we see that we can find the distance between two points by first finding the difference between the points in either order and then finding the absolute value of the resulting number.

We can now state the following definition:

Definition. The *distance between any two points on the real number line is the absolute value of the difference of the coordinates of the two points.*

Hence, on the number line, the distance between any two points A and B whose coordinates are respectively a and b can be represented by

$$AB = |a - b| \quad \text{or} \quad AB = |b - a|$$

MODEL PROBLEM

Find the distance between the points whose coordinates on the real number line are -4 and 3.

Solution:

Let A be the point on the number line whose coordinate is -4.
Let B be the point on the number line whose coordinate is 3.
Let AB represent the distance between A and B.

Then, $AB = |a - b|$
$AB = |(-4) - 3|$
$AB = |-7|$
$AB = 7$ *Ans.* 7

EXERCISES

In 1–5, graph the number on the real number line.

1. 1   **2.** 5   **3.** $2\frac{1}{2}$ **4.** -3 **5.** $-1\frac{1}{2}$

In 6–10, state the coordinate of the point using the number line pictured below.

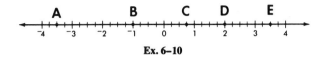

Ex. 6–10

6. *D*   **7.** *B*   **8.** *E*   **9.** *C*   **10.** *A*

In 11–14, $C = \{-2, 0, 1, 3\}$ and $D = \{-1, 0, 2, 3, 4\}$.

11. On a number line, graph the points whose coordinates are the elements of set *C*.

12. On a number line, graph the points whose coordinates are the elements of set *D*.

13. On a number line, graph the points whose coordinates are the elements of $C \cap D$.

14. On a number line, graph the points whose coordinates are the elements of $C \cup D$.

In 15–26, using the simplest numeral, represent the number without an absolute value symbolism.

15. $|7|$ **16.** $|-2|$ **17.** $|0|$
18. $|3 + 7|$ **19.** $|(-2) + (-3)|$ **20.** $|3 + (-9)|$
21. $|0 - (3)|$ **22.** $|(-6) - 0|$ **23.** $|5 - 12|$
24. $|4 - (-2)|$ **25.** $|(-9) - 6|$ **26.** $|(-3) - (-1)|$

In 27–34, use the number line pictured below to find the distance between the two points.

Ex. 27–34

27. *E* and *H*   **28.** *E* and *B*   **29.** *E* and *A*   **30.** *G* and *H*
31. *F* and *I*   **32.** *D* and *C*   **33.** *B* and *I*   **34.** *J* and *D*

In 35–42, find the distance on the number line between the two points which have the indicated coordinates.

35. 0 and 8   **36.** -7 and 0   **37.** 7 and 2   **38.** 2 and 10
39. 5 and -3 **40.** -8 and 4   **41.** -10 and -5 **42.** 15 and -5

43. The distance between points *A* and *B* on the number line is 12. The coordinate of *A* is 3. Find the coordinate of *B* if (*a*) the coordinate of *B* is a positive number and (*b*) the coordinate of *B* is a negative number.

Collinear Points

> *Definition.* A *collinear set of points* is a set of points all of which lie on the same straight line.

In Fig. 1–11, *A*, *B*, and *C* are collinear points, whereas *D*, *E*, and *F* are not collinear points.

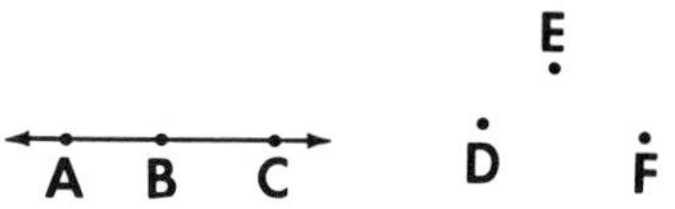

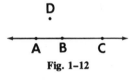

Fig. 1–11

Betweenness of Points on a Line

In your study of arithmetic and algebra, you saw that since 3 is less than 4, denoted by 3 < 4, and 4 is less than 6, denoted by 4 < 6, we may write 3 < 4 < 6, and we say that 4 is *between* 3 and 6. In general, if *a*, *b*, and *c* are real numbers, such that *a* < *b* and *b* < *c*, we may write *a* < *b* < *c*, and we say that *b* is between *a* and *c*.

Now we will discuss what we mean when we say that a point is between two other points. In Fig. 1–12, you would probably accept the statement that point *B* is *between* points *A* and *C*, and that point *D* is not between *A* and *C*. The two situations differ for the following two reasons:

Fig. 1–12

1. Points *A*, *B*, and *C* are collinear, whereas points *A*, *D*, and *C* are not collinear.
2. The sum of the distance between *A* and *B* and the distance between *B* and *C* is equal to the distance from *A* to *C*, denoted by *AB* + *BC* = *AC*. However, the sum of the distance between *A* and *D* and the distance between *D* and *C* is not equal to the distance between *A* and *C*, denoted by *AD* + *DC* ≠ *AC*.

These considerations guide us in formulating the following definition:

> *Definition.* **B is between A and C if A, B, and C are distinct collinear points and AB + BC = AC.**

We can represent a line on which *B* is between *A* and *C* by the symbol $\overrightarrow{ABC}$.

It can be shown that if point *B* is between point *A* and point *C*, then *b*, the coordinate of point *B*, is between *a*, the coordinate of point *A*, and *c*, the coordinate of point *C*. (See Fig. 1–13.)

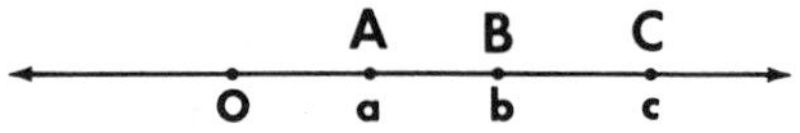

Fig. 1–13

EXERCISES

In 1–3, use the figure at the right.

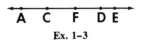

Ex. 1–3

1. Name all the points that are collinear.
2. Name a point between C and D.
3. Name a point that is between A and D, and also between C and E.

In 4–7, find the required distance if A, B, and C are collinear points and point B is between points A and C.

4. $AB = 5$, $BC = 7$, $AC = $?
5. $BC = 10$, $AB = 7$, $AC = $?
6. $AB = 3$, $AC = 12$, $BC = $?
7. $AC = 30$, $BC = 12$, $AB = $?
8. Given that $AB = 8$ and $BC = 12$. (*a*) Is AC necessarily 20? (*b*) Explain your answer in part *a*.
9. Given that $AC = 35$ and $BC = 20$. (*a*) Is AB necessarily 15? (*b*) Explain your answer in part *a*.
10. If $AB = 12$, $BC = 7$, and $AC = 19$, what must be true of points A, B, and C?
11. If $AB = 6$, $BC = 9$, and $AC = 13$, what must be true of points A, B, and C?
12. Given that A, B, and C are collinear, $AB = 13$, and $BC = 7$. (*a*) Is AC necessarily 20? (*b*) Explain your answer in part *a*.

Line Segment

Now we will define a line segment so that it will denote a segment or part of a line. In the left side of Fig. 1–14, A and B are two points on line m. Points A and B determine *line segment AB*, or *segment AB*. The right side of Fig. 1–14 also pictures the line segment AB.

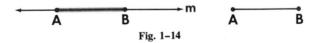

Fig. 1–14

Definition. A **line segment,** or **segment,** is a set of points consisting of two **points on a line, called endpoints, and the set of all points on the line between the endpoints.**

A line segment is named by placing a bar ($\overline{}$) over two capital letters which are the names of the endpoints of the segment. For example, the line segment whose endpoints are A and B, shown in Fig. 1–14, is denoted by $\overline{AB}$.

Observe that segment $\overline{AB}$ is a set of points consisting of the union of points A and B and all points on the line $\overleftrightarrow{AB}$ between points A and B. Note that although a line may be named by any two of its points, a line segment is always named by its two endpoints.

To indicate that C is a point on segment $\overline{AB}$ and is also between points A and B, we will use the symbol $\overline{ACB}$. (See Fig. 1–15.)

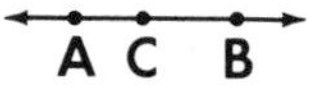

A C   B

Fig. 1–15

Half-Line and Ray

Every point in a line divides the line into two opposite sets of points called *half-lines*. The point of division itself does not belong to the half-line. In Fig. 1–16, point P divides $\overleftrightarrow{MN}$ into two half-lines. We say that points A and B are on the same side of point P. Notice that point A is between point P and point B. Also, we say that points A and C are on opposite sides of point P. Notice that point P is between point C and point A.

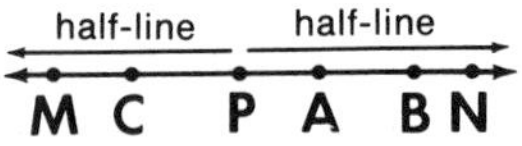

half-line   half-line

M C   P A   B N

Fig. 1–16

Definition. **A *half-line* is the set of all the points in a line on the same side of a dividing point, not including the dividing point.**

Definition. **A *ray* is the set of all the points in a half-line, including the dividing point, which is called the endpoint of the ray.**

A ray is named by placing an arrow pointing to the right over two capital letters. The first letter must be the letter which names the endpoint of the ray; the second letter may be the name of any other point on the ray. Fig. 1–17 shows ray $\overrightarrow{AB}$, which starts at the endpoint A, contains point B, and extends indefinitely in one direction. Note that point B is not the endpoint of the ray. It is any point in the infinite set of points on the ray, and is chosen merely to enable us to name the ray.

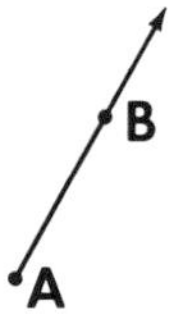

Fig. 1–17

In Fig. 1–18, the ray whose endpoint is O may be named $\overrightarrow{OA}$ or $\overrightarrow{OB}$. However, it may not be named $\overrightarrow{AB}$, since the first capital letter in the name of a ray must represent its endpoint.

B   A   O

Fig. 1–18

Any point that is between two points on a line is the common endpoint of two distinct rays called *opposite rays*. In Fig. 1–19, $\overrightarrow{AB}$ and $\overrightarrow{AC}$ are called opposite rays because points A, B, and C are collinear and point A is between points B and C.

C A   B

Fig. 1–19

Measuring a Line Segment

When we measure a line segment, we determine the distance between its endpoints.

Definition. The *length of a line segment* is the distance between its endpoints.

In Fig. 1–20, the length of segment $\overline{AB}$ is represented by AB. The length of every segment whose endpoints are distinct points is a unique positive number. Notice that we do not use an arrow or a bar when we represent the length of a segment.

A   B

Fig. 1–20

Congruence of Line Segments

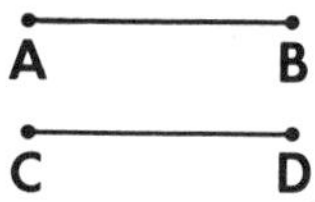

If we were to measure $\overline{AB}$ and $\overline{CD}$ in Fig. 1–21, we would find that they have the same length.

Definition. *Congruent segments* are segments that have the same length.

A   B

C   D

Fig. 1–21

The symbol for "congruent" or "is congruent to" is ≅. Hence, we write $\overline{AB} \cong \overline{CD}$ to indicate that "segment $\overline{AB}$ is congruent to segment $\overline{CD}$," or "segment $\overline{AB}$ and segment $\overline{CD}$ are congruent."

If $\overline{AB} \cong \overline{CD}$, then AB, the length of $\overline{AB}$, is the same as CD, the length of $\overline{CD}$. Hence, $\overline{AB} \cong \overline{CD}$ means that $AB = CD$. We say that the congruence $\overline{AB} \cong \overline{CD}$ is equivalent to the equality $AB = CD$. We may use either notation at any time. This does not mean, however, that the set of points in $\overline{AB}$ is the same as the set of points in $\overline{CD}$.

If we were to cut out $\overline{AB}$ and $\overline{CD}$, we could make one segment "fit" on top of the other; that is, we could make the segments "coincide." Sometimes congruent line segments are considered to be line segments that can be made to "coincide."

When two or more segments are known to be congruent, or their lengths to be equal, we may mark each segment with the same number of strokes as shown in Fig. 1–22.

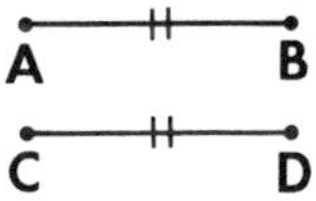

Fig. 1–22

Midpoint of a Line Segment

Definition. The *midpoint of a line segment* is the point of that line segment that divides the segment into two congruent segments.

If M is the midpoint of $\overline{AB}$, then $\overline{AM} \cong \overline{MB}$. Hence, it is also true that $AM = MB$. (See Fig. 1–23.)

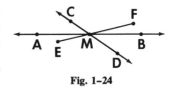

Fig. 1–23

NOTE. We may also say that $AM = \frac{1}{2}AB$, that $MB = \frac{1}{2}AB$, that $AB = 2\,AM$, and that $AB = 2\,MB$.

Bisection of a Line Segment

Definition. **A *segment is bisected at a point* if the point is the midpoint of the line segment.**

Segment $\overline{AB}$ is bisected at point M if M is the midpoint of $\overline{AB}$. (See Fig. 1–24.) Any line other than line $\overleftrightarrow{AB}$, such as $\overleftrightarrow{CD}$, or any segment other than segment $\overline{AB}$, such as $\overline{EF}$, that contains point M is called a *bisector* of segment $\overline{AB}$. We also say that line $\overleftrightarrow{CD}$ and segment $\overline{EF}$ *bisect* segment $\overline{AB}$. In all of the previous cases, $\overline{AM} \cong \overline{MB}$; also $AM = MB$.

Fig. 1–24

Note that a line cannot be bisected since it extends indefinitely in two opposite directions and therefore does not have a midpoint.

Adding and Subtracting Line Segments

Definition. **A line segment $\overline{RS}$ is the *sum of two line segments $\overline{AB}$ and $\overline{CD}$* if there is a point P between points R and S such that $AB = RP$ and $CD = PS$.**

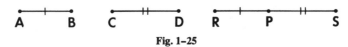

Fig. 1–25

In Fig. 1–25, observe that point P divides $\overline{RS}$ into two segments $\overline{RP}$ and $\overline{PS}$ such that:

$$RS = RP + PS$$
$$RP = RS - PS$$
$$PS = RS - RP$$

EXERCISES

In 1–9, use the following figure:

R   S   P   T   Q

Ex. 1–9

1. Name two points on the same side of P.
2. Name two points on opposite sides of S.
3. Name the segment determined by point R and point Q.
4. Name two segments indicated on the line.
5. Name two rays each of which has point T as an endpoint.
6. Name the opposite ray of ray $\overrightarrow{TQ}$.
7. Does ray $\overrightarrow{ST}$ represent the same ray as ray $\overrightarrow{TS}$? Why?
8. Is ray $\overrightarrow{ST}$ the opposite ray of ray $\overrightarrow{TS}$? Why?
9. Is point R in ray $\overrightarrow{SP}$?

10. *a.* Name all the line segments which appear in the figure.
    b. Use a ruler to measure all the line segments. Name the segments that seem to be congruent.

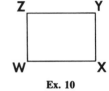
Ex. 10

11. State the number of endpoints that there are for (*a*) a line segment (*b*) a ray (*c*) a line.
12. Is the midpoint of a line segment always on the line segment?
13. Does a line have a midpoint? Why?
14. If X is the midpoint of segment $\overline{CD}$, can we say
    (*a*) $\overline{CX} \cong \overline{XD}$? Why?
    (*b*) $CX = XD$? Why?
    (*c*) $\overline{CX} = \overline{XD}$? Why?

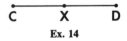
Ex. 14

15. If line $\overleftrightarrow{XY}$ is the bisector of segment $\overline{RS}$, must $\overleftrightarrow{XY}$ contain the midpoint of $\overline{RS}$? Why?
16. If $\overline{AM} \cong \overline{MB}$, does this necessarily mean that M is the midpoint of $\overline{AB}$? Why?
17. Use the symbol $\cong$ to indicate
    (*a*) $AB = CD$ (*b*) $AC = BD$

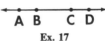
Ex. 17

In 18–21, state two conclusions that can be drawn from the given data for each figure, one conclusion using the symbol $\cong$, the other using the symbol $=$.

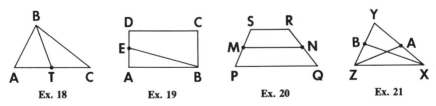

Ex. 18   Ex. 19   Ex. 20   Ex. 21

18. T is the midpoint of $\overline{AC}$.
19. E is the midpoint of $\overline{AD}$.
20. $\overline{MN}$ bisects $\overline{RQ}$.
21. $\overline{XB}$ bisects $\overline{ZY}$.

In 22 and 23, state four conclusions that can be drawn from the given data for each figure, two conclusions using the symbol ≅ and two conclusions using the symbol =.

Ex. 22

Ex. 23

22. $\overline{AC}$ and $\overline{BD}$ bisect each other.   **23.** $\overline{WY}$ and $\overline{XZ}$ bisect each other.
24. If line segment $\overline{XY}$ is the bisector of line segment $\overline{RS}$, must segment $\overline{RS}$ be the bisector of segment $\overline{XY}$? Why?
25. Use the figure in exercise 18 to complete the following statements:
   a. $AT + TC = $ _____   *b.* $AC - AT = $ _____
26. Use the figure in exercise 22 to complete the following statements:
   a. $AE + EC = $ _____   *b.* $DB - DE = $ _____

4. Definitions Involving Angles

Definition. **An** *angle* **is a set of points which is the union of two rays having the same endpoint.**

In Fig. 1–26, rays $\overrightarrow{AB}$ and $\overrightarrow{AC}$, which form an angle, are called the *sides* of the angle. A, the endpoint of each ray, is called the *vertex* of the angle. The symbol for angle is ∠ (plural, ∆).

An angle, such as the one illustrated in Fig. 1–26, may be named in any of the following ways:

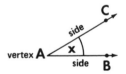

Fig. 1–26

1. By a capital letter which names its vertex. For example, ∠A.
2. By a lowercase letter or by a number placed inside the angle. For example, ∠x.
3. By three capital letters, one naming the vertex of the angle and the others naming two points, one from each of the sides of the angle. The letter at the vertex of the angle is *always* the middle letter. For example, ∠BAC or ∠CAB.

NOTE. When several angles with the same vertex are in a figure, we can avoid confusion by using three letters to name each of the angles. For example, in Fig. 1–27, it is best to name the angles ∠RPS, ∠SPT, ∠RPT.

Fig. 1–27

Sometimes we will picture an angle such as $\angle CAB$ by using segments of the rays which are the sides rather than the rays themselves. This is illustrated in Fig. 1-28.

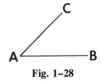

Fig. 1-28

If the two rays that form an angle are opposite rays, the angle is called a *straight angle*. Note that the sides of a straight angle belong to the same straight line. Fig. 1-29 pictures straight angle *AOB*, (st. $\angle AOB$).

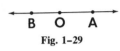

Fig. 1-29

Interior and Exterior Regions of an Angle Which Is Not a Straight Angle

An angle divides the points of a plane which are not on the angle into two sets of points called *regions*. One region is called the *interior of the angle;* the other region is called the *exterior of the angle*. (See Fig. 1-30.) We can determine the points that belong to the interior region of the angle in the following manner. In Fig. 1-30, if *M* is any point on one side of the angle and *N* is any point on the other side of the angle, neither *M* nor *N* being the vertex of the angle, then any point *P* on line segment $\overline{MN}$ between points *M* and *N* belongs to the interior region of the angle. The region consisting of all points such as *P* is called the *interior of the angle*. All other points of the plane, except the points in the angle itself, form the region called the *exterior of the angle*.

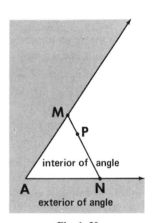

Fig. 1-30

NOTE. If *I* is any point in the interior of an angle and *E* is any point in the exterior of an angle, then the line segment $\overline{IE}$ contains a point in the angle. In the example pictured in Fig. 1-31, point *X* is a point in the angle.

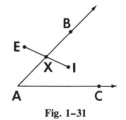

Fig. 1-31

EXERCISES

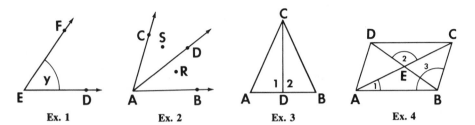

Ex. 1   Ex. 2   Ex. 3   Ex. 4

1. In the figure: (*a*) Name the vertex of the angle. (*b*) Name the sides of the angle. (*c*) Name the angle in four ways.
2. *a.* Name the vertex of ∠*BAD* in the figure.
   b. Name the sides of ∠*BAD*.
   c. Name all the angles with *A* as vertex.
   d. Name the angle whose sides are $\overrightarrow{AB}$ and $\overrightarrow{AC}$.
   e. Name the ray which is a side of both ∠*BAD* and ∠*BAC*.
   f. Name two angles in whose interior regions point *R* lies.
   g. Name the angle in whose exterior point *S* lies.
   h. Are $\overrightarrow{AB}$ and $\overrightarrow{AC}$ opposite rays? Why?
   i. Is ∠*BAC* a straight angle? Why?
3. In the figure: (*a*) Name in two ways each angle whose vertex is *C*. (*b*) Name in all possible ways each angle whose vertex is *D*.
4. In the figure:
   a. Name the angle marked 1 in four other ways.
   b. Name the angle marked 2 in two other ways.
   c. Name the angle marked 3 in two other ways.
   d. Name the point of intersection of $\overline{AC}$ and $\overline{BD}$.
   e. Name two straight angles each of which has its vertex at *E*.
5. *a.* If two rays have a point in common, can their union not be an angle?
   b. If your answer in part *a* is yes, give an illustration. If your answer in part *a* is no, give an explanation of your answer.

5. Definitions Involving Circles

Definition. A *circle* is the set of points in a plane that are a fixed distance which is a positive number from a fixed point called the *center*.

The symbol for circle is ⊙. To name a circle, we usually place a capital letter, such as *O*, near the center of the circle. The circle is then named "circle *O*" (⊙*O*).

Definition. A *radius* of a circle (plural, *radii*) is a line segment drawn from the center of the circle to any point on the circle.

In Fig. 1–32, $\overline{OB}$ is a radius of $\odot O$.

Fig. 1–32

From the definition of a circle and the definition of the radius of a circle, it follows that:

1. A point P is on a circle if the distance from the point to the center is equal to the length of a radius. The circle is said to contain point P. (See Fig. 1–33.)
2. In a circle, all radii are equal in length and are therefore congruent. For example, in Fig. 1–33, $OA = OB$; hence, $\overline{OA} \cong \overline{OB}$.

Fig. 1–33

A circle divides the points of a plane which are not on the circle into two sets of points called *regions*, an *interior region* and an *exterior region*. (See Fig. 1–34.) A point T of the plane is in the interior region of a circle, or inside the circle, if the distance from the point to the center of the circle is less than the length of a radius. A point S of the plane is in the exterior region of a circle, or outside the circle, if the distance from the point to the center is greater than the length of a radius.

Fig. 1–34

Definition. If A and B are two distinct points on a circle whose center is O, then points A and B divide the circle into two parts, each of which is called an *arc*.

In Fig. 1–35, arc AB, symbolized by $\overset{\frown}{AB}$, is the union of points A, B, and the set of points of the circle which lie in the interior region of $\angle AOB$. The other arc in the figure may be indicated by assigning a letter (for example R) to one of its points. This arc can be named arc ARB, symbolized by $\overset{\frown}{ARB}$. Arc $\overset{\frown}{ARB}$ is the union of points A, B, and the set of points of the circle which lie in the exterior region of $\angle AOB$.

Fig. 1–35

Definition. A *chord* of a circle is a line segment whose endpoints are on the circle.

In Fig. 1–35, segment $\overline{AB}$ is a chord of $\odot O$.

Definition. A *diameter* of a circle is a chord that contains the center of the circle.

In Fig. 1–36, segment $\overline{AB}$ is a diameter of $\odot O$.

Note that in a circle, the lengths of all diameters are equal. Hence, in a circle, all diameters are congruent.

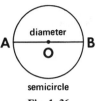

Definition. A *semicircle* is each of the parts into which a diameter divides a circle.

Fig. 1–36

In Fig. 1–36, each $\overarc{AB}$ is a semicircle in $\odot O$. Note that points A and B, the endpoints of diameter $\overline{AB}$, are also the endpoints of each of the semicircles represented by $\overarc{AB}$.

Definition. *Concentric circles* are circles which are in the same plane, which have the same center, and which have unequal radii.

In Fig. 1–37, the two circles having the common center O are concentric circles.

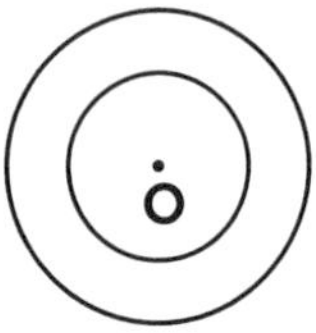

Fig. 1–37

EXERCISES

1. In a given circle O:
   a. Draw a radius $\overline{OX}$.
   b. Draw a diameter $\overline{RS}$.
   c. How does the length of diameter $\overline{RS}$ compare with the length of radius $\overline{OX}$?
   d. If P is a point in the interior of circle O, compare the length of $\overline{OP}$ with the length of radius $\overline{OX}$.
   e. If P is a point in the exterior of circle O, compare the length of $\overline{OP}$ with the length of radius $\overline{OX}$.
   f. Draw a chord $\overline{LM}$.
   g. How many radii can be drawn in circle O?
   h. What is true of the lengths of all the radii that can be drawn in circle O?
   i. How many diameters can be drawn in circle O?
   j. What is true of the lengths of all the diameters that can be drawn in circle O?
2. Draw two concentric circles which have a given point P as their common center.
3. Draw two circles whose radii are congruent and which (*a*) intersect in two points (*b*) intersect at one point (*c*) do not intersect.
4. Draw two circles O and O' whose radii are not congruent and which intersect at R and S. Draw $\overline{OR}$, $\overline{OS}$, $\overline{O'R}$, and $\overline{O'S}$. (*a*) Does $OR = OS$? (*b*) Does $O'R = O'S$? (*c*) Does $OR = O'R$?

6. Measuring Angles and Classifying Them According to Their Measures

Measuring an Angle

In order to measure an angle, we must select a unit of measure and know how this unit is to be applied. In geometry, the unit used to measure an angle is usually a *degree*. The number of degrees in an angle is called its *degree measure* or simply its *measure*. The *protractor* is an instrument that is used to measure angles. Study the model protractor in Fig. 1–38. It consists of a segment together with a semicircle whose diameter is the segment. The semicircle is divided into 180 equal parts and is marked off in units beginning with 0 and continuing through 180. Many protractors have two scales. One scale starts with 0 at the right and continues around to 180 on the left. The other scale starts with 0 at the left and continues around to 180 at the right. These two scales make it convenient to measure an angle easily, regardless of its position.

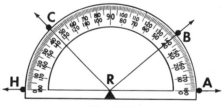

Fig. 1–38

To measure an angle, place the center of the protractor on the vertex of the angle. Place the upper part of the base of the protractor on one side of the angle. This side passes through the point marked 0 on the scale. Notice that the other side of the angle intersects that scale at a point. At this point, there is indicated a positive number which is the measure of the angle. If the sides of an angle do not reach the scale, we may extend them until they do because the sides of an angle are rays which extend indefinitely.

Notice that the measure of an angle is a real positive number. Notice also that we have set up a one-to-one correspondence between all the points on the outline of the protractor and the set of real numbers greater than or equal to 0 and less than or equal to 180.

In measuring $\angle ARB$ in Fig. 1–38, place the protractor so that $\overrightarrow{RA}$ passes through the point marked 0 on the inner scale. Side $\overrightarrow{RB}$ intersects this scale which has 0 lying on side $\overrightarrow{RA}$ at a point marked 40. Hence, the *measure* of $\angle ARB$ is 40. This indicates that $\angle ARB$ contains 40 degrees, denoted by 40°. Since we have defined the measure of an angle as a number of degrees, it is not necessary to indicate the word "degrees," or to use the symbol for degrees (°) when we give the measure of an angle. To indicate that the measure of $\angle ARB$ is 40 degrees, we write $m\angle ARB = 40$. The measures of other angles shown in Fig. 1–38 are indicated below.

$$m\angle ARC = 135 \qquad m\angle ARH = 180$$
$$m\angle HRC = 45 \qquad m\angle HRB = 140$$

Degrees, Minutes, and Seconds

In order to measure an angle with greater precision, we use units of measure smaller than a degree. These units are called a *minute* and a *second*. A degree contains 60 minutes, symbolized by 60'. A minute contains 60 seconds, symbolized by 60".

Hence, $1° = 60'$; also $1' = 60"$.

In our work, we will not deal with seconds. We will deal with minutes because we will become involved with a fractional part of a degree. For example,

$$\frac{1°}{4} = 15', \frac{1°}{2} = 30', \frac{3°}{4} = 45', \frac{1°}{3} = 20', \frac{2°}{3} = 40'$$

Classifying Angles According to Their Measures

Definition. A *right angle* is an angle whose measure is **90**.

Right Angle

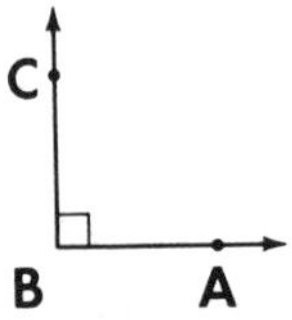

In Fig. 1–39, angle ABC is a right angle. It contains 90°. Note that the symbol ⌐ at B is used to indicate that $\angle ABC$ is a right angle.

Fig. 1–39

Definition. A *straight angle* is an angle whose measure is **180**.

In Fig. 1–40, angle DEF is a straight angle. It contains 180°. Note that $\overrightarrow{ED}$ and $\overrightarrow{EF}$, the sides of $\angle DEF$, are opposite rays and form a straight line.

Straight Angle

F   E   D

Fig. 1–40

Definition. An *acute angle* is an angle whose measure is **greater than 0 and less than 90.**

In Fig. 1–41 on the next page, if $m\angle ABC = x$, then $0 < x < 90$.

Definition. An *obtuse angle* is an angle whose measure is greater than **90** and less than **180**.

In Fig. 1–42 on the next page, if $m\angle DEF = x$, then $90 < x < 180$.

Definition. A *reflex angle* is an angle whose measure is greater than 180 and less than 360.

In Fig. 1–43, if $m\angle PQR = x$, then $180 < x < 360$.

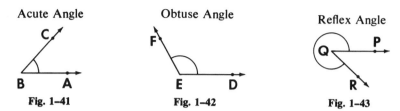

Acute Angle   Obtuse Angle   Reflex Angle

Fig. 1–41   Fig. 1–42   Fig. 1–43

NOTE. In this book, we shall not use reflex angles.

Drawing Angles

The protractor is used not only for measuring angles, but also for drawing them. Let us draw an angle whose measure is 65. (See Fig. 1–44.)

Draw a line and name it $\overleftrightarrow{OA}$. Place the protractor so that its center is at O and the zero on one of its scales lies on $\overrightarrow{OA}$. Place a point C next to the number 65 on that scale. Remove the protractor

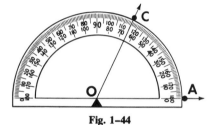

Fig. 1–44

and draw ray $\overrightarrow{OC}$ from O through the point C. The measure of angle AOC at the center of the protractor is 65.

Congruent Angles

Definition. Congruent angles are angles which have the same measure.

In Fig. 1–45, if the measure of $\angle ABC$ is 45 and the measure of $\angle DEF$ is 45, $\angle ABC$ is congruent to $\angle DEF$, symbolized by $\angle ABC \cong \angle DEF$. To indicate that the measure of $\angle ABC$ is the same as the measure of $\angle DEF$, we write $m\angle ABC = m\angle DEF$. We do not write $\angle ABC = \angle DEF$ because this would indicate that $\angle ABC$ and $\angle DEF$ represent the same set of points.

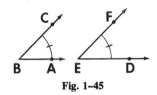

Fig. 1–45

Since $\angle ABC \cong \angle DEF$ means that $m\angle ABC = m\angle DEF$, we say that the congruence $\angle ABC \cong \angle DEF$ is equivalent to the equality $m\angle ABC = m\angle DEF$. We may use either notation at any time.

When two angles are known to be congruent, we may mark each one with the same number of strokes, as shown in Fig. 1–45, where one stroke was used for each angle.

If the representations of the congruent angles *ABC* and *DEF* are drawn on paper, we could cut them out and make one angle "fit" on top of the other; that is, we could make the congruent angles "coincide."

Bisector of an Angle

Definition. **A *bisector of an angle* is a ray in the interior of the angle such that the endpoint of the ray is the vertex of the angle and the ray divides the angle into two congruent angles.**

Fig. 1–46

For example, in Fig. 1–46, if ray $\overrightarrow{OC}$ is the bisector of $\angle AOB$, then $\angle AOC \cong \angle COB$; also $m\angle AOC = m\angle COB$. We also say that line $\overleftrightarrow{OC}$, which contains ray $\overrightarrow{OC}$, and segment $\overline{OC}$, which is part of ray $\overrightarrow{OC}$, are bisectors of $\angle AOB$. Hence, ray $\overrightarrow{OC}$, line $\overleftrightarrow{OC}$, and segment $\overline{OC}$ all *bisect* $\angle AOB$.

NOTE. If $\overrightarrow{OC}$ bisects $\angle AOB$, we may say that $m\angle AOC = \frac{1}{2}m\angle AOB$, $m\angle COB = \frac{1}{2}m\angle AOB$, $m\angle AOB = 2m\angle AOC$, and $m\angle AOB = 2m\angle COB$.

Adding and Subtracting Angles

Definition. **A *non-straight angle RST* is the sum of two angles *ABC* and *DEF* if there is a point *P* in the interior of angle *RST* such that $m\angle RSP = m\angle ABC$ and $m\angle PST = m\angle DEF$. (See Fig. 1–47.)**

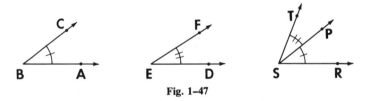

Fig. 1–47

In Fig. 1–47, observe that ray $\overrightarrow{SP}$ divides $\angle RST$ into two angles, $\angle RSP$ and $\angle PST$, such that:

$$m\angle RST = m\angle RSP + m\angle PST$$
$$m\angle RSP = m\angle RST - m\angle PST$$
$$m\angle PST = m\angle RST - m\angle RSP$$

Definition. **A *straight angle RST* is the sum of two angles *ABC* and *DEF* if there is a point *P* not on angle *RST* such that $m\angle RSP = m\angle ABC$ and $m\angle PST = m\angle DEF$. (See Fig. 1–48 on the next page.)**

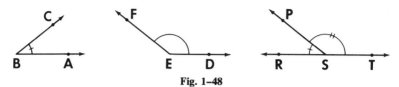

Fig. 1-48

In Fig. 1-48, observe that ray $\overrightarrow{SP}$ divides $\angle RST$ into two angles, $\angle RSP$ and $\angle PST$, such that:

$$m\angle RST = m\angle RSP + m\angle PST$$
$$m\angle RSP = m\angle RST - m\angle PST$$
$$m\angle PST = m\angle RST - m\angle RSP$$

Generating an Angle by Rotation

We can think of a ray which is rotating in a counterclockwise fashion as generating an angle whose measure is a positive number. For example, in Fig. 1-49, ray $\overrightarrow{OS}$ and ray $\overrightarrow{OT}$, which are part of the same line, have the same endpoint, O, and extend in the same direction. If ray $\overrightarrow{OS}$ is rotated counterclockwise about endpoint O, the ray generates $\angle TOS$, as shown in Fig. 1-50. $\overrightarrow{OT}$ is called the *initial side* of $\angle TOS$. $\overrightarrow{OS}$ is called the *terminal side* of $\angle TOS$. As $\overrightarrow{OS}$ continues to rotate (Figs. 1-51 and 1-52), it will complete a full revolution. Then, $\overrightarrow{OS}$ once again becomes part of the same line as $\overrightarrow{OT}$. Observe that as ray $\overrightarrow{OS}$ was rotating, it generated angles whose measures were 0 through 360.

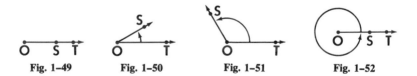

Fig. 1-49   Fig. 1-50   Fig. 1-51   Fig. 1-52

Notice that the size of an angle depends only on the amount of rotation of one of its sides. Thus, in Fig. 1-53, $m\angle a = m\angle b$ and $m\angle x > m\angle y$.

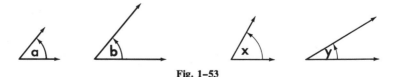

Fig. 1-53

EXERCISES

In 1–6, use a protractor to measure the angle:

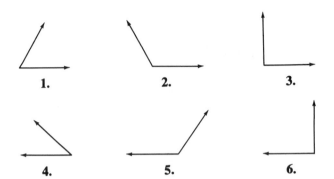

1.   **2.**   **3.**

4.   **5.**   **6.**

7. *a.* Draw a figure like the one shown in which
$\overleftrightarrow{AB}$ and $\overleftrightarrow{CD}$ are straight lines.
  b. Measure ∠1 and ∠3.
  c. What do you notice about their measures?
  d. Measure ∠2 and ∠4.
  e. What do you notice about their measures?

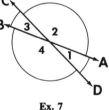

Ex. 7

8. *a.* Draw a figure like the one shown.
  b. Measure ∠A, ∠B, and ∠C.
  c. Find the sum of *m*∠A, *m*∠B, and *m*∠C.

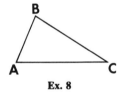

Ex. 8

In 9–14, if an angle contains the given number of degrees, state whether the angle is an acute angle, a right angle, an obtuse angle, a straight angle, or a reflex angle.

9. 18°   **10.** 98°   **11.** 210°   **12.** 90°   **13.** 64°15′   **14.** 180°

15. Find the measure of   (*a*) ½ of a right angle   (*b*) ⅔ of a right angle   (*c*) ⅗ of a straight angle.

16. Find the number of degrees contained in the sum of one-half of a right angle and one-third of a straight angle.

In 17–22, use a protractor to draw an angle whose measure is given.

17. 40   **18.** 90   **19.** 33   **20.** 120   **21.** 93   **22.** 190

In 23–25, use the information about the figure given in the exercise to (a) write a conclusion which states the congruence of two angles and (b) write a conclusion which states the equality of the measures of two angles.

Ex. 23

Ex. 24

Ex. 25

23. $\overline{CD}$ bisects $\angle ACB$.

24. $\overline{AC}$ is the bisector of $\angle DAB$.

25. $\overline{OA}$ bisects $\angle COB$.

26. If a straight angle is bisected, what type of angle is each of the resulting angles?

27. If an obtuse angle is bisected, what type of angle is each of the resulting angles?

28. Complete the following statements, which refer to the figure at the right.

a. $m\angle LMN = m\angle LMP + m\angle$ _____

b. $m\angle LMP = m\angle LMN - m\angle$ _____

c. $m\angle PMN = m\angle$ _____ $- m\angle LMP$

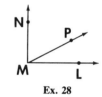

Ex. 28

29. Use the figure at the right to answer parts a through d.

a. $m\angle ABE + m\angle EBC = m\angle$ _____

b. $m\angle BEC + m\angle CED = m\angle$ _____

c. $m\angle ADC - m\angle CDE = m\angle$ _____

d. $m\angle AEC - m\angle AEB = m\angle$ _____

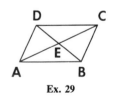

Ex. 29

7. Pairs of Angles

Definition. Adjacent angles are two angles in the same plane which have a common vertex and a common side but do not have any interior points in common.

Angles ABC and CBD in Fig. 1–54 are adjacent angles because they have B as their common vertex, $\overrightarrow{BC}$ as their common side, with no interior points in common. However, $\angle XWY$ and $\angle XWZ$ in Fig. 1–55 are not adjacent angles because, although they have W as their common vertex and $\overrightarrow{WX}$ as their common side, they do have interior points in common. For example, point P is in the interior of both $\angle XWY$ and $\angle XWZ$.

Fig. 1-54   Fig. 1-55

Definition. Vertical angles **are two angles which have a common vertex and whose sides are two pairs of opposite rays.**

In Fig. 1–56, $\angle a$ and $\angle b$ are a pair of vertical angles; $\angle x$ and $\angle y$ are also a pair of vertical angles. Observe that in each pair of vertical angles, the opposite rays, which are the sides of the angles, form the straight lines $\overleftrightarrow{AB}$ and $\overleftrightarrow{CD}$.

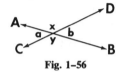

Fig. 1–56

Definition. Complementary angles **are two angles the sum of whose measures is 90.**

Each angle is called the *complement* of the other.

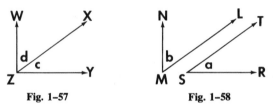

Fig. 1-57   Fig. 1-58

In Fig. 1–57, if $m\angle c = 40$ and $m\angle d = 50$, then $\angle c$ and $\angle d$ are complementary angles. In Fig. 1–58, if $m\angle a = 35$ and $m\angle b = 55$, then $\angle a$ and $\angle b$ are complementary angles. Complementary angles may be adjacent as in the case of $\angle c$ and $\angle d$, or they may be non-adjacent as in the case of $\angle a$ and $\angle b$.

Since $m\angle c + m\angle d = 40 + 50$, or 90, we say that $\angle c$, whose measure is 40, is the complement of $\angle d$, whose measure is 50. We also say that $\angle d$ is the complement of $\angle c$. We can represent the measure of the complement of an angle whose measure is m by $(90 - m)$ because $m + (90 - m) = 90$.

Definition. Supplementary angles **are two angles the sum of whose measures is 180.**

Each of the angles is called the *supplement* of the other.

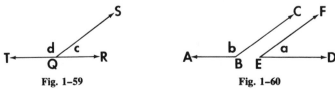

Fig. 1–59   Fig. 1–60

In Fig. 1–59, if $m\angle c = 40$ and $m\angle d = 140$, then $\angle c$ and $\angle d$ are supplementary angles. In Fig. 1–60, if $m\angle a = 35$ and $m\angle b = 145$, then $\angle a$ and $\angle b$ are supplementary angles. Supplementary angles may be adjacent as in the case of $\angle c$ and $\angle d$, or they may be non-adjacent as in the case of $\angle a$ and $\angle b$.

Since $m\angle c + m\angle d = 40 + 140$, or 180, we say that $\angle c$, whose measure is 40, is the supplement of $\angle d$, whose measure is 140. We also say that $\angle d$ is the supplement of $\angle c$. We can represent the measure of the supplement of an angle whose measure is m by $(180 - m)$ because $m + (180 - m) = 180$.

NOTE. If two adjacent angles are supplementary, their non-common sides are opposite rays which form a line. For example, in the case of $\angle c$ and $\angle d$ in Fig. 1–59, the non-common sides $\overrightarrow{QR}$ and $\overrightarrow{QT}$ form line $\overleftrightarrow{TR}$.

MODEL PROBLEMS

1. The measure of the complement of an angle is four times the measure of the angle. Find the measure of the angle.

Solution: Let x = the measure of the angle.
Then $4x$ = the measure of the complement of the angle.

The sum of the measures of an angle and its complement is 90.

1. $x + 4x = 90$

2. $\quad 5x = 90$

3. $\quad x = 18$

Answer: The measure of the angle is 18.

2. Find the measure of an angle whose measure is 40 more than the measure of its supplement.

Solution: Let x = the measure of the supplement of the angle.
Then $x + 40$ = the measure of the angle.

The sum of the measures of an angle and its supplement is 180.

1. $x + x + 40 = 180$

2. $\quad 2x + 40 = 180$

3. $\quad 2x = 140$

4. $\quad x = 70, x + 40 = 110$

Answer: The measure of the angle is 110.

EXERCISES

1. In *a–d*, tell whether angles *x* and *y* are adjacent angles. Give the reason for each answer.

    (*a*)   (*b*)   (*c*)   (*d*)

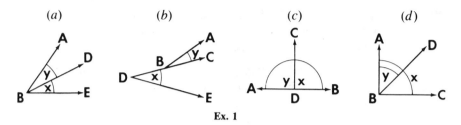

Ex. 1

2. Name two pairs of adjacent angles in the figure.
3. In the figure, $\overleftrightarrow{LM}$ and $\overleftrightarrow{PQ}$ are straight lines. (*a*) Name four pairs of adjacent angles. (*b*) Name two pairs of vertical angles.

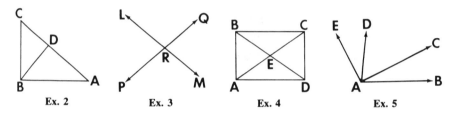

    Ex. 2   **Ex. 3**   **Ex. 4**   **Ex. 5**

4. In the straight-line figure: (*a*) Name the adjacent angles at *B*. (*b*) Name two pairs of vertical angles.
5. In the straight-line figure, name all pairs of adjacent angles.
6. If ∠*BAD* is a right angle, name two complementary angles.
7. In *a–c*, the measure of each of two angles is given. Tell whether or not the angles are complementary.
   a. 20° and 70°   *b.* 65° and 35°
   c. 65°45′ and 24°15′
8. Find the measure of the complement of an angle whose measure is:
   a. 30° *b.* 15° *c.* 36° *d.* 79° *e.* 19°30′ *f.* 68°15′
9. Express the measure of the complement of an angle whose measure is represented by:
   a. x   *b.* (3*a*)   *c.* (*y* + 10)   *d.* (*r* − 40)   *e.* (*x* + *y*)
10. The measure of an angle is equal to the measure of its complement. Find the measure of the angle.

Ex. 6

11. Two angles are complementary. The measure of the larger angle is five times the measure of the smaller angle. Find the measure of the larger angle.

12. Find the measure of an angle whose measure is 60 more than the measure of its complement.

13. Two angles are complementary, and the measure of the smaller angle is 50 less than the measure of the larger. Find the measure of the larger angle.

14. The measures of two angles which are complementary are in the ratio 7:2. Find the measure of each angle.

15. The measure of the complement of an angle exceeds the measure of the angle by 24. Find the measure of the angle.

16. If ∠XYZ is a straight angle, name two supplementary angles.

17. In *a–c*, the measure of each of two angles is given. Tell whether or not the angles are supplementary.
    a. 30° and 150°   *b.* 140° and 50°
    c. 85°30' and 94°30'

Ex. 16

18. Find the measure of the supplement of an angle whose measure is:
    a. 70°   *b.* 115°   *c.* 87°   *d.* 78°30'   *e.* 143°50'

19. Express the measure of the supplement of an angle whose measure is represented by:
    a. y   *b.* (2r)   *c.* (x + 8)   *d.* (a − 20)   *e.* (2x + 2y)

20. The measure of an angle and the measure of its supplement are equal. Find the measure of each of the supplementary angles.

21. Two angles are supplementary. The measure of the smaller angle is one-half of the measure of the greater angle. Find the measure of the greater angle.

22. The measure of an angle is 20 less than the measure of its supplement. Find the measure of the angle.

23. The measures of two supplementary angles are in the ratio of 7:2. Find the measure of each angle.

24. The measures of a pair of supplementary angles are represented by (3a + 10) and (2a − 40). Find the measure of the smaller of the two angles.

25. The measure of the supplement of an angle is 60 more than twice the measure of the angle. Find the measure of the angle.

26. The difference between the measures of two supplementary angles is 80. Find the measure of the larger of the two angles.

27. The measure of the supplement of an angle exceeds five times the

measure of the complement of the angle by 10. Find the measure of the original angle.

28. The supplement of the complement of an acute angle is always (1) an acute angle (2) an obtuse angle (3) a straight angle (4) a right angle.

In 29–32, write a conclusion that can be drawn from the figure and the information given in the exercise.

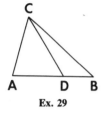
Ex. 29

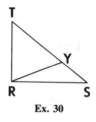
Ex. 30

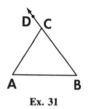
Ex. 31

29. ∠ADB is a straight angle.
30. ∠SRT is a right angle.
31. ∠BCA and ∠ACD are supplementary.
32. ∠ACD and ∠BCD are complementary.

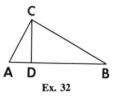
Ex. 32

8. Definitions Involving Perpendicular Lines

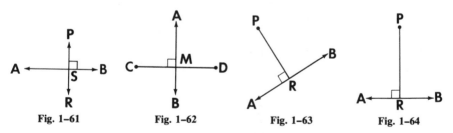

Fig. 1–61   Fig. 1–62   Fig. 1–63   Fig. 1–64

Definition. Perpendicular lines **are two lines which intersect and form right angles.**

In Fig. 1–61, $\overleftrightarrow{PR}$ is perpendicular to $\overleftrightarrow{AB}$ when $\overleftrightarrow{PR}$ and $\overleftrightarrow{AB}$ intersect at S and form right angles BSP, PSA, ASR, and RSB. "$\overleftrightarrow{PR}$ is perpendicular to $\overleftrightarrow{AB}$" is symbolized as $\overleftrightarrow{PR} \perp \overleftrightarrow{AB}$. We also speak of rays or line segments which are contained in perpendicular lines and which intersect forming right angles as being perpendicular. Notice that when two lines are perpendicular, the adjacent angles that they form at the point of intersection are congruent since each angle is a right angle whose measure is 90. Also, note that when two lines intersect and form congruent adjacent angles, the lines are perpendicular.

Definition. **The *perpendicular bisector of a line segment* is a line, a line segment, or a ray which is perpendicular to the line segment and bisects the line segment.**

In Fig. 1–62, if $\overleftrightarrow{AB}$ is the perpendicular bisector of line segment $\overline{CD}$, then $\overleftrightarrow{AB}$ is perpendicular to $\overline{CD}$, and M is the midpoint of $\overline{CD}$. Therefore, $\overline{AM} \perp \overline{CD}$ and $\overline{CM} \cong \overline{MD}$.

Definition. **The *foot of a perpendicular from a point not on a line to the line* is the point where the perpendicular meets the line.**

In Fig. 1–63, if P is a point not on line $\overleftrightarrow{AB}$, and $\overline{PR} \perp \overleftrightarrow{AB}$, then line segment $\overline{PR}$ is called the perpendicular from P to $\overleftrightarrow{AB}$, and the point R is called the foot of the perpendicular from point P to line $\overleftrightarrow{AB}$.

Definition. **The *distance from a point to a line* is the length of the perpendicular from the point to the line.**

In Fig. 1–64, the distance from point P to line $\overleftrightarrow{AB}$ is the length of segment $\overline{PR}$ when $\overline{PR} \perp \overleftrightarrow{AB}$.

EXERCISES

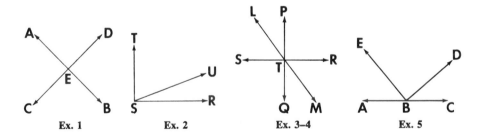

Ex. 1   Ex. 2   Ex. 3–4   Ex. 5

1. If $\overleftrightarrow{AB}$ is perpendicular to $\overleftrightarrow{CD}$, name four right angles.
2. If $\overleftrightarrow{TS} \perp \overleftrightarrow{SR}$, name a pair of complementary angles.
3. If $\overleftrightarrow{PQ} \perp \overleftrightarrow{SR}$, name two pairs of complementary angles.
4. If $\overleftrightarrow{PQ} \perp \overleftrightarrow{SR}$, tell whether the angle is acute, right, obtuse, or straight:
   a. $\angle PTR$ b. $\angle PTL$ c. $\angle LTQ$ d. $\angle STR$ e. $\angle STM$
5. $\angle ABC$ is a straight angle and $\overleftrightarrow{EB} \perp \overleftrightarrow{BD}$.   (a) If $m\angle DBC = 40$, find the number of degrees contained in $\angle ABE$.   (b) If the number of degrees contained in $\angle ABE$ is represented by y, represent the number of degrees contained in $\angle CBD$.

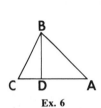
Ex. 6

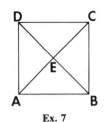
Ex. 7

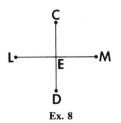
Ex. 8

6. $\overline{BD} \perp \overline{AC}$.
   a. Name two congruent adjacent angles.
   b. State the number of degrees contained in $\angle BDA$.
   c. Name the point which is the foot of the perpendicular from B to $\overline{AC}$.
   d. Name the line segment whose length measures the distance from B to $\overline{AC}$.
7. In the straight-line figure, if $\angle AEB$ is a right angle, name the lines which are perpendicular to each other.
8. Line segment $\overline{CD}$ is the perpendicular bisector of line segment $\overline{LM}$.
   a. Name two line segments that are perpendicular to each other.
   b. Name four angles that are right angles.
   c. Name two line segments that are congruent.
   d. Must $\overline{LM}$ be the perpendicular bisector of $\overline{CD}$?
   e. Give the reason for your answer to part d.

In 9–11, use the given information to name the right angle(s) in the figure.

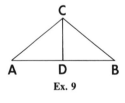
Ex. 9

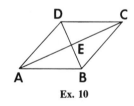
Ex. 10

Ex. 11

9. $\overline{CD} \perp \overline{AB}$ **10.** $\overline{DB} \perp \overline{AC}$ **11.** $\overline{TS} \perp \overline{RS}$

In 12–14, refer to the figures and write two conclusions that can be drawn from the given information. Give a reason for each conclusion drawn.

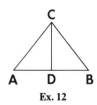
Ex. 12

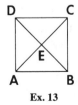
Ex. 13

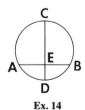
Ex. 14

12. $\overline{CD}$ is the perpendicular bisector of $\overline{AB}$.
13. $\overline{DB}$ is the perpendicular bisector of $\overline{AC}$.
14. $\overline{CD}$ is the perpendicular bisector of $\overline{AB}$.

9. Definitions Involving Triangles and Line Segments Associated With Triangles

Definition. **A** *polygon* **is a closed figure in a plane which is the union of line segments.**

In this book, we will deal with simple polygons like the ones pictured in Figs. 1–65, 1–66, and 1–67.

Union of 3 Line Segments   Union of 4 Line Segments   Union of 5 Line Segments
    (Triangle)   (Quadrilateral)   (Pentagon)

     Fig. 1–65   **Fig. 1–66**   **Fig. 1–67**

In the definition of a polygon, we will consider the word *closed* as an undefined term. We understand by the word *closed* the idea that if we start at any point on the figure and "move" along the sides, we will at some time arrive back at the starting point. In Fig. 1–68, we see a figure that is not a "closed" figure, and therefore not a polygon.

Fig. 1–68

In Fig. 1–69, the polygon is named polygon *ABCDE*.

Line segments $\overline{AB}$, $\overline{BC}$, $\overline{CD}$, $\overline{DE}$, and $\overline{EA}$ are called the *sides of the polygon*. The endpoints of these line segments — points *A*, *B*, *C*, *D*, and *E* — are called the *vertices* (singular, *vertex*) *of the polygon*.

The endpoints of a side of the polygon are called *consecutive vertices*. Examples of consecutive vertices are *A* and *B*, *B* and *C*, etc.

Angles *A*, *B*, *C*, *D*, and *E* are called the *angles of the polygon*.

The angles whose vertices are consecutive vertices of the polygon are called *consecutive angles*. Examples of consecutive angles are $\angle A$ and $\angle B$, $\angle B$ and $\angle C$, etc.

A *diagonal of a polygon* is a line segment which joins two nonconsecutive vertices. For example (Fig. 1–70), $\overline{AC}$ is a diagonal of polygon *ABCDE*.

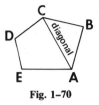

Fig. 1–70

The *perimeter of a polygon* is the sum of the measures of the sides. For example, if *P* represents the perimeter of polygon *ABCDE*, then $P = AB + BC + CD + DE + EA$.

Definition. A *triangle* is a polygon that has three sides.

The polygon shown in Fig. 1–71 is triangle *ABC*, commonly written △*ABC*. In △*ABC*, each of the points *A*, *B*, and *C* is a vertex of the triangle. The line segments $\overline{AB}$, $\overline{BC}$, and $\overline{CA}$ are the sides of the triangle. A side of a triangle may be represented by a lowercase form of the letter naming the opposite vertex. For example, in △*ABC*, side $\overline{BC}$ is labeled *a*, side $\overline{CA}$ is labeled *b*, and side $\overline{AB}$ is labeled *c*.

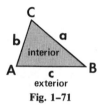

Fig. 1–71

The angles *CAB* (∠*A*), *ABC* (∠*B*), and *BCA* (∠*C*) are called the angles of the triangle. In a triangle, the three sides and the three angles are called the six *parts* of the triangle.

A triangle, which is a set of points in a plane, separates the points of the plane that are not on the triangle into two regions. One region contains all the points which are in the interior regions of the three angles of the triangle. This region is called the *interior* of the triangle. The other region is called the *exterior* of the triangle. We will assume that a line segment, one of whose endpoints is in the interior of a triangle and the other is in the exterior of the triangle, contains a point of the triangle.

Classifying Triangles According to Sides

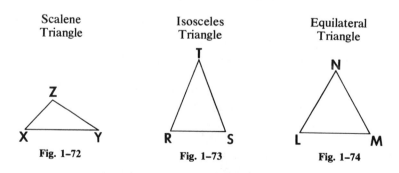

Scalene Triangle — Fig. 1–72

Isosceles Triangle — Fig. 1–73

Equilateral Triangle — Fig. 1–74

Definition. **A *scalene triangle* is a triangle that has no congruent sides.** (See Fig. 1–72.)

Definition. An *isosceles triangle* is a triangle that has two congruent sides. (See Fig. 1–73.)

Definition. An *equilateral triangle* is a triangle that has three congruent sides. (See Fig. 1–74.)

Parts of an Isosceles Triangle

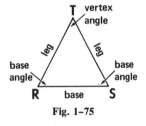

Fig. 1–75

In isosceles triangle RST, in Fig. 1–75, the two congruent sides, $\overline{TR}$ and $\overline{TS}$, are called the *legs* of the triangle. The third side, $\overline{RS}$, is called the *base*.

The angle formed by the two congruent sides of the triangle, $\angle T$, which is also sometimes referred to as "the angle opposite the base," is called the *vertex angle* of the isosceles triangle.

The angles whose vertices are the endpoints of the base of the triangle, $\angle R$ and $\angle S$, which are sometimes also referred to as "the angles opposite the congruent sides," are called the *base angles* of the isosceles triangle.

Classifying Triangles According to Angles

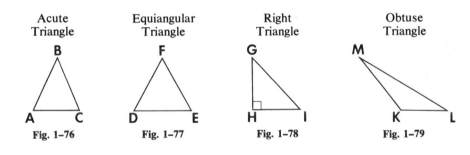

Acute Triangle	Equiangular Triangle	Right Triangle	Obtuse Triangle
Fig. 1–76	Fig. 1–77	Fig. 1–78	Fig. 1–79

Definition. An *acute triangle* is a triangle that has three acute angles. (See Fig. 1–76.)

Definition. An *equiangular triangle* is a triangle that has three congruent angles. (See Fig. 1–77.)

Definition. A *right triangle* is a triangle that has a right angle. (See Fig. 1–78.)

Definition. An *obtuse triangle* is a triangle that has an obtuse angle. (See Fig. 1–79.)

Parts of a Right Triangle

In right triangle GHI, in Fig. 1–80, the two sides of the triangle which form the right angle, $\overline{GH}$ and $\overline{HI}$, are called the *legs* or the *arms* of the right triangle. The third side of the triangle, $\overline{GI}$, which is sometimes referred to as "the side opposite the right angle," is called the *hypotenuse*.

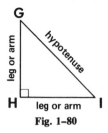

Fig. 1–80

Included Sides and Included Angles in a Triangle

In triangle ABC (see Fig. 1–81), we say that side $\overline{AB}$, whose endpoints are A and B, is included between $\angle A$ and $\angle B$; side $\overline{BC}$, whose endpoints are B and C, is included between $\angle B$ and $\angle C$; and side $\overline{CA}$, whose endpoints are C and A, is included between $\angle C$ and $\angle A$. We also say that $\angle A$, which is formed by sides $\overline{AB}$ and $\overline{AC}$, is included between sides $\overline{AB}$ and $\overline{AC}$; $\angle B$, which is formed by sides $\overline{BA}$ and $\overline{BC}$, is included between sides $\overline{BA}$ and $\overline{BC}$; and $\angle C$, which is formed by sides $\overline{CB}$ and $\overline{CA}$, is included between sides $\overline{CB}$ and $\overline{CA}$.

Fig. 1–81

Line Segments Associated with Triangles

Definition. A *median of a triangle* is a line segment which joins any vertex of the triangle to the midpoint of the opposite side.

In $\triangle ABC$ (see Fig. 1–82), if D is the midpoint of $\overline{AB}$, then $\overline{CD}$ is the median drawn from vertex C to side $\overline{AB}$.

Definition. An *altitude of a triangle* is a line segment drawn from any vertex of the triangle, perpendicular to and ending in the opposite side (extended if necessary).

Fig. 1–82

Note the altitudes in the triangles in Figs. 1–83, 1–84, and 1–85.

Fig. 1–83

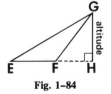

Fig. 1–84

Fig. 1–85

In $\triangle ABC$ (Fig. 1-83), the altitude from C to $\overline{AB}$ is line segment $\overline{CD}$. In $\triangle EFG$ (Fig. 1-84), the altitude from G to $\overline{EF}$ extended is line segment $\overline{GH}$.
In $\triangle RST$ (Fig. 1-85), the altitude from R to $\overline{ST}$ is line segment $\overline{RS}$.

Definition. An *angle bisector of a triangle* **is a line segment which bisects any angle of the triangle and terminates in the side opposite that angle.**

In $\triangle PQR$ (see Fig. 1-86), if $\angle PRD \cong \angle QRD$ and D is on side $\overline{PQ}$, then line segment $\overline{RD}$ is the bisector of $\angle PRQ$ in $\triangle PQR$.

Fig. 1-86

EXERCISES

1. Classify the following triangles according to *sides:*

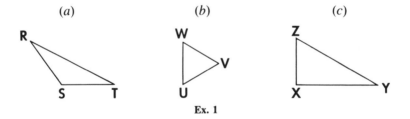

Ex. 1

2. Classify the following triangles according to *angles:*

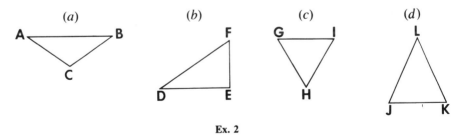

Ex. 2

3. Name the legs, base, vertex angle, and base angles in each of the isosceles triangles at the top of the next page.

(a)   (b)   (a)   (b)

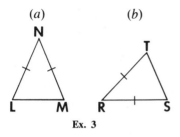
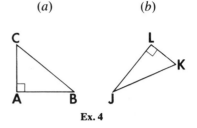

Ex. 3   Ex. 4

4. Name the legs and the hypotenuse in each of the right triangles above.

5. Draw an acute triangle that is isosceles.

6. Draw an obtuse triangle that is isosceles.

7. Draw a right triangle that is isosceles.

8. Draw an obtuse triangle that is scalene.

9. In each triangle below, name the type of line segment that $\overline{CD}$ is.

(a)   (b)   (c)   (d)

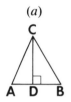
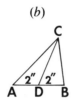

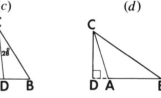

Ex. 9

10. Polygon ABC is a triangle. $\overline{CD}$ is an altitude. $\overline{CE}$ is
an angle bisector. $\overline{CF}$ is a median.

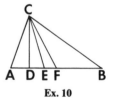

   a. Name two congruent angles, each of which has
      its vertex at C.
   b. Name two line segments which are congruent.
   c. Name two line segments which are perpendicu-
      lar to each other.
   d. Name two angles which are right angles.

Ex. 10

10. Completion Exercises

In 1–25, write a word, number, or expression that, when inserted in the
blank, will make the resulting statement true.

1. An altitude of a triangle is _____ to the side to which it is drawn.

2. A median of a triangle _____ the side to which it is drawn.

3. If two angles are supplementary, the sum of their measures is _____.

4. If the measure of an angle is represented by 4x, the measure of its supplement is represented by _____.

5. The sum of the measures of an angle and its complement is _____.

6. If the measure of an angle is represented by 90 – a, the measure of the complement of the angle is represented by _____.

7. The supplement of an acute angle is a(an) _____ angle.

8. The supplement of an obtuse angle is a(an) _____ angle.

9. The supplement of a right angle is a(an) _____ angle.

10. A ray has _____ endpoint(s).

11. A line segment has _____ endpoint(s).

12. The measure of the supplement of an angle is greater than the measure of the complement of that angle by _____.

13. If an angle is congruent to its supplement, it is a(an) _____ angle.

14. If two angles are congruent and complementary, each angle contains _____ degrees.

15. If two lines intersect forming congruent adjacent angles, the lines are _____.

16. The bisectors of two complementary adjacent angles form an angle of _____ degrees.

17. The bisectors of two supplementary adjacent angles form an angle of _____ degrees.

18. If an angle is named $\angle RTS$, the vertex of the angle is at point _____.

19. If two angles neither of which is a right angle are complementary, they must both be _____ angles.

20. If angle t is the complement of acute angle s, and angle r is the supplement of angle s, the largest of the three angles is angle _____.

21. If the length of a radius of a circle is 7 feet, the length of the diameter is _____ feet.

22. If a chord passes through the center of a circle, it must be a(an) _____ of the circle.

23. If a triangle has two congruent sides, it is called a(an) _____ triangle.

24. A line segment has no width or thickness; it has only _____.

25. In a right triangle, the side which is opposite the right angle is called the _____.

11. True-False Exercises

In 1–20, if the statement is always true, write *true;* if the statement is not always true, write *false.*

1. If two lines are perpendicular, they intersect forming right angles.
2. A ray has one and only one endpoint.
3. A straight angle contains 180°.
4. If two adjacent angles are congruent, they are supplementary.
5. If two angles are adjacent angles, they have a common vertex.
6. If two angles have a common side, they are adjacent angles.
7. If a triangle is equilateral, it is isosceles.
8. A diameter of a circle is a chord of the circle.
9. A median to a side of a triangle bisects that side of the triangle.
10. Two different circles which have the same center are concentric circles.
11. A bisector of an angle of a triangle is perpendicular to the side opposite the angle.
12. An obtuse angle is an angle whose measure is greater than 90.
13. The length of the perpendicular from a point not on a line to that line is called the distance from the point to the line.
14. In geometry, it is possible to define all terms using only previously defined terms.
15. If a triangle is isosceles, it cannot be a right triangle.
16. The sum of the measures of two acute angles is the measure of an obtuse angle.
17. If line $\overleftrightarrow{RS}$ is perpendicular to line segment $\overline{MN}$, then $\overleftrightarrow{RS}$ passes through the midpoint of $\overline{MN}$.
18. If $\overleftrightarrow{AB}$ is the perpendicular bisector of line segment $\overline{CD}$, $\overleftrightarrow{AB}$ passes through the midpoint of $\overline{CD}$.
19. An obtuse triangle has one obtuse angle.
20. A good definition is reversible.

12. "Always, Sometimes, Never" Exercises

In 1–20, if the blank space is replaced by the word *always, sometimes,* or *never,* the resulting statement will be true. Select the word which will correctly complete the statement.

1. An angle is _____ formed by two rays.
2. A point _____ has length.
3. A chord of a circle is _____ a diameter of the circle.
4. The union of line segments in a plane _____ forms a polygon.
5. An obtuse triangle is _____ isosceles.

6. A bisector of a line segment _____ passes through the midpoint of the segment.

7. The complement of an acute angle is _____ an acute angle.

8. The supplement of an angle is _____ an obtuse angle.

9. The supplement of a right angle is _____ a right angle.

10. The complement of an angle is _____ an obtuse angle.

11. The supplement of an angle _____ is congruent to the complement of the angle.

12. An altitude drawn to a side of a triangle _____ passes through the midpoint of that side.

13. Two different circles which have the same center are _____ concentric circles.

14. If line segment $\overline{AB}$ is the perpendicular bisector of line segment $\overline{CD}$, then $\overline{CD}$ is _____ the perpendicular bisector of $\overline{AB}$.

15. If two angles have a common vertex, they are _____ adjacent angles.

16. If the sum of the measures of three angles is 90, the three angles are _____ complementary.

17. The length of a radius of a circle is _____ half of the length of a diameter.

18. If two angles are complementary, a side of one angle is _____ perpendicular to a side of the other angle.

19. The bisectors of two adjacent supplementary angles are _____ perpendicular to each other.

20. If angle A and angle B are supplementary, and if the measure of angle A is greater than the measure of angle B, then angle A is _____ obtuse.

13. Multiple-Choice Exercises

In 1–20, write the letter preceding the word or expression that best completes the statement.

1. A geometric figure that can have a midpoint is (*a*) a ray (*b*) a line (*c*) a line segment.

2. A scalene triangle has (*a*) 2 congruent sides (*b*) no congruent sides (*c*) 3 congruent sides.

3. A line segment has (*a*) 2 endpoints (*b*) 1 endpoint (*c*) no endpoints.

4. A median drawn to a side of a triangle is (*a*) a line (*b*) a line segment (*c*) a ray.

5. The supplement of a 40° angle contains (*a*) 40° (*b*) 50° (*c*) 140°.

6. If two congruent angles are supplementary, the measure of each angle is   (*a*) 45   (*b*) 90   (*c*) 180.

7. An angle whose measure is 190 is   (*a*) a right angle   (*b*) an obtuse angle   (*c*) a reflex angle.

8. The difference between the measure of the supplement and the measure of the complement of an angle is the measure of   (*a*) an acute angle   (*b*) a right angle   (*c*) an obtuse angle.

9. If two adjacent angles have their non-common sides in the same straight line, they are always   (*a*) congruent   (*b*) complementary   (*c*) supplementary.

10. If the sum of the measures of two angles is an obtuse angle, one of the two angles must be   (*a*) acute   (*b*) right   (*c*) obtuse.

11. If two lines are perpendicular, they form at the point of intersection   (*a*) acute angles   (*b*) right angles   (*c*) obtuse angles.

12. If the measure of an angle is twice the measure of its supplement, the measure of the angle is   (*a*) 120   (*b*) 60   (*c*) 30.

13. An angle of one degree is formed by   (*a*) $\frac{1}{360}$ (*b*) $\frac{1}{90}$ (*c*) $\frac{1}{180}$ of a complete revolution.

14. If the measure of an angle exceeds the measure of its complement by 20°, the angle contains   (*a*) 100°   (*b*) 35°   (*c*) 55°.

15. The distance from a point not on a line to that line is the length of   (*a*) a line segment   (*b*) a line   (*c*) a ray.

16. Two angles that are both congruent and supplementary must be   (*a*) adjacent angles   (*b*) acute angles   (*c*) right angles.

17. If an acute angle varies so that its measure increases, the measure of its supplement   (*a*) increases   (*b*) decreases   (*c*) remains the same.

18. If an acute angle varies so that its measure decreases, the measure of its complement   (*a*) increases   (*b*) decreases   (*c*) remains the same.

19. If $\angle C$ is the complement of $\angle A$, and $\angle S$ is the supplement of $\angle A$, then (*a*) $m\angle C$ is greater than $m\angle S$ (*b*) $m\angle C$ is equal to $m\angle S$ (*c*) $m\angle C$ is less than $m\angle S$.

20. A ray has   (*a*) no bisectors   (*b*) one bisector   (*c*) many bisectors.

CHAPTER II

Methods of Arriving at Conclusions

1. Using Observation to Arrive at Conclusions

In our daily lives, there are many situations in which we find it necessary to investigate the truth or falsity of a statement. A statement that is either true or false we will call a *proposition*. Frequently, *direct observation* is the most efficient method of investigation to use in determining the truth or falsity of a proposition. For example, the truth or falsity of each of the following statements can be quickly and correctly determined by observation:

1. It is snowing.
2. The radio is playing.
3. There are 35 students in the room.

Scientists commonly employ the method of observation in their work. However, one may draw wrong conclusions from observation alone. For example, see how your eyes will deceive you when observing the following figures:

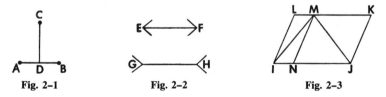

Fig. 2–1   Fig. 2–2   Fig. 2–3

1. In Fig. 2–1, does the length of $\overline{AB}$ appear to be equal to the length of $\overline{CD}$? Check your answer by measurement.
2. In Fig. 2–2, does the length of $\overline{GH}$ appear to be greater than the length of $\overline{EF}$? Check your answer by measurement.
3. In Fig. 2–3, does the length of $\overline{IM}$ appear to be less than the length of $\overline{MJ}$? Check your answer by measurement.

Fig. 2-4 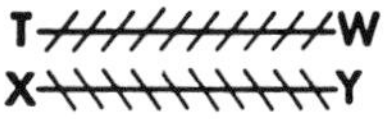   Fig. 2-5    Fig. 2-6

4. In Fig. 2-4, does the figure named by P and Q, also the figure named by R and S, appear to be curved or straight? Check your answer with a straightedge.

5. In Fig. 2-5, is the distance from T to X the same as the distance from W to Y? Check your answer by measurement.

6. In Fig. 2-6, are there 6 or 7 cubes?

Observation alone will help us arrive at conclusions in some situations. In other cases, additional methods should be used, such as reasoning or experimentation which uses measurement.

2. Using Experimentation and Measurement to Arrive at Conclusions – Inductive Reasoning

In order to determine the results that must follow from a given set of conditions, scientists often perform experiments in which measurements are made. We must realize that their results are approximate, because it is impossible to make exact measurements. *All direct measurements are approximate.*

In geometry, too, we can perform experiments in which measurements play an important role. These experiments may help us to discover properties of geometric figures and to determine geometric relationships.

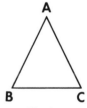

If we look at an isosceles triangle, $\triangle ABC$, in which the vertex angle, $\angle A$, is acute, and $\overline{AB} \cong \overline{AC}$, we may observe that the base angles, $\angle B$ and $\angle C$, appear to be congruent (see Fig. 2-7). In order to check our observation, we can measure $\angle B$ and $\angle C$ with a protractor. When we do, we discover that $\angle B$ and $\angle C$ have the same measure. Therefore, $\angle B \cong \angle C$.

Fig. 2-7

To convince ourselves that this relationship is also true in other isosceles triangles, we can draw another isosceles triangle and then measure its base angles. In $\triangle ABC$ (see Fig. 2-8), the vertex angle, $\angle A$, is a right angle. We can measure $\angle B$ and $\angle C$ with a protractor, and once more we would discover that the base angles have the same measure and are therefore congruent.

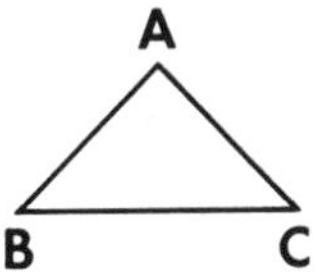

Fig. 2-8

To convince ourselves still further, we can draw an isosceles triangle, △ABC, whose vertex angle, ∠A, is an obtuse angle (see Fig. 2-9). In this triangle, too, we can measure the base angles, ∠B and ∠C, and we would discover once again that they have the same measure and are congruent.

Fig. 2-9

We may repeat the experiment several more times, changing the number of degrees in the vertex angle and changing the lengths of the sides of the isosceles triangles. In each experiment, we will find that the measure of one base angle, ∠B, is the same as the measure of the other base angle, ∠C.

From this group of experiments, dealing with various types of isosceles triangles, we are ready to arrive at the general conclusion that "the base angles of an isosceles triangle are congruent." This method of reasoning, which arrives at a general truth by studying a series of particular examples, is called *inductive reasoning*.

To discover a general geometric relationship by experimenting with particular examples, that is, to engage in inductive reasoning, we proceed as follows:

1. Carefully state the problem.
2. Perform a number of varied experiments.
3. Make the necessary measurements and observations.
4. Study and compare the results (the data).
5. Draw a proper general conclusion.

When we use inductive reasoning, we must exercise extreme care. Since our data may be based on measurement and observation which may not be absolutely accurate, our conclusion may not be accurate. Also, in inductive reasoning, we arrive at a general conclusion before we have examined every possible example. A single counterexample, that is, an example for which the general conclusion arrived at by inductive reasoning is false, is sufficient to show that the general conclusion is false. For example, after examining several isosceles triangles, Henry made the generalization that "all isosceles triangles are acute triangles." When his teacher showed him an isosceles triangle one of whose angles was a right angle, Henry realized that his generalization was false. When a general conclusion is reached by inductive reasoning alone, it can at best be called "probably true." Furthermore, although inductive reasoning may be a powerful aid in discovering new facts, it does not help us in explaining or proving them.

EXERCISES

1. *a.* Draw three right triangles that have different sizes and shapes.

    b. In each right triangle, measure the two acute angles and find the sum of their measures.

    c. Using inductive reasoning based upon the experiments just made, write a general statement about the sum of the measures of the two acute angles of a right triangle that is probably true.

In 2–8, plan and perform a series of experiments to investigate whether each statement is probably true or false.

2. If two lines intersect, the vertical angles that are formed are congruent.

3. If the bisector of the vertex angle of an isosceles triangle is drawn, it bisects the base of the triangle.

4. If the median is drawn to the base of an isosceles triangle, it bisects the vertex angle.

5. An altitude drawn to a side of a triangle bisects that side of the triangle.

6. If the diagonals of a rectangle are drawn, they are congruent.

7. If a diagonal of a polygon of four sides is drawn, it bisects the angles through whose vertices it passes.

8. The length of the line segment which joins the midpoints of two sides of a triangle is equal to one-half the length of the third side of the triangle.

In 9–12, write a conclusion; then plan and perform a series of experiments to test your conclusion.

9. If two angles are congruent, is there a relationship between the complements of these angles?

10. Is there a relationship between the lengths of the altitudes that are drawn to the two congruent legs of an isosceles triangle?

11. If two angles of one triangle are congruent to two angles of another triangle, is there a relationship between the third angle in the first triangle and the third angle in the second triangle?

12. If two sides of one triangle are congruent to two sides of a second triangle, is there a relationship between the third side of the first triangle and the third side of the second triangle?

In 13 and 14, state whether you agree with both the conclusion and the method used to arrive at it. If you do not agree with either, plan and perform a series of experiments which will help you arrive at a correct conclusion.

13. Tom drew an isosceles triangle and observed that the sum of the measures of the interior angles was 180. He concluded that the sum of the measures of the interior angles of any triangle is 180.

14. Harry drew a rectangle and observed that the sum of the measures of a pair of opposite angles was 180. He concluded that the sum of the measures of a pair of opposite angles of a polygon of four sides is 180.

In 15–20, state whether the conclusion drawn was justified. Give the reason for your answer.

15. Robert made 100% on each of his first two mathematics tests this term. He concluded that he would get 100% on every mathematics test during the term.

16. One day Mr. Peters drove home on Sunrise Highway and found traffic very heavy. He decided never again to drive on this highway on his way home.

17. Tom met two pretty Spanish girls. In talking to a friend one day, he said, "I like Spanish girls because they are all pretty."

18. One day, when Mrs. Samuels was shopping in a certain department store, she was served by an impatient saleslady. Mrs. Samuels immediately decided never to shop in that store again because all the salesladies in that store are impatient and uncooperative.

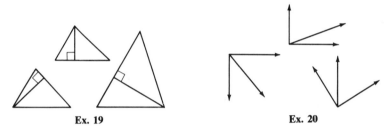

Ex. 19   Ex. 20

19. John drew the triangles shown and concluded that all points of an altitude drawn to a side of a triangle other than its endpoints always lie in the interior of the triangle.

20. From the angles shown, one can conclude that if two adjacent angles are complementary, a side of one angle is probably perpendicular to a side of the other.

3. Using Deductive Reasoning to Arrive at Conclusions

Sometimes it is difficult or inconvenient to discover the truth or falsity of a statement by observation and measurement. The average person would not like to test the truth of the statement "I shall die someday" by the method of observation. Instead, he may find the answer by reasoning through the following steps:

1. All living creatures must die someday.
2. I am a living creature.

If he accepts statements 1 and 2 as true, then he must accept as true the conclusion:

3. I shall die someday.

This is an example of valid reasoning.

If we know that an angle which contains 90° is a right angle, and that angle A contains 90°, we can conclude that angle A is a right angle by reasoning as follows:

1. All angles that contain 90° are right angles.
2. Angle A contains 90°.
3. Angle A is a right angle.

This is another example of valid reasoning.

Notice the three kinds of statements that are found in each of the preceding examples of a three-step reasoning process:

Step 1 is a general statement concerning a whole group. This statement is called the *major premise.*

Step 2 is a specific statement which indicates that an individual is a member of that group. This statement is called the *minor premise.*

Step 3 is a statement to the effect that the general statement which applies to the group also applies to the individual. This statement is called the *deduced statement,* or the *deduction.*

Such a chain of reasoning is called a *syllogism.* When we use syllogisms to arrive at conclusions, we are engaging in *deductive reasoning.* In deductive reasoning, we arrive at conclusions from accepted premises. If both the major premise and the minor premise are true, then the conclusion must be true, and the reasoning is valid.

However, unless we are very careful when using this type of reasoning, we can easily make errors in reasoning.

For example, since all seats in the orchestra at the performance of a certain play cost $8.60, are we justified in concluding that Mr. Atkins, who is sitting in the orchestra, paid $8.60 for his seat? Let us see the chain of reasoning.

1. All people who buy tickets for orchestra seats for this show pay $8.60 for a ticket.
2. Mr. Atkins is occupying an orchestra seat at this show.
3. Mr. Atkins paid $8.60 for his orchestra seat.

Notice that in step 2, Mr. Atkins failed to meet the general requirement set down for the whole group of people who bought orchestra seats. There is no statement to the effect that Mr. Atkins bought a ticket. A friend might have given him a ticket. Hence, we cannot conclude that Mr. Atkins paid $8.60 for his orchestra seat. If we did arrive at such a conclusion, our reasoning would be invalid.

When we engage in deductive reasoning using a syllogism:

KEEP IN MIND

If a major premise which is true is followed by an appropriate minor premise which is true, a conclusion can be deduced which must be true, and the reasoning is valid.

BUT

If a major premise which is true is followed by an inappropriate minor premise which is true, a conclusion cannot be deduced.

MODEL PROBLEMS

1. How may the following three statements be arranged so that the first two will make it possible to deduce the third? (*a*) An eagle has feathers. (*b*) All birds have feathers. (*c*) An eagle is a bird.

    Solution: If we arrange the sentences as a syllogism, we will have answered the question.

    Step 1 should be the major premise. (*b*) All birds have feathers.
    Step 2 should be the minor premise. (*c*) An eagle is a bird.
    Step 3 should be the conclusion. (*a*) An eagle has feathers.

    Answer: (*b*), (*c*), (*a*).

2. All residents of this state who are registered voters are over 18 years of age. If John is a resident of this state, by valid reasoning we can conclude that: (*a*) If John is over 18, he is a registered voter. (*b*) If John is a registered voter, he is over 18. (*c*) If John is not a registered voter, he is not over 18.

    Solution: The given statements and (*b*) can form a syllogism.

    1. Major premise: All residents of this state who are registered voters are over 18 years of age.
    2. Minor premise: John, a resident of this state, is a registered voter.
    3. Conclusion: John is over 18.

    Answer: (*b*).

EXERCISES

In 1–5, deduce a conclusion using a syllogism.

1. *a.* All fish swim.
  b. A trout is a fish.

2. *a.* All living human beings breathe.
  b. Sam Burns is a living human being.

3. *a.* In a certain town, teachers must be at least 21 years old.
  b. Miss Welsh teaches in that town.

4. *a.* In a right triangle, one angle is a right angle.
  b. Triangle *ABC* is a right triangle.

5. *a.* In a circle, all radii are congruent.
  b. In circle *O*, segment $\overline{OA}$ and segment $\overline{OB}$ are radii.

In 6–9, write the syllogism which justifies the conclusion.

6. Since all straight angles contain 180°, angle *A*, which is a straight angle, contains 180°.

7. Since the sides of an equilateral triangle are equal in length, in equilateral triangle *ABC*, *AB* = *BC* = *AC*.

8. Since all licensed drivers in a certain state must be over 18 years of age, Jack Welsh, who is a licensed driver in that state, is over 18 years of age.

9. Since all Presidents of the United States must be native-born citizens, President Nixon was born in the United States.

In 10–13, arrange the three statements in the proper order so that the first two will make it possible to deduce the third.

10. *a.* Harry Thompson is a student in Evans High School.
   b. All pupils in Evans High School are between 13 and 19 years of age.
   c. Harry Thompson is between 13 and 19 years of age.

11. *a.* Sam bought his newspaper at Mr. Wilson's stand.
   b. Sam always buys his newspaper at Mr. Wilson's stand.
   c. Sam bought a newspaper.

12. *a.* A triangle that has two congruent sides is an isosceles triangle.
   b. Triangle *ABC* is an isosceles triangle.
   c. Triangle *ABC* has two congruent sides.

13. *a.* Line $\overleftrightarrow{AB}$ bisects the given line segment.
   b. A line which passes through the midpoint of a given line segment bisects the given line segment.
   c. Line $\overleftrightarrow{AB}$ passes through the midpoint of the given line segment.

In 14–17, state whether the reasoning which is used to deduce the conclusion is valid. If the reasoning is not valid, state the error in reasoning.

14. Every student in West High School is a member of the Student Organization. Sue Tucker, who is a student in West High School, is a member of the Student Organization.

15. Since all children in Barter City between the ages of 6 and 17 must attend school, Harry, who is 16 years old, attends school.

16. In all isosceles triangles, there are two congruent sides. Therefore, in triangle *ABC*, there are two congruent sides.

17. All quadrilaterals with four right angles are rectangles. Therefore, a polygon in which angles *A*, *B*, *C*, and *D* are right angles is a rectangle.

18. All children of Cedar City who are pupils in East High School are over 12 years of age. If Ted is a resident of Cedar City, by valid reasoning we can conclude that: (*a*) If Ted is not a pupil in East High School, he is not over 12 years of age. (*b*) If Ted is over 12 years of age, he is a pupil in East High School. (*c*) If Ted is a pupil in East High School, he is over 12 years of age.

4. Determining the Hypothesis and Conclusion of a Statement

The Hypothesis and Conclusion in an "If-Then" Sentence

A statement which is in the form "If _____, then _____" is called a *conditional statement*.

An example of a conditional statement is: *If two sides of a triangle are congruent, then the triangle is an isosceles triangle.*

This conditional statement is a complex sentence which contains two clauses, a *dependent clause* and an *independent clause*.

1. The dependent clause is introduced by the word *if*.

If <u>two sides of a triangle are congruent</u>

The part of this clause which follows the word *if* is called the *hypothesis*, or the *given*.

If we represent "Two sides of a triangle are congruent" (the statement in the dependent clause which follows the word *if*) by *p*, then *p* is the hypothesis, or given.

2. The independent clause is introduced by the word *then*.

then <u>the triangle is an isosceles triangle</u>

The part of this clause which follows the word *then* is called the *conclusion*, or the *to prove*.

If we represent "The triangle is an isosceles triangle" (the statement in the independent clause which follows the word *then*) by *q*, then *q* is the conclusion, or to prove.

In general, in a conditional statement which is written in the form "If *p*, then *q*," the hypothesis, or given, is *p*, and the conclusion, or to prove, is *q*.

Sometimes the if-clause appears at the end of the sentence. For example, the preceding "if-then" sentence may be restated as follows: *A triangle is an isosceles triangle if two sides of the triangle are congruent.*

The Hypothesis and Conclusion in a Simple Sentence

Consider the following statement:

Right angles *A* and *B* are congruent.

This simple sentence has a subject and a predicate.

1. The subject, Right angles *A* and *B*, is the hypothesis.
2. The predicate, are congruent, is the conclusion.

In general, if a statement is written as a simple sentence, the subject of the sentence is the hypothesis and the predicate is the conclusion.

In order to help us determine the hypothesis and conclusion in a simple sentence, we can rewrite the sentence as a conditional statement. We can do this by writing the word *If* before the subject of the sentence and the word *then* before the predicate of the sentence. For example, the preceding simple sentence (Right angles *A* and *B* are congruent.) may be restated as follows: *If angles A and B are right angles, then they are congruent.*

MODEL PROBLEMS ⌇⌇⌇⌇⌇⌇⌇⌇⌇⌇⌇⌇⌇

1. Identify the hypothesis and conclusion in the statement "If Mary has a temperature, then she is probably sick."

   Solution: If Mary has a temperature, then she is probably sick.

   The if-clause, "Mary has a temperature," is the hypothesis.
   The then-clause, "she is probably sick," is the conclusion.

2. Identify the hypothesis and conclusion in the statement "The median drawn to the base of an isosceles triangle is perpendicular to the base."

   Solution: The median drawn to the base of an isosceles triangle is perpendicular to the base.

The subject of the sentence, "The median drawn to the base of an isosceles triangle," is the hypothesis.

The predicate of the sentence, "is perpendicular to the base," is the conclusion.

3. For the following statement, draw a figure, letter it, ánd state in terms of the letters of the figure what is the hypothesis and what is the conclusion:

If the bisector of the vertex angle of an isosceles triangle is drawn, the bisector is perpendicular to the base of the triangle.

Solution:

The if-clause, "the bisector of the vertex angle of an isosceles triangle is drawn," is the hypothesis.

The then-clause, "the bisector is perpendicular to the base of the triangle," is the conclusion.

Answer: Hypothesis: Isosceles triangle RST with $\overline{TR} \cong \overline{TS}$. $\overline{TQ}$ bisects $\angle RTS$.

Conclusion: $\overline{TQ} \perp \overline{RS}$.

EXERCISES

In 1–13, state the hypothesis and the conclusion.

1. If a boy has a pleasant personality, he will make friends readily.
2. If metal is cooled, then it contracts.
3. If the sun is shining, it is a clear day.
4. If the sum of the measures of two angles is 90, the angles are complementary.
5. If two angles are congruent, their measures are equal.
6. Children are polite if they have good manners.
7. A triangle is equiangular if the triangle has three congruent sides.
8. Two angles are supplementary if they are right angles.
9. Clothes which are expensive are made of better materials.
10. A well-fed child gains weight.
11. Two lines that intersect form vertical angles.
12. The bisector of an angle divides the angle into two congruent angles.

13. The median to the base of an isosceles triangle bisects the vertex angle of the triangle.

In 14–18, draw a figure, letter it, and state in terms of the letters of the figure what is the hypothesis and what is the conclusion.

14. If the altitude is drawn to the base of an isosceles triangle, the altitude bisects the base.
15. If two angles of a triangle are congruent, the sides opposite these angles are congruent.
16. A triangle is isosceles if the bisector of an angle bisects the opposite side.
17. Altitudes drawn to the congruent sides of an isosceles triangle are congruent.
18. If the opposite sides of a quadrilateral are congruent, the diagonals of the quadrilateral bisect each other.

5. Deductive Reasoning Involving a Conditional Statement

Consider the following two statements:

1. If you hit a home run, then you will score a run.
2. You hit a home run.

If we accept statements 1 and 2 as true, then we must accept as true the conclusion:

3. You scored a run.

Notice that three kinds of statements are found in the previous example.

Statement 1 is a general conditional statement in the "If ____, then ____," form in which the if-clause is the hypothesis and the then-clause is the conclusion.

Statement 2 is a statement which indicates that you satisfied the conditions of the hypothesis.

Statement 3 is a statement, a deduction, which indicates that the conclusion is true for you.

In general, if p represents the hypothesis in a conditional statement and q represents the conclusion in this conditional statement, then we can perform deductive reasoning in the following manner:

If (1) the conditional statement "If p, then q" is true, and (2) the hypothesis p is true, then (3) the conclusion q is true.

Let us see how we can perform such deductive reasoning in a geometric example. (See Fig. 2–10.)

If (1) the conditional statement "If ∠*ABC* contains
between 0° and 90°, then ∠*ABC* is an acute angle" is
accepted as true and (2) the hypothesis "∠*ABC* contains
between 0° and 90°" is asserted to be true, then (3) the
conclusion "∠*ABC* is an acute angle" is deduced to be
true.

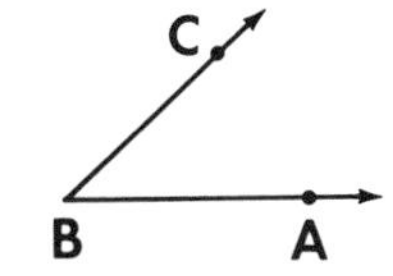

Fig. 2-10

Now let us see whether accepting the truth of a con-
ditional statement and also the truth of the conclusion of the statement per-
mits us to deduce that the hypothesis of the statement must be true. For
example,

If (1) the conditional statement "If two angles are right angles, then they
have equal measures" is accepted as true, and (2) the conclusion "Two
angles have equal measures" is asserted to be true, does it follow that the
hypothesis "The two angles are right angles" must be true? *Of course not!*
If each of the angles contains 30°, the angles would have equal measures,
yet they would not be right angles.

In general, if *p* represents the hypothesis in a conditional statement and
q represents the conclusion in this conditional statement, then:

If (1) the conditional statement "If *p*, then *q*" is true, and (2) the conclusion *q* is true, *we cannot deduce that the hypothesis p is true. The hypothesis p may or may not be true.*

EXERCISES

In 1–4, state whether accepting the truth of statements (*a*) and (*b*) makes
it possible to deduce the truth of statement (*c*). Give a reason for your
answer.

1. *a.* If it is snowing, I am at home.
   b. It is snowing.
   c. Therefore, I am at home.

2. *a.* You are a resident of the United States if you are a resident of New
      York State.
   b. You are a resident of the United States.
   c. Therefore, you are a resident of New York State.

3. *a.* If two angles are straight angles, they have equal measures.
   b. Two angles *A* and *B* are straight angles.
   c. Therefore, the two angles *A* and *B* have equal measures.

4. *a.* If two angles are adjacent angles, then they have a common vertex.
   b. Two angles *ABC* and *ABD* have a common vertex.
   c. Therefore, the two angles *ABC* and *ABD* are adjacent angles.

In 5–8, assume the truth of statements (*a*) and (*b*). If from the truth of
these statements it is possible to deduce the truth of a third statement, write

the deduced statement and tell why the deduced statement is true. If from the truth of the first two statements it is not possible to deduce the truth of a third statement, tell why this is so.

5. *a.* If you attend Highview High School, you are a male student.
   b. You attend Highview High School.

6. *a.* If you are a pretty girl, then you have many friends.
   b. You have many friends.

7. *a.* If two angles are supplementary, then the sum of the measures of the two angles is 180.
   b. Two angles *R* and *S* are supplementary.

8. *a.* Two angles are complementary if each of the two angles contains 45°.
   b. Two angles *A* and *B* are complementary.

6. Understanding the Nature of a Postulational System

In order to avoid any misunderstanding in a discussion, it is essential that words and phrases be defined so that they will have the same meaning for all people.

For example, we can define an isosceles triangle as a triangle which has two congruent sides.

Now the question arises: What is a triangle? We can define a triangle as a polygon which has three sides.

What is a polygon? It is a closed figure in a plane which is the union of line segments.

What is a line segment? It is a set of points of a line consisting of two points on the line and the set of all points on the line between these two points.

What is a plane and what is a line? Now we find that we have no simpler, previously defined terms to use.

In geometry, therefore, we must have some undefined terms with which to begin the process of defining new terms.

In our study of the use of reasoning in arriving at conclusions, we saw that, to establish the truth or falsity of a proposition, we must offer other previously accepted propositions as convincing evidence. For example, we might wish to establish the truth of the following proposition: "If two line segments are congruent to the same line segment, they are congruent to each other." To do this, we might argue as follows (see Fig. 2–11):

1. $\overline{AB} \cong \overline{EF}$.
2. $\overline{CD} \cong \overline{EF}$.

Fig. 2–11

It appears that we should now be ready to grant that $\overline{AB} \cong \overline{CD}$. Yet if we were asked to state a previously proved proposition which would justify this conclusion, we would find none.

Thus, in geometry, we must start with some propositions whose truth we assume in order to begin the process of deducing the truth of other propositions.

A proposition whose truth is assumed is called an *assumption*, a *postulate*, or an *axiom*.

Some mathematicians reserve the term *axiom* for a general statement whose truth is assumed without proof, and the term *postulate* for a geometric statement whose truth is assumed without proof. We will use the term *postulate* for both types of assumptions.

Definition. A *postulate* is a statement whose truth is accepted without proof.

In a postulational system, the *undefined terms*, the *defined terms*, and the *postulates* are the seeds from which the tree of knowledge in the subject grows. They, together with the laws of reasoning, become the instruments with which we deduce, that is, prove the truth of, new statements, called *theorems*.

Definition. A *theorem* is a statement proved by deduction.

Postulational thinking, which is the instrument used to make deductions in demonstrative geometry, is a powerful technique for several reasons:

1. It makes it possible to arrive at a conclusion in situations where observation and measurement are not practical or possible.
2. Observation and measurement may help to discover a fact, but they never explain the reason for the truth of the fact. Postulational thinking accounts for, and explains why, the reasoning used in arriving at a conclusion is valid or invalid.
3. In a postulational system, a combination of the undefined terms, the defined terms, the postulates, and the derived theorems leads to the discovery and explanation of new theorems. In this way, the entire body of knowledge known as geometry is developed.

EXERCISES

1. Define a postulate.
2. Define a theorem.
3. Answer *true* or *false*. In a postulational system, all terms are defined.
4. What are the elements in a postulational system that may be used to explain a new theorem?

7. Using Postulates in Proving Conclusions

We have seen that deductive reasoning is based upon the use of undefined terms, defined terms, and postulates. Now we are going to examine some of these postulates and learn how to use them in deductive reasoning.

Equality Postulates

When we state the relation "*a* is equal to *b*," symbolized by "*a* = *b*," we mean that the symbol *a* and the symbol *b* are two different names for the same element of a set. Very frequently *a* and *b* represent a number. For example,

1. When we write $RS = LM$, we mean that line segment $\overline{RS}$ and line segment $\overline{LM}$ have the same length.
2. When we write $m\angle A = m\angle B$, we mean that angle *A* and angle *B* contain the same number of degrees.

We should now be ready to accept the following three equality postulates, which are also referred to as the *properties of equality*.

Postulate 1. The Reflexive Property of Equality

$$a = a$$

This property, which states that if there is an element of a set named *a*, then there is only one element of that set which is named by *a*, is sometimes called the *principle of identity*. We can restate the reflexive property of equality in words as follows:

Postulate 1. **A quantity is equal to itself.**

EXAMPLE 1 (see Fig. 2–12). $LM = LM$.

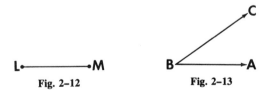

L•————————•M   B————————➤A

Fig. 2–12   Fig. 2–13

EXAMPLE 2 (see Fig. 2–13). $m\angle ABC = m\angle ABC$.

Postulate 2. The Symmetric Property of Equality

If $a = b$, then $b = a$.

This property states that if a names the same element of a set as b, then b names the same element as a. We can restate the symmetric property of equality in words as follows:

Postulate 2. **An equality may be reversed.**

EXAMPLE 1 (see Fig. 2–14). If $AB = CD$, then $CD = AB$.

EXAMPLE 2 (see Fig. 2–14). If $m\angle R = m\angle S$, then $m\angle S = m\angle R$.

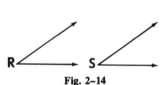

Fig. 2–14

Postulate 3. The Transitive Property of Equality

If $a = b$, and $b = c$, then $a = c$.

This property states that if a and b name the same element of a set, and b and c name the same element of that set, then a and c name the same element of the set. We can restate the transitive property of equality in words as follows:

Postulate 3. **If quantities are equal to the same quantity, they are equal to each other.**

Now we will see how the symmetric and the transitive postulates of equality can be used in deductive reasoning.

EXAMPLE 1. If we know that $m\angle x = 40$ and $m\angle y = 40$, and we wish to prove that $m\angle x = m\angle y$, we can say that since $m\angle y = 40$, then $40 = m\angle y$, using the symmetric property of equality; also, we can say that, since $m\angle x = 40$, and $40 = m\angle y$, then $m\angle x = m\angle y$, using the transitive property of equality.

It is possible to arrange the preceding proof more formally in two columns. In order to arrange a proof in a formal manner, we will:

1. State the hypothesis, which is also called the *given*, because the hypothesis contains the given facts.
2. State the conclusion, which is also called the *to prove*, because the conclusion contains what is to be proved.

NOTE. In our work, we will use the terms *given* and *to prove* rather than the terms *hypothesis* and *conclusion*.

3. Present the *proof,* the deductive reasoning, which is the series of logical arguments used in the demonstration. Each step in the proof should consist of a *statement* in one column and its *reason* in the other column. A reason may be the *given,* a *definition,* a *postulate,* or, as we shall see later, a *previously proved theorem.*

EXAMPLE 1 (see Fig. 2–15).

Given: $m\angle x = 40.$
            $m\angle y = 40.$

To prove: $m\angle x = m\angle y.$

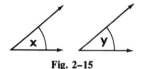

Fig. 2–15

Proof: *Statements*   *Reasons*

1. $m\angle x = 40.$	1. Given.
2. $m\angle y = 40.$	2. Given.
3. $40 = m\angle y.$	3. The symmetric property of equality: An equality may be reversed.
4. $m\angle x = m\angle y.$	4. The transitive property of equality: If quantities are equal to the same quantity, they are equal to each other.

NOTE. In the future, we will abbreviate the proof by eliminating step 3 and reason 3, the step which makes use of the symmetric property of equality. After presenting steps 1 and 2, we will immediately deduce the conclusion that $m\angle x = m\angle y.$

EXAMPLE 2 (see Fig. 2–16).

Given: $AB = LM.$
            $CD = RS.$
            $LM = RS.$

To prove: $AB = CD.$

A•————————•B L•————————•M

C•————————•D R•————————•S

Fig. 2–16

Proof: *Statements*	*Reasons*
1. $AB = LM$.	1. Given.
2. $LM = RS$.	2. Given.
3. $AB = RS$.	3. The transitive property of equality: If quantities are equal to the same quantity, they are equal to each other.
4. $CD = RS$.	4. Given.
5. $AB = CD$.	5. The transitive property of equality: If quantities are equal to the same quantity, they are equal to each other.

Notice that in example 2 we proved an illustration of the statement "If quantities are equal to equal quantities, they are equal to each other." In the future, we will feel free to use this statement, which is an expanded version of the transitive property of equality, as a reason in a proof.

EXERCISES

In 1–3, (*a*) state the postulate that can be used to show that the conclusion is valid and (*b*) write a formal proof.

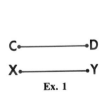

Ex. 1

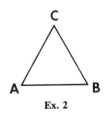

Ex. 2

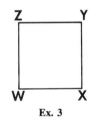

Ex. 3

1. *Given:* $CD = 2$ inches.
   $XY = 2$ inches.

   Prove: $CD = XY$.

2. *Given:* $m\angle A = m\angle B$.
   $m\angle C = m\angle B$.

   Prove: $m\angle A = m\angle C$.

3. *Given:* $WZ = XY$.
   $ZY = WX$.
   $WZ = ZY$.

   Prove: $XY = WX$.

Equivalence Relations

Relations which have the reflexive property, the symmetric property, and the transitive property are called *equivalence relations*. We would say, therefore, that "is equal to (=)" for numbers is an equivalence relation because equality has all of the three required properties. On the other hand, the relation "is perpendicular to (⊥)" for lines is not an equivalence relation. Suppose *a*, *b*, and *c* represent lines. Consider the following statements:

1. Reflexive property (see Fig. 2–17): $a \perp a$.
2. Symmetric property (see Fig. 2–18): If $a \perp b$, then $b \perp a$.
3. Transitive property (see Fig. 2–19): If $a \perp b$, and $b \perp c$, then $a \perp c$.

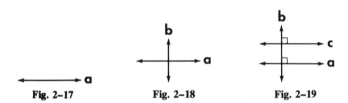

Fig. 2–17   Fig. 2–18   Fig. 2–19

Observe that the relation "is perpendicular to (⊥)" does have the symmetric property, but has neither the reflexive property nor the transitive property.

Congruence of Line Segments and Congruence of Angles

Since we have said that $\overline{AB} \cong \overline{CD}$ is equivalent to $AB = CD$, and $\overline{CD} \cong \overline{EF}$ is equivalent to $CD = EF$, it follows that the "congruence of line segments" has the same three properties as "the equality of numbers":

1. Reflexive property: $\overline{AB} \cong \overline{AB}$.
2. Symmetric property: If $\overline{AB} \cong \overline{CD}$, then $\overline{CD} \cong \overline{AB}$.
3. Transitive property: If $\overline{AB} \cong \overline{CD}$, and $\overline{CD} \cong \overline{EF}$, then $\overline{AB} \cong \overline{EF}$.

Hence, we say that "congruence of line segments" is an equivalence relation.

Since we have said that $\angle ABC \cong \angle DEF$ is equivalent to $m\angle ABC = m\angle DEF$, and $\angle DEF \cong \angle XYZ$ is equivalent to $m\angle DEF = m\angle XYZ$, it follows that the "congruence of angles" has the same three properties as "the equality of numbers":

1. Reflexive property: $\angle ABC \cong \angle ABC$.
2. Symmetric property: If $\angle ABC \cong \angle DEF$, then $\angle DEF \cong \angle ABC$.
3. Transitive property: If $\angle ABC \cong \angle DEF$, and $\angle DEF \cong \angle XYZ$, then $\angle ABC \cong \angle XYZ$.

Hence, we say that "congruence of angles" is an equivalence relation.

KEEP IN MIND

"Equality of numbers," "congruence of line segments," and "congruence of angles" are all equivalence relations. In the future, we will consider that the reflexive, the symmetric, and the transitive properties of "equality of numbers" are also to be the reflexive, the symmetric, and the transitive properties of "congruence of line segments" and of "congruence of angles."

EXERCISES

In 1–6, name the property that justifies the statement.

1. $\overline{AC} \cong \overline{AC}$.

2. If $\angle RST \cong \angle XYZ$, then $\angle XYZ \cong \angle RST$.

3. $\angle ABC \cong \angle ABC$.

4. If $\overline{LM} \cong \overline{XY}$, then $\overline{XY} \cong \overline{LM}$.

5. If $\overline{AB} \cong \overline{CD}$, and $\overline{CD} \cong \overline{ST}$, then $\overline{AB} \cong \overline{ST}$.

6. If $\angle XYZ \cong \angle RST$, and $\angle RST \cong \angle ABC$, then $\angle XYZ \cong \angle ABC$.

In 7–10, name the properties of an equivalence relation which are satisfied by the given relation.

7. "is greater than" (for natural numbers)

8. "is a factor of" (for natural numbers)

9. "is the father of" (for people)

10. "lives in the same house as" (for people)

Substitution Postulate

Postulate 4. **A quantity may be substituted for its equal in any expression.**

EXAMPLE 1 (see Fig. 2–20).

Given: $AB = 2AD$.
        $AD = DB$.
To prove: $AB = 2DB$.

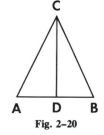

Fig. 2–20

[The proof is given on the next page.]

Proof: *Statements*	*Reasons*
1. $AB = 2AD$.	1. Given.
2. $AD = DB$.	2. Given.
3. $AB = 2DB$.	3. Substitution postulate: A quantity may be substituted for its equal in any expression.

EXAMPLE 2 (see Fig. 2–21).

Given: $m\angle a + m\angle b = 90$.
          $m\angle a = m\angle c$.

To prove: $m\angle c + m\angle b = 90$.

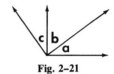

Fig. 2–21

Proof: *Statements*	*Reasons*
1. $m\angle a + m\angle b = 90$.	1. Given.
2. $m\angle a = m\angle c$.	2. Given.
3. $m\angle c + m\angle b = 90$.	3. Substitution postulate: A quantity may be substituted for its equal in any expression.

EXERCISES

In 1–4, (*a*) state the postulate that can be used to show that the conclusion is valid and (*b*) write a formal proof.

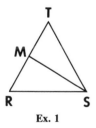

Ex. 1

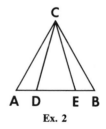

Ex. 2

1. *Given: $MT = \frac{1}{2}RT$.*
        $RM = MT$.
  Prove: $RM = \frac{1}{2}RT$.

2. *Given: $AD + DE = AE$.*
          $AD = EB$.
  Prove: $EB + DE = AE$.

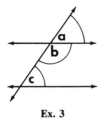

Ex. 3

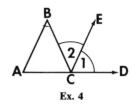

Ex. 4

3. *Given:* $m\angle a + m\angle b = 180$.
    $m\angle a = m\angle c$.
Prove: $m\angle c + m\angle b = 180$.

4. *Given:* $m\angle 1 + m\angle 2 + m\angle BCA = 180$.
    $m\angle A = m\angle 1$ and $m\angle B = m\angle 2$.
Prove: $m\angle A + m\angle B + m\angle BCA = 180$.

Partition Postulate

Postulate 5. **A whole quantity is equal to the sum of all its parts.**

EXAMPLE 1 (see Fig. 2–22). $AD = AB + BC + CD$.

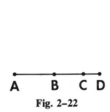

Fig. 2–22

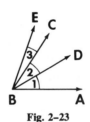

Fig. 2–23

EXAMPLE 2 (see Fig. 2–23). $m\angle ABE = m\angle 1 + m\angle 2 + m\angle 3$.

Addition Postulate

Postulate 6. **If $a = b$, and $c = d$, then $a + c = b + d$.**

We can restate the addition postulate of equality as follows:

Postulate 6. **If equal quantities are added to equal quantities, the sums are equal.**

EXAMPLE 1 (see Fig. 2–24).

Given: $AB = DE$.
           $BC = EF$.

To prove: $AC = DF$.

Fig. 2–24

[The proof is given on the next page.]

Proof: *Statements* | *Reasons*

1. $AB = DE.$ | 1. Given.

2. $BC = EF.$ | 2. Given.

3. $AB + BC = DE + EF.$ | 3. Addition postulate: If equal quantities are added to equal quantities, the sums are equal.

4. $AB + BC = AC$ and $DE + EF = DF.$ | 4. Partition postulate: A whole quantity is equal to the sum of all its parts.

5. $AC = DF.$ | 5. Substitution postulate: A quantity may be substituted for its equal in any expression.

We have learned that $\overline{AB} \cong \overline{DE}$ is equivalent to $AB = DE$, and that $\overline{BC} \cong \overline{EF}$ is equivalent to $BC = EF$. Hence, we will deal with the addition of congruent segments in the same way that we deal with the addition of segments whose lengths are equal. For example, when we are dealing with congruent segments, we will feel free to state the Addition Postulate as follows: "If congruent segments are added to congruent segments, the sums are congruent." For similar reasons, we will deal with the addition of congruent angles in the same way that we would deal with the addition of angles whose measures are equal. For example, when we are dealing with congruent angles, we will feel free to state the Addition Postulate as follows: "If congruent angles are added to congruent angles, the sums are congruent." See how this is done in the following examples.

EXAMPLE 2 (see Fig. 2–25).

Given: $\overline{AB} \cong \overline{DE}.$
$\overline{BC} \cong \overline{EF}.$

To prove: $\overline{AC} \cong \overline{DF}.$

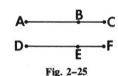

Fig. 2–25

Proof: *Statements* | *Reasons*

1. $\overline{AB} \cong \overline{DE}.$ | 1. Given.

2. $\overline{BC} \cong \overline{EF}.$ | 2. Given.

3. $\overline{AB} + \overline{BC} \cong \overline{DE} + \overline{EF}$, or $\overline{AC} \cong \overline{DF}.$ | 3. Addition postulate: If congruent segments are added to congruent segments, the sums are congruent segments.

NOTE. $\overline{AC}$ is another name for $\overline{AB} + \overline{BC}$; $\overline{DF}$ is another name for $\overline{DE} + \overline{EF}.$

EXAMPLE 3 (see Fig. 2–26).

Given: ∠*ABG* ≅ ∠*DEH*.
　　　∠*GBC* ≅ ∠*HEF*.

To prove: ∠*ABC* ≅ ∠*DEF*.

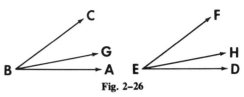
Fig. 2–26

Proof:　*Statements*　　　　　　　　　*Reasons*

1.　　　∠*ABG* ≅ ∠*DEH*.　| 1. Given.

2.　　　∠*GBC* ≅ ∠*HEF*.　| 2. Given.

3. ∠*ABG* + ∠*GBC* ≅ ∠*DEH* +　| 3. Addition postulate: If congruent
∠*HEF*, or ∠*ABC* ≅ ∠*DEF*.　| angles are added to congruent
　　　　　　　　　　　　| angles, the sums are congruent
NOTE.　∠*ABC* is another name for　| angles.
∠*ABG* + ∠*GBC*; ∠*DEF* is
another name for ∠*DEH* +
∠*HEF*.

EXERCISES

In 1–6, (*a*) state the postulate or postulates that can be used to show that the conclusion is valid and (*b*) write a formal proof.

Ex. 1

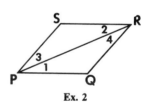
Ex. 2

1. *Given: AM = CN.*
　　　MB = ND.
Prove: AB = CD.

2. *Given: m∠1 = m∠2.*
　　　m∠3 = m∠4.
Prove: m∠QPS = m∠QRS.

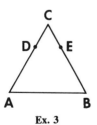
Ex. 3

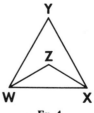
Ex. 4

3. *Given:* $\overline{CD} ≅ \overline{CE}$.
　　　$\overline{DA} ≅ \overline{EB}$.
Prove: $\overline{CA} ≅ \overline{CB}$.

4. *Given:* ∠*XWZ* ≅ ∠*WXZ*.
　　　∠*ZWY* ≅ ∠*ZXY*.
Prove: ∠*XWY* ≅ ∠*WXY*.

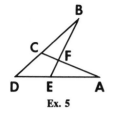

Ex. 5

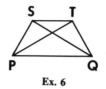

Ex. 6

5. *Given:* $\overline{AF} \cong \overline{BF}$.
   $\overline{FC} \cong \overline{FE}$.
   Prove: $\overline{AC} \cong \overline{BE}$.

6. *Given:* $\angle QST \cong \angle PTS$.
   $\angle QSP \cong \angle PTQ$.
   Prove: $\angle PST \cong \angle QTS$.

Subtraction Postulate

Postulate 7. **If** $a = b$, **and** $c = d$, **then** $a - c = b - d$.

We can restate the subtraction postulate of equality as follows:

Postulate 7. **If equal quantities are subtracted from equal quantities, the differences are equal.**

EXAMPLE 1 (see Fig. 2–27).

Given: $m\angle DAC = m\angle ECA$.
        $m\angle 1 = m\angle 2$.

To prove: $m\angle 3 = m\angle 4$.

Fig. 2–27

Proof:	*Statements*	*Reasons*
1.	$m\angle DAC = m\angle ECA$.	1. Given.
2.	$m\angle 1 = m\angle 2$.	2. Given.
3.	$m\angle DAC - m\angle 1 = m\angle ECA - m\angle 2$, or $m\angle 3 = m\angle 4$.	3. Subtraction postulate: If equal quantities are subtracted from equal quantities, the differences are equal.

We will deal with the subtraction of congruent angles in the same way that we deal with the subtraction of angles which have equal measures. Also, we will deal with the subtraction of congruent segments in the same way that we deal with the subtraction of segments whose lengths are equal. See how this is illustrated in the following example:

EXAMPLE 2 (see Fig. 2–28).

Given: $\overline{AB} \cong \overline{AC}$.
$\overline{DB} \cong \overline{EC}$.

To prove: $\overline{AD} \cong \overline{AE}$.

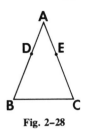

Fig. 2–28

Proof: *Statements*   *Reasons*

1. $\overline{AB} \cong \overline{AC}$.   1. Given.

2. $\overline{DB} \cong \overline{EC}$.   2. Given.

3. $\overline{AB} - \overline{DB} \cong \overline{AC} - \overline{EC}$, or   3. Subtraction postulate: If con-
   $\overline{AD} \cong \overline{AE}$.   gruent segments are subtracted
                                             from congruent segments, the
                                             differences are congruent seg-
                                             ments.

EXERCISES

In 1–6, (*a*) state the postulate or postulates that can be used to show
that the conclusion is valid and   (*b*) write a formal proof.

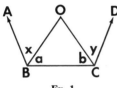

Ex. 1

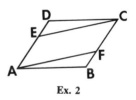

Ex. 2

1. *Given:* $m\angle ABC = m\angle DCB$.   **2.** *Given:* $AD = BC$.
      $m\angle a = m\angle b$. $AE = CF$.
   Prove: $m\angle x = m\angle y$.   *Prove:* $DE = BF$.

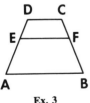

Ex. 3

Ex. 4

3. *Given:* $\overline{DA} \cong \overline{CB}$.   **4.** *Given:* $\angle WZY \cong \angle WXY$.
      $\overline{DE} \cong \overline{CF}$. $\angle RZY \cong \angle RXS$.
   Prove: $\overline{EA} \cong \overline{FB}$.   *Prove:* $\angle WZR \cong \angle YXS$.

Ex. 5

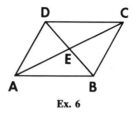

Ex. 6

5. *Given:* $\overline{FD} \cong \overline{GC}$.
           $\overline{FH} \cong \overline{GH}$.
Prove: $\overline{CH} \cong \overline{DH}$.

6. *Given:* $\angle DEB \cong \angle AEC$.
           $\angle DEA \cong \angle BEC$.
Prove: $\angle AEB \cong \angle DEC$.

Multiplication Postulate

Postulate 8. **If $a = b$, and $c = d$, then $ac = bd$.**

We can restate the multiplication postulate of equality as follows:

Postulate 8. **If equal quantities are multiplied by equal quantities, the products are equal.**

When each of two equal quantities is multiplied by the number 2, we have a special case of this postulate which is stated as follows:

Doubles of equal quantities are equal.

EXAMPLE 1 (see Fig. 2–29).

Given: $AB = CD$.
          $RS = 2AB$.
          $LM = 2CD$.

A•——•B   R•————•S

C•——•D   L•————•M

Fig. 2–29

To prove: $RS = LM$.

Proof:

Statements	Reasons
1. $AB = CD$.	1. Given.
2. $RS = 2AB$.	2. Given.
3. $LM = 2CD$.	3. Given.
4. $RS = LM$.	4. Multiplication postulate: Doubles of equal quantities are equal.

We will deal with doubles of congruent segments and doubles of congruent angles in the same way that we deal with doubles of segments whose lengths are equal, and doubles of angles which have equal measures. See how this is illustrated in the following example:

EXAMPLE 2 (see Fig. 2-30).

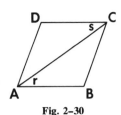

Given: $\angle r \cong \angle s$.
           $m\angle BAD = 2m\angle r$.
           $m\angle BCD = 2m\angle s$.

To prove: $\angle BAD \cong \angle BCD$.

Fig. 2-30

Proof: *Statements*

	Statements	*Reasons*
1.	$\angle r \cong \angle s$.	1. Given.
2.	$m\angle BAD = 2m\angle r$.	2. Given.
3.	$m\angle BCD = 2m\angle s$.	3. Given.
4.	$\angle BAD \cong \angle BCD$.	4. Doubles of congruent angles are congruent.

EXERCISES

In 1-6, (*a*) state the postulate or postulates that can be used to show that the conclusion is valid and (*b*) write a formal proof.

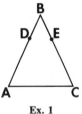

Ex. 1

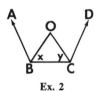

Ex. 2

1. *Given:* $BD = BE$.
           $BA = 3BD$.
           $BC = 3BE$.
    Prove: $BA = BC$.

2. *Given:* $m\angle x = m\angle y$.
           $m\angle CBA = 2m\angle x$.
           $m\angle BCD = 2m\angle y$.
    Prove: $m\angle CBA = m\angle BCD$.

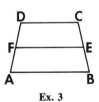

Ex. 3

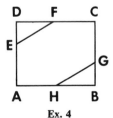

Ex. 4

3. *Given:* $AF = BE$.
           $AD = 2AF$.
           $BC = 2BE$.
    Prove: $AD = BC$.

4. *Given:* $\overline{DF} \cong \overline{HB}$.
           $DC = 2DF$.
           $AB = 2HB$.
    Prove: $\overline{DC} \cong \overline{AB}$.

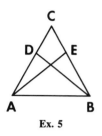

Ex. 5

Ex. 6

5. *Given:* ∠*EBD* ≅ ∠*EAD*.
   m∠*ABE* = 2*m*∠*EBD*.
   m∠*BAD* = 2*m*∠*EAD*.
Prove: ∠*ABE* ≅ ∠*BAD*.

6. *Given:* $\overline{PX} \cong \overline{PY}$.
   SP = 2*PX*.
   RP = 2*PY*.
Prove: $\overline{SP} \cong \overline{RP}$.

Division Postulate

Postulate 9. **If** $a = b$, **and** $c = d$, **then** $\dfrac{a}{c} = \dfrac{b}{d}$. (*c* **is not 0 and** *d* **is not 0.**)

We can restate the division postulate of equality as follows:

Postulate 9. **If equal quantities are divided by equal quantities (not zero), the quotients are equal.**

When each of two equal quantities is divided by the number 2, we have a special case of this postulate which is stated as follows:

Halves of equal quantities are equal.

EXAMPLE 1 (see Fig. 2–31).
Given: $m\angle LED = m\angle LFB$.
   $m\angle 1 = \frac{1}{2}m\angle LED$.
   $m\angle 2 = \frac{1}{2}m\angle LFB$.
To prove: $m\angle 1 = m\angle 2$.

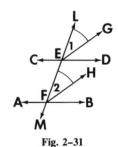

Fig. 2–31

Proof: *Statements*	*Reasons*
1. $m\angle LED = m\angle LFB$.	1. Given.
2. $m\angle 1 = \frac{1}{2}m\angle LED$.	2. Given.
3. $m\angle 2 = \frac{1}{2}m\angle LFB$.	3. Given.
4. $m\angle 1 = m\angle 2$.	4. Division postulate: Halves of equal quantities are equal.

We will deal with halves of congruent segments and halves of congruent angles in the same way that we deal with halves of segments whose lengths are equal and halves of angles whose measures are equal. See how this is illustrated in the following example:

EXAMPLE 2 (see Fig. 2–32).

Given: $\overline{AB} \cong \overline{DC}.$
$AF = \frac{1}{2}AB.$
$EC = \frac{1}{2}DC.$

To prove: $\overline{AF} \cong \overline{EC}.$

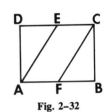

Fig. 2–32

Proof: *Statements*	*Reasons*
1. $\overline{AB} \cong \overline{DC}.$	1. Given.
2. $AF = \frac{1}{2}AB.$	2. Given.
3. $EC = \frac{1}{2}DC.$	3. Given.
4. $\overline{AF} \cong \overline{EC}.$	4. Division postulate: Halves of congruent segments are congruent segments.

EXERCISES

In 1–5, (*a*) state the postulate or postulates that can be used to show that the conclusion is valid and   (*b*) write a formal proof.

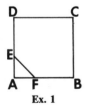

Ex. 1

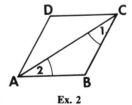

Ex. 2

1. *Given: AD = AB.*

$$AE = \frac{AD}{3}.$$

$$AF = \frac{AB}{3}.$$

Prove: AE = AF.

2. *Given: $m\angle DAB = m\angle DCB.$*
$m\angle 2 = \frac{1}{2}m\angle DAB.$
$m\angle 1 = \frac{1}{2}m\angle DCB.$
Prove: $m\angle 1 = m\angle 2.$

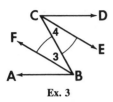

Ex. 3

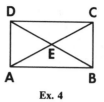

Ex. 4

3. *Given:* $m\angle DCB = m\angle ABC.$
   $m\angle 4 = \frac{1}{2}m\angle DCB.$
   $m\angle 3 = \frac{1}{2}m\angle ABC.$
   Prove: $m\angle 3 = m\angle 4.$

4. *Given:* $\overline{BD} \cong \overline{AC}.$
   $BE = \frac{1}{2}BD.$
   $AE = \frac{1}{2}AC.$
   Prove: $\overline{BE} \cong \overline{AE}.$

5. *Given:* $\angle SRX \cong \angle RSY.$
   $m\angle SRY = \frac{1}{2}m\angle SRX.$
   $m\angle RSX = \frac{1}{2}m\angle RSY.$
   Prove: $\angle SRY \cong \angle RSX.$

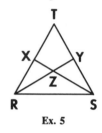

Ex. 5

Powers Postulate

Postulate 10. If $a = b$, then $a^2 = b^2$.

We can restate the powers postulate of equality as follows:

*Postulate 10. **The squares of equal quantities are equal.***

EXAMPLE. If $AB = 10$, then $(AB)^2 = (10)^2$, or $(AB)^2 = 100$.

Roots Postulate

Postulate 11. If $a = b$, then $\sqrt{a} = \sqrt{b}$.

We can restate the roots postulate of equality as follows:

*Postulate 11. **Positive square roots of equal quantities are equal.***

EXAMPLE. If $(AB)^2 = 25$, then $\sqrt{(AB)^2} = \sqrt{25}$, or $AB = 5$.

NOTE. In previous postulates which involve the phrase "equal quantities," some people use the word "equals" instead of "equal quantities."

In our work in Chapters 1 and 2, we have dealt with some geometric postulates in an informal manner. Now formal statements of these postulates will be included among the postulates that follow:

Motion Postulate

*Postulate 12. **A geometric figure may be moved without changing its size or shape. [A geometric figure may be copied.]***

Postulates Involving Lines, Line Segments, Angles, and Circles

Postulate 13. **A straight line segment can be extended indefinitely in both directions.**

EXAMPLE. Straight line segment $\overline{AB}$ can be extended indefinitely to the right and to the left. (See Fig. 2–33.)

Fig. 2–33

Postulate 14. **Through two given points one and only one straight line can be drawn. [Two points determine a straight line.]**

EXAMPLE. Through given points C and D, one and only one straight line can be drawn. (See Fig. 2–34.)

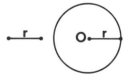

Fig. 2–34

Postulate 15. **Two straight lines cannot intersect in more than one point.**

EXAMPLE. If straight lines $\overleftrightarrow{AB}$ and $\overleftrightarrow{CD}$ intersect, they cannot intersect in more than the one point, E. (See Fig. 2–35.)

Fig. 2–35

Postulate 16. **One and only one circle can be drawn with any given point as a center and any given line segment as a radius.**

EXAMPLE. Only one circle can be drawn which has point O as its center and a radius equal in length to line segment r. (See Fig. 2–36.)

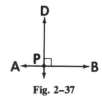

Fig. 2–36

Postulate 17. **At a given point on a given line, one and only one perpendicular can be drawn to the line.**

EXAMPLE. At point P on line $\overleftrightarrow{AB}$, only one line, $\overleftrightarrow{PD}$, can be drawn perpendicular to $\overleftrightarrow{AB}$. (See Fig. 2–37.)

Fig. 2–37

Postulate 18. **From a given point not on a given line, one and only one perpendicular can be drawn to the line.**

EXAMPLE. From point P not on line $\overleftrightarrow{CD}$, only one line, $\overleftrightarrow{PE}$, can be drawn perpendicular to line $\overleftrightarrow{CD}$. (See Fig. 2–38.)

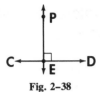

Fig. 2–38

Postulate 19. For any two distinct points, there is only one positive real number which is called the length of the line segment joining the two points.

EXAMPLE. For the distinct points A and B, there is one positive real number, represented by AB, which represents the length of $\overline{AB}$ (see Fig. 2–39). The length of $\overline{AB}$ is also called the measure of $\overline{AB}$, or the distance from A to B. We will refer to this postulate as the *distance postulate*.

Fig. 2–39

Postulate 20. The shortest path between two points is the line segment joining these two points.

EXAMPLE. Fig. 2–40 pictures three paths that can be taken in going from A to B. The length of line segment $\overline{AB}$ is less than the lengths of the other two paths. The distance between A and B is the measure of the shortest path between A and B.

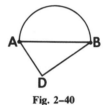

Fig. 2–40

Postulate 21. A straight line segment has one and only one midpoint.

EXAMPLE. Straight line segment $\overline{AB}$ has one and only one midpoint, point M. (See Fig. 2–41.)

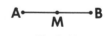

Fig. 2–41

Postulate 22. An angle has one and only one bisector.

EXAMPLE. $\angle ABC$ has one and only one bisector, ray $\overrightarrow{BD}$. (See Fig. 2–42.)

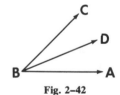

Fig. 2–42

Consider the set of points A, B, C, D, . . . , no two of which are collinear with a given point O. (See Fig. 2–43.) If each of the rays $\overrightarrow{OA}$, $\overrightarrow{OB}$, $\overrightarrow{OC}$, $\overrightarrow{OD}$, . . . , is drawn, then the sum of the measures of the consecutive angles thus formed is 360. We shall state this postulate in the following abbreviated form:

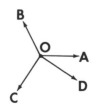

Fig. 2–43

Postulate 23. **The sum of the measures of all the angles about a given point is 360.**

EXAMPLE. The sum of the measures of all the angles about point O, $m\angle AOB + m\angle BOC + m\angle COD + m\angle DOA = 360$. (See Fig. 2–43.)

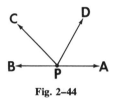

Consider $\overleftrightarrow{AB}$, which contains a given point P. (See Fig. 2–44.) Let C, D, ... be a set of points no two of which are collinear with P and such that they all lie in one of the half-planes formed by $\overleftrightarrow{AB}$. If rays $\overrightarrow{PC}, \overrightarrow{PD}$, ... are drawn, then the sum of the measures of the consecutive angles thus formed is 180. We shall state this postulate in the following abbreviated form:

Fig. 2–44

Postulate 24. **The sum of the measures of all the angles about a given point on one side of a given straight line is 180.**

EXAMPLE. The sum of all the angles about point P on one side of line $\overleftrightarrow{AB}$, $m\angle APD + m\angle DPC + m\angle CPB = 180$. (See Fig. 2–44.)

EXERCISES

In 1–17, (*a*) state the postulate or postulates that can be used to prove that the conclusion is valid and   (*b*) write a formal proof.

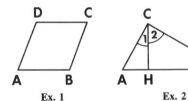
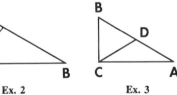
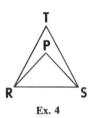

Ex. 1   Ex. 2   Ex. 3   Ex. 4

1. If $AB = AD$ and $DC = AD$, then $AB = DC$.
2. If $m\angle 1 + m\angle 2 = 90$ and $m\angle A = m\angle 2$, then $m\angle 1 + m\angle A = 90$.
3. If $\overline{AD} \cong \overline{CD}$ and $\overline{BD} \cong \overline{CD}$, then $\overline{AD} \cong \overline{BD}$.
4. If $\angle TRS \cong \angle TSR$ and $\angle PRT \cong \angle PST$, then $\angle PRS \cong \angle PSR$.

Exercises 5–8 refer to the figures on the next page.

5. If $m\angle AGH = 180$, $m\angle EHF = 180$, and $m\angle AGD = m\angle GHF$, then $m\angle DGH = m\angle GHE$.
6. If $m\angle A = m\angle B$, $m\angle 1 = m\angle B$, and $m\angle 2 = m\angle A$, then $m\angle 1 = m\angle 2$.
7. If $\angle ACG \cong \angle ADE$, and $\angle BCG \cong \angle ADF$, then $\angle 1 \cong \angle 2$.
8. If $EB = FD$, $AB = 2EB$, and $CD = 2FD$, then $AB = CD$.

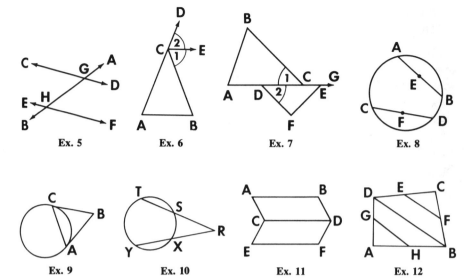

Ex. 5   Ex. 6   Ex. 7   Ex. 8

Ex. 9   Ex. 10   Ex. 11   Ex. 12

9. If $\overline{AC} \cong \overline{BC}$, and $\overline{BC} \cong \overline{BA}$, then $\overline{AC} \cong \overline{BA}$.
10. If $TS = YX$, and $SR = XR$, then $TR = YR$.
11. If $\overline{AB} \cong \overline{CD}$, and $\overline{EF} \cong \overline{CD}$, then $\overline{AB} \cong \overline{EF}$.
12. If $EF = \frac{1}{2}DB$, and $GH = \frac{1}{2}DB$, then $EF = GH$.

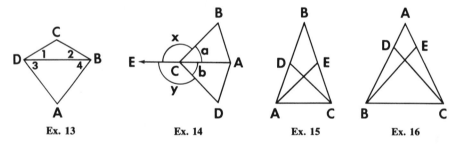

Ex. 13   Ex. 14   Ex. 15   Ex. 16

13. If $\angle 1 \cong \angle 2$, and $\angle 3 \cong \angle 4$, then $\angle CDA \cong \angle CBA$.
14. If $m\angle ECA = 180$, and $m\angle x = m\angle y$, then $m\angle a = m\angle b$.
15. If $BA = BC$, $BD = \frac{1}{2}BA$, and $BE = \frac{1}{2}BC$, then $BD = BE$.
16. If $\overline{AD} \cong \overline{AE}$, and $\overline{DB} \cong \overline{EC}$, then $\overline{AB} \cong \overline{AC}$.

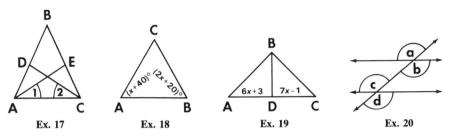

Ex. 17   Ex. 18   Ex. 19   Ex. 20

17. If $m\angle BAC = m\angle BCA$, $m\angle 1 = \frac{1}{2}m\angle BAC$, and $m\angle 2 = \frac{1}{2}m\angle BCA$, then $m\angle 1 = m\angle 2$.

18. $\angle A \cong \angle C$, and $\angle B \cong \angle C$. (*a*) Prove that $\angle A$ is congruent to $\angle B$. (*b*) Find the number of degrees in $\angle A$ and in $\angle B$.

19. $\overline{AD} \cong \overline{BD}$, and $\overline{DC} \cong \overline{BD}$. (*a*) Prove that $\overline{AD}$ is congruent to $\overline{DC}$. (*b*) Find the length of $\overline{AD}$ and of $\overline{DC}$.

20. *a.* If $m\angle a = m\angle b$, $m\angle c = m\angle d$, and $m\angle b = m\angle c$, prove that $m\angle a = m\angle d$.

    b. If $m\angle a = (2y - 60)$, and $m\angle d = (240 - y)$, find the number of degrees in $\angle a$ and in $\angle d$.

8. More Difficult Exercises in Using Postulates and Definitions in Geometric Proofs

In some problems, the hypothesis (*given*), or the conclusion (*to prove*), or both contain words and phrases that we have defined previously. It is important that we know the definitions of these terms so that we will be able to use the given information in developing the proof of the problem.

EXAMPLE 1 (see Fig. 2–45).

Given: $\overline{RT} \cong \overline{ST}$.
          A is the midpoint of $\overline{RT}$.
          B is the midpoint of $\overline{ST}$.

To prove: $\overline{RA} \cong \overline{SB}$.

Fig. 2–45

[The proof is given on the next page.]

Proof: *Statements* | *Reasons*

1. $\overline{RT} \cong \overline{ST}$, or $RT = ST$. | 1. Given.

2. A is the midpoint of $\overline{RT}$. | 2. Given.

3. $\overline{RA} \cong \overline{AT}$, or $RA = \frac{1}{2}RT$. | 3. The midpoint of a line segment is the point which divides the segment into two congruent segments.

4. B is the midpoint of $\overline{ST}$. | 4. Given.

5. $\overline{SB} \cong \overline{BT}$, or $SB = \frac{1}{2}ST$. | 5. The midpoint of a line segment is the point which divides the segment into two congruent segments.

6. $RA = SB$. | 6. Division postulate: Halves of equal quantities are equal.

7. $\overline{RA} \cong \overline{SB}$. | 7. If two segments are equal in length, they are congruent segments.

We may not assume special relationships that appear to be true in the figure drawn for a particular problem. For example, we may not assume that two line segments in a figure are congruent or are perpendicular to each other merely because they appear to be so in the figure. However, unless otherwise stated, we will assume that lines that appear to be straight lines in a figure actually are straight lines.

EXAMPLE 2 (see Fig. 2–46).

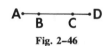

Fig. 2–46

Given: $\overline{AB} \cong \overline{CD}$.

To prove: $\overline{AC} \cong \overline{BD}$.

Proof: *Statements* | *Reasons*

1. $\overline{AB} \cong \overline{CD}$. | 1. Given.

2. $\overline{BC} \cong \overline{BC}$. | 2. Reflexive property: A segment is congruent to itself.

3. $\overline{AB} + \overline{BC} \cong \overline{CD} + \overline{BC}$, or $\overline{AC} \cong \overline{BD}$. | 3. Addition postulate: If congruent segments are added to congruent segments, the sums are congruent segments.

EXAMPLE 3 (see Fig. 2-47).

Given: ∠ABC ≅ ∠DBE.

To prove: ∠ABD ≅ ∠CBE.

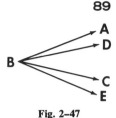

Fig. 2-47

Proof:	Statements	Reasons

Statements	Reasons
1. ∠ABC ≅ ∠DBE.	1. Given.
2. ∠DBC ≅ ∠DBC.	2. Reflexive property: An angle is congruent to itself.
3. ∠ABC − ∠DBC ≅ ∠DBE − ∠DBC, or ∠ABD ≅ ∠CBE.	3. Subtraction property: If congruent angles are subtracted from congruent angles, the differences are congruent angles.

EXERCISES

In 1-16, write a formal proof which demonstrates that the conclusion is valid.

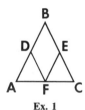

Ex. 1

Ex. 2

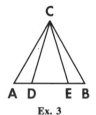

Ex. 3

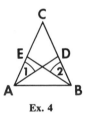

Ex. 4

1. If $\overline{AB} \cong \overline{CB}$, $\overline{FD}$ bisects $\overline{AB}$, and $\overline{FE}$ bisects $\overline{CB}$, then $\overline{AD} \cong \overline{CE}$.
2. If $\overline{CA}$ bisects both ∠DCB and ∠DAB, and ∠DCB ≅ ∠DAB, then ∠r ≅ ∠s.
3. If $\overline{AD} \cong \overline{BE}$, then $\overline{AE} \cong \overline{BD}$.
4. If $\overline{AD}$ bisects ∠CAB, $\overline{EB}$ bisects ∠CBA, and ∠CAB ≅ ∠CBA, then ∠1 ≅ ∠2.

Exercises 5-8 refer to the figures on the next page.

5. If $\overline{DF} \cong \overline{BE}$, then $\overline{DE} \cong \overline{BF}$.
6. If $\overline{AB} \cong \overline{CD}$, $\overline{OE}$ bisects $\overline{AB}$, and $\overline{OF}$ bisects $\overline{CD}$, then $\overline{AE} \cong \overline{CF}$.
7. If ∠LQM ≅ ∠NQP, then ∠LQN ≅ ∠MQP.
8. If $\overline{AB} \cong \overline{BC}$, $\overline{CD}$ is a median to $\overline{AB}$, and $\overline{AE}$ is a median to $\overline{BC}$, then $\overline{BD} \cong \overline{BE}$.

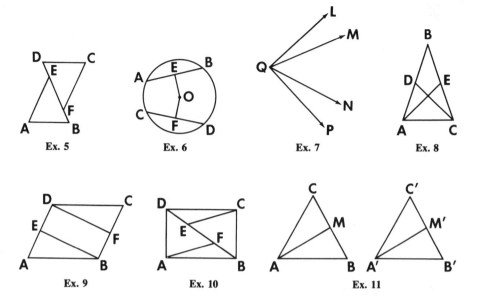

Ex. 5   Ex. 6   Ex. 7   Ex. 8

Ex. 9   Ex. 10   Ex. 11

9. If $\overline{AD} \cong \overline{BC}$, E is the midpoint of $\overline{AD}$, and F is the midpoint of $\overline{BC}$, then $\overline{AE} \cong \overline{FC}$.

10. If $\overline{DE} \cong \overline{FB}$, then $\overline{DF} \cong \overline{EB}$.

11. If $\overline{BC} \cong \overline{B'C'}$, $\overline{AM}$ is the median to $\overline{BC}$, and $\overline{A'M'}$ is the median to $\overline{B'C'}$, then $\overline{MB} \cong \overline{M'B'}$.

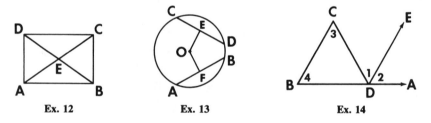

Ex. 12   Ex. 13   Ex. 14

12. If $\overline{AC} \cong \overline{DB}$, and $\overline{AC}$ and $\overline{DB}$ bisect each other, then $\overline{AE} \cong \overline{EB}$.

13. If $\overline{AF} \cong \overline{CE}$, $\overline{OF}$ bisects $\overline{AB}$, and $\overline{OE}$ bisects $\overline{CD}$, then $\overline{AB} \cong \overline{CD}$.

14. If $\overrightarrow{DE}$ bisects $\angle CDA$, $\angle 3 \cong \angle 1$, and $\angle 4 \cong \angle 2$, then $\angle 3 \cong \angle 4$.

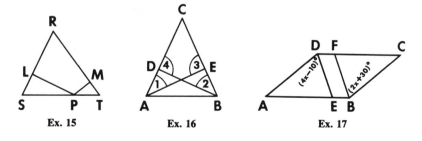

Ex. 15   Ex. 16   Ex. 17

15. If $\angle RLS$ and $\angle RMT$ are straight angles, and if $\overline{PL} \perp \overline{RS}$ and $\overline{PM} \perp \overline{RT}$, then $m\angle PLS = m\angle PMT$.

16. If $m\angle 1 + m\angle 3 + m\angle C = 180$, $m\angle 2 + m\angle 4 + m\angle C = 180$, and $m\angle 3 = m\angle 4$, then $m\angle 1 = m\angle 2$.

17. If $m\angle ADC = m\angle ABC$, $\overline{DE}$ bisects $\angle ADC$, and $\overline{BF}$ bisects $\angle ABC$: (a) Prove that $m\angle ADE = m\angle CBF$. (b) Find the number of degrees in $\angle ADE$ and in $\angle ABC$.

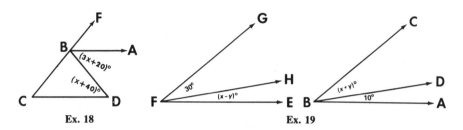

Ex. 18   Ex. 19

18. If $\overrightarrow{BA}$ bisects $\angle FBD$, and $m\angle ABD = m\angle BDC$: (a) Prove that $m\angle ABF = m\angle BDC$. (b) Find the number of degrees in $\angle ABF$.

19. If $\angle EFG \cong \angle ABC$, and $\angle EFH = \angle ABD$: (a) Prove that $\angle HFG \cong \angle DBC$. (b) Solve for x and y.

20. If $\overline{DB} \cong \overline{AC}$, and $\overline{AE} \cong \overline{EB}$: (a) Prove that $\overline{DE} \cong \overline{EC}$. (b) Find DE, EC, DB, and AC.

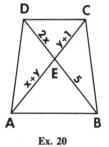

Ex. 20

9. Proving and Using Simple Angle Theorems

We already know that a theorem is a statement proved by deduction. Now we will see how we can use our undefined terms, defined terms, and postulates in proving some simple angle theorems. In theorems 1–8 that follow, the proofs of theorems 1, 3, and 8 are presented; the proofs of theorems 2, 4, 5, 6, and 7 are left to the student.

Theorem 1. **If two angles are right angles, then they are congruent.**

Given: $\angle ABC$ and $\angle DEF$ are right angles. (See Fig. 2–48.)

To prove: $\angle ABC \cong \angle DEF$.

[The proof is given on the next page.]

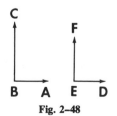

Fig. 2–48

Proof: *Statements*	*Reasons*
1. $\angle ABC$ and $\angle DEF$ are right angles.	1. Given.
2. $m\angle ABC = 90$, $m\angle DEF = 90$.	2. A right angle is an angle whose measure is 90.
3. $m\angle ABC = m\angle DEF$.	3. Transitive postulate of equality: If quantities are equal to the same quantity or equal quantities, they are equal to each other.
4. $\angle ABC \cong \angle DEF$.	4. If the measures of two angles are equal, the angles are congruent.

Note that $\angle ABC \cong \angle DEF$ is equivalent to $m\angle ABC = m\angle DEF$.

Theorem 2. If two angles are straight angles, then they are congruent.

In Fig. 2–49, if $\angle ABC$ and $\angle DEF$ are straight angles, then $\angle ABC \cong \angle DEF$.

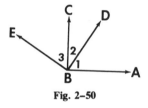

A   B   C   D   E   F

Fig. 2–49

Theorem 3. If two angles are complements of the same angle, then they are congruent.

Given: $\angle ABD$ is complementary to $\angle CBD$.
           $\angle EBC$ is complementary to $\angle CBD$.
           (See Fig. 2–50.)

To prove: $\angle ABD \cong \angle EBC$.

Fig. 2–50

Proof: *Statements*	*Reasons*
1. $\angle ABD$ is complementary to $\angle CBD$.	1. Given.
2. $m\angle ABD + m\angle CBD = 90$.	2. If two angles are complementary, the sum of their measures is 90.
3. $\angle EBC$ is complementary to $\angle CBD$.	3. Given.
4. $m\angle EBC + m\angle CBD = 90$.	4. If two angles are complementary, the sum of their measures is 90.

5. $m\angle ABD + m\angle CBD =$ $m\angle EBC + m\angle CBD.$	5. Transitive postulate of equality: If quantities are equal to the same quantity or equal quantities, they are equal to each other.
6. $m\angle CBD = m\angle CBD.$	6. Reflexive property of equality: A quantity is equal to itself.
7. $m\angle ABD = m\angle EBC.$	7. Subtraction postulate of equality: If equal quantities are subtracted from equal quantities, the differences are equal.
8. $\angle ABD \cong \angle EBC.$	8. If the measures of two angles are equal, the angles are congruent.

The following algebraic explanation can also be used to establish the truth of the theorem "If two angles are complements of the same angle, then they are congruent":

If $\angle ABD$ is complementary to $\angle CBD$ (see Fig. 2–51), then $m\angle ABD + m\angle CBD$ = 90. Therefore, if the number of degrees contained in $\angle CBD$ is represented by x, then the number of degrees contained in $\angle ABD$ can be represented by $90 - x$. Similarly, if $\angle EBC$ is complementary to $\angle CBD$, the number of degrees contained in $\angle EBC$ can be represented by $90 - x$.

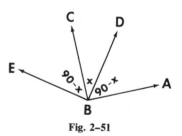

Fig. 2–51

Since $90 - x$ represents the number of degrees contained in both $\angle ABD$ and $\angle EBC$, $m\angle ABD = m\angle EBC$. Hence, $\angle ABD \cong \angle EBC$.

Theorem 4. If two angles are congruent, their complements are congruent.

In Fig. 2–52, if $\angle ABD \cong \angle EFH$, $\angle CBD$ is complementary to $\angle ABD$, and $\angle GFH$ is complementary to $\angle EFH$, then $\angle CBD \cong \angle GFH$.

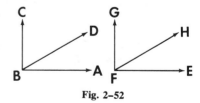

Fig. 2–52

Theorem 5. **If two angles are supplements of the same angle, then they are congruent.**

In Fig. 2-53, if ∠*ABD* is supplementary to ∠*DBC*, and ∠*EBC* is supplementary to ∠*DBC*, then ∠*ABD* ≅ ∠*EBC*.

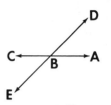

Fig. 2-53

Theorem 6. **If two angles are congruent, then their supplements are congruent.**

In Fig. 2-54, if ∠*ABD* ≅ ∠*EFH*, ∠*CBD* is supplementary to ∠*ABD*, and ∠*GFH* is supplementary to ∠*EFH*, then ∠*CBD* ≅ ∠*GFH*.

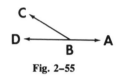

Fig. 2-54

Theorem 7. **If two adjacent angles have their non-common sides on the same straight line, they are supplementary.**

In Fig. 2-55, if $\overrightarrow{BA}$ and $\overrightarrow{BD}$, the non-common sides of adjacent angles *ABC* and *CBD*, lie on straight line $\overleftrightarrow{ABD}$, then ∠*ABC* and ∠*CBD* are supplementary.

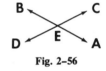

Fig. 2-55

Theorem 8. **If two angles are vertical angles, then they are congruent.**

Given: ∠*BEC* and ∠*AED* are vertical angles. (See Fig. 2-56.)

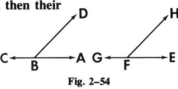

Fig. 2-56

To prove: ∠*BEC* ≅ ∠*AED*.

Proof: *Statements*   *Reasons*

Statements	Reasons
1. ∠*BEC* and ∠*AED* are vertical angles.	1. Given.
2. $\overleftrightarrow{AB}$ and $\overleftrightarrow{CD}$ are straight lines that intersect at *E*.	2. Definition of vertical angles.
3. $m\angle BEC + m\angle AEC = 180$, $m\angle AED + m\angle AEC = 180$.	3. The sum of the measures of all the angles about a point on one side of a straight line is 180.
4. $m\angle BEC + m\angle AEC = m\angle AED + m\angle AEC$.	4. Transitive postulate of equality: If quantities are equal to the same quantity, they are equal to each other.
5. $m\angle AEC = m\angle AEC$.	5. Reflexive property of equality: Any quantity is equal to itself.

| 6. $m\angle BEC = m\angle AED.$ | 6. Subtraction postulate: If equal quantities are subtracted from equal quantities, the differences are equal. |
| 7. $\angle BEC \cong \angle AED.$ | 7. If the measures of two angles are equal, the angles are congruent. |

How to Present a Formal Proof

Theorems 1–8 can be used with the undefined terms, the defined terms, and the postulates to deduce or prove new conclusions.

In order to make a formal presentation of the deductive process that is used in proving a desired conclusion from a given set of data, which we call the *hypothesis*, we will:

1. Carefully draw a good *figure* which pictures the data of the theorem or problem. Letter the figure.
2. State the *given*, which is the hypothesis of the theorem, in terms of the lettered figure.
3. State the *to prove*, which is the conclusion of the theorem, in terms of the lettered figure.
4. Present the *proof*, which is the series of logical arguments used in the demonstration. Each step in the proof should consist of a *statement* and its *reason*. A reason may be the *given*, a *definition*, a *postulate*, or a *previously proved theorem*.

KEEP IN MIND

Two angles may be proved congruent by showing that any one of the following statements is true about them:

1. They are right angles or straight angles.
2. They are complements of the same angle or congruent angles.
3. They are supplements of the same angle or congruent angles.
4. They are vertical angles formed by two intersecting straight lines.

MODEL PROBLEMS

1. Write a formal proof: If $\overleftrightarrow{CE}$ bisects $\angle ADB$, and $\overleftrightarrow{FDB}$ and $\overleftrightarrow{CDE}$ are straight lines, then $\angle a \cong \angle x$.

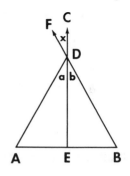

Given: $\overleftrightarrow{CE}$ bisects $\angle ADB$.
            $\overleftrightarrow{FDB}$ and $\overleftrightarrow{CDE}$ are straight lines.
To prove: $\angle a \cong \angle x$.

Proof: *Statements*   *Reasons*

1. $\overleftrightarrow{CE}$ bisects $\angle ADB$.   1. Given.

2. $\angle a \cong \angle b$.   2. A bisector of an angle divides
                                               the angle into two congruent
                                               angles.

3. $\overleftrightarrow{FDB}$ and $\overleftrightarrow{CDE}$ are straight   3. Given.
   lines.

4. $\angle x$ and $\angle b$ are vertical   4. Definition of vertical angles.
   angles.

5. $\angle b \cong \angle x$.   5. If two angles are vertical
                                               angles, then they are congruent.

6. $\angle a \cong \angle x$ 6. Transitive property of
                                               congruence of angles.

2. Write a formal proof: If $\angle ACB$ is a right angle and $\angle DAC$ is complementary to $\angle ACD$, then $\angle BCD \cong \angle DAC$.

Given: $\angle ACB$ is a right angle.
            $\angle DAC$ is complementary to $\angle ACD$.

To prove: $\angle BCD \cong \angle DAC$.

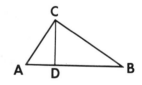

Proof: *Statements*   *Reasons*

1. $\angle ACB$ is a right angle.   1. Given.

2. $m\angle ACB = 90$.   2. The measure of a right angle
                                               is 90.

3. $m\angle ACB = m\angle ACD + m\angle BCD.$	3. The measure of a whole quantity is equal to the sum of the measures of all its parts.
4. $m\angle ACD + m\angle BCD = 90.$	4. Substitution postulate.
5. $\angle BCD$ is complementary to $\angle ACD.$	5. If the sum of the measures of two angles is 90, the angles are complementary.
6. $\angle DAC$ is complementary to $\angle ACD.$	6. Given.
7. $\angle BCD \cong \angle DAC.$	7. If two angles are complements of the same angle, then they are congruent.

3. If lines $\overleftrightarrow{AB}$ and $\overleftrightarrow{CD}$ intersect at E, find: (a) the value of x, (b) $m\angle BEC$, and (c) $m\angle CEA$.

Solution: a. Since straight lines $\overleftrightarrow{AB}$ and $\overleftrightarrow{CD}$ intersect at E, the two vertical angles that are formed, $\angle BEC$ and $\angle AED$, are congruent. Hence,

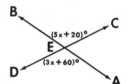

1. $m\angle BEC = m\angle AED$

2. $5x + 20 = 3x + 60$

3. $5x - 3x = 60 - 20$

4. $2x = 40$

5. $x = 20$

Answer: (a) The value of x is 20.

(b) $m\angle BEC = 5x + 20 = 5(20) + 20 = 100 + 20 \doteq 120$
Answer: (b) $m\angle BEC = 120.$

(c) Since $\overleftrightarrow{AB}$ is a straight line, $\angle CEA$ is the supplement of $\angle BEC.$

$$m\angle CEA = 180 - m\angle BEC = 180 - 120 = 60$$

Answer: (c) $m\angle CEA = 60.$

EXERCISES

In 1–17, write a formal proof using the given, definitions, postulates, and theorems as the reasons for the statements used in the proof.

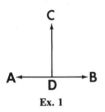

Ex. 1

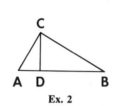

Ex. 2

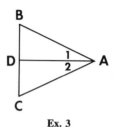

Ex. 3

1. If $\overleftrightarrow{CD} \perp \overleftrightarrow{AB}$, then $\angle CDA \cong \angle CDB$.
2. If ABC is a triangle with $\angle ACB$ a right angle and $\overline{CD} \perp \overline{AB}$, then $\angle ACB \cong \angle ADC$.
3. If $\angle 1 \cong \angle 2$, $\angle B$ is complementary to $\angle 1$, and $\angle C$ is complementary to $\angle 2$, then $\angle B \cong \angle C$.
4. If $\overleftrightarrow{AG}$ and $\overleftrightarrow{BE}$ are straight lines and $\angle a \cong \angle b$, then $\angle ADC \cong \angle BFC$.

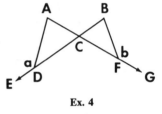

Ex. 4

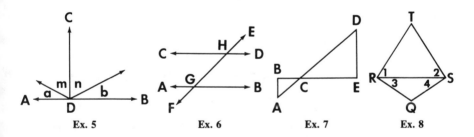

Ex. 5   Ex. 6   Ex. 7   Ex. 8

5. If $\overleftrightarrow{CD} \perp \overleftrightarrow{AB}$ and $\angle m \cong \angle n$, then $\angle a \cong \angle b$.
6. If $\overleftrightarrow{CD}$ is a straight line and $\angle AGH$ is supplementary to $\angle CHG$, then $\angle GHD \cong \angle AGH$.
7. If $\overline{BE}$ and $\overline{AD}$ intersect at C, $\angle BAC$ is complementary to $\angle ACB$, and $\angle EDC$ is complementary to $\angle ECD$, then $\angle BAC \cong \angle EDC$.
8. If $\overline{TR} \perp \overline{RQ}$, $\overline{TS} \perp \overline{SQ}$, and $\angle 3 \cong \angle 4$, then $\angle 1 \cong \angle 2$.

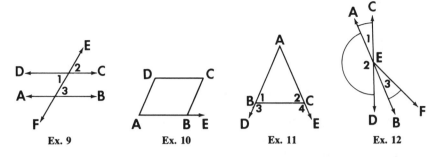

Ex. 9 Ex. 10 Ex. 11 Ex. 12

9. If $\overleftrightarrow{AB}$, $\overleftrightarrow{DC}$, and $\overleftrightarrow{EF}$ are straight lines and $\angle 3 \cong \angle 2$, then $\angle 1 \cong \angle 3$.

10. If $\overleftrightarrow{AE}$ is a straight line and $\angle CBE$ is supplementary to $\angle ADC$, then $\angle ADC \cong \angle ABC$.

11. If $\overleftrightarrow{AD}$ and $\overleftrightarrow{AE}$ are straight lines and $\angle 1 \cong \angle 2$, then $\angle 3 \cong \angle 4$.

12. If $\overleftrightarrow{AB}$, $\overleftrightarrow{CD}$, and $\overleftrightarrow{EF}$ are straight lines and $\angle 1 \cong \angle 3$, then $\angle 3$ is supplementary to $\angle 2$.

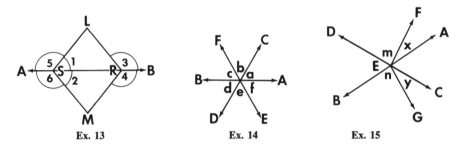

Ex. 13 Ex. 14 Ex. 15

13. If $\overleftrightarrow{AB}$ is a straight line, $\angle 5 \cong \angle 3$, $\angle 6 \cong \angle 4$, and $\angle 3 \cong \angle 4$, then $\angle 1 \cong \angle 2$.

14. If $\overleftrightarrow{AB}$, $\overleftrightarrow{CD}$, and $\overleftrightarrow{EF}$ are straight lines and $\angle a \cong \angle b$, $\angle b \cong \angle c$, then $\angle d \cong \angle e$, $\angle e \cong \angle f$.

15. If straight lines $\overleftrightarrow{AB}$ and $\overleftrightarrow{CD}$ intersect at E, and $\angle x \cong \angle y$, then $\angle m \cong \angle n$.

Exercises 16–22 on the next page refer to the following figures:

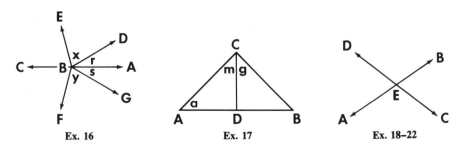

Ex. 16 Ex. 17 Ex. 18–22

16. If $\overleftrightarrow{ABC}$ is a straight line, $\angle r \cong \angle s$, $\overrightarrow{BE}$ bisects $\angle CBD$, and $\overrightarrow{BF}$ bisects $\angle CBG$, then $\angle x \cong \angle y$.

17. If $\angle ACB$ is a right angle and $\angle a$ is complementary to $\angle g$, then $\angle a \cong \angle m$.

In 18–22, $\overleftrightarrow{AB}$ and $\overleftrightarrow{CD}$ are straight lines.

18. If $m\angle BEC = 70$, find $m\angle AED$, $m\angle DEB$, and $m\angle AEC$.

19. If $m\angle DEB = 2x + 20$ and $m\angle AEC = 3x - 30$, find $m\angle DEB$, $m\angle AEC$, $m\angle AED$, and $m\angle CEB$.

20. If $m\angle BEC = 5x - 25$ and $m\angle DEA = 7x - 65$, find $m\angle BEC$, $m\angle DEA$, $m\angle DEB$, and $m\angle AEC$.

21. If $m\angle BEC = y$, $m\angle DEB = 3x$, and $m\angle DEA = 2x - y$, find $m\angle CEB$, $m\angle BED$, $m\angle DEA$, and $m\angle AEC$.

22. If $m\angle AED = 3r$, $m\angle DEB = 5s + 12$, and $m\angle BEC = r + s + 8$, find $m\angle AED$, $m\angle DEB$, $m\angle BEC$, and $m\angle CEA$.

23. $\overleftrightarrow{AB}$ intersects $\overleftrightarrow{CD}$ at E. $m\angle AEC = 2x + 30$ and $m\angle DEB = 4x - 50$. Find $m\angle AEC$ and $m\angle DEB$.

24. $\overleftrightarrow{AB}$ intersects $\overleftrightarrow{CD}$ at E. $m\angle AED = \frac{3}{2}x + 10$ and $m\angle BEC = x + 36$. Find $m\angle BEC$ and $m\angle CEA$.

25. $\overleftrightarrow{RS}$ intersects $\overleftrightarrow{LM}$ at P. $m\angle RPL = x + y$, $m\angle LPS = 3x + 2y$, $m\angle MPS = 3x - 2y$. (*a*) Solve for x and y. (*b*) Find $m\angle RPL$, $m\angle LPS$, and $m\angle MPS$.

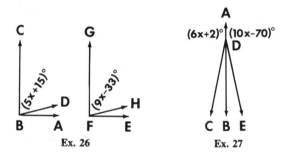

Ex. 26   Ex. 27

26. If $\overleftrightarrow{CB} \perp \overleftrightarrow{BA}$, $\overleftrightarrow{GF} \perp \overleftrightarrow{FE}$, and $\angle ABD \cong \angle EFH$: (*a*) Prove that $\angle CBD \cong \angle GFH$. (*b*) Find $m\angle CBD$ and $m\angle HFE$.

27. If $\overleftrightarrow{AB}$ bisects $\angle CDE$: (*a*) Prove that $\angle ADC \cong \angle ADE$. (*b*) Find the number of degrees in $\angle ADC$ and $\angle BDE$.

28. *Prove:* (*a*) Theorem 2 on page 92   (*b*) Theorem 4 on page 93   (*c*) Theorem 5 on page 94   (*d*) Theorem 6 on page 94   (*e*) Theorem 7 on page 94.

10. Completion Exercises

In 1–15, write a word or expression that, when inserted in the blank, will make the resulting statement true.

1. A quantity may be substituted for its _____ in any expression.
2. If two quantities are equal to the same quantity or equal quantities, they are _____.
3. If equal quantities are subtracted from equal quantities, the _____ are equal.
4. Halves of equal quantities are _____ .
5. The whole quantity is equal to the _____ of all its parts.
6. If two angles are complementary to the same angle, they are _____.
7. If $a = b$, and $b = c$, then _____.
8. If two adjacent angles have their non-common sides on a straight line, the angles are _____.
9. If equal quantities are added to equal quantities, the _____ are equal.
10. If the non-common sides of two adjacent angles are perpendicular, the angles are _____.
11. If two angles are vertical angles, they are _____.
12. A statement whose truth is assumed is called a(an) _____.
13. A statement proved by deduction is called a(an) _____.
14. Arriving at a general truth as a result of examining a set of particular examples is called _____ reasoning.
15. When we go from the general to the particular, we are engaging in _____ reasoning.

11. True-False Exercises

In 1–10, if the statement is always true, write *true;* if the statement is not always true, write *false.*

1. If two angles are supplementary to the same angle, they are supplementary to each other.
2. If two quantities are equal to the same quantity, they are equal to each other.
3. If two angles are complementary, they are congruent.
4. In a postulational system, all terms must be defined.

5. If two adjacent angles are supplementary, their non-common sides lie on a straight line.

6. If line $\overleftrightarrow{AB}$ is the perpendicular bisector of line segment $\overline{CD}$, then line $\overleftrightarrow{AB}$ must pass through the midpoint of line segment $\overline{CD}$.

7. If $\frac{1}{2}x = 10$, then $x = 5$, because halves of equal quantities are equal.

8. If $x + 9 = 19$, then $x = 10$, because when equal quantities are subtracted from equal quantities, the differences are equal.

9. In a postulational system, there are some statements whose truth is accepted without proof.

10. If the conditional statement, "If p, then q," is true, and if the conclusion, q, is true, then the hypothesis, p, is true.

12. "Always, Sometimes, Never" Exercises

In 1–10, if the blank space in the exercise is replaced by the word *always, sometimes,* or *never,* the resulting statement will be true. Select the word which will correctly complete the statement.

1. If two straight lines intersect, the vertical angles formed are _____ congruent.

2. If two straight lines intersect, the vertical angles formed are _____ supplementary.

3. If two angles are complementary to congruent angles, they are _____ congruent.

4. If two angles are complementary to the same angle, they are _____ complementary to each other.

5. If equal quantities are multiplied by equal quantities, the products are _____ equal quantities.

6. If two adjacent angles have their non-common sides on a straight line, the angles are _____ complementary.

7. A theorem is _____ a statement whose truth is assumed.

8. If two angles are supplementary to the same angle, they are _____ congruent.

9. If two angles are supplementary, they are _____ congruent.

10. If the conditional statement, "If p, then q," is true, and if the hypothesis, p, is true, then the conclusion, q, is _____ true.

13. Multiple-Choice Exercises

In 1-10, write the letter preceding the word or expression that best completes the statement.

1. A postulate is a statement which (*a*) is sometimes to be proved (*b*) is accepted without proof (*c*) is always to be proved.

2. If two straight lines intersect, the vertical angles formed are always (*a*) complementary (*b*) congruent (*c*) supplementary.

3. If two angles are congruent and supplementary, the angles are (*a*) acute angles (*b*) obtuse angles (*c*) right angles.

4. Given the statement: "The whole quantity is equal to the sum of all its parts." This statement is classified in this book as (*a*) a postulate (*b*) a theorem (*c*) a definition.

5. Given the statement: "An acute angle is an angle whose measure is greater than 0 and less than 90." This statement is classified in this book as (*a*) a postulate (*b*) a theorem (*c*) a definition.

6. The complement of an angle whose measure is 50 is an angle whose measure is (*a*) 40 (*b*) 130 (*c*) 50.

7. If the measure of an angle is represented by x, the measure of the supplement of the angle is represented by (*a*) $180 - x$ (*b*) $90 - x$ (*c*) $x - 180$.

8. If the non-common sides of two adjacent angles lie on a straight line, the angles are always (*a*) supplementary (*b*) complementary (*c*) congruent.

9. Given the following statements:

   (1) Tabby is a cat.
   (2) All cats have fur.
   (3) Tabby has fur.

   The correct order in which the statements must be arranged so that the first two will make it possible to deduce the third is (*a*) 3, 1, 2 (*b*) 1, 2, 3 (*c*) 2, 1, 3.

10. In the statement "The bisector of the vertex angle of an isosceles triangle is perpendicular to the base," the hypothesis is (*a*) an isosceles triangle (*b*) perpendicular to the base (*c*) the bisector of the vertex angle of an isosceles triangle.

CHAPTER III

Congruent Triangles

1. Understanding the Meaning of Congruent Polygons

In modern industry, it is often necessary to make many copies of a part so that each copy will have the same size and shape. For example, a machine can stamp out many duplicates of a piece of metal, each copy having the same size and shape as the original.

One way to discover whether or not two polygons have the same size and shape is to place one polygon upon the other. If the figures can be turned in such a way that the sides of one polygon *fit exactly* upon the sides of the other and the angles of one polygon *fit exactly* upon the angles of the other, we say that the polygons *coincide*. Polygons that can be made to coincide are called *congruent polygons*.

For example, we can make the two polygons shown in Fig. 3–1 coincide if we make vertex E correspond to vertex A, vertex F correspond to vertex B, vertex G correspond to vertex C, and vertex H correspond to vertex D. Therefore, we would say that "polygon $ABCD$ is congruent to polygon $EFGH$," symbolized by "polygon $ABCD \cong$ polygon $EFGH$." Notice that when we named congruent polygons, the order in which we wrote their vertices indicates the one-to-one correspondence that was set up between the vertices of polygon $ABCD$ and the vertices of polygon $EFGH$.

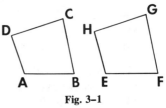

Fig. 3–1

A corresponds to E, and E corresponds to A. B corresponds to F, and F corresponds to B. C corresponds to G, and G corresponds to C. D corresponds to H, and H corresponds to D. (See Fig. 3–2.)

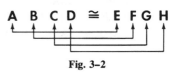

Fig. 3–2

In the future, we will name two polygons that are congruent so as to indicate the correspondences between the vertices of the polygons.

Corresponding Angles

Observe that in congruent polygons $ABCD$ and $EFGH$ (Fig. 3–1), since vertex A corresponds to vertex E, then angle E would fit exactly on angle A. Hence, $\angle A \cong \angle E$. Angles A and E are called *corresponding angles* because their vertices correspond in the one-to-one correspondence that was set up between the vertices of polygon $ABCD$ and polygon $EFGH$.

Similarly, since vertex B corresponds to vertex F, angles B and F are corresponding angles and $\angle B \cong \angle F$. Since vertex C corresponds to vertex G, angles C and G are corresponding angles and $\angle C \cong \angle G$. Since vertex D corresponds to vertex H, angles D and H are corresponding angles and $\angle D \cong \angle H$.

Hence, in these congruent polygons, *all the pairs of corresponding angles are congruent.*

Corresponding Sides

Observe that in congruent polygons $ABCD$ and $EFGH$ (Fig. 3–1), since vertex A corresponds to vertex E, and vertex B corresponds to vertex F, side $\overline{AB}$ would fit exactly on side $\overline{EF}$. Hence, $\overline{AB} \cong \overline{EF}$. Sides $\overline{AB}$ and $\overline{EF}$ are called *corresponding sides* because their endpoints correspond in the one-to-one correspondence that was set up between the vertices of polygon $ABCD$ and the vertices of polygon $EFGH$.

Similarly, since vertex B corresponds to vertex F, and vertex C corresponds to vertex G, sides $\overline{BC}$ and $\overline{FG}$ are corresponding sides and $\overline{BC} \cong \overline{FG}$. Since vertex C corresponds to vertex G, and vertex D corresponds to vertex H, sides $\overline{CD}$ and $\overline{GH}$ are corresponding sides and $\overline{CD} \cong \overline{GH}$. Since vertex D corresponds to vertex H, and vertex A corresponds to vertex E, sides $\overline{DA}$ and $\overline{HE}$ are corresponding sides and $\overline{DA} \cong \overline{HE}$.

Hence, in these congruent polygons, *all the pairs of corresponding sides are congruent.*

Now we are ready to give a formal definition of congruent polygons which will be useful in our work in geometry.

Definition: Two polygons are congruent if there is a one-to-one correspondence between their vertices such that:

1. **All pairs of corresponding angles are congruent.**
2. **All pairs of corresponding sides are congruent.**

The pairs of congruent angles and the pairs of congruent sides are called *corresponding parts of the congruent polygons.* Since a definition is reversible, we can say that:

Corresponding parts of congruent polygons are congruent.

Congruent Triangles

Consider $\triangle ABC$ and $\triangle DEF$
shown in Fig. 3-3. If we match
vertex A with vertex D, then A and
D are a pair of *corresponding vertices*. If we match vertex B with
vertex E, then B and E are a pair
of corresponding vertices. Also,
C and F are a pair of corresponding
vertices.

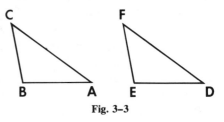

Fig. 3-3

In $\triangle ABC$ and $\triangle DEF$, angle A and angle D, which have corresponding
vertices, are *corresponding angles*. Also, $\angle B$ and $\angle E$, as well as $\angle C$ and
$\angle F$, are corresponding angles.

In $\triangle ABC$ and $\triangle DEF$, sides $\overline{AB}$ and $\overline{DE}$, which join corresponding
vertices, are *corresponding sides*. Also, $\overline{BC}$ and $\overline{EF}$, as well as $\overline{CA}$ and $\overline{FD}$,
are corresponding sides.

If we know that:

1. $\angle A \cong \angle D$, $\angle B \cong \angle E$, and $\angle C \cong \angle F$
2. $\overline{AB} \cong \overline{DE}$, $\overline{BC} \cong \overline{EF}$, and $\overline{CA} \cong \overline{FD}$

we can say that triangle ABC is congruent to triangle DEF, symbolized
$\triangle ABC \cong \triangle DEF$.

Whenever two triangles are congruent, their corresponding sides are
congruent and their corresponding angles are congruent. We can also say
that when two triangles are congruent, their corresponding parts are congruent. Hence, if we know that $\triangle ABC \cong \triangle DEF$, we immediately know six
different facts, which are listed below. In the column on the left, these six
facts are stated as congruences; in the column on the right, the same six facts
are stated as equalities.

Congruences	*Equalities*
$\overline{AB} \cong \overline{DE}$	$AB = DE$
$\overline{BC} \cong \overline{EF}$	$BC = EF$
$\overline{AC} \cong \overline{DF}$	$AC = DF$
$\angle A \cong \angle D$	$m\angle A = m\angle D$
$\angle B \cong \angle E$	$m\angle B = m\angle E$
$\angle C \cong \angle F$	$m\angle C = m\angle F$

Each congruence on the left is equivalent to the equality on its right.
Hence, at any time we may use these notations interchangeably. We will
use that notation which serves our purposes best in a particular situation.

For example, in one situation we may prefer to write $\overline{AC} \cong \overline{DF}$. In another situation, however, we may prefer to write $AC = DF$. Likewise, at one time we may prefer to write $\angle C \cong \angle F$; at another time we may prefer to write $m\angle C = m\angle F$.

In two congruent triangles, a pair of corresponding sides is always found opposite a pair of corresponding congruent angles. For example, in $\triangle ABC$ and DEF (Fig. 3-3), corresponding sides $\overline{AB}$ and $\overline{DE}$ are opposite the pair of corresponding congruent angles $\angle C$ and $\angle F$. Also, a pair of corresponding angles is always found opposite a pair of corresponding congruent sides. For example, corresponding angles A and D are found opposite the pair of corresponding congruent sides $\overline{BC}$ and $\overline{EF}$.

Properties of Congruence

Since congruence leads to a set of equations involving the equality of measures of angles and the equality of measures of line segments, the following properties hold for congruence as they hold for equality:

Reflexive Property for Congruence

Postulate 25. **Any geometric figure is congruent to itself.**

For example, $\triangle ABC \cong \triangle ABC$.

Symmetric Property for Congruence

Postulate 26. **A congruence may be reversed.**

For example, if $\triangle ABC \cong \triangle DEF$, then $\triangle DEF \cong \triangle ABC$.

Transitive Postulate for Congruence

Postulate 27. **Two geometric figures congruent to the same geometric figure are congruent to each other.**

For example, if $\triangle ABC \cong \triangle DEF$, and $\triangle DEF \cong \triangle RST$, then it follows that $\triangle ABC \cong \triangle RST$.

EXERCISES

1. Referring to the figures at the top of page 108: (*a*) Name the figures which appear to be congruent. (*b*) Use the symbol $\cong$ to write that the figures named are congruent.

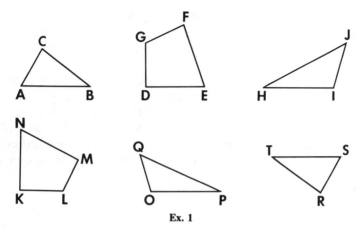

Ex. 1

In exercises 2–5, name three pairs of corresponding angles and three pairs of corresponding sides in the given congruent triangles. In each exercise, use the symbol ≅ to indicate that the angles named and also the sides named in your answers are congruent.

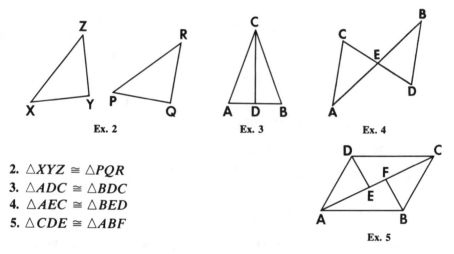

Ex. 2   Ex. 3   Ex. 4

2. △XYZ ≅ △PQR
3. △ADC ≅ △BDC
4. △AEC ≅ △BED
5. △CDE ≅ △ABF

Ex. 5

2. Proving Triangles Congruent When They Agree in Two Sides and the Included Angle

We have seen that two triangles can be proved congruent by proving that their three pairs of corresponding angles and three pairs of corresponding sides are congruent. Now let us see whether it is possible to prove two triangles congruent by proving that fewer than three pairs of sides and three pairs of angles are congruent.

Let us perform the following experiment:

In $\triangle ABC$ (see Fig. 3-4), we see that $AB = 1$ inch, $m\angle A = 45$, and $AC = \frac{3}{4}$ inch. We say that $\angle A$ is *included* between side $\overline{AB}$ and side $\overline{AC}$, because these two segments are on the sides of the angle.

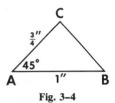

Fig. 3–4

On a sheet of paper, let us draw $\triangle A'B'C'$ so that $A'B' = 1$ inch, $A'C' = \frac{3}{4}$ inch, and the measure of the included angle A' is 45, $m\angle A' = 45$. (See Fig. 3-5.)

(1) We begin by drawing a working line on which we measure off 1 inch, the length of $\overline{A'B'}$. (2) With a protractor, we draw an angle of $45°$ whose vertex is at point A'. (3) On the side of $\angle A'$ which was last drawn, we measure off a line segment $\frac{3}{4}$ of an inch in length, beginning at point A' and ending at point C'. (4) We then draw side $\overline{C'B'}$ to complete the triangle.

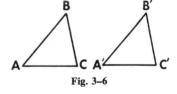

Fig. 3–5

If we measure sides $\overline{CB}$ and $\overline{C'B'}$, we find the measures equal. Hence, $\overline{CB} \cong \overline{C'B'}$. Also, if we measure $\angle C$ and $\angle C'$, we find their measures equal. $\angle B$ and $\angle B'$, if measured, are also found to have equal measures. Hence, $\angle C \cong \angle C'$ and $\angle B \cong \angle B'$. Also, if we cut out $\triangle A'B'C'$, we can make it coincide with $\triangle ABC$. Thus, $\triangle A'B'C'$ appears to be congruent to $\triangle ABC$.

If we repeat the same experiment several times with different sets of measurements for the two sides and the included angle, in each experiment the remaining pairs of corresponding parts of the triangles will appear to be congruent, and the triangles themselves will appear to be congruent. It seems reasonable, therefore, to accept the following statement, whose truth we will assume without proof:

Postulate 28. **Two triangles are congruent if two sides and the included angle of one triangle are congruent respectively to two sides and the included angle of the other. [s.a.s. $\cong$ s.a.s.]**

In $\triangle ABC$ and $\triangle A'B'C'$ (Fig. 3–6), if $\overline{AB} \cong \overline{A'B'}$, $\angle A \cong \angle A'$, $\overline{AC} \cong \overline{A'C'}$, then $\triangle ABC \cong \triangle A'B'C'$.

NOTE. In the statement of postulate 28, we did not take the trouble to state that there must exist a correspondence between the vertices of the two triangles such that two sides and the included angle of one triangle are congruent respectively to two sides and the included angle of the other. In the future, we will follow the same practice when we state other postulates or theorems involving congruent triangles. In each case, we will understand that there does exist a correspondence between the vertices of the two triangles for which the congruences stated in the hypothesis exist.

Definition. A *corollary* is a theorem that can easily be deduced from another theorem or from a postulate.

The following statement is a corollary of the preceding postulate:

Corollary P28–1. **Two right triangles are congruent if the legs of one right triangle are congruent to the legs of the other right triangle.**

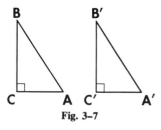

Fig. 3–7

In right triangles ABC and $A'B'C'$ (Fig. 3-7) with right angles at C and C', if leg $\overline{BC} \cong$ leg $\overline{B'C'}$ and leg $\overline{AC} \cong$ leg $\overline{A'C'}$, then $\triangle ABC \cong \triangle A'B'C'$.

Now we will see how the preceding postulate can be used to prove two triangles congruent. When we are proving triangles congruent, we can use the following device to help us show the method of congruence being used. We will write (s. $\cong$ s.) next to pairs of congruent sides and (a. $\cong$ a.) next to pairs of congruent angles that are used to establish the congruence of the triangles.

MODEL PROBLEM

In $\triangle ABC$, if $\overline{AC} \cong \overline{BC}$ and $\overline{CD}$ bisects $\angle ACB$, prove that $\triangle ACD \cong \triangle BCD$.

Given: $\triangle ABC$ with $\overline{AC} \cong \overline{BC}$.
             $\overline{CD}$ bisects $\angle ACB$.

To prove: $\triangle ACD \cong \triangle BCD$.

Plan: Prove the triangles congruent by showing that
            s.a.s. $\cong$ s.a.s.

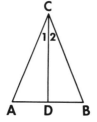

Proof: *Statements*	*Reasons*
1. In $\triangle ABC$, $\overline{AC} \cong \overline{BC}$. (s. $\cong$ s.)	1. Given.
2. $\overline{CD}$ bisects $\angle ACB$.	2. Given.
3. $\angle 1 \cong \angle 2$. (a. $\cong$ a.)	3. An angle bisector divides the angle into two congruent angles.
4. $\overline{CD} \cong \overline{CD}$. (s. $\cong$ s.)	4. Reflexive property of congruence.
5. $\triangle ACD \cong \triangle BCD$.	5. s.a.s. $\cong$ s.a.s.

EXERCISES

In 1–6, tell whether or not the triangles can be proved congruent and give the reason for your answer. (Pairs of line segments marked with the same number of strokes are congruent. Pairs of angles marked with the same number of arcs are congruent. A line segment or an angle marked with × is congruent to itself by the reflexive property of congruence.)

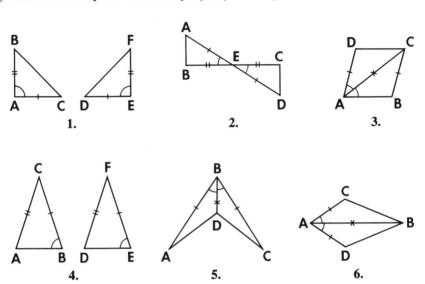

1.   2.   3.

4.   5.   6.

In 7–9, name the pair of corresponding sides or the pair of corresponding angles that would have to be proved congruent in addition to those pairs marked congruent in order to prove that the triangles are congruent by s.a.s. ≅ s.a.s.

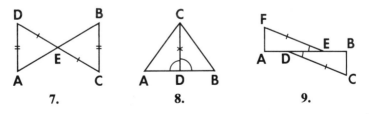

7.   8.   9.

Exercises 10 and 11 refer to the figures on the next page.

10. *Given:* $AB = 4$, $ED = 4$, $BC = 6$, $DF = 6$, $m\angle B = 70$, $m\angle D = 70$.
   Prove: $\triangle ABC \cong \triangle EDF$.

11. *Given:* $AB = 12$, $RS = 12$, $m\angle B = 120$, $m\angle S = 120$, $\overline{BC} \cong \overline{ST}$.
   Prove: $\triangle ABC \cong \triangle RST$.

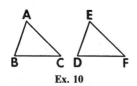

Ex. 10

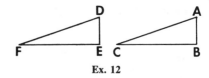

Ex. 11

12. *Given:* $\overline{DE} \cong \overline{AB}$, $\overline{EF} \cong \overline{BC}$, $\angle E$ and $\angle B$ are right angles.
Prove: $\triangle DEF \cong \triangle ABC$.

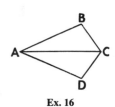

Ex. 12

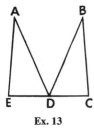

Ex. 13

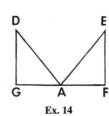

Ex. 14

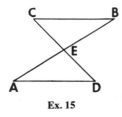

Ex. 15

Ex. 16

13. *Given:* $\overline{AE} \cong \overline{BC}$, $\angle E \cong \angle C$, D is the midpoint of $\overline{EC}$.
Prove: $\triangle ADE \cong \triangle BDC$.

14. *Given:* $\overline{DG} \cong \overline{EF}$, A is the midpoint of $\overline{GF}$, $\overline{DG} \perp \overline{GF}$, $\overline{EF} \perp \overline{GF}$.
Prove: $\triangle DGA \cong \triangle EFA$.

15. *Given:* $\overline{CD}$ bisects $\overline{AB}$, $\overline{AB}$ bisects $\overline{CD}$.
Prove: $\triangle AED \cong \triangle BEC$.

16. *Given:* $\overline{AB} \cong \overline{AD}$, $\overline{AC}$ bisects $\angle BAD$.
Prove: $\triangle ABC \cong \triangle ADC$.

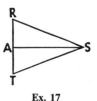

Ex. 17

Ex. 18

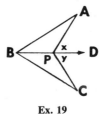

Ex. 19

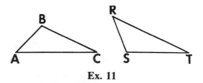

Ex. 20

17. *Given:* $\overline{AS} \perp \overline{RT}$, A is the midpoint of $\overline{RT}$.
Prove: $\triangle RAS \cong \triangle TAS$.

18. *Given:* $\overline{CD}$ is the $\perp$ bisector of $\overline{AB}$.
Prove: $\triangle ADC \cong \triangle BDC$.

19. If $\overline{AP} \cong \overline{CP}$, $\angle x \cong \angle y$, and $\overleftrightarrow{BD}$ is a straight line, prove that $\triangle ABP \cong \triangle CBP$.

20. If $\overline{DB}$ and $\overline{AC}$ bisect each other, prove that $\triangle AEB \cong \triangle CED$.

3. Proving Triangles Congruent When They Agree in Two Angles and the Included Side

Let us perform the following experiment:
In $\triangle ABC$ (see Fig. 3–8), we see that $m\angle A = 60$, $AB = 1$ inch, and $m\angle B = 50$. We say that side $\overline{AB}$ is *included* between $\angle A$ and $\angle B$, because side $\overline{AB}$ has vertex A and vertex B as its endpoints.

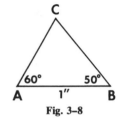

Fig. 3–8

On a sheet of paper, let us draw $\triangle A'B'C'$ so that $m\angle A' = 60$, $m\angle B' = 50$, and the length of the included side $\overline{A'B'}$ is 1 inch, $A'B' = 1$ inch. (See Fig. 3–9.)

(1) We begin by drawing a working line on which we measure off 1 inch, the length of $\overline{A'B'}$. (2) With a protractor, we draw an angle of 60° whose vertex is at point A'. (3) We then draw an angle of 50° whose vertex is at point B'. (4) To complete the triangle, we extend the sides of these angles until they intersect at point C'.

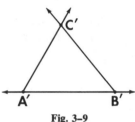

Fig. 3–9

If we measure sides $\overline{AC}$ and $\overline{A'C'}$, we find their lengths to be equal. Also, if we measure $\overline{CB}$ and $\overline{C'B'}$, we find their lengths to be equal. Hence, $\overline{AC} \cong \overline{A'C'}$ and $\overline{CB} \cong \overline{C'B'}$. $\angle C$ and $\angle C'$, if measured, are also found to have equal measures. Hence, $\angle C \cong \angle C'$. Furthermore, if we cut out $\triangle A'B'C'$, we can make it coincide with $\triangle ABC$. Therefore, it appears that $\triangle A'B'C'$ is congruent to $\triangle ABC$.

If we repeat the same experiment several times with different sets of measurements for the two angles and the included side, in each experiment the remaining pairs of corresponding parts of the triangles will appear to be congruent and the triangles themselves will appear to be congruent. It seems reasonable, therefore, to accept the following statement, whose truth we will assume without proof:

Postulate 29. **Two triangles are congruent if two angles and the included side of one triangle are congruent respectively to two angles and the included side of the other. [a.s.a. $\cong$ a.s.a.]**

If $\angle A \cong \angle A'$, $\overline{AC} \cong \overline{A'C'}$, $\angle C \cong \angle C'$, then $\triangle ABC \cong \triangle A'B'C'$. (See Fig. 3–10.)

Now we will see how the preceding postulate can be used to prove two triangles congruent.

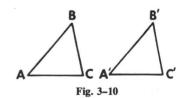

Fig. 3–10

MODEL PROBLEM ~~~~~~~~~~~~~~~~~~~~~~~~~

Given: $\overleftrightarrow{CD}$ and $\overleftrightarrow{AB}$ are straight lines which intersect at *E*.
$\overline{BA}$ bisects $\overline{CD}$. $\overline{AC} \perp \overline{CD}$, $\overline{BD} \perp \overline{CD}$

To prove: $\triangle ACE \cong \triangle BDE$.

Plan: Prove the triangles congruent by
showing that a.s.a. $\cong$ a.s.a.

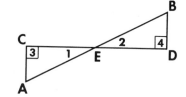

Proof: *Statements*	*Reasons*
1. $\overleftrightarrow{CD}$ and $\overleftrightarrow{AB}$ are straight lines which intersect at *E*.	1. Given.
2. $\angle 1$ and $\angle 2$ are vertical angles.	2. Definition of vertical angles.
3. $\angle 1 \cong \angle 2$. (a. $\cong$ a.)	3. If two angles are vertical angles, they are congruent.
4. $\overline{BA}$ bisects $\overline{CD}$.	4. Given.
5. $\overline{CE} \cong \overline{DE}$. (s. $\cong$ s.)	5. A bisector divides a line segment into two congruent parts.
6. $\overline{AC} \perp \overline{CD}$, $\overline{BD} \perp \overline{CD}$.	6. Given.
7. $\angle 3$ and $\angle 4$ are right angles.	7. Perpendicular lines are lines which intersect and form right angles.
8. $\angle 3 \cong \angle 4$. (a. $\cong$ a.)	8. If two angles are right angles, they are congruent.
9. $\triangle ACE \cong \triangle BDE$.	9. a.s.a. $\cong$ a.s.a.

EXERCISES

In 1–6, tell whether or not the triangles can be proved congruent by the
a.s.a. $\cong$ a.s.a. postulate, using only the marked congruent parts in establishing the congruence. Give the reason for your answer.

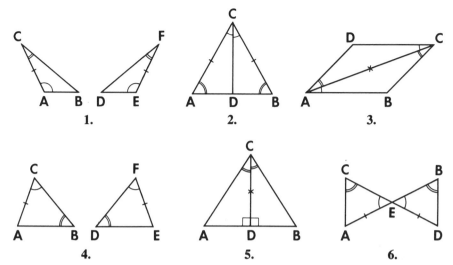

1.   2.   3.

4.   5.   6.

In 7-9, name the pair of corresponding sides or the pair of corresponding angles that would have to be proved congruent in addition to those pairs marked congruent in order to prove that the triangles are congruent by a.s.a. ≅ a.s.a.

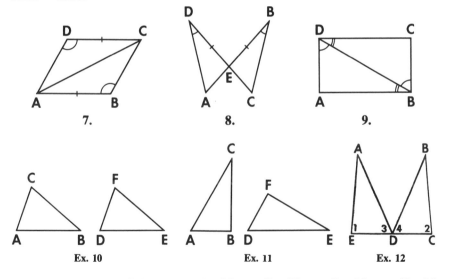

7.   8.   9.

Ex. 10   Ex. 11   Ex. 12

10. *Given: AB = 4, DE = 4, m∠A = 70, m∠D = 70, m∠B = 50, m ∠E = 50.*
    Prove: △ABC ≅ △DEF.
11. *Given: AB = 8, DF = 8, m∠B = 90, m∠F = 90, m∠A = 60, m∠D = 60.*
    Prove: △ABC ≅ △DFE.
12. *Given: ∠1 ≅ ∠2, D is the midpoint of $\overline{EC}$, ∠3 ≅ ∠4.*
    Prove: △AED ≅ △BCD.

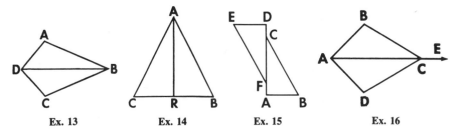

| Ex. 13 | Ex. 14 | Ex. 15 | Ex. 16 |

13. *Given:* $\overline{DB}$ bisects $\angle ADC$, $\overline{BD}$ bisects $\angle ABC$.
    Prove: $\triangle ADB \cong \triangle CDB$.
14. *Given:* $\overline{AR} \perp \overline{CB}$, $\overline{AR}$ bisects $\angle CAB$.
    Prove: $\triangle ACR \cong \triangle ABR$.
15. *Given:* $\overleftrightarrow{DA}$ is a straight line, $\angle E \cong \angle B$, $\overline{ED} \cong \overline{AB}$, $\overline{FD} \perp \overline{DE}$,
    $\overline{CA} \perp \overline{AB}$.
    Prove: $\triangle DEF \cong \triangle ABC$.
16. *Given:* $\overrightarrow{AE}$ bisects $\angle BAD$, $\angle ECB \cong \angle ECD$.
    Prove: $\triangle ABC \cong \triangle ADC$.

4. Proving Triangles Congruent When They Agree in Three Sides

Let us perform the following experiment:

In $\triangle ABC$ (see Fig. 3–11), we see that $AB = 1$ inch, $BC = \frac{7}{8}$ inch, and $AC = \frac{3}{4}$ inch.

On a sheet of paper, let us draw $\triangle A'B'C'$ so that the length of $\overline{A'B'}$ is 1 inch ($A'B' = 1$ inch), the length of $\overline{B'C'}$ is $\frac{7}{8}$ inch ($B'C' = \frac{7}{8}$ inch), and the length of $\overline{A'C'}$ is $\frac{3}{4}$ inch ($A'C' = \frac{3}{4}$ inch). (See Fig. 3–12.)

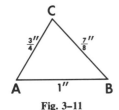

Fig. 3–11

(1) We begin by drawing a working line on which we measure off 1 inch, the length of $\overline{A'B'}$. (2) Using point A' as a center, we draw an arc of a circle whose radius is $\frac{3}{4}$ of an inch in length. (3) Using point B' as a center, we draw an arc of a circle whose radius is $\frac{7}{8}$ of an inch in length. This arc intersects the first arc at point C'. (4) We now draw sides $\overline{A'C'}$ and $\overline{B'C'}$ to complete the triangle.

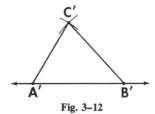

Fig. 3–12

If we measure $\angle A$ and $\angle A'$, we find their measures equal. Hence, $\angle A \cong \angle A'$. If we measure $\angle B$ and $\angle B'$, we find their measures equal. Hence, $\angle B \cong \angle B'$. If we measure $\angle C$ and $\angle C'$, we find their measures equal. Hence, $\angle C \cong \angle C'$. Also, if we cut out $\triangle A'B'C'$, we can make it coincide with $\triangle ABC$. Thus, $\triangle A'B'C'$ appears to be congruent to $\triangle ABC$.

If we repeat the same experiment several times with different sets of measurements for the three sides, in each experiment the triangles will appear to be congruent. It seems reasonable, therefore, to accept the following statement, whose truth we will assume without proof:

Postulate 30. **Two triangles are congruent if the three sides of one triangle are congruent respectively to the three sides of the other.** [s.s.s. ≅ s.s.s.]

If $\overline{AB} \cong \overline{A'B'}$, $\overline{AC} \cong \overline{A'C'}$, $\overline{BC} \cong \overline{B'C'}$, then $\triangle ABC \cong \triangle A'B'C'$. (See Fig. 3–13.)

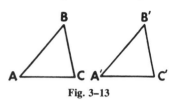

Fig. 3–13

NOTE. After theorem 9 (page 593) and theorem 10 (pages 594–595) have been proved, it is possible to prove "Two triangles are congruent if the three sides of one triangle are congruent respectively to the three sides of the other." However, since the proof is detailed, long, and difficult for the student at this early stage of the geometry course, we prefer to postulate the s.s.s. ≅ s.s.s. congruence.

Now we will see how the preceding postulate can be used to prove two triangles congruent.

MODEL PROBLEM

If a median is drawn to the base of an isosceles triangle, prove that the median divides the triangle into two congruent triangles.

Given: Isosceles triangle ABC with $\overline{CA} \cong \overline{CB}$. $\overline{CD}$ is a median to base $\overline{AB}$.

To prove: $\triangle ACD \cong \triangle BCD$.

Plan: Prove the triangles congruent by showing that s.s.s. ≅ s.s.s.

Proof: *Statements*	*Reasons*
1. In isosceles triangle ABC, $\overline{CA} \cong \overline{CB}$. (s. ≅ s.)	1. Given.
2. $\overline{CD}$ is the median to base $\overline{AB}$.	2. Given.
3. $\overline{AD} \cong \overline{BD}$. (s. ≅ s.)	3. A median in a triangle divides the side to which it is drawn into two congruent parts.
4. $\overline{CD} \cong \overline{CD}$. (s. ≅ s.)	4. Reflexive property of congruence.
5. $\triangle ACD \cong \triangle BCD$.	5. s.s.s. ≅ s.s.s.

EXERCISES

In 1–6, tell whether or not the triangles can be proved congruent using only the marked congruent parts in establishing the congruence. Give the reason for your answer.

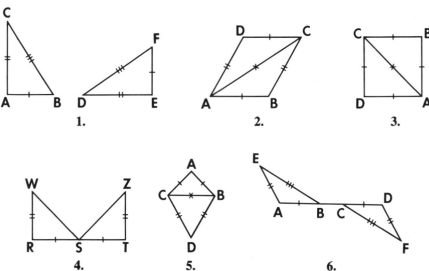

In 7–9, name the pair of corresponding sides that would have to be proved congruent in addition to those pairs marked congruent in order to prove that the triangles are congruent by s.s.s. ≅ s.s.s.

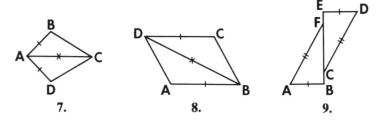

Exercises 10–12 on the next page refer to the following figures:

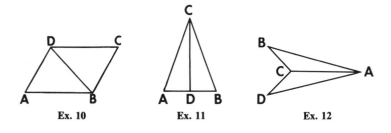

Ex. 10   Ex. 11   Ex. 12

10. *Given:* $\overline{AB} \cong \overline{CD}, \overline{AD} \cong \overline{CB}$.
   Prove: $\triangle ABD \cong \triangle CDB$.

11. *Given:* In $\triangle ABC, \overline{CA} \cong \overline{CB}$, D is the midpoint of $\overline{AB}$.
   Prove: $\triangle ADC \cong \triangle BDC$.

12. *Given:* $\overline{AB} \cong \overline{AD}, \overline{CB} \cong \overline{CD}$.
   Prove: $\triangle ABC \cong \triangle ADC$.

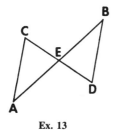

Ex. 13

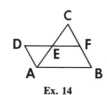

Ex. 14

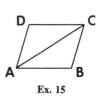

Ex. 15

13. *Given:* E is the midpoint of $\overline{CD}, \overline{CD}$ bisects $\overline{AB}, \overline{AC} \cong \overline{BD}$.
   Prove: $\triangle AEC \cong \triangle BED$.

14. *Given:* $\overline{AC}$ and $\overline{DF}$ bisect each other at $E, \overline{AD} \cong \overline{CF}$.
   Prove: $\triangle DEA \cong \triangle FEC$.

15. If both pairs of opposite sides of quadrilateral $ABCD$ (sides that do not have a common endpoint) are congruent, prove that $\triangle ABC \cong \triangle CDA$.

5. More Practice in Proving Triangles Congruent

Methods of Proving Triangles Congruent

To prove that two triangles are congruent, prove that any one of the following statements is true:

1. Two sides and the included angle of one triangle are congruent respectively to two sides and the included angle of the other. [s.a.s. $\cong$ s.a.s.]
2. Two angles and the included side of one triangle are congruent respectively to two angles and the included side of the other. [a.s.a. $\cong$ a.s.a.]
3. Three sides in one triangle are congruent respectively to the three sides of the other. [s.s.s. $\cong$ s.s.s.]

Analyzing a Congruence Problem

A process of *analysis* can help us to determine which of the three postulates can be used to prove that two triangles are congruent. Let us see how to perform such an analysis for the following congruence problems:

MODEL PROBLEMS 〜〜〜〜〜〜〜〜〜〜〜

1. *Given:* $\overleftrightarrow{AE}$ is a straight line which bisects
$\angle CAD.\ \angle CBE \cong \angle DBE.$

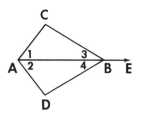

To prove: $\triangle ACB \cong \triangle ADB.$

Since $\overleftrightarrow{AE}$ bisects $\angle CAD,\ \angle 1 \cong \angle 2$, giving
us one pair of congruent angles. We see that
$\overline{AB}$ is a common side in both triangles. There-
fore, we can say that $\overline{AB} \cong \overline{AB}$, by the reflexive property of congruence, giving us a pair of congruent sides. Since we have proved one pair of sides
congruent and one pair of angles congruent, we may be able to use either the
s.a.s. postulate or the a.s.a. postulate to establish the congruence.

In order to use the s.a.s. postulate, we would have to prove that $\overline{AC} \cong$
$\overline{AD}$. Since we have no information about these sides, it appears that we
will probably not be able to use the s.a.s. postulate.

In order to use the a.s.a. postulate, we would have to prove that $\angle 3 \cong$
$\angle 4$. Since we know from the *given* that $\angle CBE \cong \angle DBE$ and that $\overleftrightarrow{AE}$ is a
straight line, we can show that $\angle 3$, which is the supplement of $\angle CBE$, must
be congruent to $\angle 4$, which is the supplement of $\angle DBE$, because "two angles
that are supplementary to congruent angles are congruent."

Therefore, we see that we can use the a.s.a. postulate to prove $\triangle ACB \cong$
$\triangle ADB$. The formal proof follows:

> *Given:* $\overleftrightarrow{AE}$ bisects $\angle CAD.$
> $\angle CBE \cong \angle DBE.$
>
> *To prove:* $\triangle ACB \cong \triangle ADB.$

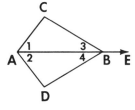

Proof: *Statements*	*Reasons*
1. $\overleftrightarrow{AE}$ bisects $\angle CAD.$	1. Given.
2. $\angle 1 \cong \angle 2.$ (a. $\cong$ a.)	2. An angle bisector divides the angle into two congruent angles.
3. $\overline{AB} \cong \overline{AB}$ (s. $\cong$ s.)	3. Reflexive property of congruence.
4. $\overleftrightarrow{AE}$ is a straight line.	4. Given.
5. $\angle CBE \cong \angle DBE.$	5. Given.
6. $\angle 3$ is supplementary to $\angle CBE.$ $\angle 4$ is supplementary to $\angle DBE.$	6. If the non-common sides of two adjacent angles lie on a straight line, the angles are supplementary.
7. $\angle 3 \cong \angle 4.$ (a. $\cong$ a.)	7. If two angles are supplements of congruent angles, they are congruent.
8. $\triangle ACB \cong \triangle ADB.$	8. a.s.a. $\cong$ a.s.a.

2. *Given:* $\overleftrightarrow{AD}$ is a straight line.
            $\overline{AE} \cong \overline{DF}.$
            $\angle A \cong \angle D.$
            $\overline{AC} \cong \overline{DB}.$

To prove: $\triangle AEB \cong \triangle DFC.$

Plan: Prove the triangles congruent by
            showing that s.a.s. $\cong$ s.a.s. In
            order to do this, it is necessary
            to prove $\overline{AB} = \overline{DC}.$

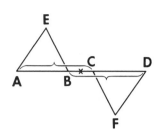

Proof: *Statements*	*Reasons*
1. $\overline{AE} \cong \overline{DF}.$ (s. $\cong$ s.)	1. Given.
2. $\angle A \cong \angle D.$ (a. $\cong$ a.)	2. Given.
3. $\overleftrightarrow{AD}$ is a straight line.	3. Given.
4. $\overline{AC} \cong \overline{DB}.$	4. Given.
5. $\overline{BC} \cong \overline{BC}.$	5. Reflexive property of congruence.
6. $\overline{AC} - \overline{BC} \cong \overline{DB} - \overline{BC}$, or $\overline{AB} \cong \overline{DC}.$ (s. $\cong$ s.)	6. If congruent segments are subtracted from congruent segments, the differences are congruent segments.
7. $\triangle AEB \cong \triangle DFC.$	7. s.a.s. $\cong$ s.a.s.

EXERCISES

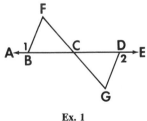

Ex. 1

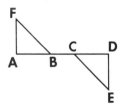

Ex. 2

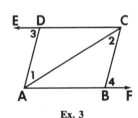

Ex. 3

1. *Given:* $\overleftrightarrow{AE}$ and $\overleftrightarrow{FG}$ are straight lines, C is the midpoint of $\overline{BD}$, $\angle 1 \cong \angle 2.$
     Prove: $\triangle BFC \cong \triangle DGC.$
2. *Given:* $\overleftrightarrow{AD}$ is a straight line, $\overline{FA} \perp \overline{AD}, \overline{ED} \perp \overline{AD}, \overline{AF} \cong \overline{DE}, \overline{AC} \cong \overline{DB}.$
     Prove: $\triangle ABF \cong \triangle DCE.$
3. *Given:* $\overleftrightarrow{EC}$ and $\overleftrightarrow{AF}$ are straight lines, $\overline{AD} \cong \overline{CB}$, $\angle 1 \cong \angle 2$, $\angle 3 \cong \angle 4.$
     Prove: $\triangle ADC \cong \triangle CBA.$

4. *Prove:* Two right triangles are congruent if the legs of one triangle are congruent to the legs of the other triangle.

5. *Given:* In triangle ABC, $\overline{CD}$ is the median to $\overline{AB}$, $\overline{CE} \cong \overline{CF}$, $\overline{EA} \cong \overline{FB}$.
   Prove: $\triangle ACD \cong \triangle BCD$.

6. *Given:* In the figure, points D and E divide segment $\overline{AB}$ into three congruent parts, $\overline{CD} \cong \overline{CE}$, $\angle x \cong \angle y$.
   Prove: $\triangle ACD \cong \triangle BCE$.

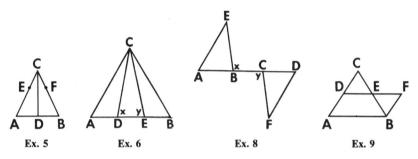

Ex. 5   Ex. 6   Ex. 8   Ex. 9

7. *Prove:* A diagonal of an equilateral quadrilateral (a quadrilateral all of whose sides are congruent) divides the quadrilateral into two congruent triangles.

8. In the figure, if $\overleftrightarrow{AD}$ is a straight line, $\overline{AC} \cong \overline{DB}$, $\angle A \cong \angle D$, and $\angle x \cong \angle y$, prove that $\triangle AEB \cong \triangle DFC$.

9. *Given:* In the figure, E is the midpoint of $\overline{BC}$, $\angle ACB \cong \angle FBC$, $\overline{AD} \cong \overline{CD}$, $\overline{FB} \cong \overline{AD}$.
   Prove: $\triangle CDE \cong \triangle BFE$.

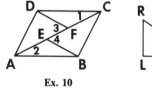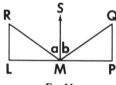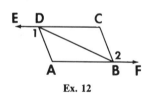

Ex. 10   Ex. 11   Ex. 12

10. *Given:* $\overleftrightarrow{AC}$, $\angle 1 \cong \angle 2$, $\angle 3 \cong \angle 4$, $\overline{AF} \cong \overline{CE}$.
    Prove: $\triangle ABE \cong \triangle CDF$.

11. *Given:* $\overleftrightarrow{SM}$ is the perpendicular bisector of $\overline{LP}$, $\overline{RM} \cong \overline{QM}$, $\angle a \cong \angle b$.
    Prove: $\triangle RLM \cong \triangle QPM$.

12. *Given:* $\overleftrightarrow{EC}$ and $\overleftrightarrow{AF}$ are straight lines, $\angle 1 \cong \angle 2$, $\angle EDB \cong \angle FBD$.
    Prove: $\triangle ADB \cong \triangle CBD$.

6. Proving Overlapping Triangles Congruent

If we are given that $\overline{AD} \cong \overline{BC}$ and $\overline{DB} \cong \overline{CA}$, can we prove that $\triangle DAB \cong \triangle CBA$?

Since these two triangles overlap, we may find it easier to visualize them if we use any one of the following devices:

1. Outline one of the triangles with a solid line, the other with a dotted line, as shown in Fig. 3–14.
2. Outline the triangles, using two contrasting colored crayons.
3. Separate the triangles, as shown in Fig. 3–15.

Fig. 3–14

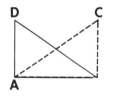 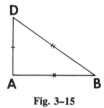 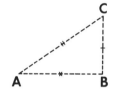

Fig. 3–15

Now we can see more clearly the relationships in $\triangle DAB$ and CBA. We were given that $\overline{AD} \cong \overline{BC}$ and $\overline{DB} \cong \overline{CA}$. Since $\overline{AB} \cong \overline{AB}$ by the reflexive property of congruence, $\triangle DAB \cong \triangle CBA$ by s.s.s. $\cong$ s.s.s.

MODEL PROBLEM

Given: In $\triangle ABC, \overline{AB} \cong \overline{AC}$.
$\overline{CD}$ and $\overline{BE}$ are me-
dians.

To prove: $\triangle ABE \cong \triangle ACD$.

Plan: Prove the triangles
congruent by showing
that s.a.s. $\cong$ s.a.s.

Separate the Triangles

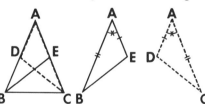

[The proof is given on the next page.]

Proof: *Statements* | *Reasons*

1. $\overline{AB} \cong \overline{AC}$.   (s. ≅ s.) | 1. Given.

2. $\angle A \cong \angle A$.   (a. ≅ a.) | 2. Reflexive property of congruence.

3. $\overline{CD}$ and $\overline{BE}$ are medians. | 3. Given.

4. $AD = \frac{1}{2}AB.$ | 4. A median divides the side to which it is drawn into two congruent parts.
$AE = \frac{1}{2}AC.$ |

5. $AD = AE.$ | 5. Halves of equal quantities are equal.

6. $\overline{AD} \cong \overline{AE}$.   (s. ≅ s.) | 6. Definition of congruent segments.

7. $\triangle ABE \cong \triangle ACD.$ | 7. s.a.s. ≅ s.a.s.

EXERCISES

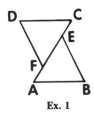

Ex. 1

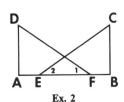

Ex. 2

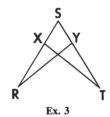

Ex. 3

1. If $\overleftrightarrow{AC}$ is a straight line, $\overline{DC} \cong \overline{BA}, \overline{DF} \cong \overline{BE}$, and $\overline{CE} \cong \overline{AF}$, prove that $\triangle AEB \cong \triangle CFD$.
2. *Given:* $\overleftrightarrow{AB}, \overline{CE} \cong \overline{DF}, \angle 1 \cong \angle 2, \overline{AE} \cong \overline{BF}$.
   Prove: $\triangle AFD \cong \triangle BEC$.
3. *Given:* $\overleftrightarrow{SR}$ and $\overleftrightarrow{ST}$ are straight lines, $\overline{SX} \cong \overline{SY}, \overline{XR} \cong \overline{YT}$.
   Prove: $\triangle RSY \cong \triangle TSX$.

Exercises 4–6 on the next page refer to the following figures:

Ex. 4

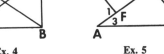

Ex. 5

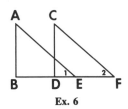

Ex. 6

4. *Given:* $\overline{DA} \cong \overline{CB}$, $\overline{DA} \perp \overline{AB}$, $\overline{CB} \perp \overline{AB}$.
   Prove: $\triangle DAB \cong \triangle CBA$.
5. *Given:* $\overleftrightarrow{AC}$, $\overline{AF} \cong \overline{EC}$, $\angle 3 \cong \angle 4$, $\angle 1 \cong \angle 2$.
   Prove: $\triangle ABE \cong \triangle CDF$.
6. *Given:* $\overline{AB} \perp \overline{BF}$, $\overline{CD} \perp \overline{BF}$, $\overline{BD} \cong \overline{FE}$, $\angle 1 \cong \angle 2$.
   Prove: $\triangle ABE \cong \triangle CDF$.

Ex. 7

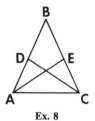
Ex. 8

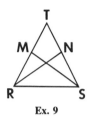
Ex. 9

7. *Given:* $\overline{LP} \perp \overline{PN}$, $\overline{MN} \perp \overline{PN}$, $\overline{LP} \cong \overline{MN}$, $\overline{PR} \cong \overline{NS}$.
   Prove: $\triangle LPS \cong \triangle MNR$.
8. *Given:* $\angle BAC \cong \angle BCA$, $\overline{CD}$ bisects $\angle BCA$, $\overline{AE}$ bisects $\angle BAC$.
   Prove: $\triangle ADC \cong \triangle CEA$.
9. *Given:* $\overline{TR} \cong \overline{TS}$, $\overline{MR} \cong \overline{NS}$.
   Prove: $\triangle RTN \cong \triangle STM$.

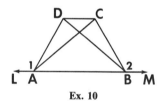
Ex. 10

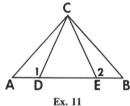
Ex. 11

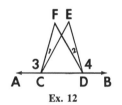
Ex. 12

10. *Given:* $\overleftrightarrow{LM}$, $\overline{CB} \cong \overline{DA}$, $\angle 2 \cong \angle 1$.
    Prove: $\triangle ABC \cong \triangle BAD$.
11. *Given:* $\overleftrightarrow{AB}$, $\overline{AD} \cong \overline{EB}$, $\angle A \cong \angle B$, $\angle 1 \cong \angle 2$.
    Prove: $\triangle AEC \cong \triangle BDC$.
12. *Given:* $\overleftrightarrow{AB}$, $\angle 1 \cong \angle 2$, $\angle 3 \cong \angle 4$.
    Prove: $\triangle CFD \cong \triangle DEC$.

Exercises 13–15 on the next page refer to the following figures:

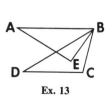
Ex. 13

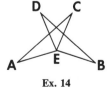
Ex. 14

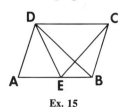
Ex. 15

13. *Given:* $\overline{AB} \cong \overline{DB}$, $\angle A \cong \angle D$, $\angle DBA \cong \angle CBE$.
    Prove: $\triangle ABE \cong \triangle DBC$.
14. *Given:* $\overline{AE} \cong \overline{BE}$, $\overline{ED} \cong \overline{EC}$, $\overline{DE} \perp \overline{AE}$, $\overline{CE} \perp \overline{EB}$.
    Prove: $\triangle AEC \cong \triangle BED$.
15. *Given:* $\overleftrightarrow{AB}$, $\overline{DA} \cong \overline{DE}$, $\angle ADE \cong \angle BDC$, $\angle DA\overline{E} \cong \angle DEC$.
    Prove: $\triangle DAB \cong \triangle DEC$.

7. Using Congruent Triangles to Prove Line Segments Congruent and Angles Congruent

To help us understand the following method of proving line segments congruent and angles congruent, let us recall that when two triangles are congruent their corresponding sides are congruent and their corresponding angles are congruent. Remember that in two congruent triangles, corresponding sides are found opposite congruent angles, and corresponding angles are found opposite congruent sides.

To prove that two line segments are congruent or two angles are congruent:

1. Choose two triangles in which the line segments to be proved congruent are sides of the triangles or in which the angles to be proved congruent are angles of the triangles.
2. Prove by any appropriate method that the triangles are congruent.
3. Show that the line segments or angles to be proved congruent are corresponding parts of the triangles proved congruent and must, therefore, be congruent.

MODEL PROBLEMS

1. Prove that in $\triangle ABC$ if $\overline{BD}$ bisects $\angle ABC$, and $\overline{BD} \perp \overline{AC}$, then $\overline{BD}$ bisects $\overline{AC}$.

   Given: In $\triangle ABC$, $\overline{BD}$ bisects $\angle ABC$.
               $\overline{BD} \perp \overline{AC}$.

   To prove: $\overline{AD} \cong \overline{CD}$.

   Plan: To prove that $\overline{AD} \cong \overline{CD}$, show that the triangles which contain these lines, $\triangle ABD$ and $\triangle CBD$, are congruent, and that $\overline{AD}$ and $\overline{CD}$ are corresponding sides of these triangles.

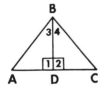

Proof: *Statements*	*Reasons*
1. $\overline{BD}$ bisects $\angle ABC$.	1. Given.
2. $\angle 3 \cong \angle 4$. (a. $\cong$ a.)	2. The bisector of an angle divides the angle into two congruent angles.
3. $\overline{BD} \perp \overline{AC}$.	3. Given.
4. $\angle 1$ and $\angle 2$ are right angles.	4. Perpendicular lines intersect and form right angles.
5. $\angle 1 \cong \angle 2$. (a. $\cong$ a.)	5. If two angles are right angles, they are congruent.
6. $\overline{BD} \cong \overline{BD}$. (s. $\cong$ s.)	6. Reflexive property of congruence.
7. $\triangle ABD \cong \triangle CBD$.	7. a.s.a. $\cong$ a.s.a.
8. $\overline{AD} \cong \overline{CD}$. ($\overline{AD}$ is opposite $\angle 3$, and $\overline{CD}$ is opposite the congruent $\angle 4$.)	8. Corresponding parts of congruent triangles are congruent.

2. a. *Given:* $\overline{CA} \cong \overline{CB}, \overline{CE} \cong \overline{CD}, \overline{BE} \cong \overline{AD}$.

To prove: $\angle EAB \cong \angle DBA$.

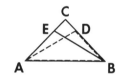

Plan: To prove that $\angle EAB \cong \angle DBA$, show that the overlapping triangles *EAB* and *DBA* are congruent, and that $\angle EAB$ and $\angle DBA$ are corresponding angles of these congruent triangles.

Separate the Triangles

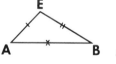 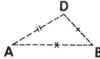

Proof: *Statements*	*Reasons*
1. $\overline{BE} \cong \overline{AD}$. (s. $\cong$ s.)	1. Given.
2. $\overline{CA} \cong \overline{CB}, \overline{CE} \cong \overline{CD}$.	2. Given.
3. $\overline{CA} - \overline{CE} \cong \overline{CB} - \overline{CD}$, or $\overline{AE} \cong \overline{BD}$. (s. $\cong$ s.)	3. If congruent segments are subtracted from congruent segments, the differences are congruent segments.

[The proof is continued on the next page.]

Proof: *Statements*	*Reasons*
4. $\overline{AB} \cong \overline{AB}$. (s. $\cong$ s.)	4. Reflexive property of congruence.
5. $\triangle EAB \cong \triangle DBA$.	5. s.s.s. $\cong$ s.s.s.
6. $\angle EAB \cong \angle DBA$. ($\angle EAB$ is opposite side $\overline{EB}$, and $\angle DBA$ is opposite the congruent side $\overline{DA}$.)	6. Corresponding parts of congruent triangles are congruent.

b. Using the results found in part *a*, find the measure of $\angle EAB$ if the measure of $\angle EAB$ is represented by $5x - 8$ and the measure of $\angle DBA$ is represented by $3x + 12$.

Solution:

1. $\angle EAB \cong \angle DBA$, or [Proved in part *a*.]

2. $m\angle EAB = m\angle DBA$

3. $5x - 8 = 3x + 12$

4. $5x - 3x = 12 + 8$

5. $2x = 20$

6. $x = 10$

7. $m\angle EAB = 5x - 8 = 5(10) - 8 = 50 - 8 = 42$.

Answer: $m\angle EAB = 42$.

EXERCISES

In 1–6, the straight-line figures have been marked to indicate the pairs of congruent angles and pairs of congruent segments.   (*a*) Name two triangles that are congruent and state the reason why the triangles are congruent.   (*b*) In these triangles, name three additional pairs of parts that are congruent because they are corresponding parts of congruent triangles.

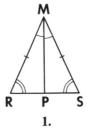

1.

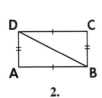

2.

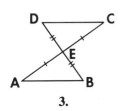

3.

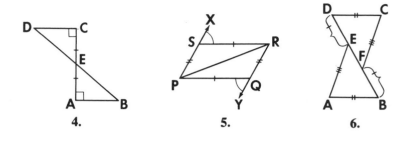

4.   5.   6.

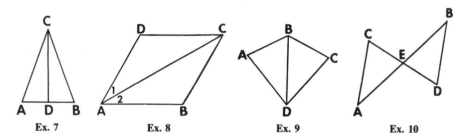

Ex. 7   Ex. 8   Ex. 9   Ex. 10

7. $\overline{CA} \cong \overline{CB}$ and $\overline{AD} \cong \overline{BD}$. (a) Prove $\triangle ADC \cong \triangle BDC$. (b) Find three pairs of congruent angles in $\triangle ADC$ and $\triangle BDC$.

8. $\overline{AD} \cong \overline{AB}$ and $\angle 1 \cong \angle 2$. (a) Prove $\triangle ADC \cong \triangle ABC$. (b) Find three more pairs of congruent parts in $\triangle ADC$ and $\triangle ABC$.

9. $\overrightarrow{BD}$ bisects $\angle ABC$, and $\overrightarrow{DB}$ bisects $\angle ADC$. (a) Prove that $\triangle ABD \cong \triangle CBD$. (b) Find three more pairs of congruent parts in $\triangle ABD$ and $\triangle CBD$.

10. If $\overleftrightarrow{AB}$ and $\overleftrightarrow{CD}$ are straight lines, $\overline{AE} \cong \overline{BE}$ and $\overline{CE} \cong \overline{DE}$, prove that $\angle C \cong \angle D$.

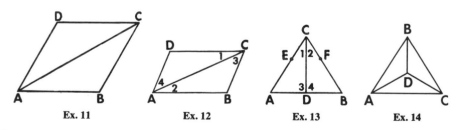

Ex. 11   Ex. 12   Ex. 13   Ex. 14

11. If $\overline{AB} \cong \overline{CD}$ and $\overline{BC} \cong \overline{DA}$, prove that $\angle B \cong \angle D$.

12. If $\angle 1 \cong \angle 2$ and $\angle 3 \cong \angle 4$, prove that $\overline{DC} \cong \overline{BA}$.

13. If $\overleftrightarrow{CA}$ and $\overleftrightarrow{CB}$ are straight lines, $\angle 1 \cong \angle 2$, $\overline{CE} \cong \overline{CF}$, and $\overline{EA} \cong \overline{FB}$, prove that $\angle 3 \cong \angle 4$.

14. If $\overline{BA} \cong \overline{BC}$ and $\overline{DA} \cong \overline{DC}$, prove that $\overline{BD}$ bisects $\angle ABC$.

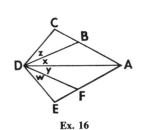

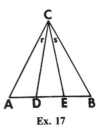

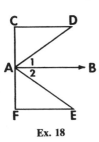

| Ex. 15 | Ex. 16 | Ex. 17 | Ex. 18 |

15. If $\overline{TQ}$ bisects $\angle RTS$ and $\overline{TQ} \perp \overline{RS}$, prove that $\overline{TQ}$ bisects $\overline{RS}$.

16. If $\overline{DC} \cong \overline{DE}$, $\angle x \cong \angle y$, and $\angle z \cong \angle w$, prove that $\overline{AE} \cong \overline{AC}$.

17. If $\overleftrightarrow{AB}$ is a straight line, $\overline{AC} \cong \overline{BC}$, $\overline{CE} \cong \overline{CD}$, and $\overline{AE} \cong \overline{BD}$, prove that $\angle r \cong \angle s$.

18. If $\overleftrightarrow{AB}$ is the perpendicular bisector of $\overline{CF}$, $\angle 1 \cong \angle 2$, and $\overline{AD} \cong \overline{AE}$, prove that $\angle D \cong \angle E$.

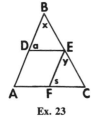

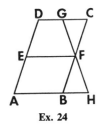

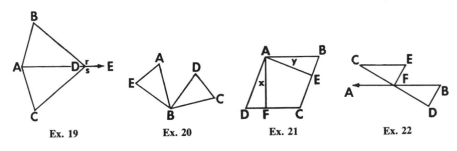

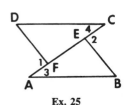

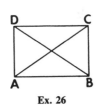

| Ex. 19 | Ex. 20 | Ex. 21 | Ex. 22 |

19. If $\overleftrightarrow{AE}$ is a straight line, $\angle r \cong \angle s$, and $\overline{BD} \cong \overline{CD}$, prove that $\overline{AB} \cong \overline{AC}$.

20. If $\overline{AB} \perp \overline{BC}$, $\overline{DB} \perp \overline{BE}$, $\overline{BC} \cong \overline{BE}$, and $\overline{DB} \cong \overline{AB}$, prove that $\angle D \cong \angle A$.

21. If $\angle D$ and $\angle B$ are both supplementary to $\angle C$, $\overline{AD} \cong \overline{AB}$, and $\overline{DF} \cong \overline{BE}$, prove that $\angle x \cong \angle y$.

22. If $\overleftrightarrow{AB}$ and $\overleftrightarrow{CD}$ are straight lines, $\angle ECF \cong \angle CFA$, $\overline{CF} \cong \overline{FD}$, and $\overline{CE} \cong \overline{FB}$, prove that $\angle E \cong \angle B$.

| Ex. 23 | Ex. 24 | Ex. 25 | Ex. 26 |

23. In triangle ABC, D is the midpoint of $\overline{AB}$, E is the midpoint of $\overline{BC}$, $\angle x \cong \angle y$, and $\overline{AD} \cong \overline{EF}$. Prove that $\angle a \cong \angle s$.

24. If F is the midpoint of $\overline{GH}$, E is the midpoint of $\overline{AD}$, $\overline{FC} \cong \overline{ED}$, $\overline{BF} \cong \overline{AE}$, and $\overleftrightarrow{BC}$ is a straight line, prove that $\overline{GC} \cong \overline{HB}$.

25. If $\overleftrightarrow{AC}$ is a straight line, $\overline{AF} \cong \overline{CE}$, $\angle 3 \cong \angle 4$, and $\angle 1 \cong \angle 2$, prove that $\angle B \cong \angle D$.

26. If $\overline{DA} \perp \overline{AB}$, $\overline{CB} \perp \overline{AB}$, and $\overline{AD} \cong \overline{BC}$, prove that $\overline{AC} \cong \overline{BD}$.

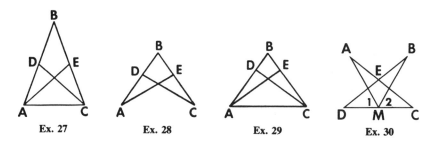

Ex. 27   Ex. 28   Ex. 29   Ex. 30

27. If $\overline{DA} \cong \overline{EC}$ and $\overline{AE} \cong \overline{CD}$, prove that $\angle EAC \cong \angle DCA$.

28. If $\overleftrightarrow{AB}$ and $\overleftrightarrow{BC}$ are straight lines, $\overline{BD} \cong \overline{BE}$, and $\overline{DA} \cong \overline{EC}$, prove that $\angle A \cong \angle C$.

29. If $\overline{CD} \perp \overline{AB}$, $\overline{AE} \perp \overline{BC}$, and $\overline{BD} \cong \overline{BE}$, prove that $\overline{AE} \cong \overline{CD}$.

30. If $\overleftrightarrow{AC}$ and $\overleftrightarrow{BD}$ are straight lines which intersect at E, $\angle D \cong \angle C$, $\angle 2 \cong \angle 1$, and M is the midpoint of $\overline{DC}$, prove that $\overline{DB} \cong \overline{CA}$.

31. If $\overleftrightarrow{EA}$ and $\overleftrightarrow{GJ}$ are straight lines, $\overline{ED} \cong \overline{BC}$, $\angle 1 \cong \angle 2$, and $\overline{FC} \cong \overline{GB}$, prove that $\angle F \cong \angle G$.

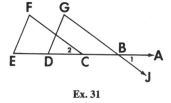

Ex. 31

32. In isosceles triangle ABC, the congruent sides $\overline{CA}$ and $\overline{CB}$ are extended through A and B to points D and E respectively so that $\overline{AD} \cong \overline{BE}$. $\overline{AE}$ and $\overline{BD}$ are drawn. Prove that triangles CDB and CEA are congruent and $\angle D \cong \angle E$.

33. Triangle ABC is congruent to triangle $A'B'C'$. If $m\angle C$ is represented by $2x - 10$ and $m\angle C'$ is represented by $x + 30$: (*a*) Find x. (*b*) Find $m\angle C$. (*c*) Find $m\angle B$ if it is represented by $x - 25$.

34. Triangle DEF is congruent to triangle $D'E'F'$. If EF is represented by $3x + 2$, $E'F'$ is represented by $x + 10$, and ED is represented by $x + 2$, find x, ED, and $E'D'$.

In 35–37, the straight-line figures have been marked to indicate pairs of congruent angles and pairs of congruent sides: (*a*) Prove two triangles congruent. (*b*) Find the value of x. (*c*) Find the measure of each side or angle which is represented in terms of x.

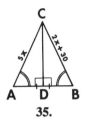

35.

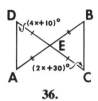

36.

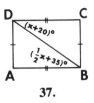

37.

38. *Given:* $\overline{AD} \cong \overline{CB}$ and $\angle 1 \cong \angle 2$. *(a) Prove:* $\triangle ADB \cong \triangle CBD$. *(b) Prove:* $\overline{AB} \cong \overline{CD}$. *(c)* Find the length of $\overline{AB}$ and of $\overline{CD}$. *(d)* Find the length of $\overline{CB}$ and of $\overline{AD}$.

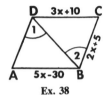

Ex. 38

39. If all sides of polygon $ABCDE$ are congruent and $\angle E \cong \angle C$, find AD and BD.

40. Triangle ABC is congruent to triangle $A'B'C'$. If AB is represented by $2x + y$, $A'B' = 7$, $BC = 11$, and $B'C'$ is represented by $4x + y$, find x and y.

41. Triangle ABC is congruent to triangle $A'B'C'$. If $m\angle A$ is represented by $x + 10$, $m\angle A'$ is represented by $y + 20$, $m\angle B$ is represented by $3x$, and $m\angle B'$ is represented by $x + 3y$, find $m\angle A$ and $m\angle B$.

42. If $\overline{AB} \perp \overline{BD}$, $\overline{CD} \perp \overline{BD}$, and $\overleftrightarrow{AC}$ bisects $\overline{BD}$, find the number of degrees in $\angle 1$ and $\angle 3$ when $m\angle 1$ is represented by $2y + 20$, $m\angle 2$ is represented by $2x + 3y$, and $m\angle 3$ is represented by $x + y$.

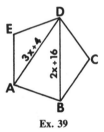

Ex. 39

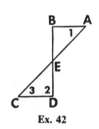

Ex. 42

8. Using Two Pairs of Congruent Triangles

Sometimes it is impossible to use the *given* in order to prove directly that a particular pair of triangles is congruent. In such cases, the *given* may contain enough information to first prove another pair of triangles congruent. Then corresponding congruent parts in these congruent triangles may be used to prove the original pair of triangles congruent. See how this is done in the following example:

MODEL PROBLEM

Given: $\overleftrightarrow{AB}$ is a straight line.
$\overline{AC} \cong \overline{AD}$.
$\overline{BC} \cong \overline{BD}$.

To prove: $\overline{CE} \cong \overline{DE}$.

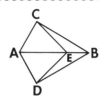

We can prove $\overline{CE} \cong \overline{DE}$ if we can prove that $\triangle ACE \cong \triangle ADE$. In these two triangles, we know only that $\overline{AC} \cong \overline{AD}$ (given) and $\overline{AE} \cong \overline{AE}$ (reflexive property of congruence). If we could prove $\angle CAE \cong \angle DAE$, then triangles ACE and ADE would be congruent by s.a.s. $\cong$ s.a.s. We can prove $\angle CAE \cong \angle DAE$ by showing that $\triangle CAB$ and $\triangle DAB$, which also contain these angles, are congruent.

In $\triangle CAB$ and DAB, $\overline{AC} \cong \overline{AD}$ (given), $\overline{BC} \cong \overline{BD}$ (given), and $\overline{AB} \cong \overline{AB}$ (reflexive property of congruence). Therefore, $\triangle CAB \cong \triangle DAB$ by s.s.s. $\cong$ s.s.s. $\angle CAB$, or $\angle CAE \cong \angle DAB$, or $\angle DAE$, because they are corresponding parts of congruent $\triangle CAB$ and DAB.

Now having proved that $\angle CAE \cong \angle DAE$, we can prove that $\triangle ACE \cong \triangle ADE$ by s.a.s. $\cong$ s.a.s. Hence, $\overline{CE} \cong \overline{DE}$ because they are corresponding sides of these congruent triangles. The formal proof follows:

Given: $\overleftrightarrow{AB}$ is a straight line.
$\overline{AC} \cong \overline{AD}$.
$\overline{BC} \cong \overline{BD}$.

To prove: $\overline{CE} \cong \overline{DE}$.

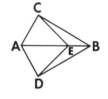

Proof: *Statements*	*Reasons*
1. In $\triangle CAB$ and DAB, $\overline{AC} \cong \overline{AD}$. (s. $\cong$ s.)	1. Given.
2. $\overline{BC} \cong \overline{BD}$. (s. $\cong$ s.)	2. Given.
3. $\overline{AB} \cong \overline{AB}$. (s. $\cong$ s.)	3. Reflexive property of congruence.
4. $\triangle CAB \cong \triangle DAB$.	4. s.s.s. $\cong$ s.s.s.
5. $\angle CAB \cong \angle DAB$, or $\angle CAE \cong \angle DAE$.	5. Corresponding parts of congruent triangles are congruent.
6. In $\triangle ACE$ and ADE, $\angle CAE \cong \angle DAE$. (a. $\cong$ a.)	6. Proved in steps 1–5.

[The proof is continued on the next page.]

Proof: *Statements*	*Reasons*
7. $\overline{AC} \cong \overline{AD}$. (s. ≅ s.)	7. Given.
8. $\overline{AE} \cong \overline{AE}$. (s. ≅ s.)	8. Reflexive property of congruence.
9. $\triangle ACE \cong \triangle ADE$.	9. s.a.s. ≅ s.a.s.
10. $\overline{CE} \cong \overline{DE}$.	10. Corresponding parts of congruent triangles are congruent.

EXERCISES

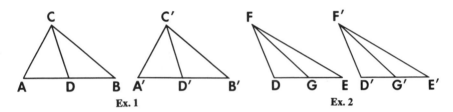

Ex. 1   Ex. 2

1. *Given:* $\triangle ABC \cong \triangle A'B'C'$, $\overline{CD}$ bisects $\angle C$, $\overline{C'D'}$ bisects $\angle C'$.
   Prove: $\overline{CD} \cong \overline{C'D'}$.

2. *Given:* $\triangle DEF \cong \triangle D'E'F'$, $\overline{FG}$ and $\overline{F'G'}$ are medians.
   Prove: $\overline{FG} \cong \overline{F'G'}$.

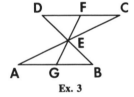 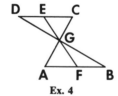 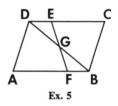

Ex. 3   Ex. 4   Ex. 5

3. *Given:* $\overleftrightarrow{AC}$, $\overleftrightarrow{BD}$, and $\overleftrightarrow{GF}$ are straight lines, $\overline{AE} \cong \overline{CE}$, $\overline{FE} \cong \overline{GE}$.
   Prove: (a) $\angle C \cong \angle A$.   (b) $\overline{DC} \cong \overline{BA}$.

4. *Given:* $\overleftrightarrow{EF}$, $\overline{AC}$ and $\overline{BD}$ bisect each other at G.
   Prove: (a) $\angle D \cong \angle B$.   (b) $\overline{GE} \cong \overline{GF}$.

5. *Given:* $\overline{AD} \cong \overline{CB}$, $\overline{DC} \cong \overline{BA}$, $\overline{EF}$ bisects $\overline{BD}$ at G.
   Prove: (a) $\angle CDB \cong \angle ABD$.   (b) $\overline{GE} \cong \overline{GF}$.

6. *Given:* $\overline{AB} \cong \overline{AC}$, $\angle RAB \cong \angle SAC$, and
           $\angle RBA \cong \angle SCA$.
   Prove: (a) $\overline{AR} \cong \overline{AS}$.   (b) $\angle ACR \cong \angle ABS$.

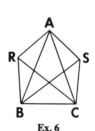

Ex. 6

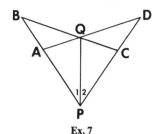
Ex. 7

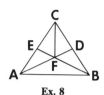
Ex. 8

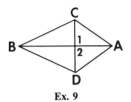
Ex. 9

7. *Given:* $\overleftrightarrow{PQ}$, $\overleftrightarrow{PAB}$, $\overleftrightarrow{PCD}$, $\overleftrightarrow{AQD}$ and $\overleftrightarrow{CQB}$. $\angle 1 \cong \angle 2$ and $\overline{AP} \cong \overline{CP}$.
   Prove: (a) $\triangle APQ \cong \triangle CPQ$.   (b) $\overline{QB} \cong \overline{QD}$.

8. *Given:* $\overline{EF} \cong \overline{DF}$, and $\angle EFC \cong \angle DFC$.
   Prove: (a) $\angle ECF \cong \angle DCF$.   (b) $\overline{AC} \cong \overline{BC}$.

9. *Given:* $\overline{AC} \cong \overline{AD}$, $\overline{BC} \cong \overline{BD}$.
   Prove: $\angle 1 \cong \angle 2$.

Ex. 10

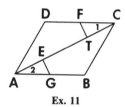
Ex. 11

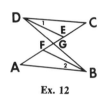
Ex. 12

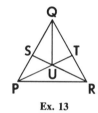
Ex. 13

10. *Given:* $\overline{RP} \cong \overline{RQ}$, $\overline{SP} \cong \overline{SQ}$.
   Prove: $\overline{RT}$ bisects $\overline{PQ}$.

11. *Given:* $\overleftrightarrow{AC}$, F is the midpoint of $\overline{DC}$, G is the midpoint of $\overline{AB}$, $\overline{FT} \perp \overline{AC}$,
   $\overline{GE} \perp \overline{AC}$, $\angle 1 \cong \angle 2$, $\overline{AT} \cong \overline{CE}$.
   Prove: $\angle B \cong \angle D$.

12. *Given:* $\overline{AC}$ and $\overline{BD}$ bisect each other at G, $\angle 1 \cong \angle 2$.
   Prove: $\overline{EC} \cong \overline{FA}$.

13. *Given:* $\overline{QP} \cong \overline{QR}$, $\overline{QS} \cong \overline{QT}$.
   Prove: $\overline{QU}$ bisects $\angle PQR$.

14. *Given:* In quadrilateral $ABCD$, $\overline{AD} \cong \overline{BC}$, and
   $\angle BAD \cong \angle ABC$.
   Prove: $\angle BCD \cong \angle ADC$.

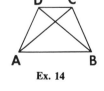
Ex. 14

15. In quadrilateral $ABCD$, $\overline{AB} \cong \overline{AD}$, and $\overline{BC} \cong \overline{DC}$.
   Diagonal $\overline{AC}$ is extended through C to E and segments $\overline{BE}$ and $\overline{DE}$ are drawn.
   Prove: $\overline{BE} \cong \overline{DE}$.

16. *Prove:* In two congruent triangles, two corresponding medians are congruent.

17. *Prove:* In two congruent triangles, two corresponding angle bisectors are congruent.

9. The Isosceles Triangle and the Equilateral Triangle

Properties of an Isosceles Triangle

Theorem 9. **If two sides of a triangle are congruent, the angles opposite these sides are congruent.**

OR

The base angles of an isosceles triangle are congruent.

[The proof for this theorem appears on page 593.]

In $\triangle ABC$ (Fig. 3–16), if $\overline{AB} \cong \overline{AC}$, then $\angle C \cong \angle B$.

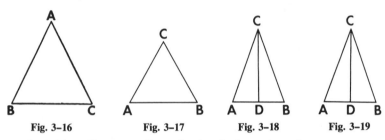

| Fig. 3–16 | Fig. 3–17 | Fig. 3–18 | Fig. 3–19 |

Corollary T9–1. **Every equilateral triangle is equiangular.**

If in $\triangle ABC$ (Fig. 3–17) $\overline{BC} \cong \overline{CA} \cong \overline{AB}$, then $\angle A \cong \angle B \cong \angle C$, or $\triangle ABC$ is equiangular.

Corollary T9–2. **The bisector of the vertex angle of an isosceles triangle bisects the base.**

If in $\triangle ABC$ (Fig. 3–18) $\overline{CA} \cong \overline{CB}$, and $\overline{CD}$ bisects $\angle ACB$ ($\angle ACD \cong \angle BCD$), then $\overline{CD}$ bisects side $\overline{AB}$ ($\overline{AD} \cong \overline{BD}$).

Corollary T9–3. **The bisector of the vertex angle of an isosceles triangle is perpendicular to the base.**

If in $\triangle ABC$ (Fig. 3–19) $\overline{CA} \cong \overline{CB}$ and $\overline{CD}$ bisects $\angle ACB$ ($\angle ACD \cong \angle BCD$), then $\overline{CD} \perp \overline{AB}$.

MODEL PROBLEM

Given: Isosceles $\triangle ABC$ with $\overline{CA} \cong \overline{CB}$.
            M is the midpoint of $\overline{AB}$. $\overline{AD} \cong \overline{BE}$.

To prove: $\overline{MD} \cong \overline{ME}$.

Plan: To prove that $\overline{MD} \cong \overline{ME}$, prove that $\triangle ADM$ and BEM, which have $\overline{MD}$ and $\overline{ME}$ as corresponding sides, are congruent by s.a.s. $\cong$ s.a.s.

Proof: *Statements*	*Reasons*
1. $\overline{AD} \cong \overline{BE}$. (s. $\cong$ s.)	1. Given.
2. M is the midpoint of $\overline{AB}$.	2. Given.
3. $\overline{AM} \cong \overline{BM}$. (s. $\cong$ s.)	3. A midpoint divides a line segment into two congruent parts.
4. $\overline{CA} \cong \overline{CB}$.	4. Given.
5. $\angle A \cong \angle B$. (a. $\cong$ a.)	5. If two sides of a triangle are congruent, the angles opposite these sides are congruent.
6. $\triangle ADM \cong \triangle BEM$.	6. s.a.s. $\cong$ s.a.s.
7. $\overline{MD} \cong \overline{ME}$.	7. Corresponding parts of congruent triangles are congruent.

EXERCISES

1. In $\triangle ABC$, if $\overline{CA} \cong \overline{CB}$ and $m\angle A = 50$, find $m\angle B$.

2. In triangle ABC, $\overline{AB} \cong \overline{BC}$. If $AB = 5x$ and $BC = 2x + 18$, find AB and BC.

3. In isosceles triangle ABC, $\overline{AB} \cong \overline{BC}$. If $AB = 5x + 10$, $BC = 3x + 40$, and $AC = 2x + 30$, find the length of each side of the triangle.

4. In triangle ABC, $\overline{AB} \cong \overline{BC}$. If $m\angle A = 7x$ and $m\angle C = 2x + 50$, find $m\angle A$ and $m\angle C$.

5. In triangle EFG, $\overline{EF} \cong \overline{FG}$. If $m\angle E = 4x + 50$, $m\angle F = 2x + 60$, and $m\angle G = 14x + 30$, find $m\angle E$, $m\angle F$, and $m\angle G$.

6. $\overline{BD}$ is the bisector of vertex angle B of isosceles triangle ABC. If $AB = 2x + 2y$, $AD = x + 2y$, $DC = 4x$, and $BC = 10$, find AB, AD, and AC.

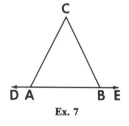
Ex. 7

Ex. 8

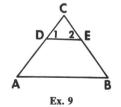
Ex. 9

7. In $\triangle ABC$, if $\overline{CA} \cong \overline{CB}$ and $\overleftrightarrow{DE}$ is a straight line, prove that $\angle CAD \cong \angle CBE$.

8. In △*RST*, if $\overline{TR} \cong \overline{TS}$, $\overline{RN}$ bisects ∠*R*, and $\overline{SM}$ bisects ∠*S*, prove that ∠*NRS* ≅ ∠*MSR*.

9. If $\overline{CA} \cong \overline{CB}$, and $\overline{DA} \cong \overline{EB}$, prove that ∠1 ≅ ∠2.

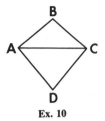
Ex. 10

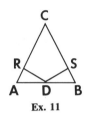
Ex. 11

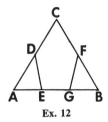
Ex. 12

10. Isosceles triangles *ABC* and *ADC* have the common base $\overline{AC}$. Prove that ∠*BAD* ≅ ∠*BCD*.

11. In △*ABC*, if $\overline{CA} \cong \overline{CB}, \overline{AR} \cong \overline{BS}, \overline{DR} \perp \overline{AC}$, and $\overline{DS} \perp \overline{BC}$, prove that $\overline{DR} \cong \overline{DS}$.

12. In isosceles triangle *ABC*, *D* and *F* are the midpoints of the congruent legs. *E* and *G* are the trisection points of the base $(\overline{AE} \cong \overline{EG} \cong \overline{GB})$. Prove that $\overline{DE} \cong \overline{FG}$.

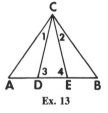
Ex. 13

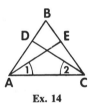
Ex. 14

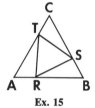
Ex. 15

13. If $\overleftrightarrow{AB}$ is a straight line, $\overline{CA} \cong \overline{CB}$, and ∠1 ≅ ∠2, prove that ∠3 ≅ ∠4.

14. If $\overleftrightarrow{AB}$ and $\overleftrightarrow{BC}$ are straight lines, $\overline{BD} \cong \overline{BE}$, and $\overline{DA} \cong \overline{EC}$, prove that ∠1 ≅ ∠2.

15. If △*ABC* is an equilateral triangle and $\overline{CT} \cong \overline{AR} \cong \overline{BS}$, prove that $\overline{TR} \cong \overline{RS} \cong \overline{ST}$.

Ex. 16

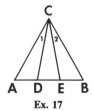
Ex. 17

Ex. 18

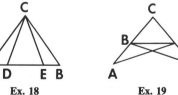
Ex. 19

16. In △*ABC*, if $\overline{AB} \cong \overline{BC}$ and $\overline{DB}$ bisects ∠*B*, prove that ∠*ACD* ≅ ∠*CAD*.

17. If in △*ABC*, $\overline{CA} \cong \overline{CB}$ and ∠1 ≅ ∠2, prove that $\overline{AE} \cong \overline{BD}$.

18. If $\overline{AD} \cong \overline{EB}$, $\overline{CD} \cong \overline{CE}$, and $\overset{\leftrightarrow}{AB}$ is a straight line, prove that $\overline{AC} \cong \overline{BC}$.
19. If $\overline{CB} \cong \overline{CD}$, $\overline{BA} \cong \overline{DE}$, and $\overset{\leftrightarrow}{CA}$ and $\overset{\leftrightarrow}{CE}$ are straight lines, prove that $\angle EBD \cong \angle ADB$.

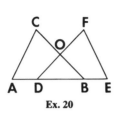

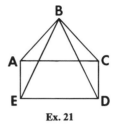

Ex. 20   Ex. 21

20. *Given:* On line $\overset{\leftrightarrow}{AE}$, $\overline{AD} \cong \overline{BE}$. $\overline{DF}$ and $\overline{BC}$ are congruent and bisect each other at O.
    Prove: $\overline{AC} \cong \overline{EF}$.
21. In the figure, $EDCA$ is a quadrilateral, $\overline{EA} \cong \overline{DC}$, $\overline{BA} \cong \overline{BC}$, $\overline{EA} \perp \overline{AC}$, and $\overline{DC} \perp \overline{AC}$.
    Prove: $\angle BED \cong \angle BDE$.
22. *Prove:* The line segments joining the midpoint of the base of an isosceles triangle to the midpoints of the legs are congruent.
23. *Prove:* The bisectors of the base angles of an isosceles triangle are congruent.
24. *Prove:* The medians to the legs of an isosceles triangle are congruent.
25. In isosceles triangle DEF, $\overline{ED} \cong \overline{EF}$. Point P is chosen between points E and D; point Q is chosen between points E and F, so that $\overline{EP} \cong \overline{EQ}$. Segments $\overline{DQ}$ and $\overline{FP}$ are drawn. *Prove:* $\triangle PDF \cong \triangle QFD$.
26. O is the midpoint of base $\overline{AB}$ of isosceles triangle ABC. $\overline{AC}$ and $\overline{BC}$ are extended through C to points E and D respectively so that $\overline{CE}$ is congruent to $\overline{CD}$. Line segments $\overline{DO}$ and $\overline{EO}$ are drawn. *Prove:* $\overline{DO} \cong \overline{EO}$.
27. In triangle CDE, $\overline{CD} \cong \overline{CE}$. R is the midpoint of $\overline{CD}$ and S is the midpoint of $\overline{CE}$. $\overset{\leftrightarrow}{RM}$ is drawn perpendicular to $\overset{\leftrightarrow}{CD}$; $\overset{\leftrightarrow}{SN}$ is drawn perpendicular to $\overset{\leftrightarrow}{CE}$, M and N being points on $\overline{DE}$ or $\overline{DE}$ extended. Prove that $\overline{RM} \cong \overline{SN}$.
28. In isosceles triangle ABC, $\overline{CA} \cong \overline{CB}$. D is a point on $\overline{CA}$ and E is a point on $\overline{CB}$. $\overline{AD} \cong \overline{BE}$. $\overline{BD}$ is drawn and extended its own length through D to X, $\overline{AE}$ is drawn and extended its own length through E to Y, and $\overline{XA}$ and $\overline{YB}$ are drawn. *Prove:* (a) $\overline{BD} \cong \overline{AE}$. (b) $\overline{XA} \cong \overline{YB}$.

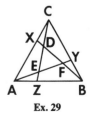

Ex. 29

29. In equilateral triangle ABC, if $\overline{CX} \cong \overline{AZ} \cong \overline{BY}$, prove that $\overline{DE} \cong \overline{EF} \cong \overline{FD}$.

10. Proving a Triangle Isosceles

The Converse of a Statement

The *converse* of a given statement is another statement which is formed by interchanging the hypothesis and the conclusion in the given statement. For example:

1. *Given Statement:*   If a man drives a Cadillac, then he drives an American car.

   Converse of Statement: If a man drives an American car, then he drives a Cadillac.

2. *Given Statement:*   If three sides of one triangle are congruent respectively to three sides of another triangle, then the triangles are congruent.

   Converse of Statement: If two triangles are congruent, then three sides of one triangle are congruent respectively to three sides of the other triangle.

In general, for a given conditional statement, we have the following:

Given Statement: If p, then q.

Converse of Statement: If q, then p.

Observe that in example 1, the original statement is true but the converse of the original statement is false. Notice, too, that in example 2, the original statement is true and the converse of the original statement is also true. Hence, we see that the converse of a true statement is not necessarily a true statement. We cannot assume that the converse of a true statement is true. We must prove it.

We will discuss the topic of converses in greater detail in the chapter dealing with "Improvement of Reasoning."

The Converse of the Isosceles Triangle Theorem

We have proved the isosceles triangle theorem, "If two sides of a triangle are congruent, the angles opposite these sides are congruent." We cannot assume that the converse of this theorem, whose statement follows, is true. We must prove it.

Theorem 10. **If two angles of a triangle are congruent, the sides opposite these angles are congruent.**

OR

If two angles of a triangle are congruent, the triangle is isosceles.

[A proof for this theorem appears on pages 594–595. An alternate proof appears on page 597.]

In △*ABC* (Fig. 3–20), if ∠*A* ≅ ∠*B*, then $\overline{BC}$ ≅ $\overline{AC}$, or △*ABC* is isosceles.

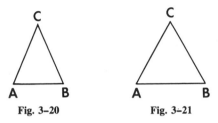

Fig. 3–20   Fig. 3–21

Corollary T10–1. **If a triangle is equiangular, it is equilateral.**

In △*ABC* (Fig. 3–21), if ∠*A* ≅ ∠*B* ≅ ∠*C*, then $\overline{BC}$ ≅ $\overline{CA}$ ≅ $\overline{AB}$, or △*ABC* is equilateral.

To prove that a triangle is isosceles, prove that one of the following statements is true:

1. Two sides of the triangle are congruent.
2. Two angles of the triangle are congruent.

Sentences Involving "If and Only If"

It is possible to write a statement and its converse in one sentence. We can do this by inserting the expression "if and only if" between the hypothesis and the conclusion. For example, Theorem 9 (page 136) and Theorem 10 (page 140) can be combined as follows:

Two sides of a triangle are congruent if and only if the angles opposite these sides are congruent.

This theorem is a short way of stating the following two theorems:

Theorem 9. **If two sides of a triangle are congruent, then the angles opposite these sides are congruent.**

Theorem 10. **If two angles of a triangle are congruent, then the sides opposite these angles are congruent.**

If we wish to prove a statement of the form "*p* if and only if *q*," where *p* and *q* are statements, we must prove the following two statements:

1. If *p*, then *q*.
2. If *q*, then *p*.

MODEL PROBLEM ～～～～～～～～～～～～～

Given: In $\triangle ABC$, $\overline{BA} \cong \overline{BC}$.
$\overline{AD}$ bisects $\angle BAC$.
$\overline{CD}$ bisects $\angle BCA$.

To prove: $\triangle ADC$ is an isosceles triangle.

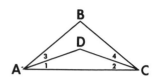

Plan: In order to prove that $\triangle ADC$ is isosceles, prove that two of its sides, $\overline{CD}$ and $\overline{AD}$, are congruent. In order to prove $\overline{CD} \cong \overline{AD}$, prove that in $\triangle ADC$ the angles opposite these sides, $\angle 1$ and $\angle 2$, are congruent.

Proof:

Statements	Reasons
1. $\overline{BA} \cong \overline{BC}$.	1. Given.
2. $\angle BAC \cong \angle BCA$.	2. If two sides of a triangle are congruent, the angles opposite these sides are congruent.
3. $\overline{AD}$ bisects $\angle BAC$. $\overline{CD}$ bisects $\angle BCA$.	3. Given.
4. $\angle 1 \cong \angle 3$, or $m\angle 1 = \frac{1}{2}m\angle BAC$. $\angle 2 \cong \angle 4$, or $m\angle 2 = \frac{1}{2}m\angle BCA$.	4. The bisector of an angle divides the angle into two angles whose measures are equal.
5. $m\angle 1 = m\angle 2$, or $\angle 1 \cong \angle 2$.	5. Halves of equal quantities are equal.
6. $\overline{CD} \cong \overline{AD}$.	6. If two angles of a triangle are congruent, the sides opposite these angles are congruent.
7. $\triangle ADC$ is an isosceles triangle.	7. If a triangle has two congruent sides, it is an isosceles triangle.

～～～～～～～～～～～～～～～～～～～～～～～～

EXERCISES

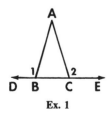

Ex. 1

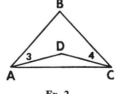

Ex. 2

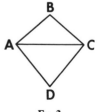

Ex. 3

1. If $\angle 1 \cong \angle 2$ and $\overleftrightarrow{DE}$ is a straight line, prove that $\triangle ABC$ is an isosceles triangle.

2. If $\overline{AB} \cong \overline{BC}$ and $\angle 3 \cong \angle 4$, prove that $\triangle ADC$ is an isosceles triangle.

3. If $\overline{BA} \cong \overline{BC}$, $\overline{DA} \perp \overline{AB}$, and $\overline{DC} \perp \overline{CB}$, prove that $\triangle ADC$ is an isosceles triangle.

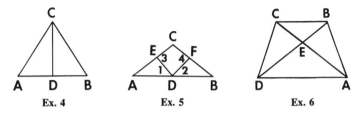

Ex. 4　　　　　Ex. 5　　　　　Ex. 6

4. If $\overline{CD} \perp \overline{AB}$, and $\overline{CD}$ bisects $\overline{AB}$, prove that $\triangle ABC$ is an isosceles triangle.

5. If $\angle 1 \cong \angle 2$, $\overline{DE} \cong \overline{DF}$, and $\angle 3 \cong \angle 4$, prove that $\triangle ABC$ is an isosceles triangle.

6. If $\overline{AB} \cong \overline{DC}$, and $\overline{AC} \cong \overline{DB}$, prove that $\triangle DEA$ is an isosceles triangle.

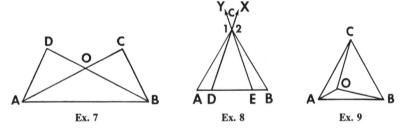

Ex. 7　　　　　Ex. 8　　　　　Ex. 9

7. In $\triangle ABC$ and ABD, if $\overline{DA} \cong \overline{CB}$ and $\angle DAB \cong \angle CBA$, prove that $\triangle AOB$ is an isosceles triangle.

8. $\overline{AC} \cong \overline{BC}$; $\overleftrightarrow{AB}$, $\overleftrightarrow{EY}$, and $\overleftrightarrow{DX}$ are straight lines; and $\angle 1 \cong \angle 2$. Prove that $\triangle DCE$ is an isosceles triangle.

9. *Given:* In $\triangle ABC$, $\overline{AB} \cong \overline{BC} \cong \overline{CA}$, and $\angle OCB \cong \angle OBC$.
   Prove: $\overline{AO}$ bisects $\angle CAB$.

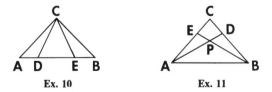

Ex. 10　　　　　Ex. 11

10. *Given:* $\overleftrightarrow{AB}$, $\overline{AD} \cong \overline{BE}$, $\angle CDE \cong \angle CED$.
    Prove: $\triangle ACB$ is an isosceles triangle.

11. *Given:* △*ACB* with $\overline{CA} \cong \overline{CB}$, and $\overline{AD}$ and $\overline{BE}$ intersecting at *P* so that ∠*PAB* ≅ ∠*PBA*.
    Prove: $\overline{PE} \cong \overline{PD}$.
12. In isosceles triangle *ABC*, $\overline{AB} \cong \overline{BC}$. Points *D* and *E* are taken on $\overline{AB}$ and $\overline{BC}$ respectively so that $\overline{BD} \cong \overline{BE}$. $\overline{AE}$ and $\overline{CD}$ are drawn and intersect at *H*. *Prove:* (*a*) $\overline{AE} \cong \overline{CD}$. (*b*) △*AHC* is an isosceles triangle.
13. *Prove:* If a triangle is equiangular, it is equilateral.

11. Proving Lines Perpendicular

We have learned that two lines are perpendicular if they intersect and form right angles. Since a definition is reversible, if line $\overleftrightarrow{MN}$ and line $\overleftrightarrow{AB}$ intersect forming two right angles, ∠*r* and ∠*s*, then line $\overleftrightarrow{MN}$ is perpendicular to line $\overleftrightarrow{AB}$. (See Fig. 3–22.)

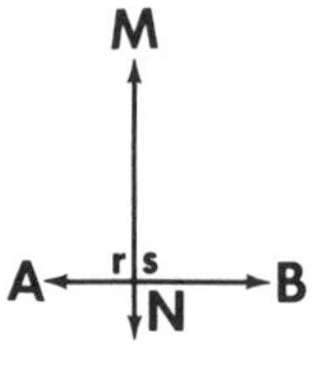

Fig. 3–22

If lines $\overleftrightarrow{MN}$ and $\overleftrightarrow{AB}$ intersect forming two congruent adjacent angles, ∠*r* and ∠*s*, then since $m\angle r + m\angle s = 180$, we can show that $m\angle r = 90$ and $m\angle s = 90$, or that both ∠*r* and ∠*s* are right angles. Hence, we have shown that $\overleftrightarrow{MN} \perp \overleftrightarrow{AB}$. From this discussion follows the truth of:

Theorem 11. If two lines intersect forming two congruent adjacent angles, the lines are perpendicular.

The Meaning of "Equidistant"

In Fig. 3–23, if *PX* = *PY*, we say that the distance from *P* to *X* is equal to the distance from *P* to *Y*, or, more simply, *P* is *equidistant* from *X* and *Y*.

If *M* is also equidistant from *X* and *Y* (*MX* = *MY*), we say that *P* and *M* are each equidistant from *X* and *Y*.

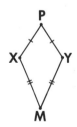

Theorem 12. Any point on the perpendicular bisector of a line segment is equidistant from the ends of the line segment.

In Fig. 3–24, if $\overleftrightarrow{CD}$ is the perpendicular bisector of line segment $\overline{AB}$ and *P* is any point on $\overleftrightarrow{CD}$, then *PA* = *PB*.

Fig. 3–23

Theorem 13. If a point is equidistant from the ends of a line segment, the point must lie on the perpendicular bisector of the line segment.

In Fig. 3–25, if *PA* = *PB*, then *P* must lie on line $\overleftrightarrow{CD}$, the perpendicular bisector of line segment $\overline{AB}$.

Theorem 14. **If two points are each equidistant from the ends of a line segment, the points determine the perpendicular bisector of the line segment.**

In Fig. 3–26, if $PA = PB$ and $QA = QB$, then the line which P and Q determine, line $\overleftrightarrow{CD}$, is the perpendicular bisector of line segment $\overline{AB}$.

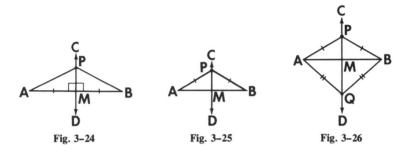

| Fig. 3–24 | Fig. 3–25 | Fig. 3–26 |

Methods of Proving Lines or Line Segments Perpendicular

To prove that two intersecting lines or line segments are perpendicular, prove that one of the following statements is true:

1. When the two lines or line segments intersect, they form right angles.
2. When the two lines or line segments intersect, they form congruent adjacent angles.
3. There are two points on one line or line segment, each of which is equidistant from the ends of the other line segment.

MODEL PROBLEM

Prove that the median to the base of an isosceles triangle is perpendicular to the base.

Given: $\triangle ABC$ with $\overline{CA} \cong \overline{CB}$.
            $\overline{CM}$ is the median to base $\overline{AB}$.

To prove: $\overline{CM} \perp \overline{AB}$.

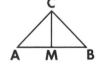

Method 1

Plan: In order to prove $\overline{CM} \perp \overline{AB}$, prove that the adjacent angles which the segments form when they intersect, $\measuredangle CMA$ and CMB, are congruent. To prove $\angle CMA \cong \angle CMB$, prove that $\triangle CMA \cong \triangle CMB$ by s.s.s. $\cong$ s.s.s.

[The proof is given on the next page.]

Proof: Statements	Reasons

1. $\overline{CA} \cong \overline{CB}$. (s. ≅ s.)	1. Given.
2. $\overline{CM}$ is the median to base $\overline{AB}$.	2. Given.
3. $\overline{AM} \cong \overline{BM}$. (s. ≅ s.)	3. A median in a triangle divides the side to which it is drawn into two congruent parts.
4. $\overline{CM} \cong \overline{CM}$. (s. ≅ s.)	4. Reflexive property of congruence.
5. $\triangle CMA \cong \triangle CMB$.	5. s.s.s. ≅ s.s.s.
6. $\angle CMA \cong \angle CMB$.	6. Corresponding parts of congruent triangles are congruent.
7. $\angle CMA$ and $\angle CMB$ are adjacent angles.	7. Two angles are adjacent angles if they have a common vertex and a common side but do not have any interior points in common.
8. $\overline{CM} \perp \overline{AB}$.	8. Two line segments are perpendicular if they intersect and form congruent adjacent angles.

Method 2

Plan: In order to prove that $\overline{CM} \perp \overline{AB}$, prove that points C and M are each equidistant from the ends of line segment $\overline{AB}$.

Proof: Statements	Reasons

1. $\overline{CA} \cong \overline{CB}$, or C is equidistant from A and B.	1. Given.
2. $\overline{CM}$ is a median.	2. Given.
3. $\overline{MA} \cong \overline{MB}$, or M is equidistant from A and B.	3. A median in a triangle divides the side to which it is drawn into two congruent parts.
4. $\overline{CM} \perp \overline{AB}$.	4. Two points each equidistant from the ends of a line segment determine the perpendicular bisector of the line segment.

EXERCISES

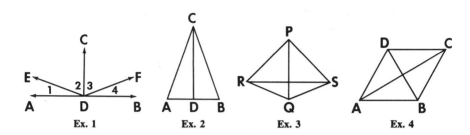

Ex. 1   Ex. 2   Ex. 3   Ex. 4

1. If $\angle 1 \cong \angle 4$ and $\angle 2 \cong \angle 3$, prove that $\overset{\leftrightarrow}{CD} \perp \overset{\leftrightarrow}{AB}$.
2. If $\overline{AC} \cong \overline{BC}$ and $\overline{CD}$ bisects $\angle ACB$, prove that $\overline{CD} \perp \overline{AB}$.
3. If $\overline{PR} \cong \overline{PS}$, and $\overline{QR} \cong \overline{QS}$, prove that $\overline{PQ} \perp \overline{RS}$.
4. If polygon $ABCD$ is equilateral, prove that $\overline{DB} \perp \overline{AC}$.

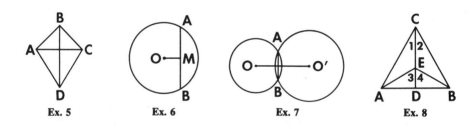

Ex. 5   Ex. 6   Ex. 7   Ex. 8

5. *Given:* Polygon $ABCD$ in which $\overline{BD}$ bisects $\angle ABC$ and $\overline{DB}$ bisects $\angle ADC$.
   Prove: $\overline{BD}$ is the perpendicular bisector of $\overline{AC}$.
6. *Given:* In circle O, M is the midpoint of chord $\overline{AB}$.
   Prove: $\overline{OM} \perp \overline{AB}$. [*Hint:* Draw auxiliary segments $\overline{OA}$ and $\overline{OB}$.]
7. *Given:* Intersecting circles O and O'.
   Prove: $\overline{OO'}$ is the perpendicular bisector of $\overline{AB}$.
8. *Given:* In $\triangle ABC$, $\overset{\leftrightarrow}{CD}$ is a straight line, $\angle 1 \cong \angle 2$, and $\angle 3 \cong \angle 4$.
   Prove: $\overline{CD}$ is the perpendicular bisector of $\overline{AB}$.

9. *Prove:* The bisector of the vertex angle of an isosceles triangle is perpendicular to the base of the triangle.
10. *Prove:* The line determined by the vertices of two isosceles triangles having a common base is perpendicular to this common base.

11. Polygon $VWXYZ$ is equiangular and equilateral. If $\overline{VT}$ bisects $\overline{XY}$, prove that $\overline{VT}$ is perpendicular to $\overline{XY}$.

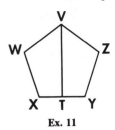

Ex. 11

12. $\overleftrightarrow{AB}$ is a straight line, $m\angle ADC = 3x + 18$, and $m\angle CDB = 4x - 6$. (*a*) Find the value of x. (*b*) Show that $\overleftrightarrow{CD} \perp \overleftrightarrow{AB}$.

13. If $\overleftrightarrow{CD} \perp \overleftrightarrow{AB}$, $m\angle ADC = 3x - y$, and $m\angle CDB = 2x + y$, find the value of x and the value of y.

14. If $\overleftrightarrow{CD} \perp \overleftrightarrow{AB}$, $m\angle CDA = 7x + y$, and $m\angle CDB = x + 4y$, find the value of x and the value of y.

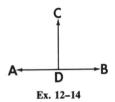

Ex. 12–14

15. At B, a point on line $\overleftrightarrow{CD}$, $\overleftrightarrow{BA}$ is drawn perpendicular to $\overleftrightarrow{CD}$. If $m\angle CBA = 7x + y$ and $m\angle DBA = 11x - y$, find x and y.

16. $\overleftrightarrow{AB}$ intersects $\overleftrightarrow{CD}$ at E. $m\angle AEC = 3x$ and $m\angle AED = 5x - 60$. (*a*) Solve for x. (*b*) Show that $\overleftrightarrow{AB}$ is perpendicular to $\overleftrightarrow{CD}$.

17. In triangle ABC, a line drawn from vertex A intersects $\overline{BC}$ in D. If $m\angle ADB = \frac{3}{2}x + 30$ and $m\angle ADC = 4x - 70$, show that $\overline{AD}$ is perpendicular to $\overline{BC}$.

18. In triangle RST, a line drawn from vertex R intersects $\overline{ST}$ in B. If $m\angle SBR = \frac{5}{2}x + 45$ and $m\angle TBR = 7x - 36$, show that $\overline{RB}$ is an altitude in triangle RST.

12. Method of Indirect Proof – Method of Elimination

In daily life, we often use a method of indirect proof, or indirect reasoning, which is illustrated by the following example:

Bill Tracy was charged with having committed a holdup in Boston on July 4, 1972 at 12 noon. At the trial, Bill's attorney, Mr. William Sawyer, said to the jury: "Bill Tracy cannot be guilty of this crime as charged because, according to the indictment, the crime was committed in Boston on July 4, 1972 at 12 noon. It is a matter of public record, reported in the newspapers, that Bill Tracy was the speaker at an Independence Day Rally that was held in New York City on July 4, 1972 at 12 noon. Your verdict in this case will have to be not guilty!"

In proving that "Bill Tracy is not guilty," the attorney, Mr. Sawyer, employed two principles of logic which we will now consider and accept without proof.

First, Mr. Sawyer showed that the proposition "Bill Tracy is guilty" led to the contradiction of the true proposition, "Bill Tracy was in New York City on July 4, 1972 at 12 noon." Therefore, he argued that the proposition "Bill Tracy is guilty" must be false. He made use of the following principle of logic, which we will now postulate.

Postulate 31. If a proposition contradicts a true proposition, then it is false. (Postulate of Contradiction.)

Second, in this case, there were only two possibilities: (1) "Bill Tracy is guilty." (2) "Bill Tracy is not guilty." One of these had to be true, the other false. Since Mr. Sawyer showed that the proposition "Bill Tracy is guilty" is false, he argued that the proposition "Bill Tracy is not guilty" must be true. He made use of the following principle of logic, which we will now postulate.

Postulate 32. If one of a given set of propositions must be true, and all but one of those propositions have been proved to be false, then this one remaining proposition must be true. (Postulate of Elimination.)

In geometry, we also use this method of indirect proof, called "the *method of elimination*," in situations where it is difficult or impossible to use the method of direct proof which we have been using up to this point. In order to prove a conclusion by this method of indirect proof, we employ the following procedure:

1. List the conclusion and all other possibilities.
2. Prove all the other possibilities false. To do this, we usually use the "Postulate of Contradiction." We assume that each of these other possibilities is true and then show that the assumption leads to a contradiction of the *given*, a *postulate*, a *definition*, or a *previously proved theorem*.
3. State that the conclusion, which is the only remaining possibility, is true, making use of the "Postulate of Elimination."

KEEP IN MIND

When using the method of elimination in indirect reasoning, be certain to list *all* the possibilities. One of these possibilities must be true.

MODEL PROBLEM

Prove that in a scalene triangle, the bisector of an angle cannot be perpendicular to the opposite side.

Given: *ABC* is a scalene triangle.
$\overline{CD}$ bisects $\angle ACB$.

To prove: $\overline{CD}$ is not $\perp \overline{AB}$.

Plan: Use the method of indirect proof. List the
possibilities: $\overline{CD} \perp \overline{AB}$ or $\overline{CD}$ is not $\perp \overline{AB}$.
Show that the possibility $\overline{CD} \perp \overline{AB}$ leads to
a contradiction of the *given*.

Proof: *Statements* | *Reasons*

Statements	Reasons
1. Either $\overline{CD} \perp \overline{AB}$ or $\overline{CD}$ is not $\perp \overline{AB}$.	1. There are only these two possibilities.
2. Suppose $\overline{CD} \perp \overline{AB}$.	2. One of the two possibilities.
3. $\angle 1 \cong \angle 2$. (a. $\cong$ a.)	3. When perpendicular line segments intersect, they form congruent adjacent angles.
4. $\overline{CD}$ bisects $\angle ACB$.	4. Given.
5. $\angle 3 \cong \angle 4$. (a. $\cong$ a.)	5. A bisector divides an angle into two congruent angles.
6. $\overline{CD} \cong \overline{CD}$. (s. $\cong$ s.)	6. Reflexive property of congruence.
7. $\triangle ACD \cong \triangle BCD$.	7. a.s.a. $\cong$ a.s.a.
8. $\overline{AC} \cong \overline{BC}$.	8. Corresponding sides of congruent triangles are congruent.
9. This contradicts the fact $\overline{AC}$ is not $\cong \overline{BC}$.	9. In a scalene triangle, no two sides are congruent.
10. Hence, the supposition that $\overline{CD} \perp \overline{AB}$ is false.	10. Postulate of Contradiction.
11. $\overline{CD}$ is not $\perp \overline{AB}$.	11. Postulate of Elimination.

EXERCISES

Indirect Proof in Geometric Situations

In each of the following, use the method of indirect proof:

1. *Prove:* If $m\angle A = 50$ and $m\angle B = 70$, then $\angle A$ and $\angle B$ are not complementary.

2. *Prove:* If $m\angle R = 130$ and $m\angle S = 80$, then $\angle R$ and $\angle S$ are not supplementary.

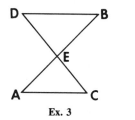 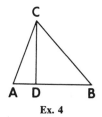 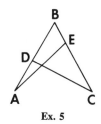

Ex. 3   Ex. 4   Ex. 5

3. *Given:* $\overline{DB}$ is not congruent to $\overline{AC}$, $\overleftrightarrow{AB}$ and $\overleftrightarrow{CD}$ are straight lines.
Prove: $\overline{AB}$ and $\overline{CD}$ do not bisect each other.

4. *Given:* $\overline{CD} \perp \overline{AB}$, $\overline{CA}$ is not congruent to $\overline{CB}$.
Prove: $\overline{AD}$ is not congruent to $\overline{DB}$.

5. *Given:* $\overline{AB} \cong \overline{BC}$, $\overline{BD}$ is not congruent to $\overline{BE}$.
Prove: $\angle A$ is not congruent to $\angle C$.

6. *Prove:* In a scalene triangle, the median to a side of the triangle cannot be perpendicular to that side.

7. *Prove:* In a scalene acute triangle, an altitude drawn to a side cannot bisect the angle which is opposite this side.

8. *Prove:* If a point is not equidistant from the ends of a line segment, the point does not lie on the perpendicular bisector of the line segment.

9. *Prove:* In a scalene triangle, no two angles are congruent.

Indirect Reasoning in Life Situations

10. One night Mr. Williams brought home a new table lamp which he tested when he bought it. He plugged the lamp into an outlet and found that it did not light. How could Mr. Williams prove by indirect reasoning that the outlet, and not the lamp, was defective?

11. A submarine sank off the coast of England. The hull was located on the ocean floor. Rescue parties worked frantically for several days in an effort to rescue survivors. At the end of this period of time, it was announced that all hands on board must be dead. Prove this conclusion by indirect reasoning.

12. Mrs. Holland told her son Dan that his friend Kenny had broken his right leg in a football game the day before. The next day, when Dan went out for football practice, he found his friend Kenny practicing placement kicks with his right leg. Show by indirect reasoning how Dan knew that his mother had been mistaken.

13. Detective Collins was trying to prove that a suspect who pretended to be deaf was not deaf. He stood behind him and fired a shot into the air. The suspect was startled and jumped. Prove by indirect reasoning that the suspect was not deaf.

14. Ralph was told by his art teacher that his works were among the best in the class and were good enough to be exhibited. When an exhibition of the works of the class was held, Ralph was not invited to exhibit any of his paintings. Show by indirect reasoning how Ralph arrived at the conclusion that his teacher had only been encouraging him with flattery.

15. On June 27, 1972, Mr. Black, in the company of his wife and several friends, attended a baseball game between the hours of 2 P.M. and 6 P.M. Several days later, Mr. Black was arrested and charged with having run into another car on June 27, 1972 at 3 P.M., having caused the death of the driver and having left the scene of the accident. Mr. Black's car, when picked up, had a badly smashed front right fender. How can Mr. Black's lawyer prove to the jury, by indirect reasoning, that Mr. Black was not guilty of the crime?

16. Ted, William, and Frank play in a dance orchestra. One plays the drums, one the clarinet, and one the piano. Ted and William hum the melody as they play their instruments. Ted brings his instrument with him to every engagement. What instrument does each boy play?

17. Give an illustration of indirect reasoning in a life situation.

13. True-False Exercises

If the statement is always true, write *true;* if the statement is not always true, write *false.*

1. Two triangles are congruent if they have two angles and the included side of one triangle congruent to the corresponding parts of the other.

2. The point of intersection of the bisectors of the base angles of an isosceles triangle and the ends of the base of the isosceles triangle are the vertices of another isosceles triangle.

3. If two angles of a triangle are congruent, the triangle is an isosceles triangle.

4. If two isosceles triangles have the same base, the line joining their vertices is perpendicular to the base.

5. If two angles of a polygon are congruent, the sides opposite these angles are congruent.

6. If the altitude drawn to the base of a triangle bisects the base, the triangle is an isosceles triangle.

7. Two triangles are congruent if three sides of one triangle are congruent respectively to three sides of the other.

8. If two adjacent angles are complementary, a side of one angle is perpendicular to a side of the other angle.

9. If two triangles have a pair of congruent sides and the altitudes drawn to these sides are also congruent, the triangles are congruent.

10. The bisectors of two supplementary angles are perpendicular to each other.

14. "Always, Sometimes, Never" Exercises

If the blank space in each of the following exercises is replaced by the word *always, sometimes,* or *never,* the resulting statement will be true. Select the word which will correctly complete each statement.

1. Two triangles are _____ congruent if two sides and the included angle of one are congruent respectively to two sides and the included angle of the other.

2. If the three sides of one triangle are congruent respectively to the three sides of another triangle, then the two triangles are _____ congruent.

3. If two angles are complementary, a side of one angle is _____ perpendicular to a side of the other angle.

4. An equilateral triangle is _____ congruent to a right triangle.

5. If two isosceles triangles have a leg and the base of one congruent to the corresponding parts of the other, the triangles are _____ congruent.

6. If the two legs of a right triangle are congruent to the corresponding legs of another right triangle, the triangles are _____ congruent.

7. Two triangles are _____ congruent if they have a pair of congruent sides and the altitudes drawn to these sides are congruent.

8. A leg of a right triangle is _____ one of the altitudes of the triangle.

9. If the three angles of a triangle are congruent, the triangle is _____ scalene.

10. In a triangle, two medians are _____ congruent.

11. The bisectors of two supplementary adjacent angles are _____ perpendicular to each other.

12. The median drawn to a side in an isosceles triangle is _____ perpendicular to that side.

13. The median to the base of an isosceles triangle _____ bisects the vertex angle.

14. The bisector of an angle of an isosceles triangle is _____ perpendicular to the opposite side.

15. A point on the perpendicular bisector of a line segment is _____ equidistant from the ends of the segment.

16. An equilateral triangle is _____ equiangular.

17. It is _____ possible to construct a right triangle if the given parts are the two legs of the triangles.

18. A median of a triangle _____ bisects the angle of the triangle through whose vertex it is drawn.

19. If two triangles are congruent, the corresponding angles are _____ congruent.

20. Two isosceles triangles are _____ congruent if they have congruent vertex angles.

15. Multiple-Choice Exercises

In 1–5, write the letter preceding the word or expression that best completes the statement.

1. If in triangle ABC, $\overline{BD}$ is the median to side $\overline{AC}$, and $\triangle ABD \cong \triangle CBD$, then triangle ABC must be   (a) scalene   (b) isosceles   (c) equilateral (d) right.

2. Two right triangles must be congruent if   (a) the hypotenuse of one triangle is congruent to the hypotenuse of the other   (b) an acute angle of one triangle is congruent to an acute angle of the other   (c) two legs of one triangle are congruent to two legs of the other   (d) the altitude drawn to the hypotenuse of one triangle is congruent to the altitude drawn to the hypotenuse of the other.

3. Two isosceles triangles are congruent if   (a) the vertex angle of one triangle is congruent to the vertex angle of the other   (b) a base angle of one triangle is congruent to a base angle of the other   (c) a leg of one triangle is congruent to a leg of the other   (d) a leg and the vertex angle of one triangle are congruent to a leg and the vertex angle of the other.

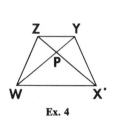

Ex. 4

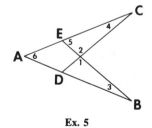

Ex. 5

4. In the figure, it can be proved that $\overline{WY} \cong \overline{XY}$ if it is known that   (*a*)
$\angle YWX \cong \angle ZXW$ (*b*) $\angle YWZ \cong \angle YXZ$ (*c*) $\angle YXW \cong \angle PWX$
(*d*) $\overline{PW} \cong \overline{PX}$.

5. If $\overline{AB} \cong \overline{AC}$ in the figure, it can be proved that $\overline{CD} \cong \overline{BE}$ if it is also
known that   (*a*) $\angle 1 \cong \angle 2$ (*b*) $\angle 3 \cong \angle 4$ (*c*) $\angle 3 \cong \angle 5$ (*d*) $\angle 4 \cong \angle 6$.

16. Construction Exercises

The following exercises are to be done with straightedge and compasses.
The basic constructions involved in these exercises appear in Chapter 14,
which begins on page 617.

1. Construct a line segment equal in length to the sum of the lengths of
two given line segments $\overline{AB}$ and $\overline{CD}$.

2. If l is the length of a given line segment $\overline{RS}$, construct a line segment
whose length is   (*a*) $2l$ (*b*) $4l$ (*c*) $1\frac{1}{2}l$ (*d*) $\frac{5}{2}l$.

3. Divide a given line segment $\overline{MN}$ into four congruent parts.

4. If x and y are the measures of two given line segments where $x > y$,
construct a line segment whose measure is   (*a*) $x + y$ (*b*) $2(x + y)$
(*c*) $\frac{1}{2}(x + y)$ (*d*) $x - y$ (*e*) $2(x - y)$ (*f*) $\frac{1}{2}(x - y)$.

5. Construct an angle congruent to a given angle B.

6. Construct the bisector of a given obtuse angle ABC.

7. In triangle ABC, construct the median to side $\overline{AC}$.

8. In obtuse triangle ABC with angle B the obtuse angle, construct the
altitude to side $\overline{AB}$.

9. In a given acute triangle, construct   (*a*) the three angle bisectors
(*b*) the three medians   (*c*) the three altitudes.

10. In a given obtuse triangle, construct   (*a*) the three angle bisectors
(*b*) the three medians   (*c*) the three altitudes.

11. In a given right triangle, construct   (*a*) the three angle bisectors   (*b*)
the three medians   (*c*) the three altitudes.

12. Construct the complement of a given acute angle.

13. Construct the supplement of a given angle.

14. If r and s are the measures of two given angles where $r > s$, construct
an angle whose measure is   (*a*) $r + s$ (*b*) $2(r + s)$ (*c*) $\frac{1}{2}(r + s)$ (*d*) $r - s$
(*e*) $2(r - s)$ (*f*) $\frac{1}{2}(r - s)$.

15. At a point on a given line, construct a perpendicular to the given line.

16. From a point C outside line $\overleftrightarrow{AB}$, construct a line perpendicular to $\overleftrightarrow{AB}$.

17. Construct an angle which contains   (*a*) $45°$ (*b*) $22\frac{1}{2}°$ (*c*) $135°$.

18. Referring to the figure, construct an equilateral triangle of side *s*.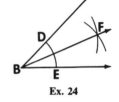

    Ex. 18

    In 19–21, construct an isosceles triangle under the stated conditions.

19. Given a leg and the base.
20. Given a leg and the vertex angle.
21. Given the base and a base angle.

22. Construct a right triangle given each of the two legs.
23. Construct an isosceles right triangle given one of the congruent legs.
24. Which one of the following statements is used in proving that $\overrightarrow{BF}$ bisects angle *B* in the figure?

    a. Two triangles are congruent if two sides and the included angle of one are congruent to the corresponding parts of the other.

    b. An angle has one and only one bisector.

    c. Two triangles are congruent if the three sides of one are congruent respectively to the three sides of the other.

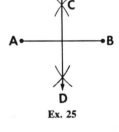

Ex. 24

25. The figure shows the usual method of constructing the perpendicular bisector of a given line segment. Which statement, *a* or *b*, may be used to prove that $\overleftrightarrow{CD}$ is the perpendicular bisector of $\overline{AB}$?

    a. Two points each equidistant from the end-points of a line segment determine the perpendicular bisector of the line segment.

    b. All points on the perpendicular bisector of a line segment are equidistant from its endpoints.

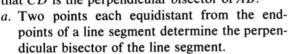

Ex. 25

26. The figure shows the usual method of constructing a line perpendicular to a given line through a given point on the line. Which two of the following statements may be used to prove that $\overleftrightarrow{EP}$ is perpendicular to $\overleftrightarrow{AB}$?

    a. When a straight angle is bisected, two right angles are formed.

    b. Two right triangles are congruent if the legs of one triangle are congruent to the legs of the other triangle.

    c. Two points, each equidistant from the ends of a line segment, determine the perpendicular bisector of the line segment.

    d. Two triangles are congruent if two angles and the included side of one triangle are congruent respectively to two angles and the included side of the other triangle.

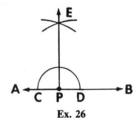

Ex. 26

27. The figure shows the usual method of constructing
    an angle congruent to a given angle. Which two
    of the following statements may be used to prove
    that angle B' is congruent to angle B?

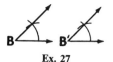

Ex. 27

   a. Two triangles are congruent if the three sides
      of one triangle are congruent respectively to
      the three sides of the other triangle.
   b. Two triangles are congruent if two sides and the included angle of
      one triangle are congruent respectively to two sides and the included
      angle of the other triangle.
   c. Corresponding parts of congruent triangles are congruent.
   d. Two triangles are congruent if two angles and the included side of
      one triangle are respectively congruent to two angles and the in-
      cluded side of the other triangle.

28. The figure shows the usual method of constructing
    a line perpendicular to a given line through a given
    point outside the line. Which two of the following
    statements may be used to prove that $\overleftrightarrow{PE}$ is
    perpendicular to $\overleftrightarrow{AB}$?

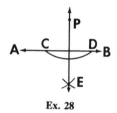

Ex. 28

   a. From a given point outside a given line, one
      and only one perpendicular can be drawn to
      the line.
   b. Two points each equidistant from the ends of a line segment deter-
      mine the perpendicular bisector of the line segment.
   c. The line which joins the vertices of two isosceles triangles on the
      same base bisects the common base at right angles.
   d. Any point on the perpendicular bisector of a line segment is equi-
      distant from the ends of the line segment.

CHAPTER IV

Parallel Lines, Angle Sums, Quadrilaterals

We have already studied many situations involving intersecting lines which lie in the same plane. When all the points or lines in a set lie in a single plane, we say that the points or the lines are *coplanar*. Now we will study situations involving coplanar lines which do not intersect.

All the points, lines, segments, and rays discussed in this chapter will be considered to be coplanar.

1. Proving Lines Parallel

Definition. Parallel lines **are two coplanar lines that do not intersect.**

The symbol for *parallel,* or *is parallel to,* is ‖.
If $\overleftrightarrow{AB}$ is parallel to $\overleftrightarrow{CD}$, we write $\overleftrightarrow{AB} \parallel \overleftrightarrow{CD}$. (See Fig. 4–1.)

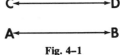

Fig. 4–1

The word *lines* in the definition means straight lines of unlimited extent. We say that line segments and rays are parallel if the lines that contain them are parallel.

Postulate 33. **Two coplanar lines are either intersecting lines or parallel lines.**

If $\overleftrightarrow{AB}$ and $\overleftrightarrow{CD}$ are two coplanar lines, they must be either intersecting lines, as in Fig. 4–2, or parallel lines, as in Fig. 4–3.

$\overleftrightarrow{AB}$ intersects $\overleftrightarrow{CD}$ $\overleftrightarrow{AB} \parallel \overleftrightarrow{CD}$

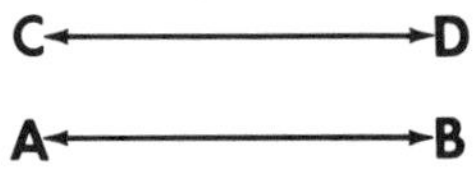

Fig. 4–2   **Fig. 4–3**

Angles Formed by a Transversal

Definition. A *transversal* is a line that intersects (cuts) two other lines in two different points.

When two lines are cut by a transversal, two sets of angles, each containing four angles, are formed. (See Fig. 4–4.)

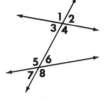

Fig. 4–4

Angles 3, 4, 5, 6 are called *interior angles.*

Angles 1, 2, 7, 8 are called *exterior angles.*

Angles 4 and 5, which are interior angles on opposite sides of the transversal and do not have the same vertex, are called *alternate interior angles.* Angles 3 and 6 are another pair of alternate interior angles.

Angles 1 and 8, which are exterior angles on opposite sides of the transversal and do not have the same vertex, are called *alternate exterior angles.* Angles 2 and 7 are another pair of alternate exterior angles.

Angles 4 and 6 are *interior angles on the same side of the transversal.* Angles 3 and 5 are another pair of interior angles on the same side of the transversal.

Angles 1 and 5, one of which is an exterior angle and the other of which is an interior angle, both being on the same side of the transversal, are called *corresponding angles.* Other pairs of corresponding angles are 2 and 6, 3 and 7, 4 and 8.

When two parallel lines are cut by a transversal, the two lines and the transversal which form a pair of alternate interior angles usually take the shape of the letter *N* or the letter *Z* in various positions. (See Fig. 4–5.)

When two parallel lines are cut by a transversal, the two lines and the transversal which form a pair of corresponding angles usually take the shape of the letter *F* in various positions. (See Fig. 4–6.)

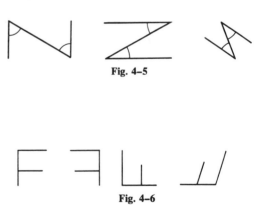

Fig. 4–5

Fig. 4–6

Postulate 34. Through a given point not on a given line, there exists one and only one line parallel to the given line.

Through point P, which is not on line $\overleftrightarrow{AB}$, there exists one and only one line, $\overleftrightarrow{LM}$, which can be drawn parallel to $\overleftrightarrow{AB}$. (See Fig. 4–7.)

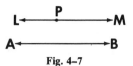

Fig. 4–7

Corollary P34–1. **If a line intersects one of two parallel lines, it intersects the other.**

In Fig. 4–8, if $\overleftrightarrow{CD} \parallel \overleftrightarrow{AB}$ and $\overleftrightarrow{EF}$ intersects $\overleftrightarrow{CD}$, then $\overleftrightarrow{EF}$ also intersects $\overleftrightarrow{AB}$.

Postulate 35. **If two lines are cut by a transversal forming a pair of alternate interior angles that are congruent, then the two lines are parallel.**

In Fig. 4–9, if transversal $\overleftrightarrow{EF}$ intersects $\overleftrightarrow{AB}$ and $\overleftrightarrow{CD}$ forming congruent alternate interior angles 1 and 2, then $\overleftrightarrow{AB} \parallel \overleftrightarrow{CD}$.

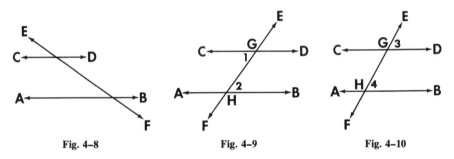

Fig. 4–8   Fig. 4–9   Fig. 4–10

Theorem 15. **If two lines are cut by a transversal forming a pair of congruent corresponding angles, then the two lines are parallel.**

In Fig. 4–10, if transversal $\overleftrightarrow{EF}$ intersects $\overleftrightarrow{AB}$ and $\overleftrightarrow{CD}$ forming congruent corresponding angles 3 and 4, then $\overleftrightarrow{AB} \parallel \overleftrightarrow{CD}$.

Theorem 16. **If two lines are cut by a transversal forming a pair of interior angles on the same side of the transversal that are supplementary, then the two lines are parallel.**

In Fig. 4–11, if transversal $\overleftrightarrow{EF}$ intersects $\overleftrightarrow{AB}$ and $\overleftrightarrow{CD}$ forming a pair of interior angles on the same side of the transversal (angles 5 and 6) that are supplementary, then $\overleftrightarrow{AB} \parallel \overleftrightarrow{CD}$.

Theorem 17. **If two lines are perpendicular to the same line, they are parallel.**

In Fig. 4–12, if $\overleftrightarrow{CD}$ and $\overleftrightarrow{EF}$ are both perpendicular to $\overleftrightarrow{AB}$, then $\overleftrightarrow{CD} \parallel \overleftrightarrow{EF}$.

Theorem 18. **If two lines are parallel to the same line, they are parallel to each other.**

In Fig. 4–13, if $\overleftrightarrow{EF} \parallel \overleftrightarrow{CD}$, and $\overleftrightarrow{AB} \parallel \overleftrightarrow{CD}$, then $\overleftrightarrow{EF} \parallel \overleftrightarrow{AB}$.

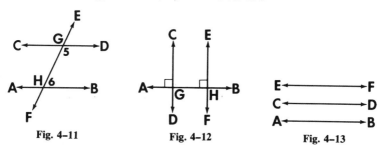

Fig. 4–11   Fig. 4–12   Fig. 4–13

Methods of Proving Lines Parallel

To prove that two coplanar lines which are cut by a transversal are parallel, prove that any one of the following statements is true:

1. A pair of alternate interior angles is congruent.
2. A pair of corresponding angles is congruent.
3. A pair of interior angles on the same side of the transversal is supplementary.

Also, two coplanar lines may be proved parallel by proving:

4. Both lines are perpendicular to the same line.
5. Both lines are parallel to the same line.

MODEL PROBLEMS

1. If $m\angle A = 100 + 3x$ and $m\angle B = 80 - 3x$, tell why $\overleftrightarrow{AD} \parallel \overleftrightarrow{BC}$.

   Solution: Since $m\angle A = 100 + 3x$ and $m\angle B = 80 - 3x$, then $m\angle A + m\angle B = 100 + 3x + 80 - 3x = 180$, or $\angle A$ and $\angle B$ are supplementary. Therefore, $\overleftrightarrow{AD} \parallel \overleftrightarrow{BC}$ because if two lines are cut by a transversal forming a pair of interior angles on the same side of the transversal that are supplementary, the lines are parallel.

2. If $\overline{BD}$ bisects angle ABC, and $\overline{BC} \cong \overline{CD}$, prove $\overleftrightarrow{CD} \parallel \overleftrightarrow{BA}$.

   Given: $\angle 1 \cong \angle 2$, and $\overline{BC} \cong \overline{CD}$.

   To prove: $\overleftrightarrow{CD} \parallel \overleftrightarrow{BA}$.

   Plan: To prove $\overleftrightarrow{CD} \parallel \overleftrightarrow{BA}$, show that transversal $\overline{BD}$ makes a pair of alternate interior angles, $\angle 2$ and $\angle 3$, congruent.

   [The proof is given on the next page.]

Proof: *Statements* | *Reasons*

Statements	*Reasons*
1. $\overline{BC} \cong \overline{CD}$.	1. Given.
2. $\angle 3 \cong \angle 1$.	2. If two sides of a triangle are congruent, the angles opposite these sides are congruent.
3. $\angle 1 \cong \angle 2$.	3. Given.
4. $\angle 3 \cong \angle 2$.	4. Transitive property of congruence.
5. $\overleftrightarrow{CD} \parallel \overleftrightarrow{BA}$.	5. If two lines are cut by a transversal forming a pair of congruent alternate interior angles, the two lines are parallel.

EXERCISES

1. Referring to the figure, prove $\overleftrightarrow{AB} \parallel \overleftrightarrow{CD}$ if:
   a. $m\angle 3 = 70$ and $m\angle 5 = 70$
   b. $m\angle 2 = 140$ and $m\angle 6 = 140$
   c. $m\angle 3 = 60$ and $m\angle 6 = 120$
   d. $m\angle 2 = 150$ and $m\angle 5 = 30$
   e. $m\angle 2 = 160$ and $m\angle 8 = 160$

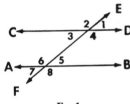

Ex. 1

2. In triangle ABC, $\overline{AC} \cong \overline{CB}$. D is a point on $\overline{AC}$ between A and C, E is a point on $\overline{CB}$ between B and C, and $\overline{DE}$ is drawn. If $m\angle CDE = 50$ and $m\angle CBA = 50$, prove $\overline{DE} \parallel \overline{AB}$.
3. In quadrilateral $ABCD$, $\overline{DC} \perp \overline{BC}$ and $m\angle ADC = 90$. Prove $\overline{AD} \parallel \overline{BC}$.
4. In quadrilateral $ABCD$, if $m\angle A = 120 + 5x$ and $m\angle B = 60 - 5x$, show $\overline{AD} \parallel \overline{BC}$.

Ex. 5   Ex. 6   Ex. 7

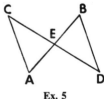

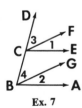

5. *Prove:* If $\overline{AB}$ and $\overline{CD}$ bisect each other, $\overline{CA} \parallel \overline{BD}$.
6. *Prove:* If $\overleftrightarrow{CD} \perp \overleftrightarrow{BC}$, $\overleftrightarrow{AB} \perp \overleftrightarrow{BC}$, $\overrightarrow{CE}$ bisects $\angle BCD$, and $\overrightarrow{BF}$ bisects $\angle ABC$, then $\overleftrightarrow{CE} \parallel \overleftrightarrow{BF}$.
7. If $\angle 1 \cong \angle 2$, and $\angle 3 \cong \angle 4$, prove $\overleftrightarrow{CE} \parallel \overleftrightarrow{BA}$.

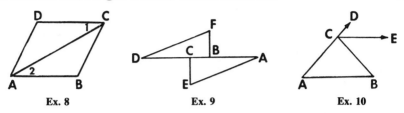

Ex. 8   Ex. 9   Ex. 10

8. *Prove:* If $\overline{AB} \cong \overline{CD}$ and $\angle 1 \cong \angle 2$, then $\overline{AD} \parallel \overline{BC}$.
9. *Prove:* If $\overline{FB} \perp \overline{AD}$, $\overline{EC} \perp \overline{AD}$, $\overline{EC} \cong \overline{FB}$, $\overline{AB} \cong \overline{DC}$, then $\overline{EA} \parallel \overline{DF}$.
10. If $\overleftrightarrow{AD}$ is a straight line, $\overline{CA} \cong \overline{CB}$, and $\angle ECB \cong \angle CAB$, then prove $\overleftrightarrow{CE} \parallel \overleftrightarrow{AB}$.

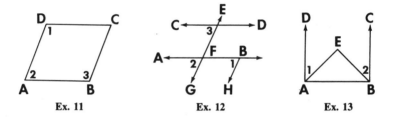

Ex. 11   Ex. 12   Ex. 13

11. If $\angle 1$ is supplementary to $\angle 2$, and $\angle 3 \cong \angle 1$, prove $\overline{AD} \parallel \overline{BC}$.
12. If $\angle 3 \cong \angle 1$, and $\angle 2 \cong \angle 3$, prove $\overleftrightarrow{EG} \parallel \overleftrightarrow{BH}$.
13. If $\overline{AE}$ bisects $\angle DAB$, $\overline{BE}$ bisects $\angle ABC$, and $m\angle 1 + m\angle 2 = 90$, prove $\overleftrightarrow{AD} \parallel \overleftrightarrow{BC}$.

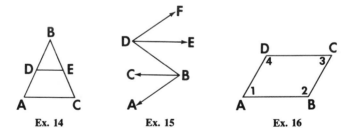

Ex. 14   Ex. 15   Ex. 16

14. If $\overline{BA} \cong \overline{BC}$ and $\angle BDE \cong \angle BCA$, prove $\overline{DE} \parallel \overline{AC}$.
15. If $\overrightarrow{DE}$ bisects $\angle FDB$, $\overrightarrow{BC}$ bisects $\angle DBA$, and $\angle EDB \cong \angle DBC$, prove $\overrightarrow{BA} \parallel \overrightarrow{DF}$.
16. If $m\angle 1 + m\angle 2 + m\angle 3 + m\angle 4 = 360$, $\angle 1 \cong \angle 3$ and $\angle 2 \cong \angle 4$, prove $\overline{AB} \parallel \overline{CD}$ and $\overline{AD} \parallel \overline{BC}$.

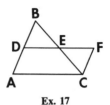
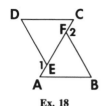
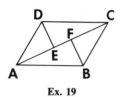

Ex. 17   Ex. 18   Ex. 19

17. If E is the midpoint of $\overline{BC}$ and E is the midpoint of $\overline{DF}$, prove $\overline{AB} \parallel \overline{CF}$.
18. If $\overleftrightarrow{AC}$ is a line, $\angle 1 \cong \angle 2$, $\overline{AE} \cong \overline{CF}$, and $\overline{DE} \cong \overline{BF}$, prove $\overline{DC} \parallel \overline{AB}$.
19. If $\overline{DE} \perp \overline{AC}$, $\overline{BF} \perp \overline{AC}$, $\overline{AF} \cong \overline{CE}$, and $\overline{DE} \cong \overline{BF}$, prove $\overline{DA} \parallel \overline{CB}$.
20. If both pairs of opposite sides of a quadrilateral are congruent, prove that both pairs of opposite sides are also parallel.

2. Properties of Parallel Lines

Theorem 19. **If two parallel lines are cut by a transversal, then the alternate interior angles are congruent.**

In Fig. 4–14, if parallel lines $\overleftrightarrow{AB}$ and $\overleftrightarrow{CD}$ are cut by transversal $\overleftrightarrow{EF}$, then alternate interior angles 1 and 2 are congruent, or $\angle 1 \cong \angle 2$. Also, $\angle DGH \cong \angle AHG$.

Theorem 20. **If two parallel lines are cut by a transversal, then the corresponding angles are congruent.**

In Fig. 4–15, if parallel lines $\overleftrightarrow{AB}$ and $\overleftrightarrow{CD}$ are cut by transversal $\overleftrightarrow{EF}$, then corresponding angles 3 and 4 are congruent, or $\angle 3 \cong \angle 4$. Also, $\angle EHC \cong \angle HGA$, $\angle FGB \cong \angle GHD$, and $\angle FGA \cong \angle GHC$.

Theorem 21. **If two parallel lines are cut by a transversal, then two interior angles on the same side of the transversal are supplementary.**

In Fig. 4–16, if parallel lines $\overleftrightarrow{AB}$ and $\overleftrightarrow{CD}$ are cut by transversal $\overleftrightarrow{EF}$, then two interior angles, 5 and 6, on the same side of the transversal are supplementary, or $\angle 5$ is supplementary to $\angle 6$. Also, $\angle CGH$ is supplementary to $\angle AHG$.

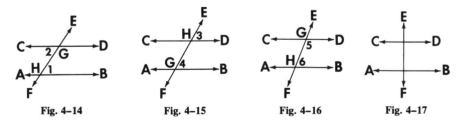

Fig. 4–14   Fig. 4–15   Fig. 4–16   Fig. 4–17

Theorem 22. **If a line is perpendicular to one of two parallel lines, it is also perpendicular to the other.**

In Fig. 4–17, if $\overleftrightarrow{AB} \parallel \overleftrightarrow{CD}$ and $\overleftrightarrow{EF} \perp \overleftrightarrow{CD}$, then $\overleftrightarrow{EF} \perp \overleftrightarrow{AB}$.

Theorem 23. **If a line is parallel to one of two parallel lines, it is also parallel to the other.**

In Fig. 4–18, if $\overleftrightarrow{AB}$ and $\overleftrightarrow{CD}$ are two parallel lines and a third line, $\overleftrightarrow{EF}$, is parallel to $\overleftrightarrow{AB}$, then $\overleftrightarrow{EF}$ must also be parallel to $\overleftrightarrow{CD}$. Or, if $\overleftrightarrow{AB} \parallel \overleftrightarrow{CD}$ and $\overleftrightarrow{EF} \parallel \overleftrightarrow{AB}$, then $\overleftrightarrow{EF} \parallel \overleftrightarrow{CD}$.

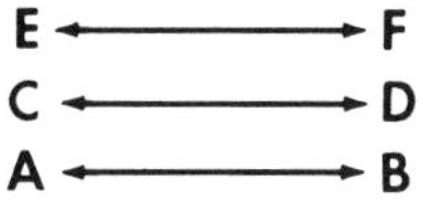

E ←————————→ F

C ←————————→ D

A ←————————→ B

Fig. 4–18

Summary of Properties of Parallel Lines

If two lines are parallel:

1. Their alternate interior angles are congruent.
2. Their corresponding angles are congruent.
3. Two interior angles on the same side of the transversal are supplementary.
4. A line perpendicular to one of them is also perpendicular to the other.
5. A line parallel to one of them is also parallel to the other.

MODEL PROBLEMS ﹏﹏﹏﹏﹏﹏﹏﹏﹏

1. If $\overleftrightarrow{AB} \parallel \overleftrightarrow{CD}$, $\overleftrightarrow{AE}$ is a line, $m\angle A = 60$, and $m\angle B = 80$:
   (a) Find $m\angle x$. (b) Find $m\angle y$.

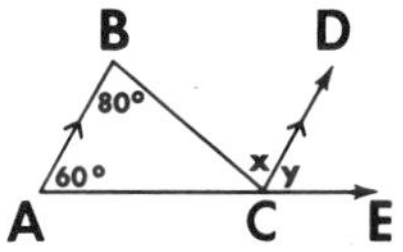

   NOTE. Arrowheads on lines $\overleftrightarrow{AB}$ and $\overleftrightarrow{CD}$, as shown in the figure, indicate that the lines are parallel.

Solution:

a. Since $\overleftrightarrow{AB} \parallel \overleftrightarrow{CD}$, transversal $\overleftrightarrow{BC}$ makes the alternate interior angles, $\angle x$ and $\angle B$, congruent.
   Since $m\angle B = 80$, $m\angle x = 80$.

Answer: $m\angle x = 80$.

b. Since $\overleftrightarrow{AB} \parallel \overleftrightarrow{CD}$, transversal $\overleftrightarrow{AC}$ makes the corresponding angles, $\angle y$ and $\angle A$, congruent.
   Since $m\angle A = 60$, $m\angle y = 60$.

Answer: $m\angle y = 60$.

2. *Given:* $\overleftrightarrow{AE}$ is a line.

$\overline{AD} \cong \overline{EC}.$

$\overline{BC} \cong \overline{HD}.$

$\overline{BC} \parallel \overline{DH}.$

To prove: $\overleftrightarrow{AB} \parallel \overleftrightarrow{EH}.$

Plan: To prove $\overleftrightarrow{AB} \parallel \overleftrightarrow{EH}$, we can show that transversal $\overleftrightarrow{AE}$ makes the alternate interior angles, $\angle A$ and $\angle E$, congruent. To prove $\angle A \cong \angle E$, prove that the triangles containing them, $\triangle ABC$ and EHD, are congruent by s.a.s. $\cong$ s.a.s.

Proof: *Statements*	*Reasons*
1. $\overline{BC} \cong \overline{HD}.$ (s. $\cong$ s.)	1. Given.
2. $\overline{BC} \parallel \overline{DH}.$	2. Given.
3. $\angle BCA \cong \angle HDE.$ (a. $\cong$ a.)	3. If two parallel lines are cut by a transversal, the alternate interior angles are congruent.
4. $\overleftrightarrow{AE}$ is a line.	4. Given.
5. $\overline{AD} \cong \overline{EC}.$	5. Given.
6. $\overline{DC} \cong \overline{DC}.$	6. Reflexive property of congruence.
7. $\overline{AC} \cong \overline{ED}.$ (s. $\cong$ s.)	7. If congruent segments are added to congruent segments, the sums are congruent segments.
8. $\triangle ABC \cong \triangle EHD.$	8. s.a.s. $\cong$ s.a.s.
9. $\angle A \cong \angle E.$	9. Corresponding parts of congruent triangles are congruent.
10. $\overleftrightarrow{AB} \parallel \overleftrightarrow{EH}.$	10. If two lines are cut by a transversal making a pair of alternate interior angles congruent, the lines are parallel.

EXERCISES

In 1–3, (*a*) Write the converse of the given statement. (*b*) State whether the converse is true or false.

1. If two lines are cut by a transversal forming a pair of alternate interior angles that are congruent, then the two lines are parallel.

2. If two lines are cut by a transversal forming a pair of corresponding angles that are congruent, then the two lines are parallel.

3. If two lines are cut by a transversal forming a pair of interior angles on the same side of the transversal that are supplementary, then the two lines are parallel.

4. In the figure, if $\overleftrightarrow{AB} \parallel \overleftrightarrow{CD}$, find:
   a. $m\angle 5$ when $m\angle 3 = 80$
   b. $m\angle 2$ when $m\angle 6 = 150$
   c. $m\angle 4$ when $m\angle 5 = 60$
   d. $m\angle 7$ when $m\angle 1 = 75$
   e. $m\angle 8$ when $m\angle 3 = 65$

Ex. 4

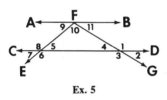

Ex. 5

Ex. 6

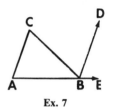

Ex. 7

5. If $\overleftrightarrow{AB} \parallel \overleftrightarrow{CD}$, $m\angle 5 = 40$, and $m\angle 4 = 30$, find the measures of the remaining angles in the figure.

6. If $\overleftrightarrow{AE} \parallel \overleftrightarrow{DC}$, $\overleftrightarrow{BC} \parallel \overleftrightarrow{AD}$, and $m\angle CBE = 80$, find $m\angle 1$, $m\angle 2$, $m\angle 3$.

7. If $\overleftrightarrow{AE}$ is a line, $\overleftrightarrow{BD} \parallel \overleftrightarrow{AC}$, $m\angle A = 65$, $m\angle C = 80$, find $m\angle CBE$.

Ex. 8

Ex. 9

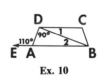

Ex. 10

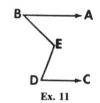

Ex. 11

8. If $\overleftrightarrow{AB} \parallel \overleftrightarrow{CD}$, $\overleftrightarrow{BC} \parallel \overleftrightarrow{DE}$, and $m\angle B = 45$, find $m\angle D$.

9. If $\overleftrightarrow{AB} \parallel \overleftrightarrow{DC}$, and $\overleftrightarrow{BC} \parallel \overleftrightarrow{AD}$, find $m\angle 1$ and $m\angle 2$.

10. If $\overleftrightarrow{EB} \parallel \overleftrightarrow{DC}$, find $m\angle 1$ and $m\angle 2$.

11. If $\overleftrightarrow{BA} \parallel \overleftrightarrow{DC}$, $m\angle B = 39$, $m\angle D = 65$, find $m\angle DEB$. [*Hint:* Through E, draw $\overleftrightarrow{GF} \parallel \overleftrightarrow{AB}$.]

12. Two parallel lines $\overleftrightarrow{AB}$ and $\overleftrightarrow{CD}$ are cut at E and F respectively by transversal $\overleftrightarrow{GH}$; $m\angle AEG = 130$. Find the number of degrees in angle CFH.

13. A transversal $\overleftrightarrow{GH}$ cuts two parallel lines $\overleftrightarrow{AB}$ and $\overleftrightarrow{CD}$ at E and F respectively, and the bisector of angle AEF meets $\overleftrightarrow{CD}$ in P. If $m\angle AEF = 64$, find the measure of angle EPF.

14. A transversal $\overleftrightarrow{GH}$ cuts two parallel lines $\overleftrightarrow{AB}$ and $\overleftrightarrow{CD}$ at E and F respectively, E being between G and F. If $m\angle AEG = 35$, find $m\angle DFE$.

15. Two parallel lines are cut by a transversal. The measures of two interior angles on the same side of the transversal are represented by x and $4x$. Find the measure of the smaller angle.

16. Two parallel lines are cut by a transversal. The measures of two interior angles on the same side of the transversal are represented by y and $3y + 20$. Find the measure of the larger angle.

17. Two parallel lines are cut by a transversal. One of two interior angles on the same side of the transversal contains $15°$ more than the other. Find the measure of the smaller angle.

In 18–21, which refer to the figure, $\overleftrightarrow{AB} \parallel \overleftrightarrow{CD}$.

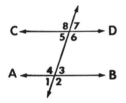

18. If $m\angle 3 = 2x + 40$ and $m\angle 7 = 3x + 20$, find $m\angle 3$.

19. If $m\angle 4 = 4x - 10$ and $m\angle 5 = 2x - 20$, find the measure of the smaller of the two angles.

20. If $m\angle 4 = 3x + 40$ and $m\angle 7 = 2x$, find $m\angle 7$.

21. If $m\angle 3 = 2y$, $m\angle 4 = x + y$, and $m\angle 5 = 2x - y$, find $m\angle 3$, $m\angle 4$, and $m\angle 5$.

                                                  Ex. 18–21

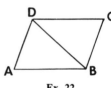

Ex. 22

Ex. 23

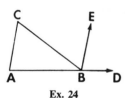

Ex. 24

22. If $\overleftrightarrow{AB} \parallel \overleftrightarrow{DC}$ and $\overline{AB} \cong \overline{CD}$, prove that $\overline{AD} \cong \overline{CB}$ and $\overleftrightarrow{AD} \parallel \overleftrightarrow{BC}$.

23. If $\overleftrightarrow{DE} \parallel \overleftrightarrow{AB}$ and $\angle 1 \cong \angle 2$, prove that $\triangle ABC$ is an isosceles triangle.

24. If $\overleftrightarrow{AD}$ is a line and $\overleftrightarrow{BE} \parallel \overleftrightarrow{AC}$, prove that $m\angle CBD = m\angle A + m\angle C$.

Ex. 25

Ex. 26

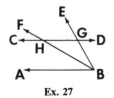

Ex. 27

25. If $\overline{BD}$ bisects angle ABC and $\overleftrightarrow{DE} \parallel \overleftrightarrow{BA}$, prove that triangle BDE is an isosceles triangle.

26. If $\overleftrightarrow{CE}$ bisects $\angle DCB$ and $\overleftrightarrow{CE} \parallel \overleftrightarrow{AB}$, prove that triangle ABC is an isosceles triangle.

27. If $\overrightarrow{BF}$ bisects $\angle ABE$ and $\overleftrightarrow{CD} \parallel \overleftrightarrow{BA}$, prove that triangle HGB is an isosceles triangle.

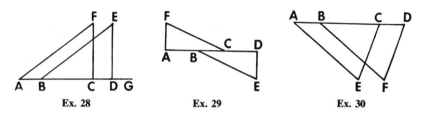

Ex. 28   Ex. 29   Ex. 30

28. If $\overleftrightarrow{AG}$ is a line, $\overline{AB} \cong \overline{DC}$, $\overline{AF} \parallel \overline{BE}$, and $\overline{AF} \cong \overline{BE}$, prove that $\overline{FC} \cong \overline{ED}$.

29. If $\overline{FA} \perp \overline{AD}$, $\overline{ED} \perp \overline{AD}$, $\overline{AB} \cong \overline{DC}$, and $\overline{FC} \parallel \overline{EB}$, prove $\overline{FC} \cong \overline{EB}$.

30. If $\overline{AB} \cong \overline{DC}$, $\overline{BF} \parallel \overline{AE}$, and $\overline{DF} \parallel \overline{CE}$, prove $\overline{AE} \cong \overline{BF}$.

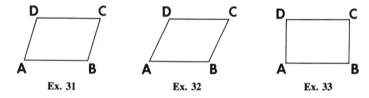

Ex. 31   Ex. 32   Ex. 33

31. If $\overline{AB} \parallel \overline{DC}$ and $\overline{BC} \parallel \overline{AD}$, prove $\angle B \cong \angle D$.

32. If $\overline{AB} \parallel \overline{DC}$, prove that $m\angle A + m\angle B + m\angle C + m\angle D = 360$.

33. If $\overline{AB} \parallel \overline{DC}$, $\overline{BC} \parallel \overline{AD}$, and $\angle A$ is a right angle, prove that $\angle B$, $\angle C$, and $\angle D$ are also right angles.

34. *Prove:* If two lines are parallel, the bisectors of a pair of alternate interior angles are parallel.

35. *Prove:* If two lines are parallel, the bisectors of a pair of corresponding angles are parallel.

36. *Prove:* If the opposite sides of a quadrilateral are parallel, then the opposite sides are congruent.

37. *Prove:* If two opposite sides of a quadrilateral are both congruent and parallel, the other two sides are both congruent and parallel.

In exercises 38 and 39, use a method of indirect proof.

38. *Prove:* If two nonparallel lines are cut by a transversal, the alternate interior angles are not congruent.

39. *Prove:* Two lines perpendicular to the same line are parallel.

3. The Sum of the Measures of the Angles of a Triangle

Theorem 24. **The sum of the measures of the angles of a triangle is 180.**

[The proof for this theorem appears on page 596.]

In triangle ABC, the sum of the measures of angles A, B, and C is 180, or $m\angle A + m\angle B + m\angle C = 180$. (See Fig. 4–19.)

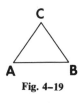

Fig. 4–19

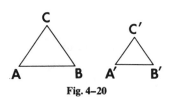

Fig. 4–20

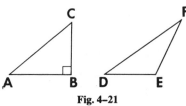

Fig. 4–21

Corollary T24–1. **If two angles of one triangle are congruent respectively to two angles of another triangle, then the third angles are congruent.**

In $\triangle ABC$ and $A'B'C'$ (Fig. 4–20), if $\angle A \cong \angle A'$, and $\angle B \cong \angle B'$, then $\angle C \cong \angle C'$.

Corollary T24–2. **A triangle can contain no more than one right angle or one obtuse angle.**

In Fig. 4–21, if $\triangle ABC$ is a right triangle, it can contain only one right angle, for example $\angle B$. Also, if $\triangle DEF$ is an obtuse triangle, it can contain only one obtuse angle, for example $\angle E$.

Corollary T24–3. **The acute angles of a right triangle are complementary.**

In right triangle ABC, if angle C is the right angle, then acute angles A and B are complementary, or $m\angle A + m\angle B = 90$. (See Fig. 4–22.)

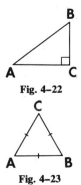

Fig. 4–22

Corollary T24–4. **Each angle of an equilateral triangle measures 60.**

In equilateral triangle ABC, each angle contains 60°, or $m\angle A = 60$, $m\angle B = 60$, and $m\angle C = 60$. (See Fig. 4–23.)

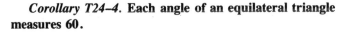

Fig. 4–23

Corollary T24–5. **Each acute angle of an isosceles right triangle measures 45.**

In isosceles right triangle ABC, if $\angle C$ contains 90° and $\overline{AC} \cong \overline{BC}$, then acute angles A and B each contain 45°, or $m\angle A = 45$ and $m\angle B = 45$. (See Fig. 4–24.)

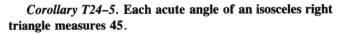

Fig. 4–24

Corollary T24–6. **The sum of the measures of the angles of a quadrilateral is 360.**

In quadrilateral $ABCD$, the sum of the measures of angles A, B, C, and D is 360, or $m\angle A + m\angle B + m\angle C + m\angle D = 360$. (See Fig. 4–25.)

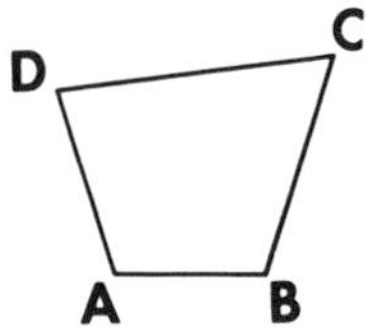

Fig. 4–25

MODEL PROBLEMS

1. The measure of the vertex angle of an isosceles triangle exceeds the measure of each base angle by 30. Find the measure of each angle of the triangle.

   Solution: Let $x =$ the measure of each base angle.
   Then $x + 30 =$ the measure of the vertex angle.

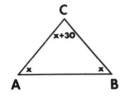

   The sum of the measures of the angles of a triangle is 180.

   1. $x + x + x + 30 = 180$

   2. $3x + 30 = 180$

   3. $3x = 150$

   4. $x = 50, x + 30 = 80$

   Answer: 50, 50, 80.

2. If in triangle ABC, $m\angle A = 9x$, $m\angle B = 3x - 6$, and $m\angle C = 11x + 2$, show that triangle ABC is a right triangle.

   Given: $m\angle A = 9x$.
   $m\angle B = 3x - 6$.
   $m\angle C = 11x + 2$.

   To show: $\triangle ABC$ is a right triangle.

   Plan: Show that one angle in the triangle has a measure of 90.

   Solution:

   1. In $\triangle ABC$, $m\angle A + m\angle B + m\angle C = 180$

   2. $9x + 3x - 6 + 11x + 2 = 180$

   3. $23x - 4 = 180$

   4. $23x = 184$

   5. $x = 8$

   [The solution continues on the next page.]

6. $m\angle A = 9x = 72$, $m\angle B = 3x - 6 = 18$, $m\angle C = 11x + 2 = 90$.

7. Since $m\angle C = 90$, $\triangle ABC$ is a right triangle.

EXERCISES

1. Which of the following can represent the measures of the three angles of a triangle?
   a. 20, 100, 60   *b.* 55, 45, 90   *c.* 30, 110, 40   *d.* 35, 125, 10

2. Find the degree measure of the third angle of a triangle if the first two angles measure:
   a. 60, 40   *b.* 130, 20   *c.* 45, 55   *d.* 102, 34   *e.* 97, 59

3. Two angles of a triangle measure 40 and 60; find the measure of the obtuse angle formed by the bisectors of these angles.

4. In triangle ABC, the measure of angle B is 80. Find the measure of the obtuse angle formed by the bisectors of angle A and angle C.

5. In triangle ABC, $m\angle A = 40$ and $m\angle C = 30$. Find the measure of the angle formed between the bisector of $\angle C$ and side $\overline{AC}$.

6. Find the measure of the vertex angle of an isosceles triangle if each base angle measures:
   a. 70   *b.* 35   *c.* 54   *d.* $37\frac{1}{2}$ *e.* 72.5

7. Find the measure of each base angle of an isosceles triangle if the vertex angle measures:
   a. 50   *b.* 70   *c.* 82   *d.* 100   *e.* 75

8. In right triangle ABC, altitude $\overline{CD}$ is drawn to hypotenuse $\overline{AB}$. If angle A measures 32, find the measure of angle BCD.

9. In a triangle, the measure of the second angle exceeds the measure of the first angle by 35. The measure of the third angle is 5 less than the measure of the first angle. Find the measure of each angle of the triangle.

10. Find the measure of each angle of a triangle if the ratio of the measures of the three angles is:
    a. 4:3:2   *b.* 2:5:8   *c.* 2:5:2   *d.* 5:3:1   *e.* 3:5:7

11. The measures of two angles of a triangle are in the ratio 3:4. The measure of the third angle is 20 more than the measure of the smaller of the first two angles. Find the measure of each angle.

12. The measure of the vertex angle of an isosceles triangle is three times the measure of each base angle. Find the measure of each angle of the triangle.

13. Each of the congruent angles of an isosceles triangle measures 9 less than four times the vertex angle. Find the measures of the angles of the triangle.

14. In triangle RST, $m\angle T = 90$ and $m\angle R = 35$. If $\overline{TH}$ is drawn perpendicular to $\overline{RS}$, find $m\angle HTS$.

15. In triangle RST, P is a point on $\overline{RT}$ such that $\overline{RS} \cong \overline{SP}$. If $m\angle RSP = 40$ and $m\angle STP = 50$, find $m\angle PST$.

16. Find the measure of the fourth angle of a quadrilateral if the first three angles measure:

a. 60, 130, 90   b. 90, 90, 140   c. 120, 110, 60

17. Find the measure of each angle of a quadrilateral if the measures of its angles are represented by $3x + 20$, $2x + 40$, $4x - 50$, $x - 10$.

18. *Prove:* If $\overline{CD}$ is the altitude drawn to the hypotenuse $\overline{AB}$ of right triangle ABC, then angle BCD is congruent to angle A.

19. *Prove:* If the measure of one angle of a triangle is equal to the sum of the measures of the other two, the triangle is a right triangle.

20. In triangle ABC, median $\overline{AM}$ is drawn to side $\overline{BC}$. If $\overline{AM} \cong \overline{CM}$, prove that triangle ABC is a right triangle.

21. In acute triangle ABC, $\overline{CD}$ is the altitude to $\overline{AB}$, and $\overline{AE}$ is the altitude to $\overline{BC}$. Prove that angle BCD is congruent to angle BAE.

22. *Prove:* If two lines are parallel, the bisectors of a pair of interior angles on the same side of the transversal are perpendicular to each other.

23. In triangle ABC, $m\angle A = 80$, $m\angle B = 50$. If $AB = 4x - 4$ and $AC = 2x + 16$, find AB and AC.

24. The measures of the angles of triangle ABC are represented by $2x$, $x + 10$, and $2x - 30$. (*a*) Express the sum of the measures of the angles in terms of x. (*b*) Find the value of x. (*c*) Show that triangle ABC is an isosceles triangle.

25. The measures of the angles of a triangle are represented by $x + 35$, $2x + 10$, and $3x - 15$. (*a*) Find the value of x. (*b*) Show that triangle ABC is an equilateral triangle.

26. The measures of the angles of triangle ABC are represented by $4x - 6$, $2x + 12$, and $\frac{5}{4}x$. Show that triangle ABC is a right triangle.

27. The measures of the angles of a triangle are represented by $3x + 18$, $4x + 9$, and $10x$. (*a*) Find the value of x. (*b*) Show that $\triangle ABC$ is an isosceles right triangle.

28. In the figure, equilateral triangles FEG and DEH are drawn on sides $\overline{FE}$ and $\overline{DE}$ of triangle DEF. *Prove:* $\overline{DG} \cong \overline{FH}$.

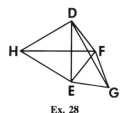

Ex. 28

In 29 and 30, use an indirect method of proof.

29. *Prove:* The base angles of an isosceles triangle are acute angles.

30. *Prove:* An obtuse triangle cannot contain a right angle.

4. Proving Triangles Congruent When They Agree in Two Angles and a Side Opposite One of Them

Theorem 25. **Two triangles are congruent if two angles and a side opposite one of them of one triangle are congruent to two angles and the corresponding side of the other. [a.a.s. ≅ a.a.s.]**

In triangles ABC and $A'B'C'$ (Fig. 4–26), if $\angle C \cong \angle C'$, $\angle A \cong \angle A'$, and $\overline{AB} \cong \overline{A'B'}$, then $\triangle ABC \cong \triangle A'B'C'$.

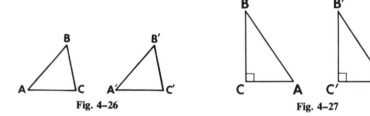

Fig. 4–26   Fig. 4–27

Corollary T25–1. **Two right triangles are congruent if the hypotenuse and an acute angle of one right triangle are congruent to the hypotenuse and an acute angle of the other right triangle.**

In right triangles ABC and $A'B'C'$ with right angles at C and C' (Fig. 4–27), if hypotenuse $\overline{AB} \cong$ hypotenuse $\overline{A'B'}$ and $\angle A \cong \angle A'$, then $\triangle ABC \cong \triangle A'B'C'$.

Must Triangles Be Congruent When a.a.a. ≅ a.a.a. or s.s.a. ≅ s.s.a.?

We have seen that two triangles must be congruent when s.s.s. ≅ s.s.s., s.a.s. ≅ s.a.s., a.s.a. ≅ a.s.a., and a.a.s. ≅ a.a.s. Must two triangles always be congruent when three angles of one triangle are congruent respectively to three angles of the other? Also, must two triangles always be congruent when two sides and an opposite angle of one triangle are congruent respectively to two sides and an opposite angle of the other?

Let us first consider the three triangles in Fig. 4–28, each of which has angles whose measures are 30, 60, 90.

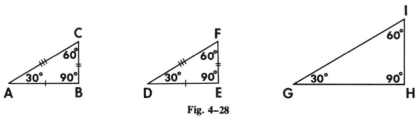

Fig. 4–28

Triangle $ABC \cong \triangle DEF$ because all pairs of corresponding angles are congruent and all pairs of corresponding sides are congruent. However, $\triangle ABC$ is not congruent to $\triangle GHI$ because the sides of $\triangle ABC$ are not congruent to the corresponding sides of $\triangle GHI$. Therefore, we cannot say that two triangles must always be congruent when three angles of one triangle are congruent respectively to three angles of the other.

Let us next consider the three triangles in Fig. 4–29, each of which has two sides whose lengths are $1\frac{1}{8}$ inches and $\frac{7}{8}$ inch, with an angle which measures 43 opposite the $\frac{7}{8}$-inch side.

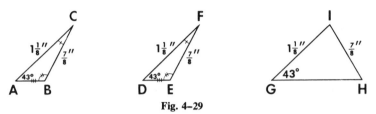

Fig. 4–29

Triangle $ABC \cong \triangle DEF$ because all pairs of corresponding sides and all pairs of corresponding angles are congruent. However, $\triangle ABC$ is not congruent to $\triangle GHI$ because not all pairs of corresponding sides are congruent and not all pairs of corresponding angles are congruent. Therefore, we cannot say that two triangles must always be congruent when two sides and an opposite angle of one triangle are congruent respectively to two sides and an opposite angle of the other.

KEEP IN MIND

Two triangles need not always be congruent when a.a.a. $\cong$ a.a.a. or s.s.a. $\cong$ s.s.a.

MODEL PROBLEM

Prove that the altitudes drawn to the legs of an isosceles triangle from the ends of the base are congruent.

Given: Isosceles $\triangle ABC$ with $\overline{BA} \cong \overline{BC}$.
$\overline{CD} \perp \overline{BA}$.
$\overline{AE} \perp \overline{BC}$.

To prove: $\overline{CD} \cong \overline{AE}$.

Plan: We can prove $\overline{CD} \cong \overline{AE}$ by proving that two triangles in which $\overline{CD}$ and $\overline{AE}$ are corresponding sides, $\triangle ADC$ and CEA, are congruent by a.a.s. $\cong$ a.a.s.

[The proof is given on the next page.]

Proof: *Statements*	*Reasons*
1. In $\triangle ABC$, $\overline{BA} \cong \overline{BC}$.	1. Given.
2. $\angle BAC \cong \angle BCA$. (a. $\cong$ a.)	2. If two sides of a triangle are congruent, the angles opposite these sides are congruent.
3. $\overline{AE} \perp \overline{BC}$, $\overline{CD} \perp \overline{BA}$.	3. Given.
4. $\angle CDA$ and $\angle AEC$ are right angles.	4. When two perpendicular lines intersect, they form right angles.
5. $\angle CDA \cong \angle AEC$. (a. $\cong$ a.)	5. All right angles are congruent.
6. $\overline{AC} \cong \overline{AC}$. (s. $\cong$ s.)	6. Reflexive property of congruence.
7. $\triangle ADC \cong \triangle CEA$.	7. a.a.s. $\cong$ a.a.s.
8. $\overline{CD} \cong \overline{AE}$.	8. Corresponding parts of congruent triangles are congruent.

EXERCISES

In 1–4, the figures have been marked to indicate the *given*. Tell whether or not the triangles must always be congruent, and give your reason.

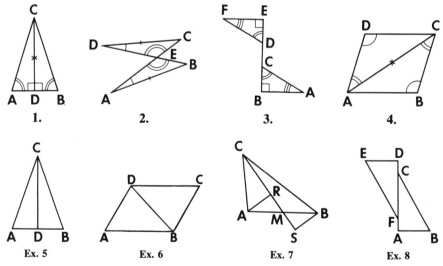

1.	2.	3.	4.

Ex. 5   Ex. 6   Ex. 7   Ex. 8

5. *Given:* $\overline{CD}$ bisects $\angle ACB$, $\angle A \cong \angle B$.
   Prove: $\triangle ACD \cong \triangle BCD$.

6. *Given:* $\overleftrightarrow{BD}$ bisects $\angle B$, $\angle A \cong \angle C$.
   Prove: $\triangle ADB \cong \triangle CDB$.
7. *Given:* M is the midpoint of $\overline{AB}$, $\overline{AR} \perp \overline{CS}$, $\overline{BS} \perp \overline{CS}$.
   Prove: $\overline{AR} \cong \overline{BS}$.
8. *Given:* $\overleftrightarrow{AD}$, $\overline{ED} \perp \overline{DA}$, $\overline{BA} \perp \overline{DA}$, $\overline{DC} \cong \overline{AF}$, $\angle E \cong \angle B$.
   Prove: $\overline{EF} \cong \overline{BC}$.

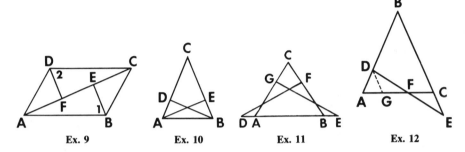

Ex. 9   Ex. 10   Ex. 11   Ex. 12

9. *Given:* $\overleftrightarrow{AC}$ is a line, $\overline{AF} \cong \overline{EC}$, $\overline{DF} \perp \overline{AC}$, $\overline{BE} \perp \overline{AC}$, $\angle 1 \cong \angle 2$.
   Prove: $\overline{AB} \cong \overline{CD}$.
10. *Given:* $\overline{AC} \cong \overline{CB}$, $\angle ADB \cong \angle BEA$.
    Prove: $\overline{AE} \cong \overline{BD}$.
11. $\overleftrightarrow{DE}$ is a line. If $\overline{CA} \cong \overline{CB}$, $\overline{EG} \perp \overline{CA}$, $\overline{DF} \perp \overline{CB}$, $\overline{DF} \cong \overline{EG}$, prove that $\angle FDA \cong \angle GEB$.
12. In triangle ABC, $\overline{AB} \cong \overline{BC}$. Side $\overline{BC}$ is extended through C to point E so that $\overline{CE} \cong \overline{DA}$. $\overline{DE}$ is drawn. Prove that $\overline{DF} \cong \overline{EF}$. [*Hint:* Draw $\overleftrightarrow{DG} \parallel \overleftrightarrow{BE}$.]
13. Prove that if perpendiculars are drawn from two vertices of a triangle upon the median drawn from the third vertex, the perpendiculars are congruent.
14. Use an indirect method of proof to prove: If a point is not equidistant from the sides of an angle, the point does not lie on the bisector of the angle.

5. Proving Right Triangles Congruent When They Agree in the Hypotenuse and a Leg

Theorem 26. **Two right triangles are congruent if the hypotenuse and a leg of one triangle are congruent to the corresponding parts of the other. [hy. leg ≅ hy. leg]**

[The proof for this theorem appears on pages 598–599.]

In right triangles ABC and $A'B'C'$ with right angles at C and C' (Fig. 4–30), if hypotenuse $\overline{AB} \cong$ hypotenuse $\overline{A'B'}$ and leg $\overline{BC} \cong$ leg $\overline{B'C'}$, then $\triangle ABC \cong \triangle A'B'C'$.

Now we will see how the preceding theorem can be used in proving triangles congruent.

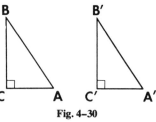

Fig. 4–30

MODEL PROBLEM

Given: $\overrightarrow{EF} \perp \overrightarrow{BA}$.
         $\overrightarrow{EG} \perp \overrightarrow{BC}$.
         $\overline{EF} \cong \overline{EG}$.

To prove: $\overrightarrow{BD}$ bisects $\angle ABC$.

Plan: To prove that $\overrightarrow{BD}$ bisects $\angle ABC$, prove that $\angle 1 \cong \angle 2$. To prove that $\angle 1 \cong \angle 2$, show that the right triangles in which they are corresponding parts, rt. $\triangle EFB$ and rt. $\triangle EGB$, are congruent by hy. leg $\cong$ hy. leg.

Proof: *Statements*   *Reasons*

Statements	Reasons
1. $\overrightarrow{EF} \perp \overrightarrow{BA}, \overrightarrow{EG} \perp \overrightarrow{BC}$.	1. Given.
2. $\angle EFB$ and $\angle EGB$ are right angles.	2. When perpendicular lines intersect, they form right angles.
3. $\triangle EFB$ and EGB are right triangles.	3. A triangle, one of whose angles is a right angle, is a right triangle.
4. $\overline{EF} \cong \overline{EG}$. (leg $\cong$ leg)	4. Given.
5. $\overline{BE} \cong \overline{BE}$. (hy. $\cong$ hy.)	5. Reflexive property of congruence.
6. Rt. $\triangle EFB \cong$ rt. $\triangle EGB$.	6. Hy. leg $\cong$ hy. leg.
7. $\angle 1 \cong \angle 2$.	7. Corresponding parts of congruent triangles are congruent.
8. $\overrightarrow{BD}$ bisects $\angle ABC$.	8. A ray which divides an angle into two congruent angles bisects the angle.

EXERCISES

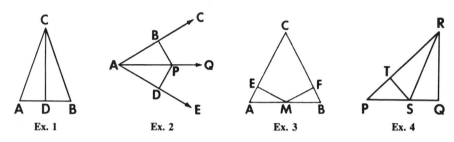

| Ex. 1 | Ex. 2 | Ex. 3 | Ex. 4 |

1. *Given:* $\overline{CD} \perp \overline{AB}$, $\overline{CA} \cong \overline{CB}$.
   Prove: $\triangle ACD \cong \triangle BCD$.
2. *Given:* $\overrightarrow{PB} \perp \overrightarrow{AC}$, $\overline{PD} \perp \overrightarrow{AE}$, $\overline{AB} \cong \overline{AD}$.
   Prove: $\triangle ABP \cong \triangle ADP$.
3. If M is the midpoint of $\overline{AB}$, $\overline{ME} \perp \overline{AC}$, $\overline{MF} \perp \overline{CB}$, and $\overline{ME} \cong \overline{MF}$, prove that $\angle CAB \cong \angle CBA$.
4. *Given:* Rt. $\triangle PQR$ with $\angle Q$ a rt. angle, $\overline{ST} \perp \overline{PR}$, $\overline{RT} \cong \overline{RQ}$.
   Prove: $\overline{RS}$ bisects $\angle PRQ$.

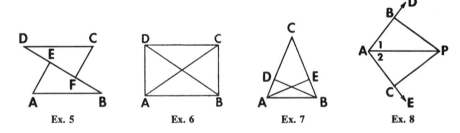

| Ex. 5 | Ex. 6 | Ex. 7 | Ex. 8 |

5. If $\overline{AE} \perp \overline{DB}$, $\overline{CF} \perp \overline{DB}$, $\overline{DE} \cong \overline{BF}$, and $\overline{DC} \cong \overline{BA}$, prove that $\overline{CF} \cong \overline{AE}$.
6. If $\overline{DA} \perp \overline{AB}$, $\overline{CB} \perp \overline{AB}$, and $\overline{AC} \cong \overline{BD}$, prove that $\overline{AD} \cong \overline{BC}$.
7. In $\triangle ABC$, $\overline{BD} \perp \overline{AC}$, $\overline{AE} \perp \overline{BC}$, and $\overline{BD} \cong \overline{AE}$. Prove that $\triangle ABC$ is an isosceles triangle.
8. If $\overrightarrow{PB} \perp \overrightarrow{AD}$, $\overline{PC} \perp \overrightarrow{AE}$, and $\overline{PB} \cong \overline{PC}$, find the measure of $\angle 1$ and $\angle 2$ if the measure of $\angle 1$ is represented by $2x + 18$ and the measure of $\angle 2$ is represented by $4x - 18$.

6. Exterior Angles of a Triangle

Definition. An *exterior angle of a triangle* is an angle formed outside a triangle by one side of the triangle and the extension of an adjacent side.

In Fig. 4–31, $\angle CBD$, which is formed outside triangle ABC by side $\overline{CB}$ and the extension
of adjacent side $\overline{AB}$, is an exterior angle of
$\triangle ABC$. Angles A and C are called *nonadjacent
interior angles* with reference to exterior angle
CBD.

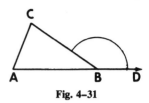

Fig. 4–31

An exterior angle of any polygon is formed
in the same way as the exterior angle of a triangle.

Theorem 27. **The measure of an exterior angle of a triangle is equal to the
sum of the measures of the two nonadjacent interior angles.**

In Fig. 4–31, the measure of exterior angle CBD is equal to the sum of
the measures of nonadjacent interior angles A and C, or $m\angle CBD = m\angle A +
m\angle C$.

MODEL PROBLEM

In $\triangle ABC$, $\overline{AC} \cong \overline{BC}$. The measure of an exterior angle at vertex C is represented by $5x + 10$. If $\angle A$ measures 30, find the value of x.

Solution:

1. Since $\overline{AC} \cong \overline{BC}$, then $m\angle B = m\angle A$, or $m\angle B =$
   30.

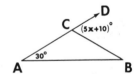

2. $m\angle DCB = m\angle A + m\angle B$

3. $\quad 5x + 10 = 30 + 30$

4. $\quad 5x + 10 = 60$

5. $\qquad 5x = 50$

6. $\qquad x = 10$

Answer: $x = 10$.

EXERCISES

1. In $\triangle RST$, if $m\angle S = 90$ and $m\angle T = 30$, find the measure of an exterior
   angle at R.

2. Find the measure of either of the exterior angles formed by extending
   the base of an isosceles triangle if the vertex angle of the triangle measures: *a.* 20   *b.* 40   *c.* 82   *d.* 120   *e.* 135

3. Find the measure of the vertex angle of an isosceles triangle if either of the exterior angles formed by extending the base measures: *a.* 100 *b.* 112   *c.* 135   *d.* 140   *e.* 157

4. In $\triangle ABC$, $m\angle B$ is four times as large as $m\angle A$. An exterior angle at C measures 125. Find the measure of $\angle A$.

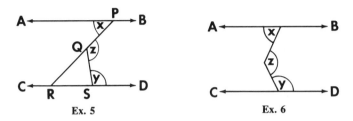

Ex. 5   Ex. 6

5. In the figure, $\overleftrightarrow{AB} \parallel \overleftrightarrow{CD}$ and $\overline{PQR}$ and $\overline{QS}$ are drawn. If $m\angle x = 44$ and $m\angle y = 98$, find the measure of angle z.

6. In the figure, $\overleftrightarrow{AB} \parallel \overleftrightarrow{CD}$, $m\angle x = 68$, and $m\angle y = 117$. Find the measure of $\angle z$.

7. In triangle ABC, an exterior angle at C measures 100 and angle B measures 20. Triangle ABC must be (1) acute (2) right (3) obtuse (4) equiangular.

8. Side $\overline{AC}$ of triangle ABC is extended through C to D. Angle BCD measures 108 and the measure of angle A is twice the measure of angle B. Triangle ABC is (1) right (2) obtuse (3) isosceles (4) scalene.

9. In $\triangle DEF$, $m\angle D = 2x + 4$, $m\angle E = 6x - 58$. The measure of an exterior angle at F is represented by $5x$.   (*a*) Find the value of x.   (*b*) Show that $\triangle DEF$ is a right triangle.

10. *Prove:* If the two exterior angles formed by extending one side of a triangle in both directions are congruent, the triangle is isosceles.

11. In $\triangle RST$, $\overline{RS} \cong \overline{ST}$. Prove that the bisector of an exterior angle at S is parallel to $\overline{RT}$.

12. *Prove:* If one exterior angle is drawn at each vertex of a triangle, the sum of the measures of the three exterior angles is 360.

7. The Sum of the Measures of the Interior Angles of a Polygon

We have learned that a polygon is a closed figure which is the union of line segments in a plane. The figure pictured in Fig. 4–32 is polygon $ABCDE$. We have already studied the properties of the triangle, the polygon which is the union of 3 sides. Other polygons which we will study are defined as follows:

Fig. 4–32

Definition. A *quadrilateral* is a polygon which is the union of 4 sides.

Definition. A *pentagon* is a polygon which is the union of 5 sides.

Definition. A *hexagon* is a polygon which is the union of 6 sides.

Definition. An *octagon* is a polygon which is the union of 8 sides.

Definition. A *decagon* is a polygon which is the union of 10 sides.

Definition. A *convex polygon* is a polygon each of whose interior angles measures less than 180.

In Fig. 4–32, polygon *ABCDE* is a convex polygon.

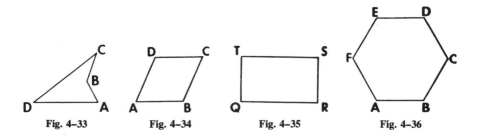

Fig. 4–33   Fig. 4–34   Fig. 4–35   Fig. 4–36

Definition. A *concave polygon* is a polygon which has at least one interior angle that measures more than 180.

In Fig. 4–33, polygon *ABCD* is a concave polygon because interior angle *B* measures more than 180.

NOTE. In this book, when the term *polygon* is used, it will mean "convex polygon" unless otherwise stated.

Definition. An *equilateral polygon* is a polygon all of whose sides are congruent.

In Fig. 4–34, if $\overline{AB} \cong \overline{BC} \cong \overline{CD} \cong \overline{DA}$, then polygon *ABCD* is an equilateral polygon.

Definition. An *equiangular polygon* is a polygon all of whose angles are congruent.

In Fig. 4–35, if $\angle Q \cong \angle R \cong \angle S \cong \angle T$, then polygon *QRST* is an equiangular polygon.

Definition. A *regular polygon* is a polygon that is both equilateral and equiangular.

In Fig. 4–36, if $\overline{AB} \cong \overline{BC} \cong \overline{CD} \cong \overline{DE} \cong \overline{EF} \cong \overline{FA}$, and $\angle A \cong \angle B \cong \angle C \cong \angle D \cong \angle E \cong \angle F$, then polygon *ABCDEF* is a regular polygon.

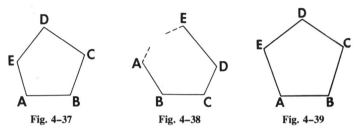

Fig. 4–37   Fig. 4–38   Fig. 4–39

Theorem 28. **The sum of the measures of the interior angles of a polygon of** *n* **sides is 180(***n* **− 2) when measured in degrees, or (***n* **− 2) when measured in straight angles.**

In Fig. 4–37, if polygon *ABCDE* represents a polygon of *n* sides, the sum of the measures of the interior angles, $m\angle A + m\angle B + m\angle C + m\angle D + m\angle E = 180(n - 2)$ when measured in degrees, or $(n - 2)$ when measured in straight angles.

NOTE. A polygon of *n* sides may also be represented as an open polygon. (See Fig. 4–38.)

Corollary T28–1. **The measure of each interior angle of an equiangular or regular polygon of** *n* **sides is** $\dfrac{180(n - 2)}{n}$ **.**

In Fig. 4–39, if polygon *ABCDE* represents a regular polygon of *n* sides, then the degree measure of each interior angle, for example, $m\angle A = \dfrac{180(n - 2)}{n}$.

MODEL PROBLEMS

1. Find the number of degrees contained in each interior angle of a regular hexagon.

Solution:

Each interior angle of a regular polygon of n sides contains $\dfrac{180(n - 2)}{n}$ *degrees.*

Since a hexagon is a polygon of 6 sides, $n = 6$.

Therefore, $\dfrac{180(n - 2)}{n} = \dfrac{180(6 - 2)}{6} = \dfrac{180(4)}{6} = 120.$

Answer: 120

2. If each interior angle of a regular polygon contains 135°, find the number of sides that the polygon has.

Solution:

Each interior angle of a regular polygon of n sides contains $\dfrac{180(n-2)}{n}$

degrees.

Since each interior angle contains 135°,

1. $135 = \dfrac{180(n-2)}{n}$

2. $135n = 180(n-2)$ [In equation 1, multiply both sides by n.]

3. $135n = 180n - 360$

4. $360 = 180n - 135n$

5. $360 = 45n$

6. $8 = n$

Answer: 8 sides.

EXERCISES

1. Find (*a*) the number of straight angles and (*b*) the sum of the degree measures of the interior angles of a polygon which has:
   a. 4 sides   *b.* 5 sides   *c.* 7 sides   *d.* 9 sides

2. Find (*a*) the number of straight angles and (*b*) the sum of the degree measures of the interior angles of:
   a. a quadrilateral   *b.* a hexagon   *c.* an octagon   *d.* a pentagon
   e. a decagon

3. Find the measure of each interior angle of a regular polygon of:
   a. 4 sides   *b.* 5 sides   *c.* 8 sides   *d.* 10 sides   *e.* 12 sides

4. How many sides has a polygon if the sum of the measures of its interior angles is:
   a. 8 straight angles   *b.* 4 straight angles   *c.* 3 straight angles

5. How many sides has a polygon if the sum of the measures of its interior angles is:
   a. 540   *b.* 720   *c.* 900   *d.* 1440   *e.* 2700

6. The sum of the measures of the interior angles of a polygon is 1800. The polygon has:
   a. 8 sides   *b.* 10 sides   *c.* 12 sides

7. If the sum of the measures of five interior angles of a hexagon is 600, find the number of degrees contained in the sixth angle.

8. Find the number of sides of a regular polygon each of whose interior angles contains:

    a. 90°   *b.* 120°   *c.* 150°   *d.* 135°   *e.* 175°

9. The angles of a quadrilateral are in the ratio 3:4:5:6. Find the number of degrees contained in the largest angle of the quadrilateral.

10. Find the smallest number of degrees that an interior angle of a regular polygon may contain.

11. As the number of sides of a regular polygon increases, what change takes place in the number of degrees contained in each interior angle of the polygon?

8. The Sum of the Measures of the Exterior Angles of a Polygon

Theorem 29. **The sum of the measures of the exterior angles of a polygon of** *n* **sides, taking one angle at each vertex, is 360 when measured in degrees, or 2 when measured in straight angles.**

In polygon *ABCD* (Fig. 4–40), the sum of the measures of the exterior angles, $m\angle 1 + m\angle 2 + m\angle 3 + m\angle 4 = 360$ when measured in degrees, or 2 when measured in straight angles.

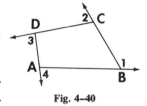

Corollary T29–1. **The measure of each exterior angle of an equiangular polygon or a regular polygon of** *n* **sides is** $\dfrac{360}{n}$ **when measured in degrees.**

Fig. 4–40

MODEL PROBLEMS

1. Find the number of degrees in the measure of each exterior angle of a regular polygon which has 12 sides.

Solution:

    Each exterior angle of a regular polygon of n sides contains $\dfrac{360}{n}$

        degrees.

    Since $n = 12$, $\dfrac{360}{n} = \dfrac{360}{12} = 30$.

Answer: 30°.

2. Each interior angle of a regular polygon contains 120°. How many sides does the polygon have?

Solution: Since at each vertex of the polygon the exterior angle is supplementary to the interior angle, when the interior angle contains 120°, the exterior angle contains 60°.

Each exterior angle of a regular polygon of n sides contains $\dfrac{360}{n}$ degrees.

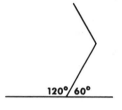

1. Since each exterior angle contains 60°,

$$60 = \frac{360}{n}$$

2. $60n = 360$

3. $n = 6$

Answer: 6 sides.

EXERCISES

1. Find (*a*) in degrees and (*b*) in straight angles, the sum of the measures of the exterior angles of a polygon which has:
   a. 4 sides   *b.* 5 sides   *c.* 7 sides   *d.* 9 sides   *e.* 12 sides

2. Find (*a*) in degrees and (*b*) in straight angles, the sum of the measures of the exterior angles of:
   a. a quadrilateral   *b.* a hexagon   *c.* an octagon   *d.* a decagon

3. Find the degree measure of each exterior angle of a regular polygon of:
   a. 4 sides   *b.* 5 sides   *c.* 6 sides   *d.* 8 sides   *e.* 10 sides

4. Find the number of sides of a polygon each of whose exterior angles contains:
   a. 30°   *b.* 40°   *c.* 45°   *d.* 60°   *e.* 90°

5. How many sides has a polygon if the sum of the measures of its interior angles equals the sum of the measures of its exterior angles?

6. How many sides has a polygon if the sum of the measures of its interior angles is four times the sum of the measures of its exterior angles?

7. Is there a regular polygon such that each exterior angle measures 50? Give a reason for your answer.

8. As the number of sides of a polygon increases, the number of degrees in the sum of the measures of the exterior angles (*a*) increases (*b*) decreases (*c*) remains the same.

9. How many sides does a polygon have if the sum of the measures of its interior angles is five times the sum of the measures of its exterior angles?

10. The measure of each exterior angle of a regular polygon is twice the measure of each interior angle. How many sides does the polygon have?

11. The measure of each interior angle of a regular polygon is t times the measure of each exterior angle of the polygon. Show that the polygon has $2(t + 1)$ sides.

9. The Parallelogram

We have learned that a quadrilateral is a polygon which is the union of four sides. Now we are going to investigate the properties of various types of quadrilaterals. We will begin our study with the following definition:

Definition. **A** *parallelogram* **is a quadrilateral in which both pairs of opposite sides are parallel.**

In quadrilateral $ABCD$ (Fig. 4–41), if $\overline{AB} \parallel \overline{DC}$ and $\overline{AD} \parallel \overline{BC}$, the quadrilateral is a parallelogram. The symbol for parallelogram $ABCD$ is $\square ABCD$.

In a quadrilateral, vertices which are endpoints of the same side are called *consecutive vertices*. For example, in $\square ABCD$ (Fig. 4–41), vertices A and B, B and C, C and D, also D and E, are called consecutive vertices. Sides of a quadrilateral which have a common endpoint are called *consecutive sides,* or *adjacent sides.* For example, in $\square ABCD$ (Fig. 4–41), sides $\overline{AB}$ and $\overline{BC}$, $\overline{BC}$ and $\overline{CD}$, $\overline{CD}$ and $\overline{DA}$, also $\overline{DA}$ and $\overline{AB}$, are called consecutive sides, or adjacent sides. Sides of a quadrilateral which do not have a common endpoint are called *opposite sides.* For example, in $\square ABCD$ (Fig. 4–41), $\overline{AB}$ and $\overline{DC}$, also $\overline{BC}$ and $\overline{AD}$, are called opposite sides. Angles of a quadrilateral whose vertices are consecutive vertices are called *consecutive angles.* For example, in $\square ABCD$ (Fig. 4–41), $\angle A$ and $\angle B$, $\angle B$ and $\angle C$, $\angle C$ and $\angle D$, also $\angle D$ and $\angle E$, are called consecutive angles. Angles of a quadrilateral whose vertices are nonconsecutive vertices are called *opposite angles.* For example, in $\square ABCD$ (Fig. 4–41), $\angle A$ and $\angle C$, also $\angle B$ and $\angle D$, are called opposite angles. A line segment which joins two nonconsecutive vertices of a quadrilateral is called a *diagonal.* For example, in $\square ABCD$ (Fig. 4–43), $\overline{AC}$ and $\overline{BD}$ are diagonals.

Fig. 4–41

Fig. 4–42

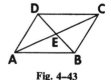

Fig. 4–43

Theorem 30. **A diagonal divides a parallelogram into two congruent triangles.**

In $\square ABCD$ (Fig. 4–42), diagonal $\overline{AC}$ divides the parallelogram into two congruent triangles. $\triangle ABC \cong \triangle CDA$.

Corollary T30–1. **Both pairs of opposite sides of a parallelogram are congruent.**

In $\square ABCD$ (Fig. 4–41), $\overline{AB} \cong \overline{DC}$ and $\overline{BC} \cong \overline{AD}$.

Corollary T30–2. **Both pairs of opposite angles of a parallelogram are congruent.**

In $\square ABCD$ (Fig. 4–41), $\angle A \cong \angle C$ and $\angle B \cong \angle D$.

Corollary T30–3. **Two consecutive angles of a parallelogram are supplementary.**

In $\square ABCD$ (Fig. 4–41), $\angle A$ is supplementary to $\angle B$, $\angle B$ is supplementary to $\angle C$, $\angle C$ is supplementary to $\angle D$, and $\angle D$ is supplementary to $\angle A$.

Corollary T30–4. **The diagonals of a parallelogram bisect each other.**

In $\square ABCD$ (Fig. 4–43), $\overline{AC}$ bisects $\overline{BD}$, so that $\overline{BE} \cong \overline{DE}$; also, $\overline{BD}$ bisects $\overline{AC}$, so that $\overline{AE} \cong \overline{CE}$.

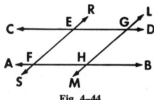

Fig. 4–44

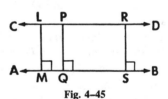

Fig. 4–45

Definition. **If a transversal intersects two lines in two points, we say that the lines *intercept* or *cut off* on the transversal the segment whose endpoints are the points of intersection.**

In Fig. 4–44, lines $\overleftrightarrow{CD}$ and $\overleftrightarrow{AB}$ intercept or cut off the segment $\overline{EF}$ on transversal $\overleftrightarrow{RS}$.

Corollary T30–5. **Segments of parallel lines intercepted between parallel lines are congruent.**

In Fig. 4–44, if $\overleftrightarrow{AB} \parallel \overleftrightarrow{CD}$ and $\overleftrightarrow{RS} \parallel \overleftrightarrow{LM}$, then $\overline{EF} \cong \overline{GH}$.

Definition. **The *distance between two parallel lines* is the distance from any point on one line to the other line.**

In Fig. 4–45, if $\overleftrightarrow{AB} \parallel \overleftrightarrow{CD}$, P is a point on $\overleftrightarrow{CD}$, and $\overleftrightarrow{PQ} \perp \overleftrightarrow{AB}$, then PQ is the distance between parallel lines $\overleftrightarrow{AB}$ and $\overleftrightarrow{CD}$.

Corollary T30–6. **Parallel lines are everywhere equidistant.**

In Fig. 4–45, if $\overleftrightarrow{AB} \parallel \overleftrightarrow{CD}$, $\overleftrightarrow{LM} \perp \overleftrightarrow{AB}$, $\overleftrightarrow{PQ} \perp \overleftrightarrow{AB}$, and $\overleftrightarrow{RS} \perp \overleftrightarrow{AB}$, then $LM = PQ = RS$.

Properties of a Parallelogram

1. Both pairs of opposite sides are parallel.
2. A diagonal divides it into two congruent triangles.
3. Both pairs of opposite sides are congruent.
4. Both pairs of opposite angles are congruent.
5. Two consecutive angles are supplementary.
6. The diagonals bisect each other.

MODEL PROBLEMS

1. In parallelogram $ABCD$, if $m\angle B$ exceeds $m\angle A$ by 50, find the measure of $\angle B$.

Solution:　　　　Let $x =$ the measure of $\angle A$.
　　　　　Then $x + 50 =$ the measure of $\angle B$.

Since two consecutive angles of a parallelogram are supplementary,

1. $m\angle A + m\angle B = 180$

2. $x + x + 50 = 180$

3. $2x + 50 = 180$

4. $2x = 130$

5. $x = 65$

6. $x + 50 = 115$

Answer: $m\angle B = 115$.

2. *Given:*　　In $\square ABCD$, $\overline{DE} \perp \overline{AB}$, $\overline{BF} \perp \overline{DC}$.

To prove: $\overline{DE} \cong \overline{BF}$.

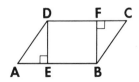

Plan:　　To prove that $\overline{DE} \cong \overline{BF}$, prove that the triangles which have these line segments as corresponding sides, $\triangle AED$ and CFB, are congruent by a.a.s. $\cong$ a.a.s.

[The proof is given on the next page.]

Proof: *Statements*	*Reasons*
1. $ABCD$ is a $\Box$.	1. Given.
2. $\overline{AD} \cong \overline{CB}$. (s. $\cong$ s.)	2. A pair of opposite sides of a $\Box$ are congruent.
3. $\angle A \cong \angle C$. (a. $\cong$ a.)	3. A pair of opposite angles of a $\Box$ are congruent.
4. $\overline{DE} \perp \overline{AB}, \overline{BF} \perp \overline{DC}$.	4. Given.
5. $\angle E$ and $\angle F$ are right angles.	5. When perpendicular lines intersect, they form right angles.
6. $\angle E \cong \angle F$. (a. $\cong$ a.)	6. All right angles are congruent.
7. $\triangle AED \cong \triangle CFB$.	7. a.a.s. $\cong$ a.a.s.
8. $\overline{DE} \cong \overline{BF}$.	8. Corresponding parts of congruent triangles are congruent.

EXERCISES

1. Find the measures of the other three angles of a parallelogram if one angle measures:
   a. 60   *b.* 68   *c.* 73   *d.* 110   *e.* 138   *f.* 160

2. In parallelogram $ABCD$, the measure of angle A is represented by x and the measure of angle B by $2x + 60$. Find the measure of angle A.

3. In parallelogram $ABCD$, angle A measures x degrees and angle B measures $(2x - 30)$ degrees. Find the measure of angle A.

4. The measures of angles A and B of parallelogram $ABCD$ are in the ratio 2:7. Find the measure of angle A.

5. In parallelogram $ABCD$, the measure of angle A exceeds the measure of angle B by 30. Find the measure of angle B.

6. In parallelogram $ABCD$, diagonal $\overline{AC}$ is perpendicular to side $\overline{CD}$. If $m\angle ACB = 50$, find the measure of angle ADC.

7. In parallelogram $ABCD$, $m\angle ABC = 3x - 12$ and $m\angle CDA = x + 40$. Find $m\angle ABC$, $m\angle CDA$, $m\angle BCD$, and $m\angle DAB$.

8. In parallelogram $ABCD$, $AB = 7x - 4$ and $CD = 2x + 21$. Find AB and CD.

9. In parallelogram $ABCD$, $BC = 9y + 10$, $AD = 6y + 40$, $AB = \frac{1}{2}y + 50$. Find BC, AD, AB, and DC.

Exercises 10–13 refer to parallelogram $ABCD$ in the figure.

10. If $m \angle DAB = 4x - 60$ and $m \angle DCB = 30 - x$, find $m \angle DAB$, $m \angle DCB$, $m \angle ABC$, and $m \angle CDA$.

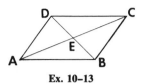

Ex. 10–13

11. If $m \angle DCB = a + 12$ and $m \angle CDA = 4a + 18$, find the measures of the angles of the parallelogram.

12. If $AB = 4x + y$, $BC = y + 4$, $CD = 3x + 6$, $DA = 2x + y$, find the lengths of the sides of the parallelogram.

13. If $AE = 5x - 3$ and $EC = 15 - x$, find AC.

14. In parallelogram $ABCD$, $AB = 2x + y$, $BC = x + 2$, $CD = x + 12$, and $DA = y + 6$. (*a*) Find x and y. (*b*) Find AB, BC, CD, and DA.

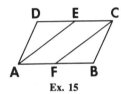

Ex. 15

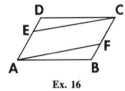

Ex. 16

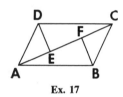

Ex. 17

15. *Given: $ABCD$ is a $\square$, E is the midpoint of $\overline{DC}$, F is the midpoint of $\overline{AB}$.*
    Prove: $\overline{AE} \cong \overline{CF}$.

16. *Given: $ABCD$ is a $\square$, $\overline{AE} \cong \overline{CF}$.*
    Prove: $\overline{EC} \cong \overline{FA}$.

17. *Given: $ABCD$ is a $\square$, $\overline{DE} \perp \overline{AC}$, $\overline{BF} \perp \overline{AC}$.*
    Prove: $\overline{AE} \cong \overline{CF}$.

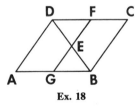

Ex. 18

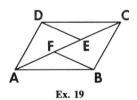

Ex. 19

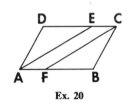

Ex. 20

18. *Given: $ABCD$ is a $\square$, $\overline{FG}$ bisects $\overline{DB}$.*
    Prove: $\overline{DB}$ bisects $\overline{FG}$.

19. *Given: $\overline{AC}$ is a diagonal in $\square ABCD$, $\overline{AF} \cong \overline{CE}$.*
    Prove: $\overline{DE} \parallel \overline{BF}$.

20. *Given: $ABCD$ is a $\square$, $\overline{AE}$ bisects $\angle DAB$, $\overline{CF}$ bisects $\angle DCB$.*
    Prove: $\overline{AF} \cong \overline{CE}$.

21. In $\square ABCD$, $\overline{DE} \perp \overline{AB}$ and $\overline{CF} \perp \overline{AF}$. Prove that $\overline{DE} \cong \overline{CF}$.

22. Prove that in a parallelogram, the distances to a diagonal from two opposite vertices are equal.

23. Prove that a line segment drawn through the midpoint of a diagonal of a parallelogram and ending in a pair of opposite sides is bisected by the diagonal.

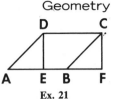

Ex. 21

24. *Prove:* If a parallelogram is not equilateral, the bisectors of a pair of opposite angles in the parallelogram are congruent.

25. In parallelogram $ABCD$, $\overline{AD}$ is longer than $\overline{DC}$ and diagonal $\overline{AC}$ is drawn. Use an indirect method of proof to prove that $\overline{AC}$ does not bisect angle C.

Proving That a Quadrilateral Is a Parallelogram

If we wish to prove that a certain quadrilateral is a parallelogram, we can do so by proving its opposite sides parallel, thus satisfying the definition of a parallelogram. There are other conditions which are sufficient to show that a quadrilateral is a parallelogram. We now proceed to study some of these conditions.

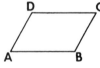

Fig. 4–46

Fig. 4–47

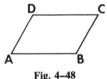

Fig. 4–48

Theorem 31. **If both pairs of opposite sides of a quadrilateral are congruent, the quadrilateral is a parallelogram.**

In quadrilateral $ABCD$ (Fig. 4–46), if $\overline{AB} \cong \overline{DC}$ and $\overline{BC} \cong \overline{AD}$, then quadrilateral $ABCD$ is a parallelogram.

Theorem 32. **If two opposite sides of a quadrilateral are both congruent and parallel, the quadrilateral is a parallelogram.**

In quadrilateral $ABCD$ (Fig. 4–46), if $\overline{AB} \cong \overline{DC}$ and $\overline{AB} \parallel \overline{DC}$, then quadrilateral $ABCD$ is a parallelogram.

Theorem 33. **If the diagonals of a quadrilateral bisect each other, the quadrilateral is a parallelogram.**

In quadrilateral $ABCD$ (Fig. 4–47), if diagonals $\overline{AC}$ and $\overline{BD}$ bisect each other (that is, if $\overline{AE} \cong \overline{EC}$ and $\overline{BE} \cong \overline{ED}$), then quadrilateral $ABCD$ is a parallelogram.

Theorem 34. **If both pairs of opposite angles of a quadrilateral are congruent, the quadrilateral is a parallelogram.**

In quadrilateral $ABCD$ (Fig. 4–48), if $\angle A \cong \angle C$ and $\angle B \cong \angle D$, then $ABCD$ is a parallelogram.

Methods of Proving a Quadrilateral a Parallelogram

To prove that a quadrilateral is a parallelogram, prove that any one of the following statements is true:

1. Both pairs of opposite sides of the quadrilateral are parallel.
2. Both pairs of opposite sides of the quadrilateral are congruent.
3. Two opposite sides of the quadrilateral are congruent and parallel.
4. The diagonals of the quadrilateral bisect each other.
5. Both pairs of opposite angles of the quadrilateral are congruent.

MODEL PROBLEM

In triangle ABC, D is the midpoint of $\overline{AC}$, and E is the midpoint of $\overline{CB}$. If $\overline{DE}$ is extended its own length to F and $\overline{FB}$ is drawn, prove that $ABFD$ is a parallelogram.

Given: Segments $\overline{AC}$, $\overline{CB}$, $\overline{FB}$.
$\overline{DC} \cong \overline{DA}$.
$\overline{CE} \cong \overline{BE}$.
$\overline{DE} \cong \overline{FE}$.

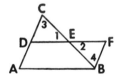

To prove: $ABFD$ is a parallelogram.

Plan: Prove that quadrilateral $ABFD$ is a parallelogram by showing that two of its opposite sides, $\overline{BF}$ and $\overline{AD}$, are both congruent and parallel.

[The proof is given on the next page.]

Proof: *Statements*	*Reasons*
1. $\overline{CE} \cong \overline{BE}$. (s. $\cong$ s.)	1. Given.
2. $\overline{DE} \cong \overline{FE}$. (s. $\cong$ s.)	2. Given.
3. $\angle 1 \cong \angle 2$. (a. $\cong$ a.)	3. If two angles are vertical angles, they are congruent.
4. $\triangle CED \cong \triangle BEF$.	4. s.a.s. $\cong$ s.a.s.
5. $\angle 3 \cong \angle 4$.	5. Corresponding parts of congruent triangles are congruent.
6. $\overleftrightarrow{FB} \parallel \overleftrightarrow{CA}$, or $\overline{FB} \parallel \overline{DA}$.	6. If two lines are cut by a transversal making a pair of alternate interior angles congruent, the lines are parallel.
7. $\overline{FB} \cong \overline{DC}$.	7. Same as reason 5.
8. $\overline{DC} \cong \overline{DA}$.	8. Given.
9. $\overline{FB} \cong \overline{DA}$.	9. Transitive property of congruence.
10. $ABFD$ is a $\square$.	10. A quadrilateral is a $\square$ if two opposite sides are both congruent and parallel.

EXERCISES

1. In (*a*) to (*e*), the *given* is marked on the figure. Tell why each quadrilateral $ABCD$ is a parallelogram.

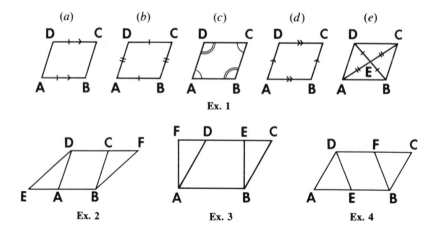

Ex. 1

Ex. 2   Ex. 3   Ex. 4

2. *Given:* $ABCD$ is a $\square$, $\overleftrightarrow{EB}$ and $\overleftrightarrow{DF}$ are lines, $\overline{CF} \cong \overline{AE}$.
   Prove: $EBFD$ is a $\square$.
3. *Given:* $ABCD$ is a $\square$, $\overline{FC}$ is a line segment, $\overline{BE} \perp \overline{FC}$, $\overline{AF} \perp \overline{FC}$.
   Prove: $ABEF$ is a $\square$.
4. *Given:* $ABCD$ is a $\square$, E is the midpoint of $\overline{AB}$, F is the midpoint of $\overline{DC}$.
   Prove: $EBFD$ is a $\square$.

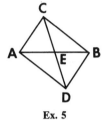

Ex. 5

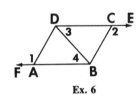

Ex. 6

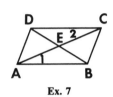

Ex. 7

5. *Given:* In $\triangle ABC$, $\overline{CE}$ is a median, $\overline{CE}$ is extended its own length to D.
   $\overline{AD}$ and $\overline{DB}$ are drawn.
   Prove: $ADBC$ is a $\square$.
6. *Given:* $\overrightarrow{BF}$ and $\overrightarrow{DE}$, $\angle 1 \cong \angle 2$, $\angle 3 \cong \angle 4$.
   Prove: $ABCD$ is a $\square$.
7. *Given:* $\overline{DB}$ bisects $\overline{AC}$, $\angle 1 \cong \angle 2$.
   Prove: $ABCD$ is a $\square$.

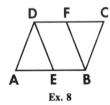

Ex. 8

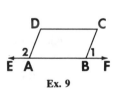

Ex. 9

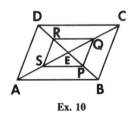

Ex. 10

8. *Given:* $ABCD$ is a $\square$, $\overline{AE} \cong \overline{CF}$.
   Prove: $EBFD$ is a $\square$.
9. *Given:* $\overleftrightarrow{EF}$ is a line, $\angle 2$ is supplementary to $\angle 1$, $\angle C \cong \angle 1$.
   Prove: $ABCD$ is a $\square$.
10. *Given:* $ABCD$ is a $\square$ with diagonals $\overline{AC}$ and $\overline{BD}$, S, P, Q, R are respectively the midpoints of $\overline{AE}$, $\overline{BE}$, $\overline{CE}$, and $\overline{DE}$.
    Prove: $PQRS$ is a $\square$.

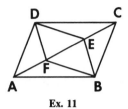
Ex. 11

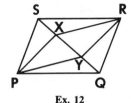
Ex. 12

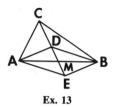
Ex. 13

11. *Given:* $\overline{AC}$ is a diagonal in $\square ABCD$, $\overline{AF} \cong \overline{CE}$.
    Prove: BEDF is a $\square$.

12. *Given:* $\overline{QS}$ is a diagonal in $\square PQRS$, $\angle SXR \cong \angle PYQ$.
    Prove: PYRX is a $\square$.

13. *Given:* In $\triangle ABC$, $\overline{CM}$ is a median extended to E, $\overline{AD} \perp \overline{CM}$,
    $\overline{BE} \perp \overline{CE}$.
    Prove: AEBD is a $\square$.

14. If *ABCD* is a parallelogram and *CDFE*
    is a parallelogram, prove:
    a. ABEF is a $\square$.
    b. $\overline{FA} \cong \overline{EB}$ and $\overline{FA} \parallel \overline{EB}$.

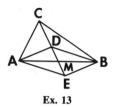

Ex. 14

15. In quadrilateral *ABCD*, *E* is the mid-
    point of $\overline{AB}$ and *F* is the midpoint of $\overline{DC}$.
    Diagonal $\overline{AC}$ and line segment $\overline{EF}$ bi-
    sect each other. (*a*) Prove that $\overline{AB}$ is congruent to $\overline{DC}$. (*b*) Prove that
    $\overline{AB}$ is parallel to $\overline{DC}$. (*c*) Prove that *ABCD* is a parallelogram.

16. Prove that the line segment joining the midpoints of two opposite sides
    of a parallelogram is parallel to the other two sides.

17. Prove that in a parallelogram the line segments joining two opposite
    vertices to the midpoints of their opposite sides are parallel and con-
    gruent.

18. Prove that if the successive midpoints of the sides of a parallelogram are
    joined, the figure formed is a parallelogram.

19. Use an indirect method of proof to prove: Two line segments drawn
    inside a triangle from the ends of one side and terminating in the other
    two sides cannot bisect each other.

10. The Rectangle

Definition. A *rectangle* is a **parallelogram one of whose angles is a right
angle.**

If one angle, $\angle A$, in $\square ABCD$ (Fig. 4–49) is a right angle, then $\square ABCD$
is a rectangle.

Any side of rectangle *ABCD* (Fig. 4–49) may be called a *base* of the
rectangle. If side $\overline{AB}$ is considered as a base, then either consecutive side
$\overline{AD}$ or $\overline{BC}$ is called an *altitude* of the rectangle.

Fig. 4-49

Fig. 4-50

Fig. 4-51

Since a rectangle is a special kind of parallelogram, a rectangle has all the properties of a parallelogram. In addition to these properties, a rectangle has special properties.

Theorem 35. **All angles of a rectangle are right angles.**

In rectangle $ABCD$ (Fig. 4-49), $\angle A$, $\angle B$, $\angle C$, and $\angle D$ are all right angles.

Theorem 36. **The diagonals of a rectangle are congruent.**

If $ABCD$ is a rectangle (Fig. 4-50), its diagonals, $\overline{AC}$ and $\overline{BD}$, are congruent, or $\overline{AC} \cong \overline{BD}$.

Properties of a Rectangle

1. A rectangle has all the properties of a parallelogram.
2. A rectangle contains four right angles and is therefore equiangular.
3. The diagonals of a rectangle are congruent.

Theorem 37. **If the diagonals of a parallelogram are congruent, the parallelogram is a rectangle.**

In $\square ABCD$ (Fig. 4-51), if the diagonals, $\overline{AC}$ and $\overline{BD}$, are congruent, or if $\overline{AC} \cong \overline{BD}$, then $\square ABCD$ is a rectangle.

Methods of Proving a Quadrilateral a Rectangle

To prove that a quadrilateral is a rectangle, prove that any one of the following statements is true:

1. The quadrilateral is a parallelogram one of whose angles is a right angle.
2. The quadrilateral is equiangular.
3. The quadrilateral is a parallelogram whose diagonals are congruent.

MODEL PROBLEM

Given: $ABCD$ is a $\square$.

$\overline{DE} \perp \overleftrightarrow{AB}$.

$\overline{CF} \perp \overleftrightarrow{AB}$.

To prove: $DEFC$ is a rectangle.

Plan: To prove that *DEFC* is a rectangle, prove that *DEFC* is a
▱ which contains a right angle at *E*.

Proof: *Statements* | *Reasons*

Statements	Reasons
1. *ABCD* is a ▱.	1. Given.
2. $\overline{DC} \parallel \overline{AB}$.	2. A pair of opposite sides of a ▱ are parallel.
3. $\overline{DE} \perp \overleftrightarrow{AB}, \overline{CF} \perp \overleftrightarrow{AB}$.	3. Given.
4. $\overline{DE} \parallel \overline{CF}$.	4. Two lines perpendicular to the same line are parallel.
5. *DEFC* is a ▱.	5. If both pairs of opposite sides of a quadrilateral are parallel, the quadrilateral is a ▱.
6. ∠*DEB* is a right angle.	6. When perpendicular lines intersect, they form right angles.
7. *DEFC* is a rectangle.	7. If one angle of a ▱ is a right angle, the ▱ is a rectangle.

EXERCISES

Ex. 1

Ex. 2

Ex. 3

1. *Given:* *ABCD* is a rectangle, *M* is the midpoint of $\overline{AB}$.
   Prove: $\overline{DM} \cong \overline{CM}$.
2. *Given:* *ABCD* is a rectangle. (*a*) *Prove:* $\overline{AC} \cong \overline{BD}$. (*b*) *Prove:*
   △*AEB* is isosceles.
3. *Given:* *ABCD* is a rectangle, $\overline{BE} \cong \overline{CF}$.
   Prove: $\overline{DE} \cong \overline{AF}$.
4. In rectangle *ABCD*, diagonals $\overline{BD}$ and $\overline{AC}$ are drawn. Prove that
   ∠*DBA* ≅ ∠*CAB*.
5. In rectangle *ABCD*, the length of diagonal $\overline{AC}$ is represented by $6x - 2$
   and the length of diagonal $\overline{BD}$ is represented by $4x + 2$. (*a*) Find the
   value of x. (*b*) Find *AC* and *BD*.
6. In rectangle *ABCD*, diagonals $\overline{AC}$ and $\overline{BD}$ intersect in *E*. If $AE = 3x + y$,
   $BE = 4x - 2y$, and $CE = 20$, find x and y.

7. In (*a*), (*b*), and (*c*), the *given* is marked on the figure. Tell why each parallelogram *ABCD* is a rectangle.

(*a*)

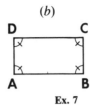

(*b*)

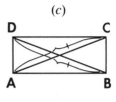

(*c*)

Ex. 7

8. In quadrilateral *ABCD*, $AB = 8$, $BC = 6$, $CD = 8$, $DA = 6$, $AC = 10$, and $BD = 10$. Prove that *ABCD* is a rectangle.

9. *a.* In $\square ABCD$, $AE = 7x - 1$, and $EC = 5x + 5$. Find *AC*.

b. If $DB = 10x + 10$, find *DB*.

c. What kind of parallelogram is *ABCD?* Why?

Ex. 9

10. *Prove:* If the diagonals of a parallelogram are congruent, the parallelogram is a rectangle.

11. *Prove:* If the consecutive angles of a quadrilateral are congruent, the quadrilateral is a rectangle.

12. *Prove:* If two opposite angles of a parallelogram are supplementary, the parallelogram is a rectangle.

13. In right triangle *ABC*, $\overline{AM}$ is the median to hypotenuse $\overline{BC}$. If $\overline{AM}$ is extended its own length through *M* to *D*, and $\overline{DC}$ and $\overline{DB}$ are drawn, prove that *ABDC* is a rectangle.

14. *ABCDEF* is a regular hexagon. If diagonals $\overline{AE}$ and $\overline{BD}$ are drawn, prove that *ABDE* is a rectangle.

15. *Prove:* In an isosceles triangle, the sum of the lengths of the perpendiculars drawn to the legs from any point on the base is equal to the length of an altitude drawn to one of the legs. [*Hint:* Draw $\overline{PF} \perp \overline{AG}.$]

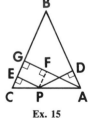

Ex. 15

16. *Prove:* If from any point inside an equilateral triangle perpendiculars are drawn to each of the sides of the triangle, the sum of the lengths of these perpendiculars is equal to the length of an altitude of the equilateral triangle. [*Hint:* Through the chosen point, draw a line segment parallel to one side of the equilateral triangle, the endpoints of the segment being on the other two sides of the triangle.]

17. Use an indirect method of proof to prove: If the diagonals of a parallelogram are not congruent, the parallelogram is not a rectangle.

11. The Rhombus

Definition. A *rhombus* is a parallelogram which has two congruent consecutive sides.

In □*ABCD* (Fig. 4–52), if the consecutive sides $\overline{AB}$ and $\overline{AD}$ are congruent. of if $\overline{AB} \cong \overline{AD}$, then □*ABCD* is a rhombus.

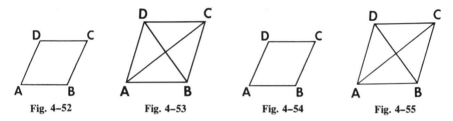

| Fig. 4–52 | Fig. 4–53 | Fig. 4–54 | Fig. 4–55 |

Since a rhombus is a special kind of parallelogram, a rhombus has all the properties of a parallelogram. In addition to these properties, a rhombus has some special properties.

Theorem 38. **All sides of a rhombus are congruent.**

In rhombus *ABCD* (Fig. 4–52), all sides, $\overline{AB}$, $\overline{BC}$, $\overline{CD}$, and $\overline{DA}$, are congruent, or $\overline{AB} \cong \overline{BC} \cong \overline{CD} \cong \overline{DA}$.

Theorem 39. **The diagonals of a rhombus are perpendicular to each other.**

In rhombus *ABCD* (Fig. 4–53), diagonals $\overline{AC}$ and $\overline{DB}$ are perpendicular to each other, or $\overline{AC} \perp \overline{DB}$.

Theorem 40. **The diagonals of a rhombus bisect its angles.**

In rhombus *ABCD* (Fig. 4–53), diagonal $\overline{AC}$ bisects ∠*DAB* and ∠*DCB*, and diagonal $\overline{BD}$ bisects ∠*ABC* and ∠*ADC*.

Properties of a Rhombus

1. A rhombus has all the properties of a parallelogram.
2. A rhombus is equilateral.
3. The diagonals of a rhombus are perpendicular to each other.
4. The diagonals of a rhombus bisect its angles.

Theorem 41. **If a quadrilateral is equilateral, it is a rhombus.**

In quadrilateral *ABCD* (Fig. 4–54), if all the sides, $\overline{AB}$, $\overline{BC}$, $\overline{CD}$, and $\overline{DA}$, are congruent, or if $\overline{AB} \cong \overline{BC} \cong \overline{CD} \cong \overline{DA}$, then quadrilateral *ABCD* is a rhombus.

Theorem 42. **If the diagonals of a parallelogram are perpendicular to each other, the parallelogram is a rhombus.**

In $\square ABCD$ (Fig. 4-55), if diagonals $\overline{AC}$ and $\overline{BD}$ are perpendicular to each other, or if $\overline{AC} \perp \overline{BD}$, then $ABCD$ is a rhombus.

Theorem 43. If a diagonal of a parallelogram bisects the angles whose vertices it joins, then the parallelogram is a rhombus.

In $\square ABCD$ (Fig. 4-55), if diagonal $\overline{AC}$ bisects $\angle A$ and $\angle C$, or if diagonal $\overline{BD}$ bisects $\angle B$ and $\angle D$, then $\square ABCD$ is a rhombus.

Methods of Proving a Quadrilateral a Rhombus

To prove that a quadrilateral is a rhombus, prove that any one of the following statements is true:

1. The quadrilateral is a parallelogram with two congruent consecutive sides.
2. The quadrilateral is equilateral.
3. The quadrilateral is a parallelogram whose diagonals are perpendicular to each other.
4. The quadrilateral is a parallelogram, and a diagonal bisects the angles whose vertices it joins.

MODEL PROBLEM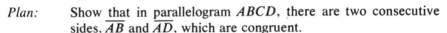

Given: $ABCD$ is a parallelogram.
$AB = 2x + 1$.
$DC = 3x - 11$.
$AD = x + 13$.

To show: $ABCD$ is a rhombus.

Plan: Show that in parallelogram $ABCD$, there are two consecutive sides, $\overline{AB}$ and $\overline{AD}$, which are congruent.

Solution: Since the opposite sides of a $\square$ are congruent, they are also equal in length. Hence,

1. $DC = AB$

2. $3x - 11 = 2x + 1$

3. $3x - 2x = 1 + 11$

4. $x = 12$

5. $AB = 2x + 1 = 2(12) + 1 = 25.$

6. $AD = x + 13 = 12 + 13 = 25.$

7. Therefore, $AB = AD$ and $\overline{AB} \cong \overline{AD}$.

8. Therefore, $ABCD$ is a rhombus, since it is a parallelogram in which two consecutive sides are congruent.

EXERCISES

1. Prove that when the diagonals of a rhombus intersect, four congruent triangles are formed.

2. In rhombus $ABCD$, diagonal $\overline{BD} \cong$ side $\overline{AB}$. (*a*) Prove that $\triangle ADB$ is equilateral. (*b*) Find the measure of each angle of the rhombus.

3. *Prove:* In rhombus $ABCD$, diagonal $\overline{AC}$ is the perpendicular bisector of diagonal $\overline{BD}$.

4. *Prove:* In rhombus $ABCD$, diagonal $\overline{AC}$ bisects $\angle A$ and $\angle C$.

5. *Given:* $ABCD$ is a rhombus.
   F is the midpoint of $\overline{DE}$.
   G is the midpoint of $\overline{BE}$.
   H is a point on $\overline{AE}$.
   Prove: $\triangle GHF$ is an isosceles triangle.

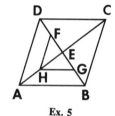

Ex. 5

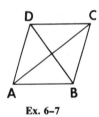

Ex. 6–7

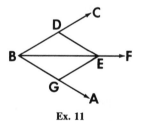

Ex. 11

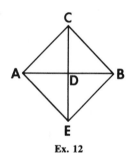

Ex. 12

6. *a.* In $\square ABCD$, if $m\angle ACD = 4x - 2$, $m\angle CAB = 3x + 6$, find $m\angle ACD$ and $m\angle CAB$.
   b. In $\square ABCD$, if $m\angle CAD = 2x + 14$, find $m\angle CAD$.
   c. What type of parallelogram is $ABCD$?

7. In parallelogram $ABCD$, $AB = x + 4$, $DC = 3x - 36$, and $BC = 2x - 16$. Show that $ABCD$ is a rhombus.

8. *Prove:* If a quadrilateral is equilateral, it is a rhombus.

9. *Prove:* If the diagonals of a parallelogram are perpendicular to each other, the parallelogram is a rhombus.

10. *Prove:* If a diagonal of a parallelogram bisects the angles whose vertices it joins, then the parallelogram is a rhombus.

11. *Given:* $\overrightarrow{BF}$ bisects $\angle CBA$, $\overline{DE} \parallel \overrightarrow{BA}$, $\overline{GE} \parallel \overrightarrow{BC}$.
    Prove: $GEDB$ is a rhombus.

12. *Prove:* If $\overline{CD}$, the bisector of vertex angle C in isosceles triangle ACB, is extended its own length to E, and $\overline{AE}$ and $\overline{BE}$ are drawn, then quadrilateral $ACBE$ is a rhombus.

13. Use an indirect method of proof to prove: If a diagonal of a parallelogram does not bisect the angles through whose vertices the diagonal is drawn, the parallelogram is not a rhombus.

12. The Square

Definition. **A *square* is a rectangle which has two congruent consecutive sides.**

In rectangle $ABCD$ (Fig. 4–56), if consecutive sides $\overline{AB}$ and $\overline{AD}$ are congruent, or if $\overline{AB} \cong \overline{AD}$, then rectangle $ABCD$ is a square.

Fig. 4–56

Theorem 44. **A square is an equilateral quadrilateral.**

In square $ABCD$ (Fig. 4–56), sides $\overline{AB}$, $\overline{BC}$, $\overline{CD}$, and $\overline{DA}$ are congruent, or $\overline{AB} \cong \overline{BC} \cong \overline{CD} \cong \overline{DA}$.

Corollary T44–1. **A square is a rhombus.**

Any square, for example $ABCD$ (Fig. 4–56), is a rhombus.

Since a square is a special kind of rectangle and also a special kind of rhombus, a square has all the properties of a rectangle and all the properties of a rhombus.

Properties of a Square

1. A square has all the properties of a rectangle.
2. A square has all the properties of a rhombus.

Theorem 45. **If one of the angles of a rhombus is a right angle, the rhombus is a square.**

In rhombus $ABCD$ (Fig. 4–56), if one angle, $\angle A$, is a right angle, then rhombus $ABCD$ is a square.

Methods of Proving a Quadrilateral a Square

To prove that a quadrilateral is a square, prove that either one of the following statements is true:

1. The quadrilateral is a rectangle with two consecutive sides congruent.
2. The quadrilateral is a rhombus one of whose angles is a right angle.

MODEL PROBLEM

Given: *ABC* is an isosceles right triangle with ∠*ABC* a
            right angle and $\overline{AB} \cong \overline{BC}$.
            $\overline{BD}$, which bisects $\overline{CA}$, is extended to *E*, so that
            $\overline{BD} \cong \overline{DE}$.

To prove: *BAEC* is a square.

Plan: To prove that *BAEC* is a square, show that *BAEC*
            is a rectangle which has two consecutive sides, $\overline{AB}$
            and $\overline{BC}$, congruent.

Proof: *Statements*	*Reasons*
1. $\overline{BD} \cong \overline{DE}$ and $\overline{AD} \cong \overline{DC}$.	1. Given.
2. *BAEC* is a ▱.	2. If the diagonals of a quadrilateral bisect each other, the quadrilateral is a parallelogram.
3. ∠*ABC* is a right angle.	3. Given.
4. *BAEC* is a rectangle.	4. A parallelogram, one of whose angles is a right angle, is a rectangle.
5. $\overline{AB} \cong \overline{BC}$.	5. Given.
6. *BAEC* is a square.	6. If a rectangle has two congruent consecutive sides, the rectangle is a square.

EXERCISES

1. *Prove:* A square is an equilateral quadrilateral.

2. *Prove:* The diagonals of a square are perpendicular to each other.

3. In square *ABCD*, diagonal $\overline{AC}$ is drawn. Find *m*∠*ACB* and *m*∠*DCA*.

4. *Prove:* The diagonals of a square divide the square into four congruent isosceles triangles.

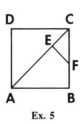

Ex. 5

Ex. 6

5. *Given:* $ABCD$ is a square.
   $\overline{AE} \cong \overline{AB}$.
   $\overline{FE} \perp \overline{AC}$.
   Prove: a. $\overline{CE} \cong \overline{EF}$.
   b. $\overline{FE} \cong \overline{FB}$.

6. *Given:* $WXYZ$ is a square.
   $\overline{AW} \cong \overline{BX} \cong \overline{CY} \cong \overline{DZ}$.
   $\overleftrightarrow{BW}, \overleftrightarrow{CX}, \overleftrightarrow{DY}$, and $\overleftrightarrow{AZ}$.
   Prove: $ABCD$ is a square.

7. In isosceles right triangle ABC, $\angle CAB$ is a right angle and $\overline{BA} \cong \overline{AC}$. Median $\overline{AM}$ is extended its own length through M to D. $\overline{DC}$ and $\overline{DB}$ are drawn. Prove that $ABDC$ is a square.

8. *Prove:* If the midpoints of the sides of a square are joined in order, another square is formed.

9. In isosceles right triangle ABC, $\overline{AB}$ and $\overline{AC}$ are the congruent sides. If the midpoints of $\overline{AC}, \overline{CB}$, and $\overline{BA}$ are respectively D, E, and F, prove that $DEFA$ is a square.

13. The Trapezoid

Definition. **A *trapezoid* is a quadrilateral that has two and only two sides parallel.**

In quadrilateral $ABCD$ (Fig. 4–57), if $\overline{AB} \parallel \overline{DC}$ and $\overline{AD}$ is not $\parallel \overline{BC}$, then $ABCD$ is a trapezoid. The parallel sides $\overline{AB}$ and $\overline{DC}$ are called the *bases* of the trapezoid; the nonparallel sides $\overline{AD}$ and $\overline{BC}$, the *legs* of the trapezoid.

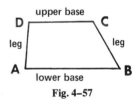

Fig. 4–57

The Isosceles Trapezoid and Its Properties

Definition. **An *isosceles trapezoid* is a trapezoid in which the nonparallel sides are congruent.**

In trapezoid $QRST$ (Fig. 4–58), if $\overline{QT} \cong \overline{RS}$, then trapezoid $QRST$ is isosceles. The angles at the ends of a base are called *base angles*. Hence, $\angle Q$ and $\angle R$, which are at the ends of base $\overline{QR}$, are base angles.

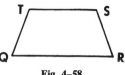

Fig. 4–58

Theorem 46. **The base angles of an isosceles trapezoid are congruent.**

In isosceles trapezoid $QRST$ (Fig. 4–58), $\angle Q \cong \angle R$.

Theorem 47. **The diagonals of an isosceles trapezoid are congruent.**

In isosceles trapezoid $PQRS$ (Fig. 4–59), the diagonals $\overline{PR}$ and $\overline{QS}$ are congruent, or $\overline{PR} \cong \overline{QS}$.

Fig. 4–59

Method of Proving a Quadrilateral an Isosceles Trapezoid

To prove that a quadrilateral is an isosceles trapezoid, prove that the quadrilateral has only two parallel sides, and that the nonparallel sides are congruent.

MODEL PROBLEM ~~~~~~~~~~~~~~~~~~~~

Given: $ABCD$ is a $\square$.
            $\overleftrightarrow{AE}$ is a line.
            $\angle CBE \cong \angle CEB$.

To prove: $AECD$ is an isosceles trapezoid.

Plan: To prove that $AECD$ is an isosceles trapezoid, prove that $\overline{DC} \parallel \overline{AE}$ and $\overline{DA} \cong \overline{CE}$. To prove that $\overline{DA} \cong \overline{CE}$, prove that $\overline{DA}$ and $\overline{CE}$ are each congruent to $\overline{CB}$.

Proof: *Statements*	*Reasons*
1. $ABCD$ is a $\square$.	1. Given.
2. $\overline{DC} \parallel \overline{AB}$, or $\overline{DC} \parallel \overline{AE}$.	2. The opposite sides of a parallelogram are parallel.
3. $AECD$ is a trapezoid.	3. A trapezoid is a quadrilateral that has two and only two sides parallel.

Proof: *Statements*	*Reasons*
4. $\overline{DA} \cong \overline{CB}$.	4. A pair of opposite sides of a parallelogram are congruent.
5. $\angle CBE \cong \angle CEB$.	5. Given.
6. $\overline{CB} \cong \overline{CE}$.	6. If two angles of a triangle are congruent, the sides opposite those angles are congruent.
7. $\overline{DA} \cong \overline{CE}$.	7. Transitive property of congruence.
8. $AECD$ is an isosceles trapezoid.	8. An isosceles trapezoid is a trapezoid whose nonparallel sides are congruent.

EXERCISES

Ex. 1

Ex. 2

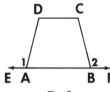
Ex. 5

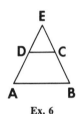
Ex. 6

1. *Given:* $ABCD$ is an isosceles trapezoid.
   $\overline{DC} \parallel \overline{AB}$.
   $\overline{DE} \perp \overline{AB}$.
   $\overline{CF} \perp \overline{AB}$.
   Prove: $\triangle DEA \cong \triangle CFB$.

2. *Given:* $ABCD$ is a trapezoid.
   $\overline{DC} \parallel \overline{AB}$.
   $\overline{CE} \parallel \overline{DA}$.
   $\angle DCE \cong \angle CBE$.
   Prove: a. $\angle CBA \cong \angle BAD$.
   b. $\overline{CB} \cong \overline{DA}$.

3. *Prove:* The diagonals of an isosceles trapezoid are congruent.

4. *Prove:* The base angles of an isosceles trapezoid are congruent.

5. *Given:* $ABCD$ is an isosceles trapezoid.
   $\overline{DC} \parallel \overline{AB}$.
   $\overleftrightarrow{EF}$ is a line.
   Prove: $\angle 1 \cong \angle 2$.

6. *Given:* $ABCD$ is an isosceles trapezoid.
   $\overline{AB} \parallel \overline{CD}$.
   $\overline{AD}$ and $\overline{BC}$ are extended until they intersect at E.
   Prove: $\triangle ABE$ and DCE are isosceles triangles.

7. In trapezoid $ABCD$, $\overline{AB}$ is the lower base. The bisector of angle A intersects $\overline{DC}$ at P. Prove that triangle ADP is isosceles.

8. *Prove:* If the diagonals of a trapezoid are congruent, the trapezoid is isosceles.

9. *Prove:* If the base angles of a trapezoid are congruent, the trapezoid is isosceles.

10. *Prove:* A line which intersects two sides of an isosceles triangle and is parallel to the base of the triangle cuts off an isosceles trapezoid.

11. *Given:* $ABCD$ is a $\square$.
    $\overleftrightarrow{AE}$ is a line.
    $\angle ADC$ is supplementary to $\angle CEB$.
    Prove: $AECD$ is an isosceles trapezoid.

12. Use an indirect method of proof to prove: The diagonals of a trapezoid cannot bisect each other.

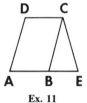

Ex. 11

14. Transversals to Three or More Parallel Lines and Medians

Theorem 48. **If three or more parallel lines intercept congruent segments on one transversal, then they intercept congruent segments on any transversal.**

In Fig. 4–60, if $\overleftrightarrow{AB} \parallel \overleftrightarrow{CD} \parallel \overleftrightarrow{EF}$, and $\overline{AC} \cong \overline{CE}$, then $\overline{BD} \cong \overline{DF}$.

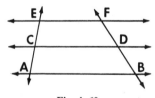

Fig. 4–60

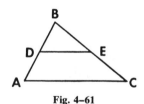

Fig. 4–61

Theorem 49. **If a line is parallel to one side of a triangle and bisects a second side, then it bisects the third side also.**

In Fig. 4–61, if $\overleftrightarrow{DE} \parallel \overline{AC}$, and $\overline{BD} \cong \overline{DA}$, then $\overline{BE} \cong \overline{EC}$.

Theorem 50. **If a line segment joins the midpoints of two sides of a triangle, the segment is parallel to the third side and its length is one-half the length of the third side.**

In Fig. 4–61, if $\overline{BD} \cong \overline{DA}$ and $\overline{BE} \cong \overline{EC}$, then $\overline{DE} \parallel \overline{AC}$ and $DE = \frac{1}{2}AC$, or $AC = 2DE$.

The Median of a Trapezoid

Definition. The *median of a trapezoid* is the line segment which joins the midpoints of the nonparallel sides.

In trapezoid $ABCD$ (Fig. 4–62), if F is the midpoint of $\overline{AD}$ and E is the midpoint of $\overline{BC}$, then $\overline{FE}$ is the median of the trapezoid.

Theorem 51. The median of a trapezoid is parallel to the bases and its length is equal to one-half the sum of the lengths of the bases.

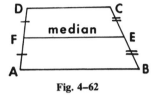

Fig. 4–62

In trapezoid $ABCD$ (Fig. 4–62), if $\overline{AF} \cong \overline{FD}$ and $\overline{BE} \cong \overline{EC}$, then median $\overline{FE} \parallel \overline{AB}$, $\overline{FE} \parallel \overline{DC}$, and $FE = \frac{1}{2}(AB + DC)$, or $2FE = AB + DC$.

Concurrency of Medians of a Triangle

Definition. Three or more lines (or rays or segments) are *concurrent* if there is one point common to all of the lines (or rays or segments).

In Fig. 4–63, lines $\overleftrightarrow{AB}$, $\overleftrightarrow{CD}$, and $\overleftrightarrow{EF}$ are concurrent at P.

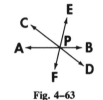

Fig. 4–63

Theorem 52. The medians of a triangle are concurrent at a point whose distance from any vertex is two-thirds the distance from that vertex to the midpoint of the opposite side.

In triangle ABC (Fig. 4–64), if $\overline{AE}$, $\overline{BF}$, and $\overline{CD}$ are medians, then $AG = \frac{2}{3}AE$, $BG = \frac{2}{3}BF$, and $CG = \frac{2}{3}CD$.

Definition. The point of concurrency of the medians of a triangle is called the *centroid* of the triangle.

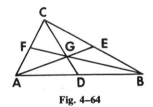

Fig. 4–64

In Fig. 4–64, if $\overline{AE}$, $\overline{BF}$, and $\overline{CD}$ are medians in triangle ABC, then G is the centroid of triangle ABC. If $\triangle ABC$ is a triangular piece of a sheet of metal of uniform thickness, this triangular sheet will balance in a horizontal position with only one support, such as the tip of a pencil, at G. For this reason, the centroid of such a triangular sheet is called its *center of gravity.*

Theorem 53. **The length of the median to the hypotenuse of a right triangle is equal to one-half the length of the hypotenuse.**

In right triangle ABC (Fig. 4–65), if $\overline{CM}$ is the median to hypotenuse $\overline{AB}$, then $CM = \frac{1}{2}AB$, or $AB = 2CM$.

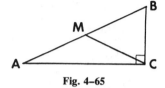

Fig. 4–65

MODEL PROBLEMS

1. In triangle ABC, D is the midpoint of $\overline{AB}$ and E is the midpoint of $\overline{AC}$. If $BC = 7x + 1$ and $DE = 4x - 2$, find x, DE, and BC.

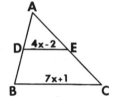

   Solution: Since D and E are the midpoints of two sides of triangle ABC,

   1. $BC = 2DE$

   2. $7x + 1 = 2(4x - 2)$

   3. $7x + 1 = 8x - 4$

   4. $4 + 1 = 8x - 7x$

   5. $5 = x$

   6. $DE = 4x - 2 = 20 - 2 = 18.$

   7. $BC = 7x + 1 = 35 + 1 = 36.$

   Answer: $x = 5$, $DE = 18$, $BC = 36$.

2. In triangle ABC, medians $\overline{AD}$, $\overline{BE}$, and $\overline{CF}$ intersect at P. If $AD = 24$ in., find the length of $\overline{AP}$.

   Solution: Since the medians of a triangle are concurrent at a point whose distance from any vertex is two-thirds the distance from that vertex to the midpoint of the opposite side,

   $$AP = \tfrac{2}{3}AD = \tfrac{2}{3}(24) = 16$$

   Answer: $AP = 16$ in.

3. The length of the median drawn to the hypotenuse of a right triangle is 12 inches. Find the length of the hypotenuse.

Solution: Since the length of the median drawn to the hypotenuse of a right triangle is equal to one-half of the length of the hypotenuse,

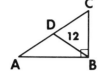

$$BD = \tfrac{1}{2}AC, \quad \text{or} \quad AC = 2BD = 2(12) = 24$$

Answer: $AC = 24$ in.

EXERCISES

1. Find the length of a line segment which joins the midpoints of two sides of a triangle if the length of the third side is:
   a. 10   *b.* 12   *c.* 24   *d.* 50   *e.* 9   *f.* 15

2. Find the length of the third side of a triangle if the length of the line segment which joins the midpoints of the other two sides is:
   a. 4   *b.* 3   *c.* 6   *d.* 15   *e.* 8.5   *f.* 6.25

3. D is the midpoint of side $\overline{AB}$ of triangle ABC, and a line through D parallel to $\overline{AC}$ intersects $\overline{BC}$ in E. If $AC = 9$ inches, then $DE = $ _____ inches.

4. D is the midpoint of side $\overline{AB}$ of triangle ABC, and a line through D parallel to $\overline{BC}$ intersects $\overline{AC}$ at E. If $DE = 12$, find BC.

5. The line joining the midpoints of two consecutive sides of a rectangle is 20. Find the length of a diagonal of the rectangle.

6. In triangle ABC, a line joins D and E, the midpoints of $\overline{AB}$ and $\overline{CB}$ respectively. If $m\angle A = 40$, find $m\angle BDE$.

7. Find the length of the line segment joining the midpoints of the non-parallel sides of a trapezoid if the lengths of the bases are:
   a. 6 and 10   *b.* 20 and 8   *c.* 9 and 13   *d.* 8 and 5   *e.* 23 and 16

8. In triangle ABC, the medians $\overline{AD}$, $\overline{BE}$, and $\overline{CF}$ are concurrent at point P. If $AP = 8$, find the length of median $\overline{AD}$.

9. In triangle RST, the medians $\overline{SL}$, $\overline{RN}$, and $\overline{TM}$ are concurrent at point P. If $SP = 10$, find PL.

10. Find the length of the median to the hypotenuse of a right triangle the length of whose hypotenuse is:
    a. 10   *b.* 20   *c.* 24   *d.* 5   *e.* 13   *f.* 25

11. Find the length of the hypotenuse of a right triangle if the length of the median to the hypotenuse is:
    a. 5   *b.* 8   *c.* 3   *d.* 10   *e.* 12   *f.* 13

12. If in right isosceles triangle ABC the bisector of the right angle C is 6 inches in length, then the hypotenuse $\overline{AB}$ is _____ inches in length.

13. If the lengths of the sides of triangle ABC are represented by a, b, and c, represent the perimeter of the triangle whose vertices are the midpoints of the sides of triangle ABC.

14. In equilateral triangle ABC, $AB = 14$. Find the perimeter of the triangle which joins the midpoints of the sides of triangle ABC.

15. Points D, E, and F are the midpoints of the sides of equilateral triangle RST. If the perimeter of triangle DEF is 24, find the length of each side of triangle RST.

16. In equilateral triangle ABC, the length of side $\overline{AB}$ is represented by s. Represent the perimeter of the triangle which joins the midpoints of the sides of triangle ABC.

17. In triangle ABC, D is the midpoint of AB and E is the midpoint of $\overline{AC}$. If $DE = 3y - 2$ and $BC = 4y + 4$, find y, DE, and BC.

18. In triangle ABC, D is the midpoint of $\overline{AB}$. A line through D, drawn parallel to $\overline{BC}$, intersects $\overline{AC}$ in E. If $AE = 4x + 2$ and $EC = 8x - 10$, find x, AE, EC, and AC.

19. In right triangle RST, median $\overline{TM}$ is drawn to hypotenuse $\overline{RS}$. If $RS = 4x + 10$ and $TM = 3x - 5$, find RS and TM.

20. In right triangle ABC, $\overline{BD}$ is the median to hypotenuse $\overline{AC}$. If $BD = x + 3$, $AD = 6y + 1$, and $DC = x + y + 1$, find x, y, BD, and AC.

21. In triangle ABC, medians $\overline{BE}$ and $\overline{AD}$ are concurrent at P. If $AP = 8x - 12$ and $PD = 2x$, find x, PD, AP, and AD.

22. In triangle ABC, medians $\overline{BD}$ and $\overline{AE}$ intersect at P. If $AP = 2x + y$, $PE = 3x - 2$, $BP = y + 2$, and $PD = x + 1$, find x, y, BD, and AE.

23. *Prove:* The median of a trapezoid bisects each diagonal of the trapezoid.

24. In triangle RST, D is the midpoint of $\overline{RS}$, E is the midpoint of $\overline{ST}$, and F is the midpoint of $\overline{RT}$. If $\overline{DF}$ and $\overline{FE}$ are drawn, prove that $SDFE$ is a parallelogram.

25. In right triangle ABC, $m\angle A = 90$. The midpoints of sides $\overline{AB}$, $\overline{BC}$, and $\overline{CA}$ are respectively R, S, and T. Prove that $ARST$ is a rectangle.

26. *Prove:* If the midpoint of the base of an isosceles triangle is joined to the midpoints of the congruent sides, a rhombus is formed.

27. *Prove:* The lines joining the midpoints of the sides of an isosceles triangle form an isosceles triangle.

28. *Prove:* The lines which join the consecutive midpoints of the sides of a rectangle form a rhombus.

15. More About Concurrent Lines in a Triangle

We have learned that the medians of a triangle are concurrent in a point whose distance from any vertex is two-thirds the distance from that vertex to the midpoint of the opposite side. Now we will learn about the concurrency of three additional sets of lines that are associated with a triangle.

Concurrency of the Perpendicular Bisectors of the Sides of a Triangle

Theorem 54. **The perpendicular bisectors of the sides of a triangle are concurrent at a point that is equidistant from the vertices of the triangle.**

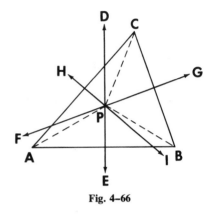

In triangle ABC (Fig. 4–66), $\overleftrightarrow{DE}$, the $\perp$ bisector of $\overline{AB}$, $\overleftrightarrow{FG}$, the $\perp$ bisector of $\overline{BC}$, and $\overleftrightarrow{HI}$, the $\perp$ bisector of $\overline{AC}$, are concurrent in point P such that $PA = PB = PC$.

Later it can be proved that a circle can be drawn through the three vertices of any triangle, or through any three points that are not collinear. The circle which passes through the three vertices of a triangle is called the *circumscribed circle* of the triangle. The center of this circle, which is the point at which the perpendicular bisectors of the sides

Fig. 4–66

of the triangle are concurrent, is called the *circumcenter* of the triangle. See constructions 5 and 21 on pages 619 and 629.

Concurrency of the Bisectors of the Angles of a Triangle

Theorem 55. **The bisectors of the angles of a triangle are concurrent at a point that is equidistant from the sides of the triangle.**

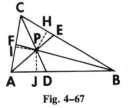

In triangle ABC (Fig. 4–67), $\overline{AE}$, the bisector of $\angle A$, $\overline{BF}$, the bisector of $\angle B$, and $\overline{CD}$, the bisector of $\angle C$, are concurrent at point P.

If $\overline{PJ} \perp \overline{AB}$, $\overline{PH} \perp \overline{BC}$, and $\overline{PI} \perp \overline{AC}$, then $PJ = PH = PI$.

Later it can be proved that a circle can be drawn that "touches" all three sides of a triangle. This circle is called the *inscribed circle* of the triangle. The

Fig. 4–67

center of this circle, which is the point at which the bisectors of the angles of the triangle are concurrent, is called the *incenter* of the triangle. See construction 22 on page 630.

Concurrency of the Altitudes of a Triangle

Theorem 56. The altitudes, or the lines containing the altitudes, of a triangle are concurrent.

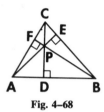

Fig. 4–68

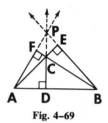

Fig. 4–69

In triangle *ABC* (Fig. 4–68), the altitudes of the triangle, $\overline{CD}$, $\overline{AE}$, and $\overline{BF}$, are concurrent at point *P*. In triangle *ABC* (Fig. 4–69), the altitudes of the triangle, $\overline{CD}$, $\overline{AE}$, and $\overline{BF}$, are not concurrent. However, the lines which contain the altitudes are concurrent at point *P*.

The point at which the altitudes of a triangle, or the lines containing the altitudes of a triangle, are concurrent is called the *orthocenter* of the triangle.

EXERCISES

In 1–4, after performing several experiments, state whether the indicated center of the triangle appears to be on a side of the triangle, in the interior of the triangle, or in the exterior of the triangle.

1. The centroid of   (*a*) an acute triangle   (*b*) a right triangle   (*c*) an obtuse triangle.

2. The circumcenter of   (*a*) an acute triangle   (*b*) a right triangle   (*c*) an obtuse triangle.

3. The incenter of   (*a*) an acute triangle   (*b*) a right triangle   (*c*) an obtuse triangle.

4. The orthocenter of   (*a*) an acute triangle   (*b*) a right triangle   (*c*) an obtuse triangle.

5. From the four points—the centroid, the circumcenter, the incenter, and the orthocenter of a triangle—select those points which appear to be in the interior region of the triangle in all triangles.

6. If two altitudes of a given triangle fall outside the triangle, the triangle is   (*a*) right   (*b*) acute   (*c*) obtuse.

7. If the point at which the perpendicular bisectors of the sides of a triangle are concurrent is outside the triangle, the triangle is   (*a*) acute   (*b*) right   (*c*) obtuse.

8. The altitudes of a right triangle intersect   (*a*) outside the triangle   (*b*) inside the triangle   (*c*) at one of the vertices of the triangle.
9. The bisectors of angle *A* and angle *B* of triangle *ABC* intersect in point *P*. The bisector of angle *C*   (*a*) always passes through *P*   (*b*) sometimes passes through *P*   (*c*) never passes through *P*.

16. Completion Exercises

Write a word or expression that, when inserted in the blank, will make the resulting statement true.

1. If two parallel lines are cut by a transversal, the bisectors of a pair of corresponding angles are _____ to each other.
2. If two lines are cut by a transversal, making two alternate interior angles congruent, the sum of the measures of two interior angles on the same side of the transversal is _____ degrees.
3. If two parallel lines are cut by a transversal, the bisectors of a pair of interior angles on the same side of the transversal are _____ to each other.
4. If a line is parallel to one of two parallel lines, it is _____ to the other.
5. If a line is perpendicular to one of two parallel lines, it is _____ to the other.
6. If a line is parallel to one of two perpendicular lines, it is _____ to the other.
7. In an isosceles right triangle, the measure of each acute angle is _____.
8. The acute angles of a right triangle are _____.
9. If the diagonals of a parallelogram are congruent, the parallelogram must be a(an) _____.
10. In a parallelogram, any two consecutive angles are _____.
11. If the diagonals of a parallelogram are unequal in length and bisect the angles through which they are drawn, then the figure must be a(an) _____.
12. If the midpoints of two consecutive sides of a rhombus are joined, the triangle formed is _____.
13. If one side of a rhombus is congruent to the shorter diagonal, then one of the acute angles of the rhombus contains _____ degrees.
14. A line which joins the midpoints of two sides of a triangle is _____ to the third side.
15. In an isosceles trapezoid, the base angles are _____.
16. If two parallel lines are cut by a transversal, the two interior angles on the same side of the transversal are _____.

17. If line a is perpendicular to line b and line b is parallel to line c, then line a is ———— to line c.

18. The median of a trapezoid is ———— to the bases of the trapezoid.

19. Each angle of an equilateral triangle contains ————.

20. If a pair of opposite angles of a parallelogram are supplementary, the parallelogram is a(an) ————.

17. True-False Exercises

If the statement is always true, write *true;* if the statement is not always true, write *false.*

1. When two straight lines are cut by a transversal, if the interior angles on the same side of the transversal contain $x°$ and $(180 - x)°$, the two lines are parallel.

2. The exterior angles at the base of an isosceles triangle are acute.

3. One of the exterior angles of a right triangle may be an acute angle.

4. A parallelogram is defined as a polygon whose opposite sides are parallel.

5. If a line is parallel to one of two perpendicular lines, it is parallel to the other also.

6. If the diagonals of a parallelogram are congruent and perpendicular to each other, the parallelogram is always a square.

7. If one angle of a parallelogram is a right angle, all the other angles of the parallelogram are also right angles.

8. If a quadrilateral is equilateral, the quadrilateral is a square.

9. A rhombus is equiangular.

10. A diagonal divides a parallelogram into two congruent triangles.

11. The median to the hypotenuse of a right triangle divides the right triangle into two isosceles triangles.

12. The diagonals of a trapezoid are congruent.

13. The diagonals of a parallelogram divide it into four congruent triangles.

14. If the consecutive midpoints of the sides of a rhombus are joined, the figure thus formed is a rectangle.

15. The diagonals of a rhombus are congruent.

16. The diagonals of an isosceles trapezoid bisect each other.

17. A diagonal of an isosceles trapezoid divides the trapezoid into two congruent triangles.

18. A trapezoid has at least one acute angle.

19. If a line segment which intersects two sides of a triangle is equal in length to one-half the length of the third side, the segment is parallel to the third side.

20. If the midpoint of the hypotenuse of a right triangle is joined to each of the midpoints of the two legs of the right triangle, a rectangle is formed.

21. If a rhombus is defined as a parallelogram in which two consecutive sides are congruent, then it follows from this definition that a square is a rhombus.

22. In parallelogram $ABCD$, if angle A is a right angle, then diagonal $\overline{AC}$ is congruent to diagonal $\overline{BD}$.

23. If the diagonals of a quadrilateral are congruent, the quadrilateral is a rectangle.

18. "Always, Sometimes, Never" Exercises

If the blank space in each of the following exercises is replaced by the word *always, sometimes,* or *never,* the resulting statement will be true. Select the word which will correctly complete each statement.

1. If two parallel lines are cut by a transversal, the interior angles on the same side of the transversal are _____ congruent.

2. When two parallel lines are cut by a transversal which is not perpendicular to them, all the acute angles formed are _____ congruent.

3. If the sum of the measures of two angles of a triangle is equal to the measure of the third angle, then two sides of the triangle are _____ perpendicular to each other.

4. An exterior angle of a right triangle is _____ an acute angle.

5. All three exterior angles of a triangle are _____ acute.

6. The opposite angles of a quadrilateral are _____ supplementary.

7. The diagonals of a parallelogram are _____ congruent.

8. The diagonals of a quadrilateral _____ divide it into four congruent triangles.

9. The diagonals of a rectangle are _____ congruent.

10. A parallelogram whose diagonals are congruent and are perpendicular to each other is _____ a square.

11. If the diagonals of a quadrilateral are perpendicular to each other, the quadrilateral is _____ a parallelogram.

12. If the diagonals of a quadrilateral bisect each other, the quadrilateral is _____ a rhombus.

13. A quadrilateral whose angles are congruent is _____ a rectangle.

14. If two sides of a quadrilateral are parallel and the other two sides are congruent, then the quadrilateral is _____ a parallelogram.

15. The diagonals of a trapezoid are _____ congruent.
16. The sum of the measures of the interior angles of a quadrilateral is _____ equal to the sum of the measures of the exterior angles.
17. If the number of sides of a polygon is increased by 2, the sum of the measures of the exterior angles of this polygon, made by extending each of its sides in succession, _____ remains the same.
18. If two lines are cut by a transversal, then the bisectors of a pair of interior angles on the same side of the transversal are _____ perpendicular to each other.
19. The sum of the measures of the interior angles of a polygon is _____ equal to the sum of the measures of the exterior angles of the polygon.
20. The measure of an exterior angle of a regular polygon _____ equals 70.
21. If the opposite sides of a polygon which has four sides are parallel, the polygon is _____ a parallelogram.
22. If the diagonals of a quadrilateral are congruent, the quadrilateral is _____ a rectangle.
23. The bisectors of two opposite angles of a parallelogram _____ coincide.
24. The diagonals of a rectangle _____ bisect each other.
25. If the diagonals of a parallelogram are unequal in length and are perpendicular to each other, the parallelogram is _____ a square.

19. Multiple-Choice Exercises

Write the letter preceding the word or expression that best completes the statement.

1. If two parallel lines are cut by a transversal, the corresponding angles are always (*a*) supplementary (*b*) congruent (*c*) acute.
2. Which of the following statements is false? (*a*) A parallelogram is a quadrilateral. (*b*) A rectangle is a square. (*c*) A rectangle is a parallelogram.
3. If the diagonals of a quadrilateral bisect each other, the quadrilateral is always (*a*) a rhombus (*b*) a rectangle (*c*) a parallelogram.
4. If in quadrilateral $ABCD$, $\overline{AB} \cong \overline{BC}$ and $\overline{CD} \cong \overline{DA}$, then diagonals $\overline{AC}$ and $\overline{BD}$ (*a*) bisect each other (*b*) are perpendicular to each other (*c*) are congruent.
5. All quadrilaterals whose diagonals are congruent and bisect each other are (*a*) rectangles (*b*) squares (*c*) rhombuses.
6. The diagonals of a rectangle are always (*a*) congruent to each other (*b*) perpendicular to each other (*c*) bisectors of the angles through which they pass.

7. Two consecutive angles of a parallelogram are always (*a*) congruent (*b*) complementary (*c*) supplementary.

8. The diagonals of a rectangle are always (*a*) congruent and perpendicular to each other (*b*) perpendicular to each other and bisect each other (*c*) congruent and bisect each other.

9. The sum of the measures of the exterior angles of a polygon of *n* sides is (*a*) *n* straight angles (*b*) 2 straight angles (*c*) $(n - 2)$ straight angles.

10. By definition, a parallelogram is a quadrilateral (*a*) whose diagonals bisect each other (*b*) both pairs of whose opposite sides are congruent (*c*) both pairs of whose opposite sides are parallel.

11. Two opposite angles of a parallelogram are always (*a*) congruent (*b*) supplementary (*c*) complementary.

12. The diagonals of an isosceles trapezoid always (*a*) are perpendicular to each other (*b*) are congruent (*c*) bisect each other.

13. If one angle of a trapezoid is a right angle, the greatest number of additional right angles that the trapezoid may have is (*a*) 1 (*b*) 2 (*c*) 3.

14. If one angle of a parallelogram is a right angle, the parallelogram is (*a*) a square (*b*) a rhombus (*c*) a rectangle.

15. The sum of the measures of the interior angles of a polygon of *n* sides is (*a*) *n* straight angles (*b*) 2 straight angles (*c*) $(n - 2)$ straight angles.

16. The sum of the measures of the exterior angles of a quadrilateral made by extending each of its sides in order is (*a*) equal to (*b*) less than (*c*) greater than the sum of the measures of its interior angles.

17. An exterior angle at the base of an isosceles triangle is always (*a*) an acute angle (*b*) an obtuse angle (*c*) a right angle.

18. The midpoint of the hypotenuse of a right triangle is the point of intersection of (*a*) the three medians (*b*) the bisectors of the three angles (*c*) the perpendicular bisectors of the three sides.

19. If the lengths of the bases of a trapezoid are represented by b and b', then the length of the median of the trapezoid, represented in terms of b and b', is (*a*) $\frac{1}{2}bb'$ (*b*) $\frac{1}{2}(b + b')$ (*c*) $2(b + b')$.

20. If the measures of the angles of a triangle are represented by x, y, and $(x + y)$, the triangle is (*a*) an isosceles triangle (*b*) an equilateral triangle (*c*) a right triangle.

21. If the midpoints of the sides of a quadrilateral are joined consecutively, the resulting figure is always (*a*) a rhombus (*b*) a rectangle (*c*) a parallelogram.

22. Which of the following statements is *not always* true? (*a*) The diagonals of a rectangle are congruent. (*b*) The diagonals of an isosceles trapezoid are congruent. (*c*) The diagonals of a parallelogram bisect the angles of the parallelogram.

23. A parallelogram must be a rectangle if its diagonals (a) bisect each other   (b) are perpendicular to each other   (c) are congruent.

24. Diagonals $\overline{AC}$ and $\overline{BD}$ of quadrilateral $ABCD$ intersect at E. $ABCD$ is a parallelogram if (a) $A\overline{E} \cong \overline{BE}$, and $\overline{DE} \cong \overline{CE}$ (b) $\overline{AB} \cong \overline{BC}$, and $\overline{CD} \cong \overline{DA}$ (c) $\overline{AE} \cong \overline{EC}$, and $\overline{BE} \cong \overline{ED}$.

25. Two opposite angles of an isosceles trapezoid are (a) congruent (b) complementary   (c) supplementary.

20. Construction Exercises

The following exercises are to be done with straightedge and compasses. The basic constructions involved in these exercises appear in Chapter 14, which begins on page 617.

1. Through point C outside given line $\overleftrightarrow{AB}$, construct a line parallel to $\overleftrightarrow{AB}$.

2. Construct a line parallel to two parallel lines $\overleftrightarrow{AB}$ and $\overleftrightarrow{CD}$ and midway between them.

3. Angle A and angle B are two given angles of triangle ABC. Construct angle C.

4. If given acute angle A is a base angle of an isosceles triangle, construct the vertex angle of the triangle.

5. Construct an angle of (a) 60° (b) 30° (c) 15° (d) 120° (e) 75°.

6. At point P on given line m, construct a line making an angle of 30° with line m.

7. Divide a given line segment $\overline{AB}$ into three congruent parts.

8. Construct an equilateral triangle whose perimeter is a given line segment $\overline{CD}$.

In 9–11, construct a right triangle under the stated conditions.

9. Given the hypotenuse and one of the acute angles.

10. Given a leg and an acute angle adjacent to that leg.

11. Given a leg and an acute angle opposite that leg.

12. If given line segment $\overline{AB}$ is the hypotenuse of a right triangle, determine by construction the length of the median drawn to the hypotenuse.

13. Construct a parallelogram which will have two given segments, m and n, and a given angle B as two sides and the included angle.

14. Construct a square given (a) a side (b) its perimeter   (c) a diagonal.

15. Construct a rhombus given (a) an angle and a side (b) a side and a diagonal   (c) the diagonals.

16. The diagram shows the construction of a line parallel to a given line through a given point outside the line. Which one of the following statements is used to prove that the construction is correct?

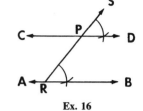

Ex. 16

   a. Through a given point, only one line can be constructed parallel to a given line.
   b. Two lines are parallel if their corresponding angles are congruent.
   c. If two lines are parallel, their corresponding angles are congruent.

17. The diagram shows the construction for dividing a given line segment into any number of congruent parts. Which one of the following statements is used to prove that the construction is correct?

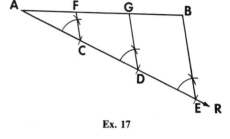

Ex. 17

   a. Parallel lines are everywhere equidistant.
   b. Three or more parallel lines cut off equal lengths on any transversal.
   c. If three or more parallel lines cut off equal lengths on one transversal, they cut off equal lengths on any transversal.

CHAPTER V

Circles

1. Definitions and Fundamental Relations

Previously, on page 24, we learned the definition of a *circle*. We also learned the definitions of *radius*, *chord*, and *diameter*, which are line segments associated with the circle. In circle O (Fig. 5–1), $\overline{OC}$ is a radius, $\overline{AB}$ is a diameter, and $\overline{DE}$ is a chord. Now we will define several additional terms.

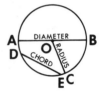

Fig. 5–1

Arcs and Central Angles

Definition. A *central angle* of a circle is an angle whose vertex is the center of the circle.

In circle O (Fig. 5–2), $\angle AOB$ is a central angle. We say that central $\angle AOB$ "intercepts," or "has," the arc $\widehat{AB}$. We also say that arc $\widehat{AB}$ "subtends," or "has," the central $\angle AOB$.

Fig. 5–2

Fig. 5–3

Definition. A *minor arc* of a circle is the union of two points of the circle that are not the ends of a diameter and the set of points of the circle which lie in the interior of the central angle whose sides contain the two points.

In circle O (Fig. 5–3), "arc AB," or $\widehat{AB}$, is a minor arc.

222

Definition. A *major arc* of a circle is the union of two points of a circle that are not the ends of a diameter and the set of points of the circle which lie in the exterior of the central angle whose sides contain the two points.

In circle O (Fig. 5-3), "arc ACB," or $\overparen{ACB}$, is a major arc.

NOTE. When we refer to an arc, we will mean the minor arc, unless we state otherwise.

We say that a chord "subtends" the arcs that it cuts off from a circle. Unless we state otherwise, the arc subtended by a chord will always mean the minor arc subtended by the chord.

The Measure of an Arc

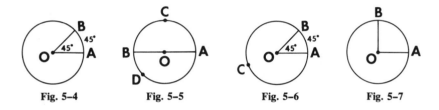

Fig. 5–4   Fig. 5–5   Fig. 5–6   Fig. 5–7

Definition. The *measure of a minor arc* is the measure of the central angle that intercepts the arc.

In circle O (Fig. 5-4), the measure of arc $\overparen{AB}$, symbolized by $m\overparen{AB}$, is the measure of the central angle AOB, or $m\angle AOB$. If $m\angle AOB = 45$, then $m\overparen{AB} = 45$.

Definition. The *measure of a semicircle* is 180.

In circle O (Fig. 5-5), the measure of semicircle $\overparen{ACB}$, symbolized by $m\overparen{ACB}$, is 180. Also, $m\overparen{BDA}$ is 180. Hence, the entire circle will have a measure of 360.

Definition. The *measure of a major arc* is 360 minus the measure of the minor arc which has the same endpoints as the major arc.

In circle O (Fig. 5-6), the measure of major arc BCA, symbolized by $m\overparen{BCA}$, is 360 minus the measure of $\overparen{BA}$. If $m\angle AOB = 45$, then $m\overparen{BA} = 45$. Hence, $m\overparen{BCA} = 360 - 45 = 315$.

Definition. A *quadrant* is an arc whose measure is 90.

In circle O (Fig. 5-7), $\overparen{AB}$ is a quadrant if $m\overparen{AB} = 90$.

Angle Degrees and Arc Degrees

We have learned that $m\angle AOB = 5$ (Fig. 5–8) indicates that $\angle AOB$ is an angle of 5 degrees where the unit of measure for the size of an angle is the degree. Likewise, we will write $m\widehat{AB} = 5$ to indicate that $\widehat{AB}$ is an arc of 5 degrees where the unit of measure for the size of an arc is the degree. However, to distinguish the unit of measure for the angle from that of the arc, we will call the former an *angle degree,* whereas we will call the latter an *arc degree.*

Fig. 5–8

Linear Measure of an Arc

In Fig. 5–9, we see that $m\angle AOB = 45$; therefore, $\widehat{AB}$ contains 45 arc degrees. We also see that $m\angle COD = 45$; therefore, $\widehat{CD}$ contains 45 arc degrees. Although both arcs contain 45 arc degrees, they are not equal in length; that is, they do not have the same *linear measure* because the length of $\widehat{AB}$ is $\frac{45}{360}$, or $\frac{1}{8}$, of the length of the smaller circle, whereas the length of $\widehat{CD}$ is $\frac{45}{360}$, or $\frac{1}{8}$, of the length of the larger circle.

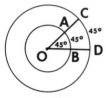

Fig. 5–9

In a later chapter, we will learn how to compute the length of a circle and the length of an arc. For the present, we can find the approximate length of an arc by fitting a string tightly around the arc and measuring the length of the piece that fits around the arc. We assume that with every arc there is associated a number which expresses the length of the arc in terms of a unit such as inches or feet. We will symbolize "the length of arc AB" by $\widehat{AB}$. Previously, we indicated that $\widehat{AB}$ means arc $\widehat{AB}$ itself. In the future, the context in which the symbol $\widehat{AB}$ is used will determine whether it represents arc $\widehat{AB}$ itself, or the length of arc $\widehat{AB}$.

Caution: Do not confuse the number of degrees contained in an arc with the length of the arc.

The Sum of Two Arcs

Consider two arcs in a circle the sum of whose measures is less than 360. By the sum of these two arcs, we will mean an arc of the circle whose length is equal to the sum of the lengths of the two arcs.

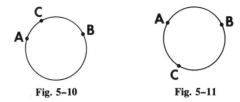

Fig. 5–10   Fig. 5–11

In Fig. 5–10 and Fig. 5–11, if the intersection of $\widehat{AC}$ and $\widehat{CB}$ is the unique point C, then $\widehat{AC}$ and $\widehat{CB}$ have as their sum $\widehat{ACB}$. Thus, length of $\widehat{AC}$ + length of $\widehat{CB}$ = length of $\widehat{ACB}$. We may write this statement in a more concise form as follows: $\widehat{AC} + \widehat{CB} = \widehat{ACB}$.

Congruent Circles, Equal Circles, Congruent Arcs, and Equal Arcs

Definition. **Congruent circles** are circles whose radii are congruent.

In Fig. 5–12, if radius $\overline{OA} \cong$ radius $\overline{O'A'}$, then circle $O \cong$ circle O'.

Definition. **Equal circles** are circles whose radii are equal in length.

Fig. 5–12

In Fig. 5–12, if $OA = O'A'$, then circle O = circle O'.

From the definitions of a circle, congruent circles, and equal circles, the following relationships, which we will use in future proofs, readily follow:

1. In a circle or in congruent circles, radii are congruent and diameters are congruent.
2. In a circle or in equal circles, radii are equal in length and diameters are equal in length.

Definition. **Congruent arcs** are arcs that have equal degree measures (arc measures) and equal lengths (linear measures).

In circle O (Fig. 5–13), if $\widehat{AB}$ and $\widehat{CD}$ have equal degree measures, $m\widehat{AB} = m\widehat{CD}$, and $\widehat{AB}$ and $\widehat{CD}$ have equal lengths, $\widehat{AB} = \widehat{CD}$, then $\widehat{AB}$ is congruent to $\widehat{CD}$, $\widehat{AB} \cong \widehat{CD}$.

Postulate 36. **In the same circle or in equal circles, arcs that have equal degree measures have equal lengths.**

Fig. 5–13

In circle O (Fig. 5–13), if $m\overarc{AB} = m\overarc{CD}$, then $\overarc{AB} = \overarc{CD}$.

Hence, in a circle or in equal circles, when the degree measures of two arcs are equal, or when the lengths of two arcs are equal, we will say that the two arcs are equal. Furthermore, we can also say that in the same circle or in equal circles, when two arcs are equal, the arcs are congruent. In the future, when we write that in a circle or in equal circles, $\overarc{AB} = \overarc{CD}$, the context will determine whether we mean $m\overarc{AB} = m\overarc{CD}$ or length of $\overarc{AB}$ = length of $\overarc{CD}$.

In dealing with theorems concerning arcs, we will at times talk about *equal* arcs rather than *congruent* arcs. We will do this in order to be able to make use of the addition, subtraction, multiplication and division properties of equality. Thus, if we are discussing arcs which are in the same circle or in equal circles, we may say *"equal arcs"* rather than *"congruent arcs."*

Definition. The *midpoint of an arc* is the point that divides the arc into two congruent arcs or two equal arcs.

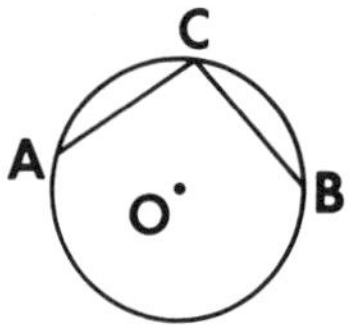

In circle O (Fig. 5–14), if $\overarc{AC} \cong \overarc{CB}$ or $\overarc{AC} = \overarc{CB}$, then C is the midpoint of $\overarc{AB}$.

Fig. 5–14

Circle Circumscribed About a Polygon

Definition. A *circle circumscribed about a polygon* is a circle that passes through each vertex of the polygon.

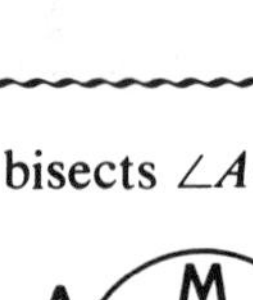

If circle O (Fig. 5–15) passes through every vertex of polygon $ABCD$, then the circle is circumscribed about polygon $ABCD$. We can also say that polygon $ABCD$ is "inscribed in circle O."

Fig. 5–15

MODEL PROBLEM ⎯⎯⎯⎯⎯⎯⎯⎯

In circle O, M is the midpoint of chord $\overline{AB}$. Prove that $\overline{OM}$ bisects $\angle AOB$.

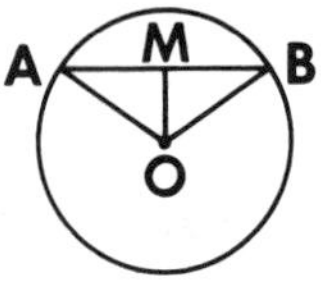

Given: Circle O.
             $\overline{AM} \cong \overline{MB}$.

To prove: $\angle AOM \cong \angle BOM$.

Plan: To prove that $\angle AOM \cong \angle BOM$, prove that
             $\triangle AOM$ and BOM, which contain $\angle AOM$ and
             $\angle BOM$, are congruent by s.s.s. $\cong$ s.s.s.

Proof: *Statements*	*Reasons*
1. $\overline{AM} \cong \overline{MB}$. (s. $\cong$ s.)	1. Given.
2. $\overline{OM} \cong \overline{OM}$. (s. $\cong$ s.)	2. Reflexive property of congruence.
3. $\overline{OA} \cong \overline{OB}$. (s. $\cong$ s.)	3. Radii of a circle are congruent.
4. $\triangle AOM \cong \triangle BOM$.	4. s.s.s. $\cong$ s.s.s.
5. $\angle AOM \cong \angle BOM$.	5. Corresponding parts of congruent triangles are congruent.

EXERCISES

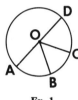
Ex. 1

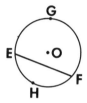
Ex. 2

Ex. 3

1. Name   (*a*) a radius   (*b*) a diameter   (*c*) a semicircle.
2. Name   (*a*) a chord   (*b*) a minor arc   (*c*) a major arc.
3. Name   (*a*) a central angle   (*b*) the arc intercepted by $\angle KOJ$.

4. If circle O = circle O' and the length of radius $\overline{OA}$ is 10, find the length of radius $\overline{O'A'}$.

5. In circle O, radii $\overline{OA}$ and $\overline{OB}$ are drawn. If $OA = 5x + 6$ and $OB = 2x + 24$, find the length of a radius of the circle.

6. In circle O, radii $\overline{OA}$, $\overline{OB}$, and chord $\overline{AB}$ are drawn. If $\overline{OA} = 2x + 8$, $\overline{OB} = x + 24$, and $\overline{AB} = 3x - 8$, find   (*a*) the length of $\overline{OA}$,   (*b*) the length of $\overline{AB}$, and   (*c*) the measure of $\angle AOB$.

7. In circle O, radii $\overline{OR}$ and $\overline{OS}$ are drawn. If $OR = \frac{2}{3}x - 4$ and $OS = x - 12$, find the length of a diameter of the circle.

8. In circle O, radii $\overline{OA}$ and $\overline{OB}$ are drawn. If radius $\overline{OC}$ bisects $\angle AOB$, prove $\overline{AC} \cong \overline{BC}$.

9. In circle O, diameter $\overline{AB}$ is drawn. At A, $\overline{CA}$ is drawn perpendicular to $\overline{AB}$. At B, $\overline{DB}$ is drawn perpendicular to $\overline{AB}$. If $\overline{AC} \cong \overline{BD}$, prove $\overline{OC} \cong \overline{OD}$.

10. $\overline{AB}$ is a diameter of circle O, $\overline{AC}$ is any chord, and radius $\overline{OC}$ is drawn. Prove that the bisector of angle BOC is parallel to $\overrightarrow{AC}$.

11. On diameter $\overline{AB}$ of semicircle O, two points C and D are located on opposite sides of the center O so that $\overline{AC} \cong \overline{BD}$. At C and D, perpendiculars are erected to $\overline{AB}$ and extended to meet $\widehat{AB}$ in points E and F respectively. Prove that $\overline{CE} \cong \overline{DF}$.

12. In circle O, diameter $\overline{AB}$ is extended to C. Line $\overleftrightarrow{CF}$ intersects the circle in D and E. If $\overline{DC} \cong \overline{OE}$, show that $m\angle EOA$ is three times as large as $m\angle ACE$. [*Hint:* Draw radius $\overline{OD}$.]

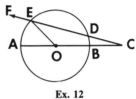

Ex. 12

2. Proving Arcs Equal or Congruent

Theorem 57. **In a circle or in equal circles, central angles whose measures are equal have equal arcs.**

In circle O (Fig. 5–16), if $m\angle AOB = m\angle BOC$, then $\widehat{AB} = \widehat{BC}$. We can also say that if $\angle AOB \cong \angle BOC$, then $\widehat{AB} \cong \widehat{BC}$.

Corollary T57–1. **A diameter divides a circle into two equal arcs.**

In Fig. 5–17, diameter $\overline{AB}$ divides circle O into two equal arcs, each of which is a semicircle.

Theorem 58. **In a circle or in equal circles, equal arcs have central angles whose measures are equal.**

In circle O (Fig. 5–16), if $\widehat{AB} = \widehat{BC}$, then $m\angle AOB = m\angle BOC$. We can also say that if $\widehat{AB} \cong \widehat{BC}$, then $\angle AOB \cong \angle BOC$.

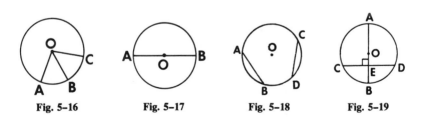

Fig. 5–16   Fig. 5–17   Fig. 5–18   Fig. 5–19

Theorem 59. **In a circle or in equal circles, congruent chords have equal arcs.**

In circle O (Fig. 5–18), if chord $\overline{AB} \cong$ chord $\overline{CD}$, then $\widehat{AB} = \widehat{CD}$. We can also say that: (1) if chord $\overline{AB} \cong$ chord $\overline{CD}$, then $\widehat{AB} \cong \widehat{CD}$ and   (2) if $AB = CD$, then $\widehat{AB} = \widehat{CD}$.

Theorem 60. **A diameter perpendicular to a chord of a circle bisects the chord and its arcs.**

[The proof for this theorem appears on pages 599–600.]

In circle O (Fig. 5–19), if diameter $\overline{AB} \perp$ chord $\overline{CD}$, then   (1) $\overline{CE} \cong \overline{ED}$ or $CE = ED$ (2) $\widehat{CB} \cong \widehat{BD}$ or $\widehat{CB} = \widehat{BD}$ (3) $\widehat{CA} \cong \widehat{AD}$ or $\widehat{CA} = \widehat{AD}$.

Corollary T60–1. **The perpendicular bisector of a chord of a circle passes through the center of the circle.**

In circle O (Fig. 5–19), if $\overleftrightarrow{AB}$ is the perpendicular bisector of chord $\overline{CD}$, then $\overleftrightarrow{AB}$ passes through O, the center of the circle, and $\overline{AB}$ is thus a diameter of the circle.

Methods of Proving Arcs in the Same or Equal Circles Equal or Congruent

To prove that arcs in a circle or in equal circles are equal or congruent, prove that either one of the following statements is true:

1. The central angles of the arcs are equal in angular measure, or are congruent.
2. The chords of the arcs are equal in linear measure, or are congruent.

MODEL PROBLEM ~~~~~~~~~~~~~~~~~~~~~~~~~~~~~~~~~

Given: In circle O, $\overline{BC}$ is a diameter.
            Radius $\overline{OE} \parallel$ chord $\overline{CD}$.

To prove: $\widehat{BE} = \widehat{ED}$.

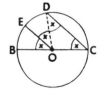

Plan: In order to prove that $\widehat{BE} = \widehat{ED}$, we can show that these arcs have central angles whose measures are equal. Draw $\overline{OD}$ to form central angle EOD. Prove $m\angle BOE = m\angle EOD$.

            [The proof is given on the next page.]

Proof: *Statements*	*Reasons*
1. Draw radius $\overline{OD}$.	1. One and only one straight line may be drawn through two points.
2. $\overline{OE} \parallel \overline{CD}$.	2. Given.
3. $m\angle EOD = m\angle CDO = x$.	3. If two parallel lines are cut by a transversal, the alternate interior angles are congruent.
4. $\overline{OD} \cong \overline{OC}$.	4. Radii of a circle are congruent.
5. $m\angle OCD = m\angle CDO = x$.	5. If two sides of a triangle are congruent, the angles opposite these sides are congruent.
6. $m\angle BOE = m\angle OCD = x$.	6. If two parallel lines are cut by a transversal, the corresponding angles are congruent.
7. $m\angle BOE = m\angle EOD$.	7. If quantities are equal to the same quantity or equal quantities, they are equal to each other.
8. $\overset{\frown}{BE} = \overset{\frown}{ED}$.	8. In a circle, central angles whose measures are equal have equal arcs.

EXERCISES

Ex. 1   Ex. 2–3   Ex. 6   Ex. 7

1. *Given:* In circle O, B is the midpoint of $\overset{\frown}{AC}$.
   Prove: $\overline{AB} \cong \overline{BC}$.
2. *Given:* In circle O, $\overline{BE} \perp \overline{OA}$, $\overline{BD} \perp \overline{OC}$, B is the midpoint of $\overset{\frown}{AC}$.
   Prove: $\overline{BE} \cong \overline{BD}$.

3. *Given:* In circle O, $\overline{BO}$ bisects $\angle EBD$, B is the midpoint of $\overparen{AC}$.
   Prove: $\overline{OE} \cong \overline{OD}$.
4. *Prove:* If an equilateral triangle is inscribed in a circle, it divides the circle into three equal arcs.
5. If triangle ABC is inscribed in a circle and $\angle A \cong \angle C$, prove $\overparen{AB} = \overparen{BC}$.
6. *Given:* In circle O, $\overline{AD} \cong \overline{DC}$.
   Prove: $\overparen{AB} = \overparen{BC}$.
7. *Given:* In circle O, $\overline{OS} \perp \overline{RT}$.
   Prove: $\overparen{RS} \cong \overparen{ST}$.

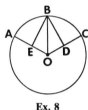

Ex. 8

Ex. 9

Ex. 10

Ex. 11

8. *Given:* In circle O, $\overline{BE} \cong \overline{BD}$, $\overline{BE} \perp \overline{OA}$, $\overline{BD} \perp \overline{OC}$.
   Prove: $\overparen{AB} \cong \overparen{BC}$.
9. *Given:* $\overline{BA} \perp \overline{AD}$, $\overline{BC} \perp \overline{CD}$, $\overline{BD}$ bisects $\angle ABC$.
   Prove: $\overparen{AB} = \overparen{BC}$.
10. *Given:* $\overline{ED} \parallel \overline{FG}$, $\overline{BD} \cong \overline{AF}$, $\overline{DB} \perp \overline{EG}$, $\overline{FA} \perp \overline{EG}$.
    Prove: $\overparen{DE} \cong \overparen{FG}$.
11. $\overline{AB}$ is the perpendicular bisector of $\overline{CD}$. Prove $\overparen{AC} \cong \overparen{AD}$.

Ex. 12

Ex. 13

Ex. 14–15

Ex. 16

12. If $\overline{AB} \cong \overline{CD}$, prove $\overparen{BAC} = \overparen{DCA}$.
13. If $\overline{AB} \cong \overline{CD}$, prove $\overparen{AC} = \overparen{BD}$.
14. In circle O, if $\overline{AD} \cong \overline{AC}$ and $\angle 1 \cong \angle 2$, prove $\overparen{DB} = \overparen{BC}$.
15. In circle O, if $\overline{AB}$ is a diameter and $\angle 1 \cong \angle 2$, prove $\overparen{DB} \cong \overparen{BC}$.
16. *Given:* $\overleftrightarrow{WZ}$ intersects the two concentric circles whose centers are O.
    Prove: $\overline{WX} \cong \overline{YZ}$. [*Hint:* Draw $\overline{OM} \perp \overline{WZ}$, M being a point on $\overline{WZ}$.]
17. In a circle, chord $\overline{CD}$ is parallel to diameter $\overline{AB}$. Prove $\overparen{AC} \cong \overparen{BD}$.

18. *Prove:* The diagonals of a parallelogram that is inscribed in a circle are, congruent.
19. *Prove:* The diagonals of a regular pentagon that is inscribed in a circle are congruent.
20. In circle O, diameter $\overline{AB}$ is perpendicular to chord $\overline{FH}$ at C. If $\overline{FC}$ is 4 inches long, how many inches are there in the length of $\overline{HC}$?
21. In circle O, $\overline{OD}$ is drawn perpendicular to chord $\overline{RS}$, D being a point on $\overline{RS}$. If $RD = 6x + 8$ and $SD = 10x - 36$, find RD and SD.
22. In circle O, $\overline{OC}$ is drawn perpendicular to chord $\overline{AB}$, C being a point on $\overline{AB}$. If $AC = 5x - 1$ and $CB = 13 - 2x$, find the length of chord $\overline{AB}$.

3. Proving Chords Congruent

Theorem 61. In a circle or in equal circles, equal arcs have congruent chords.

In circle O (Fig. 5–20), if $\overset{\frown}{AB} = \overset{\frown}{CD}$, then chord $\overline{AB} \cong$ chord $\overline{CD}$. We can also say that if $\overset{\frown}{AB} \cong \overset{\frown}{CD}$, then chord $\overline{AB} \cong$ chord $\overline{CD}$.

| Fig. 5–20 | Fig. 5–21 |

Theorem 62. In a circle, if two chords are congruent, they are equally distant from the center of that circle.

In circle O (Fig. 5–21), if chord $\overline{AB} \cong$ chord $\overline{CD}$, $\overline{OE} \perp \overline{AB}$, and $\overline{OF} \perp \overline{CD}$, then $\overline{OE} \cong \overline{OF}$. Hence, $OE = OF$.

Theorem 63. In a circle, if two chords are equidistant from the center, they are congruent.

In circle O (Fig. 5–21), if $\overline{OE} \perp \overline{AB}$, $\overline{OF} \perp \overline{CD}$, and $OE = OF$, then chord $\overline{AB} \cong$ chord $\overline{CD}$. Hence, $AB = CD$.

Methods of Proving Chords in the Same or Equal Circles Equal in Length or Congruent

To prove that two chords in a circle or in equal circles are equal in length or congruent, prove that either one of the following statements is true:

1. The arcs of the chords are equal or congruent.
2. The chords are equidistant from the center of the circle.

MODEL PROBLEM

Given: $\overline{AB}$ is a diameter in circle O.
Chord $\overline{AC}$ ∥ chord $\overline{DB}$.

To prove: Chord $\overline{AC} \cong$ chord $\overline{DB}$.

Plan: To prove that chord $\overline{AC}$ and chord $\overline{DB}$ are congruent, show that their distances from O, the center of the circle, are equal. Draw $\overline{OE} \perp \overline{AC}$ and $\overline{OF} \perp \overline{DB}$. Prove $\overline{OE} \cong \overline{OF}$ by proving $\triangle OEA \cong \triangle OFB$ by s.a.a. $\cong$ s.a.a.

Proof: *Statements*	*Reasons*
1. Draw $\overline{OE} \perp \overline{AC}, \overline{OF} \perp \overline{DB}$.	1. From a given point outside a line, one and only one perpendicular can be drawn to the line.
2. $\angle E \cong \angle F$. (a. $\cong$ a.)	2. All right angles are congruent.
3. $\overline{AC} \parallel \overline{DB}$.	3. Given.
4. $\angle EAO \cong \angle FBO$. (a. $\cong$ a.)	4. If two parallel lines are cut by a transversal, the alternate interior angles are congruent.
5. $\overline{OA} \cong \overline{OB}$. (s. $\cong$ s.)	5. Radii of a circle are congruent.
6. $\triangle OEA \cong \triangle OFB$.	6. s.a.a. $\cong$ s.a.a.
7. $\overline{OE} \cong \overline{OF}$, or $OE = OF$.	7. Corresponding parts of congruent triangles are congruent.
8. Chord $\overline{AC} \cong$ chord $\overline{DB}$.	8. In a circle, if two chords are equidistant from the center, they are congruent.

EXERCISES

1. If a circle is divided into three equal arcs, and lines are drawn connecting the points of division, prove that an equilateral triangle is formed.

234   Geometry

| Ex. 2 | Ex. 3 | Ex. 4 | Ex. 5 |

2. *Given:* $\overline{BE} \perp \overline{AC}$, B is the midpoint of $\overparen{AC}$.
 Prove: $\overline{AE} \cong \overline{CE}$.
3. *Given:* B is the midpoint of chord $\overline{CD}$, A is the midpoint of $\overparen{CD}$.
 Prove: $\overline{AB} \perp \overline{CD}$.
4. *Given:* $\overleftrightarrow{AC}$ is a line, $\overparen{BC} = \overparen{AD}$, $\overline{BC} \parallel \overline{AD}$, $\angle B \cong \angle D$.
 Prove: $\overline{AE} \cong \overline{CF}$.
5. *Given:* $\overparen{AB} \cong \overparen{CD}$, E is the midpoint of $\overline{BC}$, $\overline{AB} \perp \overline{BC}$, $\overline{DC} \perp \overline{BC}$.
 Prove: $\overline{AE} \cong \overline{DE}$.

   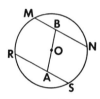

| Ex. 6 | Ex. 7 | Ex. 8 | Ex. 9 |

6. *Given:* $\overline{AB} \cong \overline{CD}$, $\overline{AF} \cong \overline{DE}$.
 Prove: $\overline{BF} \cong \overline{CE}$.
7. *Given:* $\overparen{AB} \cong \overparen{DC}$, $\overparen{AD} \cong \overparen{BC}$.
 Prove: $ABCD$ is a parallelogram.
8. *Given:* In circle O, $\overline{AB}$ is a diameter, $\angle DAB \cong \angle CBA$.
 Prove: $\overline{AD} \cong \overline{BC}$.
9. *Given:* In circle O, $\overline{MN} \parallel \overline{RS}$, $\overline{OB} \cong \overline{OA}$, $\overleftrightarrow{AOB}$ is a line.
 Prove: $\overline{MN} \cong \overline{RS}$.

| Ex. 10 | Ex. 11 | Ex. 12 | Ex. 13 |

10. If chord $\overline{AD}$ is congruent to chord $\overline{CB}$, prove that chord $\overline{AB}$ is congruent to chord $\overline{CD}$.

11. If chord $\overline{AB}$ is congruent to chord $\overline{CD}$, prove that $\triangle DAB \cong \triangle BCD$.

12. In circle O, $\overline{PD}$ and $\overline{PB}$ form congruent angles with $\overline{PO}$. Prove that $\overline{AB} \cong \overline{CD}$.

13. In circle O, if $\angle COD \cong \angle FOE$, prove that $\overline{CE} \cong \overline{DF}$.

14. A is a point on circle O. Radius $\overline{OA}$ is drawn. Chords $\overline{AB}$ and $\overline{AC}$ are drawn on opposite sides of $\overline{OA}$ so that $\angle BAO \cong \angle CAO$. Prove that chord $\overline{AB}$ is congruent to chord $\overline{AC}$.

15. If two chords which intersect on a circle make congruent angles with the radius drawn to the point of intersection, prove that the chords are congruent.

16. *Prove:* The line that bisects the minor arc and the major arc of a chord is the perpendicular bisector of the chord.

17. *Prove:* If equilateral triangles are inscribed in two congruent circles, the triangles are congruent.

18. *Prove:* In a circle, two chords perpendicular to a third chord at its endpoints are congruent.

19. *Prove:* A radius of a circle which bisects an arc in the circle is the perpendicular bisector of the chord of that arc.

20. In circle O, $\widehat{AB} = \widehat{CD}$. If $AB = 9x + 10$ and $CD = 4x + 60$, find AB.

21. In circle O, chord $\overline{LM} \cong$ chord $\overline{NP}$. If $\widehat{LM} = \frac{2}{3}y + 20$ and $\widehat{NP} = 2y - 20$, find $\widehat{NP}$.

22. Chords $\overline{AB}$ and $\overline{CD}$ are drawn in circle O. $\overline{OE} \perp \overline{AB}$, and $\overline{OF} \perp \overline{CD}$, point E being on $\overline{AB}$ and point F being on $\overline{CD}$.
a. If $\overline{AB} \cong \overline{CD}$, $OE = 5x + 1$, and $OF = 8x - 11$, find OE.
b. If $\overline{OE} \cong \overline{OF}$, $AB = 3x + 7$, and $CD = 5x - 7$, find AE.

23. Use an indirect method of proof to prove: In the same or in equal circles, chords that are not congruent are unequally distant from the center.

4. Tangents and Tangent Circles

A Tangent to a Circle

Definition. **A *tangent to a circle* is a line in the plane of the circle which intersects the circle at one and only one point. The point at which the tangent intersects the circle is called the "point of tangency," or "point of contact."**

In Fig. 5–22 on the next page, $\overleftrightarrow{AB}$ is a tangent to circle O; and point P is the point of tangency, or point of contact.

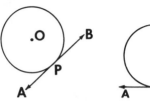

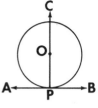

Fig. 5–22   Fig. 5–23   Fig. 5–24   Fig. 5–25

Theorem 64. If a line is tangent to a circle, the line is perpendicular to the radius drawn to the point of contact.

In Fig. 5–23, if $\overleftrightarrow{AB}$ is tangent to circle O, then tangent $\overleftrightarrow{AB} \perp$ radius $\overline{OP}$ at P.

Theorem 65. If a line is perpendicular to a radius of a circle at its outer endpoint, then the line is a tangent to the circle.

In circle O (Fig. 5–23), if $\overleftrightarrow{AB} \perp$ radius $\overline{OP}$ at P, then $\overleftrightarrow{AB}$ is tangent to circle O.

Theorem 66. If a line is perpendicular to a tangent to a circle at the point of contact, the line passes through the center of the circle.

In Fig. 5–24, if $\overleftrightarrow{AB}$ is tangent to circle O at point P and $\overleftrightarrow{CP} \perp \overleftrightarrow{AB}$ at P, then $\overleftrightarrow{CP}$ passes through the center of circle O.

Definition. A *circle is inscribed in a polygon* when all the sides of the polygon are tangent to the circle.

In Fig. 5–25, if all sides of polygon $ABCD$ are tangent to circle O, then circle O is inscribed in polygon $ABCD$. We can also say that polygon $ABCD$ is "circumscribed about circle O."

Tangents to a Circle From an External Point

Definition. The *length of a tangent from an external point to a circle* is the length of the line segment whose endpoints are the external point and the point of contact of the tangent to the circle.

In Fig. 5–26, if $\overleftrightarrow{AB}$ is tangent to circle O at point P, the length of the tangent from point A to circle O is the length of line segment $\overline{AP}$. Note that this length does not measure the length of tangent $\overleftrightarrow{AB}$. Since $\overleftrightarrow{AB}$ is a line and not a line segment, $\overleftrightarrow{AB}$ has no length. For convenience, segment $\overline{AP}$ may be referred to as the tangent from A. Segment $\overline{AP}$ may also be referred to as a *tangent segment*.

Fig. 5–26

Theorem 67. **If two tangents are drawn to a circle from an external point, these tangents are equal in length.**

In Fig. 5–27, if $\overleftrightarrow{PA}$ and $\overleftrightarrow{PB}$ are tangent to circle O, then $PA = PB$.

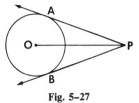

Corollary T67–1. **If two tangents are drawn to a circle from an external point, the line passing through that point and the center of the circle bisects the angle formed by the tangents.**

Fig. 5–27

In Fig. 5–27, if $\overleftrightarrow{PA}$ and $\overleftrightarrow{PB}$ are tangents drawn to circle O, then $\overleftrightarrow{PO}$ bisects $\angle APB$, or $\angle APO \cong \angle BPO$.

Line of Centers of Two Circles

Definition. **The *line of centers of two circles* is the line segment whose end-points are the centers of the circles.**

In Fig. 5–28, $\overline{OO'}$ is the line of centers of circles O and O'.

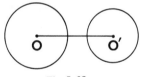   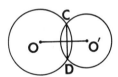

Fig. 5–28   Fig. 5–29

Theorem 68. **If two circles intersect in two points, their line of centers is the perpendicular bisector of their common chord.**

If circles O and O' intersect in point C and point D (Fig. 5–29), their line of centers $\overline{OO'}$ is the perpendicular bisector of common chord $\overline{CD}$. When two circles intersect in two points, their *common chord* is the line segment whose endpoints are the two points of intersection.

Common Tangents

Definition. **A *common tangent* to two circles is a line which is tangent to each of the circles.**

On the next page are shown some examples of common tangents drawn to circles:

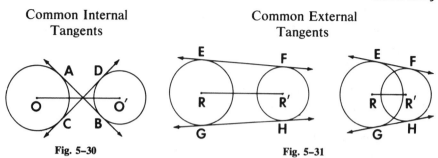

Common Internal Tangents

Common External Tangents

Fig. 5–30   Fig. 5–31

Definition. A *common internal tangent* to two circles is a line which is tangent to both circles and intersects their line of centers.

In Fig. 5–30, $\overleftrightarrow{AB}$ and $\overleftrightarrow{CD}$ are common internal tangents to circles O and O'. Both $\overleftrightarrow{AB}$ and $\overleftrightarrow{CD}$ intersect $\overline{OO'}$, the line of centers. The length of common internal tangent $\overleftrightarrow{AB}$ is the length of line segment $\overline{AB}$, whose endpoints are the points of contact A and B.

Definition. A *common external tangent* to two circles is a line which is tangent to both circles and does not intersect their line of centers.

In Fig. 5–31, $\overleftrightarrow{EF}$ and $\overleftrightarrow{GH}$ are common external tangents to circles R and R'. Neither $\overleftrightarrow{EF}$ nor $\overleftrightarrow{GH}$ intersects $\overline{RR'}$, the line of centers. The length of common external tangent $\overleftrightarrow{EF}$ is the length of line segment $\overline{EF}$, whose endpoints are the points of contact E and F.

Tangent Circles

Definition. *Tangent circles* are circles in a plane that are tangent to the same line at the same point.

Following are examples of tangent circles:

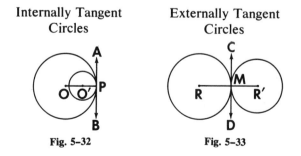

Internally Tangent Circles

Externally Tangent Circles

Fig. 5–32   Fig. 5–33

Definition. *Internally tangent circles* are tangent circles which lie on the same side of the common tangent.

In Fig. 5–32, circles O and O' are internally tangent because they both lie to the left of common tangent $\overleftrightarrow{AB}$.

*Definition. **Externally tangent circles** are tangent circles which lie on opposite sides of the common tangent.*

In Fig. 5–33, circles R and R' are externally tangent because circle R lies to the left of common tangent $\overleftrightarrow{CD}$, and circle R' lies to the right of $\overleftrightarrow{CD}$.

Theorem 69. If two circles are tangent, their line of centers, extended if necessary, passes through the point of contact and is perpendicular to their common tangent.

In Fig. 5–32, the line of centers $\overline{OO'}$, extended, passes through the point of contact P and is perpendicular to common tangent $\overleftrightarrow{AB}$.

Also, in Fig. 5–33, the line of centers RR' passes through the point of contact M and is perpendicular to common tangent $\overleftrightarrow{CD}$.

MODEL PROBLEMS

1. $\overleftrightarrow{AB}$, $\overleftrightarrow{BC}$, and $\overleftrightarrow{CA}$ are tangents to circle O. $AD = 5$ and $BE = 4$. Find the length of $\overline{AB}$.

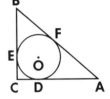

Solution: Since the lengths of the tangents drawn to a circle from an external point are equal,

$$AF = AD = 5 \quad \text{and} \quad BF = BE = 4$$

Therefore, $AB = AF + BF = 5 + 4 = 9$.

Answer: $AB = 9$.

2. Prove that if two circles are tangent externally, tangents drawn to the circles from any point in their common internal tangent are equal in length.

Given: Circles O and O' are externally tangent.
$\overleftrightarrow{PA}$ is their common internal tangent.
$\overleftrightarrow{PD}$ is tangent to circle O.
$\overleftrightarrow{PE}$ is tangent to circle O'.

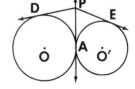

To prove: $PD = PE$.

Plan: To prove that the length of tangent $\overleftrightarrow{PD}$ is equal to the length of tangent $\overleftrightarrow{PE}$, prove that both PD and PE are equal to PA, the length of tangent $\overleftrightarrow{PA}$.

[The proof is given on the next page.]

Proof: *Statements*	*Reasons*
1. $\overleftrightarrow{PD}$ and $\overleftrightarrow{PA}$ are tangents to circle O.	1. Given.
2. $PD = PA$.	2. The lengths of tangents drawn to a circle from an external point are equal.
3. $\overleftrightarrow{PE}$ and $\overleftrightarrow{PA}$ are tangents to circle O'.	3. Given.
4. $PA = PE$.	4. The lengths of tangents drawn to a circle from an external point are equal.
5. $PD = PE$.	5. Transitive property of equality.

EXERCISES

In 1–3, find the value of *x*, or *x* and *y*, as indicated.

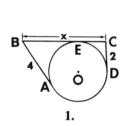

1.

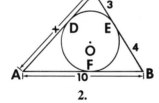

2.

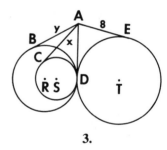

3.

4. $\overleftrightarrow{PA}$ and $\overleftrightarrow{PB}$ are tangents to circle O from point P. Chord $\overline{AB}$ is drawn. Find the number of degrees contained in $\angle PAB$ if $\angle APB$ contains:
a. 80°   *b.* 40°   *c.* 60°   *d.* 90°   *e.* 120°

5. $\overleftrightarrow{PA}$ and $\overleftrightarrow{PB}$ are tangents to circle O from point P, and chord $\overline{AB}$ is drawn. Express the number of degrees contained in angle PAB if the number of degrees contained in angle APB is represented by:
a. x   *b.* 2m   *c.* (180 − x)   *d.* (90 − x)   *e.* (x + y)

6. $\overleftrightarrow{PC}$ and $\overleftrightarrow{PD}$ are tangents to circle O at C and D respectively. $\overline{OC}$ and $\overline{OD}$ are drawn. Find $m\angle CPD$ if $m\angle COD$ is:
a. 160   *b.* 140   *c.* 120   *d.* 90   *e.* 60   *f.* x   *g.* (180 − x)

7. Prove that tangents drawn to a circle at the ends of a diameter are parallel.

8. *Prove:* Tangents to a circle from a point outside the circle form congruent angles with the chord joining their points of contact.

9. *Prove:* If two circles are tangent externally, their common internal tangent bisects their common external tangents.

10. *Prove:* If two nonintersecting circles, each outside the other, are congruent, their line of centers bisects a common internal tangent.

11. *Prove:* The common internal tangents to two nonintersecting circles, each outside the other, are congruent.

12. *Prove:* The common external tangents to two unequal nonintersecting circles, each outside the other, are congruent.

13. Points C and D are on circle O. Tangents drawn to circle O at points C and D intersect at P. Prove that $\overline{PO}$ bisects minor arc $\overset{\frown}{CD}$.

14. *Prove:* If two tangents drawn to a circle from an external point meet at an angle of 60°, the chord joining their points of contact is congruent to each tangent.

15. *Prove:* An angle formed by two tangents drawn to a circle from an external point is supplementary to the angle formed by the radii drawn to the points of contact.

16. *Prove:* The sum of the lengths of two opposite sides of a quadrilateral that is circumscribed about a circle is equal to the sum of the lengths of the other two sides.

17. *Prove:* If two circles are tangent externally, the common internal tangent bisects a common external tangent.

18. *Prove:* If a circle is inscribed in a right triangle, the sum of the length of the hypotenuse of the triangle and the length of the diameter of the circle is equal to the sum of the lengths of the legs of the triangle.

19. Draw two circles which will have the indicated number of common tangents. (a) 0 (b) 1 (c) 2 (d) 3 (e) 4

20. Draw two circles whose radii are 3 and 4 if the length of the line of centers is:
   a. 10   *b.* 6   *c.* 7   *d.* 1

21. State the number of common tangents that can be drawn to: (a) two circles which intersect in two points (b) two circles, each outside the other, that do not intersect (c) two circles that are externally tangent (d) two circles that are internally tangent.

22. If the radius of circle O is represented by r, the radius of circle O' is represented by R, and the length of the line of centers OO' is represented by D, express the relationship among D, r, and R when (a) the two circles are tangent externally (b) the two circles are tangent internally (c) the two circles intersect in two points (d) the two circles are nonintersecting, with each circle outside the other.

23. *Prove:* If a tangent to a circle is parallel to a chord of a circle, the lines intercept congruent arcs on the circle.

24. *Prove:* Two parallel chords intercept congruent arcs on a circle.

25. *Prove:* Two parallel tangents intercept congruent arcs on a circle.

26. *Prove:* A chord of a circle is parallel to a tangent to the circle drawn at the midpoint of the minor arc of the chord.

27. $\overleftrightarrow{PA}$ and $\overleftrightarrow{PB}$ are tangents drawn to circle O from point P. If $PA = 8r - 7$ and $PB = 2r + 35$, find r, PA, and PB.

28. $\overleftrightarrow{PC}$ and $\overleftrightarrow{PD}$ are tangents drawn to circle O from point P. If $m\angle DOC = 2x + 40$ and $m\angle CPD = x - 10$, find $m\angle DOC$, $m\angle CPD$, and $m\angle CPO$.

29. $\overleftrightarrow{PA}$ and $\overleftrightarrow{PB}$ are tangents drawn to circle O from point P. If $m\angle APB = 60$, $AP = 2x - 2y$, $PB = \frac{1}{3}x + 6$, and $AB = x + y$, find x, y, and AP.

30. *Given:* $\overleftrightarrow{CD}$ is a common internal tangent to circles O and O'. $\overline{AB}$ is a common external tangent to circles O and O'.

Prove: a. D is the midpoint of $\overline{AB}$.
b. $\angle ACB$ is a right angle.
[*Hint:* Let $m\angle BCD = x$; let $m\angle ACD = y$.]

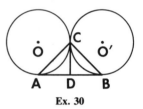

Ex. 30

5. Measurements of Angles and Arcs

Measuring a Central Angle

We have learned that in a circle a central angle is an angle whose vertex is the center of the circle. Also, we have defined the measure of a minor arc as the measure of the central angle that intercepts the arc. Since a definition is reversible we can also say that:

The measure of a central angle is the measure of its intercepted arc.

In circle O (Fig. 5–34), if $\angle AOB$ is a central angle, then $m\angle AOB = m\widehat{AB}$, or $m\angle AOB = b$.

Theorem 70. **In a circle or in equal circles, two arcs which contain the same number of arc degrees are equal.**

Fig. 5–34

In equal circles O and O' (Fig. 5–35), if the number of degrees in $\widehat{AB}$ is equal to the number of degrees in $\widehat{A'B'}$, then $\widehat{AB} = \widehat{A'B'}$.

Fig. 5–35

Method of Proving Angles Congruent Using Central Angles

To prove that two angles are congruent or equal in measure, prove that they are central angles in a circle or in equal circles and that they intercept the same or equal arcs.

MODEL PROBLEM

In circle O, $m\widehat{AB} = 80$. Find the measure of $\angle A$.

Solution: Since $\angle AOB$ is a central angle, $m\angle AOB = m\widehat{AB}$, or $m\angle AOB = 80$.
Since radius $\overline{OA} \cong$ radius $\overline{OB}$, $m\angle A = m\angle B$.

1. $m\angle A + m\angle B + m\angle AOB = 180$

2. $m\angle A + m\angle A + 80 = 180$

3. $\qquad 2m\angle A + 80 = 180$

4. $\qquad 2m\angle A = 100$

5. $\qquad m\angle A = 50$

Answer: $m\angle A = 50$.

EXERCISES

1. Find the measure of a central angle which intercepts an arc whose measure is:
   a. 50   *b.* 20   *c.* 70   *d.* 90   *e. r*   *f.* 4x

2. Find the measure of the arc intercepted by a central angle whose measure is:
   a. 30   *b.* 60   *c.* 75   *d.* 120   *e. b*   *f.* 180 − x

3. A central angle whose measure is 40 intercepts an arc whose measure is _____ degrees.

4. Angle AOB is a central angle of circle O, and chord $\overline{AB}$ is drawn. If the length of chord $\overline{AB}$ is equal to the length of a radius, find the measure of angle AOB.

In 5–9, O is the center of each circle. Find the value of x.

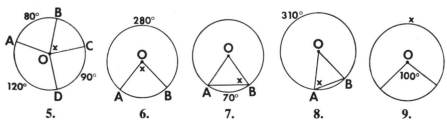

    5.   **6.**   **7.**   **8.**   **9.**

10. As the number of degrees in an arc of a circle increases, what change takes place in its central angle?

11. If the measure of an arc which is less than 180 is doubled, what change takes place in the measure of its central angle?

12. If the measure of an arc is halved, what change takes place in the measure of its central angle?

Measuring an Inscribed Angle

Definition. **In a circle, an *inscribed angle* is an angle whose vertex lies on the circle and whose sides are chords of the circle.**

In circle O (Fig. 5–36), $\angle ACB$ is called an inscribed angle and is said to be inscribed in the circle.

Definition. **An *angle is inscribed in an arc* of a circle if its vertex lies on the arc and its sides are chords which join the vertex and the ends of the arc.**

Fig. 5–36

In Fig. 5–36, $\angle ACB$ is inscribed in $\overset{\frown}{ACB}$. Angle ACB *intercepts*, or cuts off, $\overset{\frown}{AB}$.

Fig. 5–37

Fig. 5–38

Fig. 5–39

Fig. 5–40

Theorem 71. **The measure of an angle inscribed in a circle is equal to one-half the measure of its intercepted arc.**

[The proof of this theorem appears on pages 601–603.]

In circle O (Fig. 5–37), $m\angle ABC = \frac{1}{2}m\overset{\frown}{AC}$, or $m\angle ABC = \frac{1}{2}b$.

Corollary T71–1. **An angle inscribed in a semicircle is a right angle.**

In Fig. 5–38, if $\overline{AC}$ is a diameter in circle O, angle CBA is a right angle.

Corollary T71–2. **In a circle or in equal circles, if inscribed angles intercept the same or equal arcs, then the inscribed angles are equal in measure.**

In circle O (Fig. 5–39), $m\angle ABC$, which intercepts $\overset{\frown}{AC}$, and $m\angle ADC$, which also intercepts $\overset{\frown}{AC}$, are equal, or $m\angle ABC = m\angle ADC$.

Corollary T71–3. **In a circle or in equal circles, if inscribed angles are equal in measure, then they intercept equal arcs.**

In circle O (Fig. 5–40), if $m\angle ABC = m\angle DEF$, then $\overset{\frown}{AC} = \overset{\frown}{DF}$.

Fig. 5–41

Fig. 5–42

Fig. 5–43

Corollary T71–4. **In a circle, angles inscribed in the same arc are equal in measure.**

In circle O (Fig. 5–41), $\angle ABC$, which is inscribed in $\overarc{ABDC}$, is equal in measure to $\angle ADC$, which is also inscribed in $\overarc{ABDC}$, or $m\angle ABC = m\angle ADC$.

Corollary T71–5. **In a circle, the opposite angles of an inscribed quadrilateral are supplementary.**

In Fig. 5–42, if quadrilateral $ABCD$ is inscribed in circle O, then $m\angle A + m\angle C = 180$ and $m\angle B + m\angle D = 180$. If $m\angle A = x$, then $m\angle C = 180 - x$.

Corollary T71–6. **Parallel lines which intersect a circle intercept equal arcs on a circle.**

In circle O (Fig. 5–43), if $\overleftrightarrow{AB} \parallel \overleftrightarrow{CD}$, then $\overarc{CA} = \overarc{DB}$.

Method of Proving Angles Congruent Using Inscribed Angles

To prove that two angles are congruent or equal in measure, prove that they are inscribed angles in the same circle or in equal circles and that they intercept, or are inscribed in, the same arc or equal arcs.

MODEL PROBLEM

In circle O, the measure of central angle AOB is 80. If point C is on minor arc $\overarc{AB}$, find the measure of $\angle ACB$.

Solution:

1. Since $m\angle AOB = 80$, the measure of intercepted $\overarc{AB} = 80$.

2. Since the measure of minor $\overarc{AB} = 80$, the measure of major $\overarc{AMB} = 360 - 80$, or 280.

3. The measure of inscribed $\angle ACB$ is equal to one-half the measure of major arc $\overarc{AMB}$.

4. $m\angle ACB = \frac{1}{2} m\overarc{AMB}$

5. $m\angle ACB = \frac{1}{2}(280) = 140$

Answer: The measure of $\angle ACB$ is 140.

EXERCISES

1. Find the measure of an inscribed angle which intercepts an arc whose measure is:
   a. 40   *b.* 80   *c.* 105   *d.* 120   *e. a*   *f.* 4*y*

2. Find the measure of the arc intercepted by an inscribed angle whose measure is:
   a. 30   *b.* 75   *c.* 22½   *d.* 45   *e. b*   *f.* 6*a*

3. Inscribed angle *ABC* of circle *O* measures 75. Radii $\overline{AO}$ and $\overline{CO}$ are drawn. Find the measure of angle *AOC*.

4. $\overline{AB}$ is a diameter of a circle, $\overline{AC}$ is a chord, and arc $\widehat{AC}$ contains 100°. Angle *BAC* contains _____ degrees.

5. If the vertices of an inscribed triangle divide the circle into three arcs whose measures are in the ratio 3:4:5, what is the measure of the largest angle of the triangle?

6. An inscribed angle and a central angle intercept the same arc of a circle. The ratio of the measure of the inscribed angle to the measure of the central angle is _____.

7. In circle *O*, central angle *DOE* measures 80. Find the measure of angle *DFE*, which is inscribed in minor arc *DE*.

8. Central angle *AOB* in circle *O* measures 120, and *X* is any point on minor arc $\widehat{AB}$. Find the measure of angle *AXB*.

   In 9–13, *O* is the center of each circle. Find the value of *x*, or *x* and *y*.

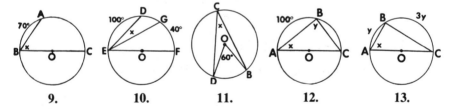

9.   10.   11.   12.   13.

14. In a circle, two parallel chords on opposite sides of the center have arcs which measure 100 and 120. Find the measure of one of the arcs included between the chords.

   In 15–19, *O* is the center of the circle and $\overline{AB} \parallel \overline{CD}$. Find the value of *x*.

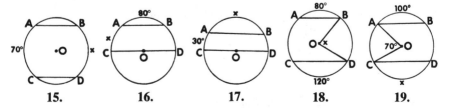

15.   16.   17.   18.   19.

20. If quadrilateral *ABCD* is inscribed in a circle, find the measure of angle *B* if its opposite angle *D* measures:
    a. 65   *b.* 90   *c.* 110   *d. a*   *e.* 180 − 2*x*

21. Quadrilateral *ABCD* is inscribed in a circle. If angle *A* measures 95, find the measure of angle *C*.

22. Quadrilateral *ABCD* is inscribed in a circle. If $m\widehat{AB} = 119$, $m\widehat{BC} = 73$, and $m\widehat{CD} = 60$, what is the measure of angle *ABC*?

23. Prove that when a circle whose diameter is one of the congruent sides of an isosceles triangle is drawn, the circle bisects the base of the triangle.

Measuring an Angle Formed by a Tangent and a Chord

Theorem 72. The measure of an angle formed by a tangent and a chord drawn from the point of contact is equal to one-half the measure of its intercepted arc.

In circle *O* (Fig. 5–44), the measure of ∠*ABC*, which is formed by tangent $\overleftrightarrow{AB}$ and chord $\overline{BC}$, is equal to one-half the measure of its intercepted arc $\widehat{BC}$. $m\angle ABC = \frac{1}{2}m\widehat{BC}$, or $m\angle ABC = \frac{1}{2}b$.

Fig. 5–44

MODEL PROBLEM ⎯⎯⎯⎯⎯⎯⎯⎯⎯

In the figure shown, triangle *ABC* is inscribed in the circle. $m\widehat{BC}:m\widehat{CA}:m\widehat{AB}$ = 2:3:5. Find the measure of the acute angle formed by side $\overline{BC}$ and the tangent to the circle at *B*.

Solution: Represent the measures of arcs $\widehat{BC}$, $\widehat{CA}$, and $\widehat{AB}$ by 2*x*, 3*x*, and 5*x* respectively.

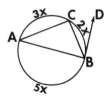

1. $2x + 3x + 5x = 360$

2. $\quad\quad 10x = 360$

3. $\quad\quad\quad x = 36$

4. $\quad\quad\quad 2x = 72$

5. $m\angle DBC = \frac{1}{2}m\widehat{BC}$, or $m\angle DBC = \frac{1}{2}(72) = 36$.

Answer: $m\angle DBC = 36$.

EXERCISES

1. Find the measure of the angle formed by a tangent and a chord drawn from the point of contact if the angle intercepts an arc whose measure is:
   a. 40   *b.* 80   *c.* 65   *d.* 140   *e. b*   *f.* $180 - 2x$

2. Find the measure of the arc intercepted by an angle formed by a tangent and a chord drawn from the point of contact if the angle measures:
   a. 30   *b.* 50   *c.* $22\frac{1}{2}$ *d.* 70   *e. m*   *f.* $\frac{3}{2}x$

3. Triangle ABC is inscribed in a circle, side $\overline{AB}$ is a diameter of the circle, and arc $\overset{\frown}{AC}$ measures 100. The measure of the acute angle formed by the tangent at B and side $\overline{BC}$ of the triangle is _____.

4. Equilateral triangle ABC is inscribed in a circle. Find the measure of the acute angle formed by side $\overline{AB}$ and the tangent at B.

5. A regular pentagon $ABCDE$ is inscribed in a circle. Find the measure of the acute angle formed by side $\overline{AB}$ and the tangent at B.

6. Triangle ABC is inscribed in circle O. $m\overset{\frown}{AB}:m\overset{\frown}{BC}:m\overset{\frown}{CA} = 3:3:4$. Find the measure of the acute angle formed by side $\overline{AB}$ and the tangent to the circle at A.

In 7–11, O is the center of the circle and $\overset{\leftrightarrow}{BT}$ is tangent to the circle. Find the value of x, or x and y, as indicated.

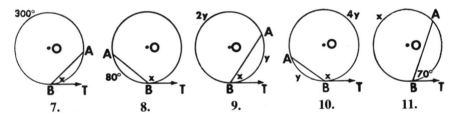

7.   8.   9.   10.   11.

Measuring an Angle Formed by Two Chords Intersecting Within a Circle

Theorem 73. The measure of an angle formed by two chords intersecting within a circle is equal to one-half the sum of the measures of the intercepted arcs.

[The proof for this theorem appears on page 604.]

In circle O (Fig. 5–45), if chords $\overline{AB}$ and $\overline{CD}$ intersect at E, then the measure of $\angle CEA$ is equal to one-half the sum of the measures of arcs $\overset{\frown}{AC}$ and $\overset{\frown}{BD}$. $m\angle CEA = \frac{1}{2}(m\overset{\frown}{AC} + m\overset{\frown}{BD})$, or $m\angle CEA = \frac{1}{2}(a + b)$.

Fig. 5–45

MODEL PROBLEM

In circle O, chords $\overline{AB}$ and $\overline{CD}$ intersect at E. If $m\angle CEB = 50$ and $m\widehat{CB} =$ 40, find the measure of minor arc $\widehat{AD}$.

Solution: Let $x =$ the measure of minor arc $\widehat{AD}$.

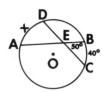

1. $m\angle CEB = \frac{1}{2}(m\widehat{BC} + m\widehat{AD})$

2. $50 = \frac{1}{2}(40 + x)$ Multiply by 2.

3. $100 = 40 + x$

4. $60 = x$

Answer: The measure of minor arc $\widehat{AD}$ is 60.

EXERCISES

1. Find the measure of the angle formed by two chords intersecting within a circle if the opposite arcs they intercept measure:
   a. 40 and 60   *b.* 90 and 20   *c.* 110 and 44   *d.* $4x$ and $6x$

2. Find the sum of the measures of the opposite arcs intercepted by two chords which meet inside a circle if the chords form an angle whose measure is:
   a. 50   *b.* 70   *c.* 90   *d.* $37\frac{1}{2}$ *e.* $67\frac{1}{2}$ *f.* $a + b$

3. Chords $\overline{AB}$ and $\overline{CD}$ of a circle intersect at point E within the circle. If $m\widehat{AC} = 120$ and $m\widehat{BD} = 80$, find the measure of angle CEB.

4. Regular pentagon $ABCDE$ is inscribed in circle O. Diagonals $\overline{AD}$ and $\overline{EB}$ intersect at F. Find the measure of angle BFD.

5. Two chords intersecting within a circle form an angle whose measure is 60. If one of the intercepted arcs measures 80, what is the measure of the other intercepted arc?

6. In a circle, chords $\overline{AB}$ and $\overline{CD}$ are perpendicular, and they intersect at E. If $m\widehat{AC} = 80$, find the measure of arc $\widehat{BD}$.

In 7–11, O is the center of the circle. Chords $\overline{AB}$ and $\overline{CD}$ intersect inside circle O. Find the value of x, or x and y, as indicated.

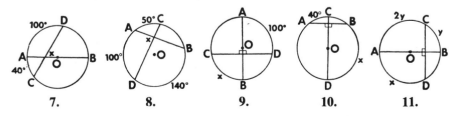

    7.   **8.**   **9.**   **10.**   **11.**

Measuring Angles Formed by Secants and Tangents Drawn to a Circle From an Outside Point

Definition. A *secant* is a line which intersects a circle in two points.

In circle O (Fig. 5–46), $\overleftrightarrow{EF}$ is a secant.

Theorem 74. The measure of an angle formed by two secants drawn to a circle from an outside point is equal to one-half the difference of the measures of the intercepted arcs.

Fig. 5–46

[The proof for this theorem appears on page 605.]

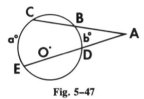

In circle O (Fig. 5–47), if secants $\overleftrightarrow{AC}$ and $\overleftrightarrow{AE}$ are drawn from point A, then the measure of $\angle CAE$ is equal to one-half the difference of the measures of the intercepted arcs $\widehat{CE}$ and $\widehat{BD}$. $m\angle CAE = \frac{1}{2}(m\widehat{CE} - m\widehat{BD})$, or $m\angle CAE = \frac{1}{2}(a - b)$.

Fig. 5–47

Theorem 75. The measure of an angle formed by a tangent and a secant drawn to a circle from an outside point is equal to one-half the difference of the measures of the intercepted arcs.

[The proof for this theorem appears on page 606.]

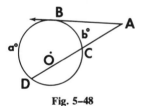

In circle O (Fig. 5–48), if tangent $\overleftrightarrow{AB}$ and secant $\overleftrightarrow{AD}$ are drawn from point A, then the measure of $\angle BAD$ is equal to one-half the difference of the measures of intercepted arcs $\widehat{BD}$ and $\widehat{BC}$. $m\angle BAD = \frac{1}{2}(m\widehat{BD} - m\widehat{BC})$, or $m\angle BAD = \frac{1}{2}(a - b)$.

Fig. 5–48

Theorem 76. The measure of an angle formed by two tangents drawn to a circle from an outside point is equal to one-half the difference of the measures of the intercepted arcs.

[The proof for this theorem appears on page 607.]

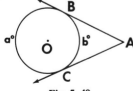

In circle O (Fig. 5–49), if tangents $\overleftrightarrow{AB}$ and $\overleftrightarrow{AC}$ are drawn from point A, then the measure of $\angle BAC$ is equal to one-half the difference of the measures of the intercepted arcs, major arc $\widehat{BC}$ and minor arc $\widehat{BC}$. $m\angle BAC = \frac{1}{2}(m \text{ major } \widehat{BC} - m \text{ minor } \widehat{BC})$, or $m\angle BAC = \frac{1}{2}(a - b)$.

Fig. 5–49

MODEL PROBLEM

The angle formed by two tangents drawn to a circle from the same external point measures 80. Find the measure of the smaller of the intercepted arcs.

Solution: Let x = the measure of minor $\widehat{BC}$.
Then $360 - x$ = the measure of major $\widehat{BC}$.

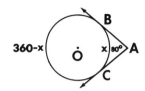

1. $m\angle BAC = \frac{1}{2}(m \text{ major } \widehat{BC} - m \text{ minor } \widehat{BC})$

2. $\quad 80 = \frac{1}{2}(360 - x - x)$

3. $\quad 80 = \frac{1}{2}(360 - 2x)$

4. $\quad 80 = 180 - x$

5. $\quad x = 180 - 80$

6. $\quad x = 100$

Answer: The measure of the smaller intercepted arc is 100.

NOTE. Another solution is possible. If $\overline{BC}$ is drawn, $\triangle ABC$ is an isosceles triangle and $m\angle ABC = 50$. Since $m\angle ABC = \frac{1}{2}m\widehat{BC}$, it follows that $m\widehat{BC} = 2m\angle ABC$. Hence, $m\widehat{BC} = 2(50) = 100$.

EXERCISES

1. Find the measure of the angle formed by two tangents drawn to a circle from an external point if they intercept a minor arc whose measure is:
   a. 160   *b.* 140   *c.* 120   *d.* 145   *e.* 135   *f.* 90

2. If two tangents drawn from an external point to a circle intercept a major arc whose measure is 210, the angle between the tangents measures _____.

3. One of the arcs intercepted by two tangents drawn to a circle from an external point measures 260. The measure of the angle formed by the tangents is _____.

4. If two tangents to a circle form an angle whose measure is 30, then the minor intercepted arc measures _____.

5. Tangents $\overline{PA}$ and $\overline{PB}$ from an external point P to circle O form an angle whose measure is 70. If radii $\overline{OA}$ and $\overline{OB}$ are drawn, what is the measure of angle AOB?

6. Two tangents $\overline{PA}$ and $\overline{PB}$ are drawn from point P to a circle. The measure of the major arc intercepted by the tangents is twice the measure of the minor arc. Find the measure of angle APB.

7. Find the measure of the angle formed by a tangent and a secant drawn to a circle from an external point if they intercept arcs whose measures are:
   a. 110 and 50   *b.* 120 and 65   *c.* *a* and *b*   *d.* 6*a* and 2*a*

8. The sides of an angle formed by a tangent and a secant drawn to a circle from an external point intercept arcs whose measures are 140 and 30. What is the measure of the angle?

9. An angle formed by a tangent and a secant drawn to a circle from an external point measures 65. If the greater intercepted arc measures 170, find the measure of the smaller intercepted arc.

10. An angle formed by a tangent and a secant drawn to a circle from an external point measures 40. Find the measure of the intercepted arcs if the measure of the larger arc is twice the measure of the smaller arc.

11. Find the measure of the angle formed by two secants drawn to a circle from an external point if they intercept arcs whose measures are:
    a. 100 and 40   *b.* 110 and 60   *c.* *m* and *n*   *d.* 7*x* and 3*x*

12. Two secants drawn to a circle from an external point P intercept arcs of 90° and 20° on the circle. Find the measure of angle P.

13. Two sides of an angle formed by two secants drawn to a circle from the same point intercept arcs of 144° and 92°. Find the measure of the angle.

14. From point P outside a circle, two secants $\overline{PAC}$ and $\overline{PBD}$ are drawn. Angle P contains 32° and minor arc $\overarc{AB}$ contains 50°. Find the number of degrees in minor arc $\overarc{CD}$.

In 15–19, O is the center of the circle. Tangents to the circle are marked "tan." Find the value of x, or x and y, as indicated.

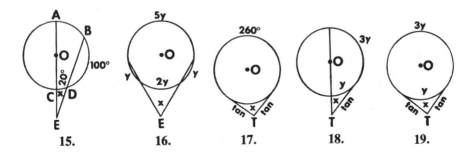

15.   16.   17.   18.   19.

More Difficult Exercises in Angle Measurements

MODEL PROBLEMS

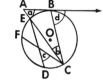

1. In the figure, $\overleftrightarrow{AB}$ is a tangent to circle O at point B; $\overleftrightarrow{AEC}$ is a secant; and $\overline{DE}$, $\overline{FC}$, and $\overline{BC}$ are chords. $m\widehat{EB} = 50$, $m\widehat{BC} = (4x - 50)$, $m\widehat{CD} = x$, $m\widehat{DF} = (x + 25)$, $m\widehat{FE} = (x - 15)$.

   a. Find $m\widehat{BC}$, $m\widehat{CD}$, $m\widehat{DF}$, and $m\widehat{FE}$.

   b. Find $m\angle a$, $m\angle b$, $m\angle c$, $m\angle d$.

Solution:

a. 1. $m\widehat{EB} + m\widehat{BC} + m\widehat{CD} + m\widehat{DF} + m\widehat{FE} = 360$

   2. $50 + 4x - 50 + x + x + 25 + x - 15 = 360$

   3. $\qquad\qquad\qquad 7x + 10 = 360$

   4. $\qquad\qquad\qquad\qquad 7x = 350$

   5. $\qquad\qquad\qquad\qquad\quad x = 50$

   6. $m\widehat{BC} = 4x - 50 = 4(50) - 50 = 200 - 50 = 150.$
      Ans. $m\widehat{BC} = 150.$

   7. $m\widehat{CD} = x = 50.$ *Ans.* $m\widehat{CD} = 50.$

   8. $m\widehat{DF} = x + 25 = 50 + 25 = 75.$ *Ans.* $m\widehat{DF} = 75.$

   9. $m\widehat{FE} = x - 15 = 50 - 15 = 35.$ *Ans.* $m\widehat{FE} = 35.$

b. 10. $m\angle a = \frac{1}{2}(m\widehat{BC} - m\widehat{EB}) = \frac{1}{2}(150 - 50) = \frac{1}{2}(100) = 50.$
      Ans. $m\angle a = 50.$

   11. $m\angle b = \frac{1}{2}m\widehat{EB} = \frac{1}{2}(50) = 25.$ *Ans.* $m\angle b = 25.$

   12. $m\angle c = \frac{1}{2}(m\widehat{CD} + m\widehat{FE}) = \frac{1}{2}(50 + 35) = \frac{1}{2}(85) = 42\frac{1}{2}.$
      Ans. $m\angle c = 42\frac{1}{2}.$

   13. $m\angle d = \frac{1}{2}(m\widehat{BC}) = \frac{1}{2}(150) = 75.$ *Ans.* $m\angle d = 75.$

2. $\overleftrightarrow{PA}$ is a tangent and $\overleftrightarrow{PCB}$ is a secant drawn to the circle. The measure of angle P is represented by x and the measures of $\widehat{AB}$, $\widehat{BC}$, and $\widehat{CA}$ are represented by $(3x - 20)$, $6x$, and y respectively.

   a. In terms of x and y, write a set of equations that can be used to solve for x and y.

   b. Solve the set of equations written in answer to part a.

   c. Find the number of degrees contained in $\widehat{BAC}$.

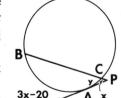

[The solution is given on the next page.]

Solution:

a. 1. $m\angle BPA = \frac{1}{2}(m\overset{\frown}{BA} - m\overset{\frown}{AC})$

2. $x = \frac{1}{2}(3x - 20 - y)$

3. $2x = 3x - 20 - y$

4. $20 = 3x - 2x - y$

5. $20 = x - y$

6. $m\overset{\frown}{AC} + m\overset{\frown}{CB} + m\overset{\frown}{BA} = 360$

7. $y + 6x + 3x - 20 = 360$

8. $9x + y - 20 = 360$

9. $9x + y = 360 + 20$

10. $9x + y = 380$

Answer: A set of equations is $x - y = 20$
$\qquad\qquad\qquad\qquad\qquad\quad 9x + y = 380$

b. 11. $x - y = 20$

12. $9x + y = 380$ Add the corresponding members of equation 11 and equation 12.

13. $10x = 400$

14. $x = 40$

15. $9x + y = 380$

16. $9(40) + y = 380$ In equation 15, replace x by 40.

17. $360 + y = 380$

18. $y = 20$

Answer: $x = 40$, $y = 20$.

c. 19. $m\overset{\frown}{BAC} = m\overset{\frown}{BA} + m\overset{\frown}{AC}$

20. $m\overset{\frown}{BAC} = 3x - 20 + y$

21. $m\overset{\frown}{BAC} = 3(40) - 20 + 20 = 120 - 20 + 20 = 120$

Answer: $\overset{\frown}{BAC}$ contains $120°$.

EXERCISES

1. Quadrilateral *ABCD* is inscribed in circle *O;* and the measures of arcs $\overarc{AB}$, $\overarc{BC}$, $\overarc{CD}$, and $\overarc{DA}$ are in the ratio 2:5:3:8 respectively. (*a*) Find the measure of each arc. (*b*) Find $m\angle BAD$.

2. In the circle shown, $\overleftrightarrow{PT}$ is a tangent, $\overleftrightarrow{PAB}$ is a secant, and $\overline{TA}$ a chord. $m\overarc{BT} = 112$ and $m\angle PTA = 34$.
   a. Find the measure of angle *BAT*.
   b. Find the measure of angle *TPB*.
   c. Show that $\overline{AB}$ is a diameter of the circle.

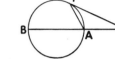

Ex. 2

3. Chord $\overline{AC}$ and diameter $\overline{BD}$ intersect at *E*. $m\overarc{AB} = 56$ and $m\angle BAC = 72$. Find the measures of $\overarc{AD}$, $\overarc{BC}$, angle *BEC*, and angle *ABC*.

Ex. 3

4. The tangent to the circle at *C* intersects chord $\overline{DB}$ extended at *F;* chord $\overline{AB}$ extended intersects $\overline{FC}$ at *E;* $\overline{DB}$ intersects $\overline{AC}$ at *R*.

   $$m\overarc{AB}:m\overarc{BC}:m\overarc{CD}:m\overarc{DA} = 8:7:10:11$$

   a. Find the measures of $\overarc{AB}$, $\overarc{BC}$, $\overarc{CD}$, and $\overarc{DA}$.
   b. Find $m\angle 1$, $m\angle 2$, and $m\angle 3$.

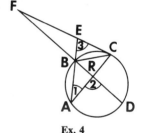

Ex. 4

5. $\overline{AB}$ and $\overline{CD}$ are chords. Chords $\overline{AC}$ and $\overline{DB}$ intersect at *E*. The tangent at *C* intersects $\overline{DB}$ extended at *K*. $m\overarc{AB} = 80$; and the measures of arcs $\overarc{BC}$, $\overarc{CD}$, and $\overarc{DA}$ are represented by *x*, (*2x* − 8), and (*x* + 32) respectively.
   a. Find $m\overarc{BC}$, $m\overarc{CD}$, and $m\overarc{DA}$.
   b. Find $m\angle r$, $m\angle s$, and $m\angle t$.

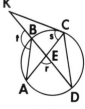

Ex. 5

6. $ABCD$ is a quadrilateral inscribed in a circle; $m\overarc{AB} = (4x - 25)$, $m\overarc{BC} = x$, $m\overarc{CD} = (2x + 20)$, $m\overarc{DA} = (3x - 35)$. Chords $\overline{AC}$ and $\overline{BD}$ are drawn; also chords $\overline{AB}$ and $\overline{DC}$ are extended to intersect at E, and the tangent at A intersects $\overline{CD}$ extended at F. Find the number of degrees contained in angle a, angle b, angle c, angle d, and angle e.

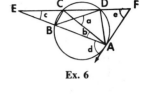

Ex. 6

7. $ABCD$ is a quadrilateral inscribed in circle O. Chord $\overline{BA} \cong$ chord $\overline{CD}$, and $\overline{BA}$ and $\overline{CD}$ extended intersect in point E. A tangent at B intersects $\overline{DA}$ extended in point F. Diagonals $\overline{BD}$ and $\overline{AC}$ are drawn. $m\overarc{AD} = 50$ and $m\overarc{BC} = 140$. Find $m\angle a$, $m\angle b$, $m\angle c$, $m\angle d$, and $m\angle e$.

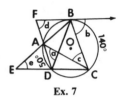

Ex. 7

8. Two secants $\overline{PDA}$ and $\overline{PCB}$ are drawn from external point P to a circle. Chords $\overline{AC}$ and $\overline{BD}$ intersect in F. If $m\overarc{AB} = 128$ and $m\overarc{CD} = 32$, find $m\angle P$, $m\angle ADB$, and $m\angle BFC$.

9. Tangent $\overleftrightarrow{PC}$ and secant $\overleftrightarrow{PBA}$ are drawn from point P to a circle, and chords $\overline{BC}$ and $\overline{AC}$ are drawn. $m\angle APC = 37$ and $m\overarc{ABC} = 236$. Find $m\overarc{BC}$, $m\angle BCP$, and $m\angle ACB$.

10. Congruent chords $\overline{AB}$ and $\overline{CD}$ of a circle are extended through B and D to intersect in P. $\overline{AD}$ and $\overline{BC}$ intersect in E, and $\overline{AC}$ is drawn. $m\angle P = 18$ and $m\overarc{AC} = 60$. Find $m\overarc{BD}$, $m\angle BCD$, $m\angle AEC$, and $m\angle ACB$.

11. $\overleftrightarrow{AB}$ is a tangent and $\overleftrightarrow{ACD}$ is a secant to a circle. $m\angle A$ is represented by x and $m\overarc{DB}$, $m\overarc{BC}$, and $m\overarc{CD}$ are represented by $(x + 3y)$, y, and $3y$ respectively.
   a. In terms of x and y, write a set of equations that can be used to solve for x and y.
   b. Solve the set of equations written in part *a*.
   c. Find the number of degrees contained in arc $\overarc{DBC}$.

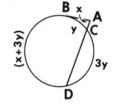

Ex. 11

12. Chords $\overline{AB}$ and $\overline{CD}$ intersect at point E, and chord $\overline{BC}$ is drawn. The measures of arcs $\overarc{AC}$ and $\overarc{BD}$ are represented by $(2x + 4y)$ and $(4x + 2y)$ respectively. The measure of angle ABC is represented by $(2x + 25)$ and the measure of angle AEC is 60.
   a. In terms of x and y, write a set of equations that can be used to solve for x and y.

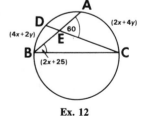

Ex. 12

   b. Solve the set of equations written in answer to *a* to obtain the values of *x* and *y*.

   c. Find $m\widehat{AC}$ and $m\widehat{BD}$.

13. Secants $\overline{PQR}$ and $\overline{PST}$ are drawn to a circle from external point *P* so that $m\angle P = 20$ and $m\angle QTS = 10$. If $m\widehat{QS}$ is represented by $(3x + y)$ and $m\widehat{RT}$ by $(8x + 4y)$:

   a. Write a pair of equations that can be used to solve for *x* and *y*.

   b. Solve these equations to find values for *x* and *y*.

   c. Find $m\angle RQT$.

14. The sides of a triangle inscribed in a circle have arcs whose measures are represented by $(x + 15)$, $(6x + 10)$, and $(8x - 40)$. Show that the triangle is an isosceles triangle.

15. The sides of a quadrilateral inscribed in a circle have arcs whose measures are represented by $(4x - 6)$, $(2x + 42)$, $(5x - 30)$, and $(3x + 18)$. Show that the quadrilateral is a square.

6. Using Angle Measurement in Proving Angles Congruent and Arcs Equal

Summary of Methods of Proving Angles Congruent and Arcs Equal

To prove that two or more angles are congruent, prove that any one of the following statements is true:

1. The measures of the angles are equal.
2. The angles are central angles that intercept the same arc or equal arcs in a circle or in equal circles.
3. The angles are inscribed in the same arc or in equal arcs in a circle or in equal circles.
4. The angles are inscribed angles or angles formed by a tangent and a chord that intercept the same arc or equal arcs in a circle or in equal circles.

To prove that two or more arcs are equal, prove that any one of the following statements is true:

1. The measures of the arcs are equal.
2. The arcs are intercepted by congruent central angles in a circle or in equal circles.
3. The arcs are intercepted by congruent inscribed angles, or congruent angles formed by a tangent and a chord, in a circle or in equal circles.

MODEL PROBLEMS ~~~~~~~~~~~~

1. *Given:*   In circle O, $\overline{BD}$ bisects inscribed $\angle ABC$. $\overleftrightarrow{EC}$
        is a tangent to circle O at C.

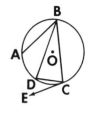

   To prove: $\angle ABD \cong \angle DCE$.

   Plan: To prove $\angle ABD \cong \angle DCE$, first use the
        "given" to prove that $\angle ABD \cong \angle DBC$. Then
        prove that $\angle DBC \cong \angle DCE$ by showing that
        $m\angle DBC = m\angle DCE$, since the measure of
        each angle is equal to $\frac{1}{2}m\widehat{DC}$. Therefore,
        $\angle ABD \cong \angle DCE$ by the transitive property of
        congruence.

Proof: *Statements*	*Reasons*
1. $\overline{BD}$ bisects $\angle ABC$.	1. Given.
2. $\angle ABD \cong \angle DBC$.	2. A bisector divides an angle into two congruent angles.
3. $\overleftrightarrow{EC}$ is tangent to circle O.	3. Given.
4. $m\angle DCE = \frac{1}{2}m\widehat{DC}$.	4. The measure of an angle formed by a tangent and a chord at the point of contact is equal to one-half the measure of the intercepted arc.
5. $m\angle DBC = \frac{1}{2}m\widehat{DC}$.	5. The measure of an inscribed angle is equal to one-half the measure of the intercepted arc.
6. $m\angle DBC = m\angle DCE$.	6. Transitive property of equality.
7. $\angle DBC \cong \angle DCE$.	7. Two angles are congruent if their measures are equal.
8. $\angle ABD \cong \angle DCE$.	8. Transitive property of congruence.

2. In a circle, congruent chords $\overline{AB}$ and $\overline{CD}$ are extended through B and D respectively until they intersect at P. Prove that triangle APC is an isosceles triangle.

Given: Chord $\overline{AB} \cong$ chord $\overline{CD}$. Chords $\overline{AB}$ and $\overline{CD}$ are extended to intersect at P.

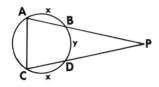

To prove: $\triangle APC$ is an isosceles triangle.

Plan: To prove that $\triangle APC$ is an isosceles triangle, show that $\angle A \cong \angle C$. It can be shown that $\angle A \cong \angle C$ by proving that both angles are inscribed angles whose measures are equal to one-half the measures of the equal arcs $\overset{\frown}{CDB}$ and $\overset{\frown}{ABD}$. Let $m\overset{\frown}{AB} = x$ and $m\overset{\frown}{BD} = y$.

Proof:

Statements	*Reasons*
1. Chord $\overline{AB} \cong$ chord $\overline{CD}$.	1. Given.
2. $m\overset{\frown}{AB} = m\overset{\frown}{CD} = x$.	2. In a circle, congruent chords have equal arcs.
3. $m\overset{\frown}{ABD} = x + y$, and $m\overset{\frown}{CDB} = x + y$.	3. The measure of an arc is equal to the sum of the measures of its parts.
4. $m\overset{\frown}{ABD} = m\overset{\frown}{CDB}$.	4. Transitive property of equality.
5. $\angle A \cong \angle C$.	5. In a circle, if inscribed angles intercept equal arcs, the angles are congruent.
6. $\overline{PA} \cong \overline{PC}$.	6. In a triangle, if two angles are congruent, the sides opposite these angles are congruent.
7. $\triangle APC$ is an isosceles triangle.	7. An isosceles triangle is a triangle that has two congruent sides.

3. *Given:* $\overline{CD}$ is a diameter in circle O. $\overleftrightarrow{AD}$ is tangent to circle O. $\overleftrightarrow{ABC}$ is a line.

To prove: $\triangle ABD$ and $\triangle DBC$ are mutually equiangular.

Plan: To prove that $\triangle ABD$ and DBC are mutually equiangular means that we must prove that three angles in $\triangle ABD$ are congruent to three angles in $\triangle DBC$.

[The proof is given on the next page.]

Proof: *Statements*   *Reasons*

1. $\overline{CD}$ is a diameter in circle O.	1. Given.
2. $\angle CBD$ is a right angle.	2. An angle inscribed in a semi-circle is a right angle.
3. $\overleftrightarrow{ABC}$ is a line.	3. Given.
4. $\angle ABD$ is supplementary to $\angle CBD$.	4. If two adjacent angles have their non-common sides on a straight line, the angles are supplementary.
5. $\angle ABD$ is a right angle, or $m\angle ABD = 90$.	5. The supplement of a right angle is a right angle.
6. $\angle CBD \cong \angle ABD$. (a. $\cong$ a.)	6. All right angles are congruent.
7. $\overleftrightarrow{AD}$ is tangent to circle O.	7. Given.
8. $\angle CDA$ is a right angle.	8. A tangent to a circle is perpendicular to a radius at the point of contact.
9. $\angle ADB$ is complementary to $\angle BDC$.	9. Two angles are complementary if the sum of their measures is 90.
10. $\angle BCD$ is complementary to $\angle BDC$.	10. The acute angles of a right triangle are complementary.
11. $\angle BCD \cong \angle ADB$. (a. $\cong$ a.)	11. If two angles are complements of the same angle, they are congruent.
12. $\angle BDC \cong \angle BAD$. (a. $\cong$ a.)	12. If two angles in one triangle are congruent to two angles in another triangle, the third angles in these triangles are congruent.
13. $\triangle ABD$ and $\triangle DBC$ are mutually equiangular.	13. If three angles in one triangle are congruent to three angles in another triangle, the triangles are mutually equiangular.

EXERCISES

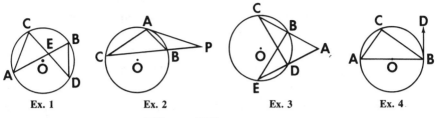

Ex. 1   Ex. 2   Ex. 3   Ex. 4

1. In circle O, chords $\overline{AB}$ and $\overline{CD}$ intersect in E. Prove that $\angle CAB \cong \angle BDC$.

2. If $\overline{PBC}$ is a secant and $\overleftrightarrow{PA}$ is a tangent to circle O at A, prove that $\angle PAB \cong \angle ACB$.

3. In circle O, $\overline{ABC}$ and $\overline{ADE}$ are secants. Prove that $\angle ADC \cong \angle ABE$.

4. In circle O, $\overline{AB}$ is a diameter. $\overleftrightarrow{DB}$ is tangent to circle O at B. Prove that $\angle ACB \cong \angle ABD$.

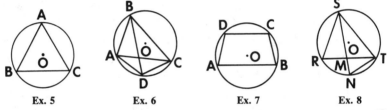

Ex. 5   Ex. 6   Ex. 7   Ex. 8

5. Triangle ABC is inscribed in circle O. If $\angle B \cong \angle C$, prove that $\overparen{ABC} = \overparen{ACB}$.

6. In circle O, $\overline{BD}$ bisects inscribed $\angle ABC$. Prove that $\triangle ADC$ is isosceles.

7. Quadrilateral $ABCD$ is inscribed in circle O, and $\angle DAB \cong \angle CBA$. (a) Prove: $\overline{DA} \cong \overline{CB}$. (b) Prove: $\overline{DC} \parallel \overline{AB}$.

8. Triangle RST is inscribed in circle O. $\overline{SN}$ bisects $\angle RST$. Prove: $\angle SMR \cong \angle STN$.

9. *Prove:* The bisector of an angle inscribed in a circle bisects the arc intercepted by the angle.

10. *Prove:* A trapezoid inscribed in a circle is isosceles.

11. Isosceles triangle ABC with $\overline{AB} \cong \overline{AC}$ is inscribed in a circle. Prove that if $\overleftrightarrow{ED}$ is a tangent to the circle at vertex A, $\overleftrightarrow{ED}$ is parallel to $\overleftrightarrow{BC}$.

12. *Prove:* A parallelogram inscribed in a circle is a rectangle.

13. In a circle, chord $\overline{AB}$ is parallel to tangent $\overleftrightarrow{CD}$, which intersects the circle at P. Prove that angle CPA is congruent to angle DPB.

14. From P, a point outside a circle, congruent secants $\overline{PAB}$ and $\overline{PCD}$ are drawn to the circle. Prove that chord $\overline{AB} \cong$ chord $\overline{CD}$.

15. In circle O, $\overline{AB}$ is a diameter and $\overline{AC}$ is a chord. Prove that $\overline{OD}$, the radius which bisects arc $\overparen{CB}$, is parallel to chord $\overline{AC}$.

16. A, B, C, and D are four points taken consecutively on a circle and so located that the measure of $\overparen{BC}$ is twice each of the measures of $\overparen{AB}$ and $\overparen{CD}$. Chords $\overline{AC}$ and $\overline{BD}$ are drawn intersecting in M, and chord $\overline{DC}$ is drawn. Prove that triangle DCM is isosceles.

17. $\overline{AB}$ is a diameter of a circle and C is any point on the circle. Chord $\overline{AC}$ is drawn and extended to D so that $\overline{AC} \cong \overline{CD}$, and $\overline{DB}$ is drawn. Prove that $\overline{DB} \cong \overline{AB}$.

18. Angle ABC is inscribed in a circle. Chord $\overline{BD}$ bisects angle ABC, and chord $\overline{DE}$ is drawn parallel to $\overline{AB}$. Prove that chord $\overline{DE}$ is congruent to chord $\overline{BC}$.

19. Quadrilateral $ABCD$ is inscribed in a circle. Diagonals $\overline{AC}$ and $\overline{BD}$ intersect in E, and $\overline{BE} \cong \overline{CE}$. Prove that chord $\overline{AB} \cong$ chord $\overline{CD}$.

20. *Prove:* A parallelogram circumscribed about a circle is a rhombus.

21. In a circle, chords $\overline{LM}$ and $\overline{RS}$ intersect at P. Prove that three angles in $\triangle LPR$ are congruent to three angles in $\triangle SPM$.

22. From point P outside a circle, tangent $\overleftrightarrow{PA}$, A being the point of tangency, and secant $\overline{PBC}$ are drawn. Prove that three angles in $\triangle PAB$ are congruent to three angles in $\triangle PCA$.

23. From point P outside a circle, two secants $\overline{PAB}$ and $\overline{PCD}$ are drawn. Prove that $\triangle PAD$ and $\triangle PCB$ are mutually equiangular.

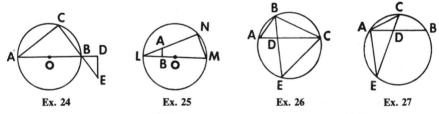

Ex. 24   Ex. 25   Ex. 26   Ex. 27

24. In circle O, diameter $\overline{AB}$ is extended through B to D, $\overline{DE} \perp \overline{AD}$, and $\overleftrightarrow{CBE}$ is a line. Prove that $\triangle ACB$ and $\triangle EDB$ are mutually equiangular.

25. In circle O, $\overline{LM}$ is a diameter and $\overline{AB} \perp \overline{LM}$. Prove that three angles in $\triangle ABL$ are congruent to three angles in $\triangle MNL$.

26. Triangle ABC is inscribed in a circle. $\overline{BDE}$ is the bisector of angle B. Prove that $\triangle ABD$ and $\triangle EBC$ are mutually equiangular.

27. C is the midpoint of $\overparen{AB}$. $\overleftrightarrow{CDE}$ is a line. Prove that three angles in $\triangle ACD$ are congruent to three angles in $\triangle ECA$.

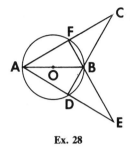

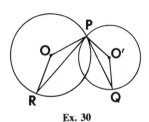

| Ex. 28 | Ex. 29 | Ex. 30 |

28. If $\overline{AB}$ is a diameter in circle O and $\overline{CA}$, $\overline{CD}$, $\overline{EF}$, and $\overline{EA}$ are secants, prove that $\triangle DBE$ and FBC are mutually equiangular.

29. $\overleftrightarrow{RQ}$ is the common tangent to two circles that are internally tangent at P. $\overline{PX}$ and $\overline{PY}$ are chords of the larger circle which intersect the smaller circle in S and T respectively. (a) Prove that $\overline{ST} \parallel \overline{XY}$. (b) Prove that $\triangle PST$ and PXY are mutually equiangular.

30. Unequal circles O and O' intersect at P. Chord $\overline{PR}$ is tangent to circle O' and chord $\overline{PQ}$ is tangent to circle O. Radii $\overline{OP}$, $\overline{OR}$, $\overline{O'P}$, and $\overline{O'Q}$ are drawn. (a) Prove that $\angle OPR \cong \angle O'PQ$. (b) Prove that $\triangle OPR$ and $O'PQ$ are mutually equiangular.

7. Completion Exercises

Write a word or expression that, when inserted in the blank, will make the resulting statement true.

1. The measure of an angle formed by a tangent and a secant intersecting in the exterior region of a circle is equal to one-half the _____ of the intercepted arcs.

2. The measure of an angle formed by two chords intersecting in the interior region of a circle is equal to one-half the _____ of the intercepted arcs.

3. The measure of an angle formed by two secants intersecting in the exterior region of a circle is equal to one-half the _____ of the intercepted arcs.

4. The measure of an angle formed by a tangent and a chord drawn to the point of contact is equal to _____ its intercepted arc.

5. If two chords of a circle bisect each other, the chords must be _____ of the circle.

6. If quadrilateral $ABCD$ is inscribed in a circle O, the sum of the measures of angles A and C is _____ degrees.

7. In a circle, a central angle and an inscribed angle intercept the same arc. The ratio of the measure of the central angle to the measure of the inscribed angle is _____.

8. An angle inscribed in a(an) _____ is a right angle.

9. An angle inscribed in an arc which contains less than 180° is a(an) _____ angle.

10. An angle inscribed in an arc whose measure is greater than the measure of a semicircle is a(an) _____ angle.

11. In a circle, if two inscribed angles intercept the same arc, the ratio of their measures is _____.

12. If two circles are tangent externally, the distance between their centers is equal to the _____ of the lengths of their radii.

13. Tangents to a circle at the ends of a diameter are _____ to each other.

14. In a circle, a chord which is the perpendicular bisector of another chord must be a(an) _____.

15. Two externally tangent circles have _____ common tangents.

16. In two concentric circles, all chords of the larger circle which are tangent to the smaller circle are _____.

17. Chords $\overline{AB}$ and $\overline{CD}$ of a circle intersect in E. If $m\overset{\frown}{AD} = 6x$ and $m\overset{\frown}{BC} = 4x$, then angle AED contains _____ degrees.

18. To circumscribe a circle about a triangle, it is necessary to bisect two of the _____ of the triangle.

19. The center of a circle circumscribed about a triangle is equidistant from the three _____ of the triangle.

20. To inscribe a circle in a triangle, it is necessary to bisect two of the _____ of the triangle.

21. The hypotenuse of a right triangle which is inscribed in a circle is _____ times as long as the radius of the circle.

22. If a parallelogram is inscribed in a circle, then the parallelogram must be a(an) _____.

23. If a line is perpendicular to a radius of a circle at its outer extremity, then the line is _____ to the circle.

24. Two internally tangent circles have _____ common tangent(s).

25. Two parallel chords intercept _____ arc(s) on a circle.

8. True-False Exercises

If the statement is always true, write *true;* if the statement is not always true, write *false.*

1. If chord $\overline{LM}$ bisects chord $\overline{AB}$, then $\overline{LM}$ must be perpendicular to $\overline{AB}$.

2. The length of the median to the hypotenuse of a right triangle is equal to half the length of the hypotenuse.

3. A bisector of a chord passes through the center of the circle.

4. The bisector of an inscribed angle bisects the intercepted arc.

5. In equal circles, congruent central angles intercept arcs of the same number of degrees.

6. If in a circle point P is the midpoint of $\overarc{CD}$, then the length of chord $\overline{CP}$ is one-half the length of chord $\overline{CD}$.

7. If a secant and a tangent to a circle are parallel, the diameter drawn to the point of tangency is perpendicular to the secant.

8. A parallelogram inscribed in a circle is a rectangle.

9. A trapezoid inscribed in a circle is isosceles.

10. A diameter which bisects one of two parallel chords, neither of which is a diameter, bisects the other chord also.

11. If parallelogram $ABCD$ is inscribed in a circle, sides $\overline{AB}$ and $\overline{DC}$ are equidistant from the center of the circle.

12. If two chords intercept equal arcs on a circle, the chords are parallel.

13. An angle inscribed in an arc which contains more than 180° is an obtuse angle.

14. A line which passes through the midpoint of a chord and the midpoint of its minor arc passes through the center of the circle.

15. If two circles are concentric, chords of the larger circle which are tangent to the smaller circle are congruent.

16. The opposite angles of an inscribed quadrilateral are complementary.

17. If two chords intersecting in a circle intercept opposite arcs the sum of whose measures is 180, then the chords are perpendicular to each other.

18. If two chords of a circle are perpendicular to each other, then one chord is a diameter.

19. There are two and only two circles of radius r which are tangent to each of two intersecting lines.

20. Congruent chords must have equal arcs.

21. If two circles are externally tangent to each other, the greatest number of common tangents that can be drawn to both circles is four.

22. If two chords intercept equal arcs on a circle, the chords are equidistant from the center of the circle.

23. If a circle is circumscribed about a parallelogram, each diagonal of the parallelogram is a diameter of the circle.

24. An angle inscribed in a major arc of a circle is an obtuse angle.

25. If two circles do not intersect, they must have four common tangents.

9. "Always, Sometimes, Never" Exercises

If the blank space in each of the following exercises is replaced by the word *always, sometimes,* or *never,* the resulting statement will be true. Select the word which will correctly complete each statement.

1. If two arcs of a circle are equal, the chords of these arcs are _____ parallel.

2. If the perpendiculars drawn from the center of a circle upon two chords are congruent, then the minor arcs subtended by these chords are _____ equal.

3. The perpendicular bisector of a chord of a circle _____ passes through the center of the circle.

4. A line passing through the midpoint of a chord of a circle _____ passes through the center of the circle.

5. If in a given circle $\overarc{AB}$ equals $\overarc{BC}$, then the length of chord $\overline{AC}$ is _____ twice the length of chord $\overline{AB}$.

6. Tangents drawn from an external point to a circle _____ make congruent angles with the chord joining the points of tangency.

7. Chord $\overline{AB}$ of circle O passes through the midpoints of two parallel chords. $\overline{AB}$ is _____ a diameter of the circle.

8. If in the same circle or in equal circles two chords are congruent, they are _____ equidistant from the center.

9. A parallelogram inscribed in a circle _____ has two acute angles.

10. If two chords of a circle are perpendicular to a third chord at its endpoints, the two chords are _____ congruent.

11. If the perpendicular bisectors of the sides of a triangle intersect on a side of the triangle, the triangle is _____ a right triangle.

12. Quadrilateral $ABCD$ is circumscribed about a circle whose center is O. The bisector of angle A _____ passes through O.

13. If from point A on a circle chord $\overline{AB}$ and tangent $\overleftrightarrow{AP}$ are drawn, then $m\angle PAB$ is _____ less than 90.

14. If two circles are concentric, any two chords of the larger circle which are tangent to the smaller circle are _____ congruent.

15. From external point A, tangents $\overleftrightarrow{AB}$ and $\overleftrightarrow{AC}$ are drawn to a circle, and chord $\overline{BC}$ is drawn. Triangle ABC is _____ equilateral.

16. If two chords of a circle are parallel, the minor arc of one chord is _____ equal to the minor arc of the other.

17. If the measure of the angle between two tangents to a circle is 60, the

triangle formed by these tangents and the chord joining the points of contact is _____ equiangular.

18. Two externally tangent circles _____ have three common tangents.

19. Two right triangles inscribed in the same or equal circles are _____ congruent.

20. Two triangles are inscribed in congruent circles and have their angles respectively congruent. The triangles are _____ congruent.

21. In circle O, chord $\overline{AB}$ is drawn. The length of $\overarc{AB}$ is _____ equal to the length of chord $\overline{AB}$.

22. An inscribed angle which intercepts an arc whose measure is less than 180 is _____ an obtuse angle.

23. An angle inscribed in an arc whose measure is less than 180 is _____ an obtuse angle.

24. If two angles intercept the same arc of a circle, they are _____ congruent.

25. If a chord in one circle is congruent to a chord in another circle, the minor arcs of these chords are _____ congruent.

26. At least one common tangent can _____ be drawn to two given circles.

27. A circle can _____ be constructed which will pass through three given points.

28. The center of the circle circumscribed about a triangle is _____ in the exterior region of the triangle.

29. The center of the circle circumscribed about a triangle _____ lies in the interior region of the triangle.

30. The bisectors of the angles of a triangle are collinear at a point which is _____ equidistant from the three sides of the triangle.

10. Multiple-Choice Exercises

Write the letter preceding the word or expression that best completes the statement.

1. In a circle, a central angle of $x°$ intercepts an arc of   (a) $\frac{1}{2}x°$ (b) $x°$ (c) $2x°$.

2. If an angle inscribed in a circle intercepts an arc of $y°$, the angle contains   (a) $\frac{1}{2}y°$ (b) $y°$ (c) $2y°$.

3. If two tangents are drawn to a circle at the ends of a chord whose arc measures 100°, the triangle formed is   (a) acute   (b) right   (c) obtuse.

4. The angle whose measure is equal to one-half the difference of the measures of its intercepted arcs has its vertex (*a*) in the interior region of the circle (*b*) on the circle (*c*) in the exterior region of the circle.

5. The angle whose measure is equal to one-half the sum of the measures of its intercepted arcs has its vertex (*a*) in the exterior region of the circle (*b*) in the interior region of the circle (*c*) on the circle.

6. An angle inscribed in an arc which measures less than 180° is (*a*) acute (*b*) right (*c*) obtuse.

7. The opposite angles of a quadrilateral inscribed in a circle are always (*a*) congruent (*b*) complementary (*c*) supplementary.

8. The two chords that form the sides of an angle inscribed in a semicircle are always (*a*) congruent (*b*) unequal in length (*c*) perpendicular to each other.

9. A circle can always be circumscribed about (*a*) a parallelogram (*b*) a rectangle (*c*) a rhombus.

10. If the length of a median of a triangle is equal to one-half the length of the side to which it is drawn, the triangle is (*a*) acute (*b*) obtuse (*c*) right.

11. If a parallelogram is inscribed in a circle, the diagonals always (*a*) are not congruent (*b*) are diameters (*c*) are perpendicular to each other.

12. If two chords intersecting within a circle intercept opposite arcs the sum of whose measures is 180, the angle formed by the two chords is (*a*) acute (*b*) right (*c*) obtuse.

13. If two circles have a common chord, then the sum of the lengths of their radii is (*a*) greater than (*b*) equal to (*c*) less than the distance between their centers.

14. If for two given circles only two common tangents exist, the circles (*a*) intersect in two points (*b*) are tangent internally (*c*) are tangent externally.

15. If two circles are tangent internally, the distance between their centers is equal to (*a*) the sum of the lengths of their radii (*b*) the difference of the lengths of their radii (*c*) the product of the lengths of their radii.

16. Two circles are externally tangent. The number of common tangents which these circles can have is (*a*) one (*b*) three (*c*) four.

17. The number of circles that can be tangent to each of two intersecting lines is (*a*) two (*b*) four (*c*) infinite.

18. Two unequal circles are tangent externally. From a point on their common internal tangent, tangents are drawn to the circles. The length of the tangent to the larger circle is (*a*) greater than the length of the tangent to the smaller circle (*b*) equal to the length of the tangent to the smaller circle (*c*) less than the length of the tangent to the smaller circle.

19. If two tangents are drawn to a circle at the endpoints of a chord which has an arc of 60°, the triangle formed by the tangents and the chord is (*a*) acute   (*b*) equilateral   (*c*) obtuse.

20. If *A, B, C,* and *D* are four consecutive points on a circle such that $\overset{\frown}{AB}$ = $\overset{\frown}{CD}$, then chords $\overline{BC}$ and $\overline{AD}$ always   (*a*) are congruent   (*b*) intersect   (*c*) are parallel.

21. In a circle, an inscribed angle and a central angle intercept the same arc. The ratio of the number of degrees in the inscribed angle to the number of degrees in the central angle is   (*a*) 1:2   (*b*) 1:1   (*c*) 2:1.

22. Two circles with radii 5 and 10 respectively are internally tangent to each other. The distance between their centers is   (*a*) 2   (*b*) 15   (*c*) 5.

23. Tangents $\overset{\leftrightarrow}{PA}$ and $\overset{\leftrightarrow}{PB}$ are drawn from external point *P* to circle *O*, points *A* and *B* being the points of contact. Angle *PAB* is always   (*a*) an acute angle   (*b*) the supplement of angle *AOB*   (*c*) congruent to angle *APB*.

24. The center of a circle which circumscribes a triangle is always the point of concurrency of   (*a*) the altitudes of the triangle   (*b*) the bisectors of the angles of the triangle   (*c*) the perpendicular bisectors of the sides of the triangle.

25. The center of a circle circumscribed about a triangle lies in the interior region of the triangle if the triangle is   (*a*) acute   (*b*) right   (*c*) obtuse.

11. Construction Exercises

The basic constructions involved in the following exercises, which are to be done with straightedge and compasses, appear in Chapter 14, which begins on page 617.

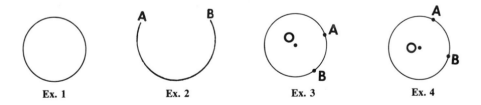

Ex. 1   Ex. 2   Ex. 3   Ex. 4

1. Find by construction the center of the circle.

2. Find by construction the center of the circle of which $\overset{\frown}{AB}$ is a part.

3. Locate by construction the midpoint *M* of minor $\overset{\frown}{AB}$ in circle *O*.

4. Locate by construction two points *M* and *N* on circle *O* each of which is equidistant from points *A* and *B*.

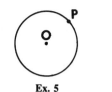

Ex. 5   Ex. 6   Ex. 7

5. Construct a tangent to circle O at point P.
6. Through point P; construct a tangent to circle O.
7. Through point A, construct the chord of circle O whose midpoint is A.
8. Through a point inside a circle, construct the smallest chord.
9. In a given circle, construct two chords that are congruent and parallel.
10. Construct two parallel lines which are tangent to the same circle.
11. Construct a tangent to a circle which is parallel to a given line in the exterior region of the circle.
12. Find the center of the circle that can be inscribed in a given   (a) acute triangle   (b) obtuse triangle   (c) right triangle.
13. Find the center of the circle that can be circumscribed about a given (a) acute triangle   (b) obtuse triangle   (c) right triangle.
14. Inscribe a circle in a given   (a) acute triangle   (b) obtuse triangle   (c) right triangle.
15. Circumscribe a circle about a given   (a) acute triangle   (b) obtuse triangle   (c) right triangle.
16. Circumscribe a circle about a given rectangle.
17. Inscribe a circle in a given rhombus.
18. Inscribe an equilateral triangle in a given circle.
19. Construct a circle which will pass through three given points A, B, and C which are not collinear.
20. Construct triangle ABC, having given angle A, angle B, and the included side c.

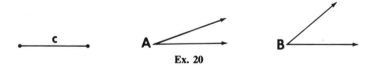

Ex. 20

21. Construct triangle RST in which $\angle R \cong \angle A$, $RS = c$, and $RT = b$.

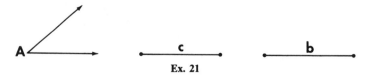

Ex. 21

22. Construct an isosceles triangle whose base is the given line segment b and whose altitude upon b is the given line segment h.

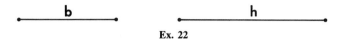

Ex. 22

23. To construct a tangent to circle O at point P, a line is drawn perpendicular to $\overleftrightarrow{OP}$ at point P as shown in the diagram. Which one of the following statements is the theorem used to prove that $\overleftrightarrow{BP}$ is tangent to circle O?

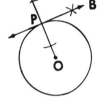

Ex. 23

   a. A tangent to a circle is a line in the plane of the circle which intersects the circle in one and only one point.
   b. A line perpendicular to a radius at its endpoint on the circle is tangent to the circle.
   c. A tangent to a circle is perpendicular to the radius drawn to the point of contact.

24. The construction of tangents to circle O from external point B is shown. Which one of the following statements is used to prove the construction?

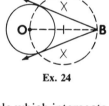

Ex. 24

   a. In a circle, a line perpendicular to a radius at its outer extremity is tangent to the circle.
   b. A tangent to a circle is perpendicular to the radius drawn to the point of contact.
   c. A tangent to a circle is a line in the plane of the circle which intersects the circle in one and only one point.

25. The diagram shows the construction of a tangent $\overleftrightarrow{PA}$ to circle O from external point P. Which theorem is used in the proof of this construction to show that $\overleftrightarrow{PA}$ is a tangent?

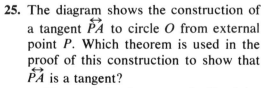

Ex. 25

   a. If two circles intersect, the line joining their centers is the perpendicular bisector of the common chord.
   b. An angle inscribed in a semicircle is a right angle.
   c. Tangents to a circle from an external point are congruent.

26. The construction for circumscribing a circle about a given triangle is shown. Which two of the following statements are used in proving the construction?

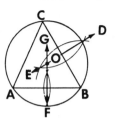

Ex. 26

   a. If two quantities are equal to the same quantity, they are equal to each other.

   b. If a point is equidistant from the endpoints of a line segment, then the point is on the perpendicular bisector of the line segment.

   c. If a point is on the perpendicular bisector of a line segment, then the point is equidistant from the endpoints of the line segment.

27. The construction for inscribing a circle in a given triangle is shown. Which two of the following statements are used in proving the construction?

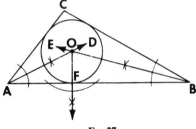

Ex. 27

   a. If a point is on the bisector of an angle, the point is equidistant from the sides of the angle.

   b. If two quantities are equal to the same quantity, they are equal to each other.

   c. If a point is equidistant from the sides of an angle, then the point is on the bisector of the angle.

CHAPTER VI

Proportions Involving Line Segments and Similar Triangles

Up to this point, we have studied the conditions under which polygons, particularly triangles, would be congruent; that is, they would have the same "size" and the same "shape." Now we will study the conditions under which two polygons, particularly triangles, will have the same "shape" but will not necessarily have the same "size." In order to engage in this study, it would be best for us to have a clear understanding of *ratio* and *proportion*, particularly in relation to line segments.

1. Ratio and Proportion

The Meaning of Ratio

If line segment $\overline{AB}$ is 8 feet long and line segment $\overline{CD}$ is 4 feet long, we can compare their lengths by using division. If we divide 8 by 4, we have $\frac{8}{4}$, or $\frac{2}{1}$, which tells us that $\overline{AB}$ is twice as long as $\overline{CD}$. Such a comparison is called a *ratio*.

Definition. The ratio of two numbers a and b, where b is not zero, is the number $\frac{a}{b}$.

Thus, the ratio of 8 to 4 is $\frac{8}{4}$, which is read "8 to 4" or "8 is to 4." The numbers 8 and 4 are called the *terms* of the ratio.

Keep in mind that we do not find the ratio of two objects. We find the ratio of two numbers which are the measures of the two objects in terms of the *same unit of measure*.

For example, if $\overline{AB}$ has a measure of 1 foot and $\overline{CD}$ has a measure of 1 inch, to find the ratio of AB to CD, we first convert 1 foot to 12 inches and then divide 12 by 1, obtaining $\frac{AB}{CD} = \frac{12}{1}$. The inch is the common unit.

Likewise, if $\angle A$ measures 45 and $\angle B$ is a right angle, to find the ratio of $m\angle A$ to $m\angle B$, we first find that the measure of the right angle is 90 and then divide 45 by 90, obtaining $\dfrac{m\angle A}{m\angle B} = \dfrac{45}{90}$ or $\dfrac{1}{2}$. The degree is the common unit of measure.

However, if in the future we should talk about the *ratio of two angles* or *the ratio of two segments*, we will mean the number which is the quotient of their measures in terms of the same unit of measure.

The ratio of a to b may also be written in the form $a:b$. An advantage of this form is that it can be used to express the comparison among three or more numbers. The statement that three numbers are in the ratio $4:5:9$ means that the ratio of the first to the second is $4:5$, the ratio of the second to the third is $5:9$, and the ratio of the first to the third is $4:9$. This does not mean that the numbers must be 4, 5, and 9. There are many sets of numbers whose ratio is $4:5:9$. For example, 8, 10, 18; also 12, 15, 27. In general, a set of numbers whose ratio is $4:5:9$ can be represented by $4x$, $5x$, and $9x$ where $x \neq 0$.

The Meaning of Proportion

Since the ratio $\frac{4}{12}$ is equal to the ratio $\frac{1}{3}$, we may write $\frac{4}{12} = \frac{1}{3}$. The equation $\frac{4}{12} = \frac{1}{3}$ is called a *proportion*. Another way of writing the proportion $\frac{4}{12} = \frac{1}{3}$ is $4:12 = 1:3$, which is read "4 is to 12 as 1 is to 3."

Definition. A *proportion* is an equation which states that two ratios are equal.

The proportion $\dfrac{a}{b} = \dfrac{c}{d}$, or $a:b = c:d$, is read "a is to b as c is to d," or "a divided by b is equal to c divided by d."

The four numbers a, b, c, and d are called the *terms* of the proportion. The number a is called the first term, b is called the second term, c is called the third term, and d is called the fourth term.

The first and fourth terms, a and d, are called the *extremes* of the proportion. (See Fig. 6–1.)

The second and third terms, b and c, are called the *means* of the proportion.

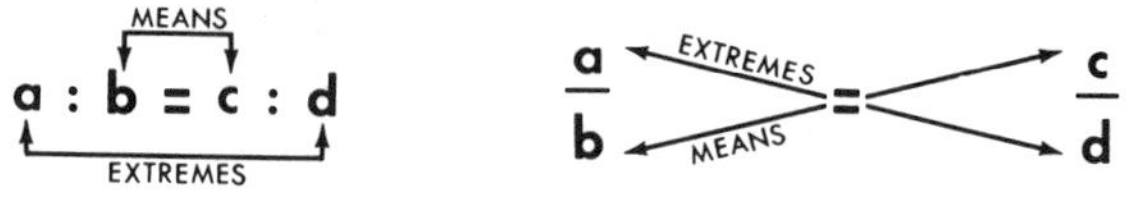

Fig. 6–1

The fact that the four ratios $\frac{1}{2}$, $\frac{2}{4}$, $\frac{3}{6}$, and $\frac{4}{8}$ represent the same number may be expressed in the form of the extended proportion $\frac{1}{2} = \frac{2}{4} = \frac{3}{6} = \frac{4}{8}$. In general: $\dfrac{a}{b} = \dfrac{c}{d} = \dfrac{e}{f} = \dfrac{g}{h}$ states that the four ratios represent the same number.

The Fourth Proportional

In a proportion in which no terms are equal, the fourth term is called the *fourth proportional* to the other three. In the proportion $a:b = c:d$, the term d is the fourth proportional to a, b, and c.

The Mean Proportional and the Third Proportional

If the two means of a proportion are equal, either mean is called the *mean proportional* between the first and fourth terms of the proportion. In the proportion $a:b = b:c$, the term b is the mean proportional between a and c. Also, the fourth term is called the *third proportional* to the other two terms. Thus, c is the third proportional to a and b.

Theorems Involving Proportions

Keep in mind that since a proportion is an equation, all properties of equality can be used to transform a proportion into an equivalent equation. For example, we can transform the proportion $\dfrac{a}{b} = \dfrac{c}{d}$ to the equation $ad = bc$ by using the *multiplication property of equality*, multiplying both members by bd.

Theorem 77. **In a proportion, the product of the means is equal to the product of the extremes.**

Thus, if $\frac{4}{8} = \frac{5}{10}$, then $8 \times 5 = 4 \times 10$.

And if $\dfrac{a}{b} = \dfrac{c}{d}$, then $bc = ad$.

Theorem 78. **If the product of two numbers (not zero) is equal to the product of two other numbers (not zero), either pair of numbers may be made the means and the other pair may be made the extremes in a proportion.**

Thus if $6 \times 5 = 3 \times 10$, then $\frac{6}{3} = \frac{10}{5}$ or $\frac{3}{6} = \frac{5}{10}$.

And, if $ad = bc$, then $\dfrac{a}{b} = \dfrac{c}{d}$ or $\dfrac{b}{a} = \dfrac{d}{c}$.

Theorem 79. **If any three terms of one proportion are equal respectively to the three corresponding terms of another proportion, the fourth terms are equal.**

Thus, if $\dfrac{4}{8} = \dfrac{x}{16}$ and $\dfrac{4}{8} = \dfrac{y}{16}$, then $x = y$.

And, if $\dfrac{a}{b} = \dfrac{c}{d}$ and $\dfrac{a}{b} = \dfrac{c}{e}$, then $d = e$.

Theorem 80. **If the numerators of the ratios of a proportion are equal (not zero), the denominators are equal; also, if the denominators of the ratios of a proportion are equal, the numerators are equal.**

Thus, if $\dfrac{a}{b} = \dfrac{c}{d}$ and $a = c$, then $b = d$.

And, if $\dfrac{a}{b} = \dfrac{c}{d}$ and $a = c$, then $a = c$.

Theorem 81. **If four numbers (not zero) are in proportion, they are also in proportion by inversion; that is, the second term is to the first as the fourth is to the third.**

Thus, if $\dfrac{3}{9} = \dfrac{4}{12}$, then $\dfrac{9}{3} = \dfrac{12}{4}$. And, if $\dfrac{a}{b} = \dfrac{c}{d}$, then $\dfrac{b}{a} = \dfrac{d}{c}$.

Theorem 82. **If four numbers (not zero) are in proportion, they are also in proportion by alternation; that is, the first term is to the third as the second is to the fourth.**

Thus, if $\dfrac{10}{15} = \dfrac{8}{12}$, then it is also true that $\dfrac{10}{8} = \dfrac{15}{12}$.

And, if $\dfrac{a}{b} = \dfrac{c}{d}$, then it is also true that $\dfrac{a}{c} = \dfrac{b}{d}$.

Theorem 83. **If four numbers are in proportion, they are also in proportion by addition; that is, the first term plus the second term is to the second term as the third term plus the fourth term is to the fourth term.**

Thus, if $\dfrac{3}{6} = \dfrac{4}{8}$, then it is also true that $\dfrac{3+6}{6} = \dfrac{4+8}{8}$ or $\dfrac{9}{6} = \dfrac{12}{8}$.

And, if $\dfrac{a}{b} = \dfrac{c}{d}$, then it is also true that $\dfrac{a+b}{b} = \dfrac{c+d}{d}$.

Theorem 84. **If four numbers are in proportion, they are also in proportion by subtraction; that is, the first term minus the second term is to the second term as the third term minus the fourth term is to the fourth term.**

Thus, if $\dfrac{15}{5} = \dfrac{12}{4}$, then it is also true that $\dfrac{15-5}{5} = \dfrac{12-4}{4}$ or $\dfrac{10}{5} = \dfrac{8}{4}$.

And, if $\dfrac{a}{b} = \dfrac{c}{d}$, then it is also true that $\dfrac{a-b}{b} = \dfrac{c-d}{d}$.

Theorem 85. **In a sequence of equal ratios, the sum of the numerators of the ratios is to the sum of the denominators as any numerator is to its denominator.**

Thus, if $\dfrac{1}{2} = \dfrac{3}{6} = \dfrac{5}{10}$, then it is also true that $\dfrac{1+3+5}{2+6+10} = \dfrac{1}{2}$ or $\dfrac{9}{18} = \dfrac{1}{2}$.

And, if $\dfrac{a}{b} = \dfrac{c}{d} = \dfrac{e}{f}$, then it is also true that $\dfrac{a+c+e}{b+d+f} = \dfrac{a}{b}$.

MODEL PROBLEMS ~~~~~~~~~~~~~~~~~

1. Is $\frac{12}{20} = \frac{36}{60}$ a proportion?

Solution: Since $\frac{12}{20} = \frac{3}{5}$ and $\frac{36}{60} = \frac{3}{5}$, the ratios $\frac{12}{20}$ and $\frac{36}{60}$ are equal.

Therefore, $\frac{12}{20} = \frac{36}{60}$ is a proportion.

Answer: Yes.

NOTE. We can also show that $\frac{12}{20} = \frac{36}{60}$ is a proportion by showing that the product of the second and third terms, 20×36, is equal to the product of the first and fourth terms, 12×60.

2. Solve for c in the proportion $18:6 = c:9$.

Solution:

1. $18:6 = c:9$	In a proportion, the product of the means is equal
2. $6c = 18 \times 9$	to the product of the extremes.
3. $6c = 162$	
4. $c = 27$	*Check:* $18:6 \overset{?}{=} 27:9$
	$3:1 = 3:1$

Answer: $c = 27$.

3. Find the fourth proportional to 3, 4, and 9.

Solution:

1. Let $x =$ the fourth proportional to 3, 4, and 9.
2. Then $3:4 = 9:x$
3. $\quad\quad 3x = 36$
4. $\quad\quad x = 12$ $\quad$ *Check:* $3:4 \overset{?}{=} 9:12$
$\quad\quad\quad\quad\quad\quad\quad\quad\quad\quad\quad 3:4 = 3:4$

Answer: 12.

4. Find the mean proportional between 4 and 16.

Solution:

1. Let $x =$ the mean proportional between 4 and 16.
2. Then $4:x = x:16$
3. $\quad\quad x^2 = 64$
4. $\quad\quad x = \pm 8$ $\quad$ Find the square root of both numbers in the preceding equation.

[The solution continues on the next page.]

In our work in geometry, we will restrict our discussion to positive values.

Check: $4:8 \overset{?}{=} 8:16$

$\qquad$ $1:2 = 1:2$

Answer: $x = 8$.

EXERCISES

1. Use a colon to represent in simplest form the ratio of the first number to the second number:

   a. 8, 2   *b.* 50, 30   *c.* 48, 28   *d.* 15, 45   *e.* 8, 9

2. Express in simplest form the ratio of the first measure to the second measure:

   a. 6 in., 18 in.   *b.* 2 ft., 4 in.   *c.* 1 right angle, 30°

   d. 2 lb., 8 oz.   *e.* 3 dollars, 50 cents   *f.* 2 feet, 4 yards

3. Does an equal ratio result when both terms of a given ratio are:

   a. multiplied by the same non-zero number?

   b. divided by the same non-zero number?

   c. increased by the same number?

   d. decreased by the same number?

4. Given $XZ = 4$ and $ZY = 6$. State each of the following ratios:

   a. $XZ{:}ZY$ *b.* $ZY{:}XZ$ *c.* $XZ{:}XY$

   d. $XY{:}ZY$

   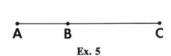
   Ex. 4

5. B is a point on $\overline{AC}$ such that $\dfrac{AB}{BC} = \dfrac{1}{2}$. State each of the following ratios:

   a. $BC{:}AB$ *b.* $AB{:}AC$ *c.* $BC{:}AC$

   d. $AC{:}BC$

   Ex. 5

6. In which of the following may the ratios form a proportion?

   a. $\frac{2}{3}, \frac{24}{36}$ *b.* $\frac{4}{5}, \frac{32}{40}$ *c.* $\frac{3}{4}, \frac{9}{16}$ *d.* $\frac{2}{9}, \frac{10}{54}$ *e.* $\frac{9}{12}, \frac{15}{20}$

7. Use each of the following sets of numbers to form two proportions:

   a. 40, 10, 1, 4   *b.* 4, 6, 18, 12   *c.* 2, 9, 6, 3   *d.* 28, 6, 24, 7

8. Discover which one of the following is a true statement:

   a. $5{:}10 = 10{:}20$ *b.* $3{:}4 = 15{:}30$ *c.* $12{:}18 = 36{:}72$

9. Find and check the value of x in each of the following proportions:

   a. $\dfrac{x}{10} = \dfrac{3}{20}$ *b.* $\dfrac{20}{x} = \dfrac{10}{24}$ *c.* $\dfrac{4}{12} = \dfrac{x}{x+8}$ *d.* $\dfrac{32}{16} = \dfrac{21-x}{x}$

   e. $5{:}x = 8{:}24$ *f.* $x{:}10 = 65{:}5$ *g.* $2r{:}s = x{:}t$

10. Express x in terms of r, s, and t:
    a. $r:s = t:x$ *b.* $s:2r = t:x$ *c.* $3r:2t = x:4s$

11. Find the fourth proportional to:
    a. 1, 4, 5   *b.* 2, 3, 18   *c.* 10, 8, 30   *d.* 4, 18, 16   *e.* r, s, t *f.* $2a$, b, c

12. Find the mean proportional between:
    a. 4 and 9   *b.* 2 and 32   *c.* 4 and 25   *d.* $\frac{1}{2}$ and $\frac{1}{8}$ *e.* .3 and 1.2   *f.* c and d

13. Find the third proportional to:
    a. 1 and 4   *b.* 4 and 6   *c.* 50 and 10   *d.* .4 and .8   *e.* r and s

14. M is a point on $\overline{LN}$ such that $LM:MN = 3:4$.
    a. If $LM = 9$, find MN.   *b.* If $MN = 20$, find LN.

    L   M   N

    Ex. 14

15. Divide a line segment 36 inches long into two parts whose measures are in the ratio 1:8.

16. The measure of an angle and the measure of its complement have the ratio 7:2. Find the number of degrees contained in the angle and in the complement of the angle.

17. The measures of two supplementary angles are in the ratio 1:9. Find the number of degrees contained in the measures of the two angles.

18. If $\dfrac{r}{s} = \dfrac{t}{x}$ and $\dfrac{r}{s} = \dfrac{t}{y}$, why does $x = y$?

19. Use a theorem of proportions to find the ratio $x:y$ if:
    a. $5x = 10y$ *b.* $3x = 4y$ *c.* $2x = y$ *d.* $x = 8y$

20. Write a proportion that can be used to prove:
    a. $AE \times EB = CE \times DE$ if $\overline{AE}$, $\overline{EB}$, $\overline{CE}$, and $\overline{DE}$ are line segments.
    b. $PC \times PB = PA \times PA$ if $\overline{PC}$, $\overline{PB}$, and $\overline{PA}$ are line segments.

21. Use each given proportion to form a new proportion by inversion:
    a. $3:4 = 6:8$ *b.* $5:3 = 50:30$ *c.* $\frac{12}{15} = \frac{36}{45}$ *d.* $\frac{5}{12} = \frac{10}{24}$

22. Use each given proportion to form a new proportion by alternation:
    a. $1:2 = 8:16$ *b.* $4:5 = 16:20$ *c.* $\frac{3}{4} = \frac{15}{20}$ *d.* $\frac{20}{5} = \frac{80}{20}$

23. Use the addition or subtraction theorem of proportions to solve each of the following equations:

    a. $\dfrac{12 - x}{x} = \dfrac{16}{8}$ *b.* $\dfrac{20 - x}{x} = \dfrac{6}{4}$ *c.* $\dfrac{10 + x}{x} = \dfrac{6}{2}$ *d.* $\dfrac{x + 8}{x} = \dfrac{15}{5}$

24. If $\dfrac{u}{v} = \dfrac{w}{x} = \dfrac{y}{z} = \dfrac{3}{4}$, find $\dfrac{u + w + y}{v + x + z}$.

25. *a.* If $\dfrac{5}{x} = \dfrac{5}{7}$, find x.   *b.* If $\dfrac{y}{6} = \dfrac{3}{6}$, find y.

26. Write a proportion in which x is the fourth term and which when solved for x will give:

    a. $x = \dfrac{ab}{c}$ *b.* $x = \dfrac{rt}{s}$ *c.* $x = \dfrac{mn}{n}$ *d.* $x = \dfrac{r^2}{s}$ *e.* $x = \dfrac{a^2}{b}$

27. In $\triangle ABC$, $\dfrac{AD}{DB} = \dfrac{AE}{EC}$.

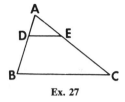

Ex. 27

  a. Write a new proportion using inversion.
  b. Write a new proportion using alternation.
  c. Write a new proportion using addition; then name the single line segments whose measures represent the first and third terms of this new proportion.
  d. If $AD = 5$, $DB = 15$, and $AE = 8$, find EC.
  e. If $AD = 2$, $AE = 6$, and $EC = 18$, find DB.
  f. If $DB = 6$, $AE = 12$, and $AC = 36$, find AD.
  g. If $AB = 25$, $AD = 10$, and $AC = 30$, find EC.

28. *a.* *Given:* In $\triangle ABC$, $CD{:}BD = BD{:}DA$. Find AD if $BD = 10$ and $CD = 4$.
  b. *Given:* In $\triangle ABC$, $CD{:}BC = BC{:}CA$. Find BC if $CD = 4$ and $CA = 16$.

Ex. 28

2. Proportions Involving Line Segments

Definition, **Two line segments are divided proportionally** when the ratio of the lengths of the segments of one of them is equal to the ratio of the lengths of the segments of the other.

In Fig. 6–2, $\overset{\leftrightarrow}{DE}$ divides $\overline{AB}$ and $\overline{AC}$ proportionally if:

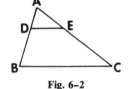

Fig. 6–2

$$\dfrac{AD}{DB} = \dfrac{AE}{EC} \quad \begin{bmatrix} \text{length of upper segment} \\ \text{length of lower segment} \end{bmatrix}$$

OR

$$\dfrac{DB}{AD} = \dfrac{EC}{AE} \quad \begin{bmatrix} \text{length of lower segment} \\ \text{length of upper segment} \end{bmatrix}$$

Postulate 37. **If a line is parallel to one side of a triangle and intersects the other two sides, the line divides those sides proportionally.**

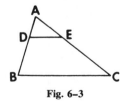

Fig. 6–3

If $\overset{\leftrightarrow}{DE} \parallel \overline{BC}$ and $\overset{\leftrightarrow}{DE}$ intersects $\overline{AB}$ and $\overline{AC}$ (Fig. 6–3), then

1. $\dfrac{AD}{DB} = \dfrac{AE}{EC}$ $\begin{bmatrix} \dfrac{\text{length of upper segment}}{\text{length of lower segment}} = \dfrac{\text{length of upper segment}}{\text{length of lower segment}} \end{bmatrix}$

2. $\dfrac{DB}{AD} = \dfrac{EC}{AE}$ $\left[\dfrac{\text{length of lower segment}}{\text{length of upper segment}} = \dfrac{\text{length of lower segment}}{\text{length of upper segment}}\right]$

If we apply the theorems of proportions that we have learned, we can obtain the following additional proportions:

3. $\dfrac{AD}{AE} = \dfrac{DB}{EC}$ $\left[\dfrac{\text{length of upper segment}}{\text{length of upper segment}} = \dfrac{\text{length of lower segment}}{\text{length of lower segment}}\right]$

4. $\dfrac{AE}{AD} = \dfrac{EC}{DB}$ $\left[\dfrac{\text{length of upper segment}}{\text{length of upper segment}} = \dfrac{\text{length of lower segment}}{\text{length of lower segment}}\right]$

5. $\dfrac{AB}{AD} = \dfrac{AC}{AE}$ $\left[\dfrac{\text{length of whole side}}{\text{length of upper segment}} = \dfrac{\text{length of whole side}}{\text{length of upper segment}}\right]$

6. $\dfrac{AB}{DB} = \dfrac{AC}{EC}$ $\left[\dfrac{\text{length of whole side}}{\text{length of lower segment}} = \dfrac{\text{length of whole side}}{\text{length of lower segment}}\right]$

7. $\dfrac{AD}{AE} = \dfrac{AB}{AC}$ $\left[\dfrac{\text{length of upper segment}}{\text{length of upper segment}} = \dfrac{\text{length of whole side}}{\text{length of whole side}}\right]$

8. $\dfrac{DB}{EC} = \dfrac{AB}{AC}$ $\left[\dfrac{\text{length of lower segment}}{\text{length of lower segment}} = \dfrac{\text{length of whole side}}{\text{length of whole side}}\right]$

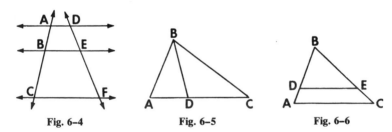

Fig. 6–4   Fig. 6–5   Fig. 6–6

Theorem 86. **Three or more parallel lines intercept proportional segments on any two transversals.**

In Fig. 6–4, if $\overleftrightarrow{AD} \parallel \overleftrightarrow{BE} \parallel \overleftrightarrow{CF}$, then $AB:BC = DE:EF$.

Theorem 87. **The bisector of an angle of a triangle divides the opposite side into segments whose lengths are proportional to the lengths of the two adjacent sides.**

In Fig. 6–5, if $\overline{BD}$ bisects angle B, then $AD:DC = AB:CB$.

Postulate 38. **If a line divides two sides of a triangle proportionally, the line is parallel to the third side.**

In Fig. 6–6, if $BD:DA = BE:EC$, then $\overleftrightarrow{DE} \parallel \overline{AC}$.
Also, if $BA:BD = BC:BE$, then $\overleftrightarrow{DE} \parallel \overline{AC}$.

MODEL PROBLEMS

1. In triangle RST, a line is drawn parallel to $\overline{ST}$ intersecting $\overline{RS}$ in K and $\overline{RT}$ in L. If $RK = 5$, $KS = 10$, and $RT = 18$, find RL.

Solution: *Method* 1   *Method* 2

Let $RL = x$ and $LT = 18 - x$. | Let $x = RL$.

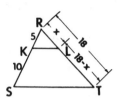

1. If $\overleftrightarrow{KL} \parallel \overline{ST}$, $\dfrac{RL}{LT} = \dfrac{RK}{KS}$ | 1. $\dfrac{RL}{RT} = \dfrac{RK}{RS}$

2. $\dfrac{x}{18 - x} = \dfrac{5}{10}$ | 2. $\dfrac{x}{18} = \dfrac{5}{15}$

3. $\qquad 10x = 90 - 5x$ | 3. $15x = 90$

4. $\qquad 15x = 90$ | 4. $\quad x = 6$

5. $\qquad\quad x = 6$

Answer: $RL = 6$.

2. In triangle ABC, $CD = 6$, $DA = 5$, $CE = 12$, and $EB = 10$. Is $\overleftrightarrow{DE}$ parallel to $\overline{AB}$?

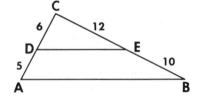

Solution: Since $\dfrac{CD}{DA} = \dfrac{6}{5}$,

and $\dfrac{CE}{EB} = \dfrac{12}{10} = \dfrac{6}{5}$,

then $\dfrac{CD}{DA} = \dfrac{CE}{EB}$.

Therefore, $\overleftrightarrow{DE}$ divides two sides of $\triangle ABC$, $\overline{CA}$ and $\overline{CB}$, proportionally; and $\overleftrightarrow{DE}$ must be parallel to the third side, $\overline{AB}$.

Answer: Yes.

EXERCISES

1. If $\overleftrightarrow{DE} \parallel \overline{AC}$, complete the following proportions:

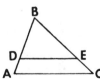

   a. $BD:DA = BE:$ _____.
   b. $BC:BE =$ _____$:BD$.
   c. $AD:EC =$ _____ : _____.
   d. $BE:BD =$ _____ : _____.

Ex. 1–7

2. If $\overleftrightarrow{DE} \parallel \overline{AC}$ and $BD:DA = 1:2$, find the ratio $BE:EC$.

3. If $BD = 8$, $DA = 4$, $BE = 10$, and $EC = 5$, is $\overleftrightarrow{DE} \parallel \overline{AC}$?

4. If $AD = 9$, $BD = 6$, $EC = 12$, and $BE = 4$, is $\overleftrightarrow{DE} \parallel \overline{AC}$?
5. If $\overleftrightarrow{DE} \parallel \overline{AC}$, $BD = 6$, $DA = 2$, and $BE = 9$, find EC.
6. If $\overleftrightarrow{DE} \parallel \overline{AC}$, $BD:DA = 1:4$, and $BC = 40$, find EC.
7. If $\overleftrightarrow{DE} \parallel \overline{AC}$, $BE = 7$, $EC = 3$, and $BA = 12$, find BD.

8. In triangle ABC, D is a point on $\overline{AB}$, E is a point on $\overline{AC}$, and $\overline{DE}$ is drawn. If $AB = 8$, $AC = 12$, $DB = 3$, and $EC = 4$, is $\overline{DE} \parallel \overline{BC}$?
9. In triangle ABC, D is a point on $\overline{AB}$, E is a point on $\overline{AC}$, and $\overline{DE}$ is drawn. $AD = 6$, $DB = 4$, $AC = 15$. In order for $\overline{DE}$ to be parallel to $\overline{BC}$, what must be the length of $\overline{EC}$?
10. A line parallel to side $\overline{AB}$ of triangle ABC intersects $\overline{AC}$ at D and $\overline{BC}$ at E. If $DC = 15$, $AD = 5$, and $EC = 18$, find BE.
11. A line parallel to side $\overline{AB}$ of triangle ABC intersects $\overline{CA}$ at D and $\overline{CB}$ at E. If $CD = 4$, $DA = 2$, and $BC = 9$, find CE.
12. Given triangle ABC with a line drawn parallel to $\overline{AC}$ intersecting $\overline{AB}$ at D and $\overline{CB}$ at E. If $AB = 8$, $BC = 12$, and $BD = 6$, find BE.
13. A line parallel to side $\overline{AC}$ of triangle ABC intersects $\overline{AB}$ at D and $\overline{BC}$ at E. If $BD = m$, $DA = n$, and $BE = p$, represent EC in terms of m, n, and p.
14. In triangle ABC, $\overline{BD}$ is the bisector of angle B. If $AB = 6$ and $BC = 8$, find the ratio $AD:DC$.
15. The nonparallel sides of a trapezoid measure 12 and 16 respectively. A line parallel to the bases divides the side whose measure is 12 into two segments whose measures are in the ratio 1:3. Find the measures of the segments of the side whose measure is 16.
16. The bisector of an angle of a triangle divides the opposite side into segments whose measures are 4 inches and 3 inches. If the side of the triangle adjacent to the 4-inch segment is 12 inches, find the measure of the side of the triangle adjacent to the 3-inch segment.

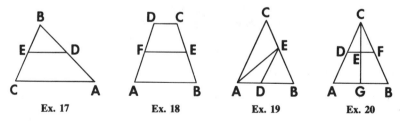

Ex. 17　　　　　Ex. 18　　　　　Ex. 19　　　　　Ex. 20

17. If $\angle BDE \cong \angle BAC$, prove that $BE:EC = BD:DA$.
18. If $\overleftrightarrow{DC} \parallel \overleftrightarrow{FE} \parallel \overleftrightarrow{AB}$, prove that $AF:FD = BE:EC$.
19. If $\angle DEA \cong \angle CAE$, prove that $AB:BD = CB:BE$.
20. If $CD:DA = CF:FB$, prove that $CE:CG = CD:CA$.

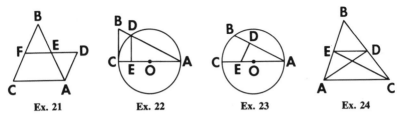

Ex. 21   Ex. 22   Ex. 23   Ex. 24

21. If $ADFC$ is a parallelogram, prove that $BE:EA = BF:DA$.

22. If in circle O, $\overline{DE} \perp$ diameter $\overline{CA}$, and $\overleftrightarrow{BC}$ is a tangent, prove that $AB:BD = AC:CE$.

23. If in circle O, $\overline{ED} \perp \overline{AB}$, and $\overline{CA}$ is a diameter, prove that $AD:AE = AB:AC$.

24. If $\overline{BC} \cong \overline{BA}$, $\overline{CE}$ bisects angle BCA, and $\overline{AD}$ bisects angle BAC, prove that $\overline{ED} \parallel \overline{AC}$.

25. In $\triangle RST$, P is a point on $\overline{RT}$. Through P, a line is drawn parallel to $\overline{ST}$ which intersects $\overline{RS}$ in Y. Through P, a line is drawn parallel to $\overline{RS}$ which intersects $\overline{ST}$ in X. Prove $RY:YS = SX:XT$.

3. Understanding the Meaning of Similar Polygons

In Fig. 6–7, we see two polygons which have the "same shape" but not the "same size." We call such polygons *similar polygons*. The symbol for the word *similar* is $\sim$.

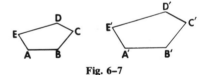

Fig. 6–7

If we study these polygons carefully, we find that they appear to have the same shape because their corresponding angles are congruent and the ratios of the measures of their corresponding sides are equal, (1:2).

We will use this description as a guide in stating a formal definition of similar polygons which will be useful in our work in geometry. Our definition of similar polygons will follow the same pattern that was used in defining congruent polygons.

Definition. *Two polygons are similar* if there is a one-to-one correspondence between their vertices such that:

1. All pairs of corresponding angles are congruent.
2. The ratios of the measures of all pairs of corresponding sides are equal.

In this definition, it is to be understood that the three phrases (1) "a one-to-one correspondence between the vertices of the polygons," (2) "corresponding angles of the two polygons," and (3) "corresponding sides of the two polygons" have the same meanings that they had when we dealt with congruent polygons.

In Fig. 6-7, polygon $ABCDE$ is similar to polygon $A'B'C'D'E'$, symbolized polygon $ABCDE \sim$ polygon $A'B'C'D'E'$, if:

1. $\angle A \cong \angle A'$, $\angle B \cong \angle B'$, $\angle C \cong \angle C'$, $\angle D \cong \angle D'$, $\angle E \cong \angle E'$

AND

2. $\dfrac{AB}{A'B'} = \dfrac{BC}{B'C'} = \dfrac{CD}{C'D'} = \dfrac{DE}{D'E'} = \dfrac{EA}{E'A'}$

NOTE. When the ratios of the measures of the corresponding sides of two polygons are equal, we say that "the corresponding sides of the two polygons are in proportion."

It is possible for two polygons to have their corresponding sides in proportion and yet not be similar.

Thus, in Fig. 6-8, polygons $ABCD$ and $A'B'C'D'$ have their corresponding sides in proportion. Yet the polygons are not similar because their corresponding angles are not congruent.

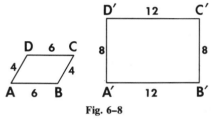

Fig. 6-8

It is also possible for two polygons to have their corresponding angles congruent and yet not be similar.

Thus, in Fig. 6-9, polygons $WXYZ$ and $W'X'Y'Z'$ have their corresponding angles congruent. Yet the polygons are not similar because their corresponding sides are not in proportion.

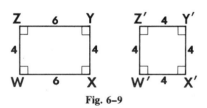

Fig. 6-9

We see that in order for two polygons to be similar, two conditions must be satisfied:

1. All pairs of corresponding angles must be congruent.
2. Their corresponding sides must be in proportion; that is, the ratios of the measures of their corresponding sides must be equal.

Since a definition is reversible, it follows that when two polygons are similar:

1. All pairs of corresponding angles are congruent.
2. Their corresponding sides are in proportion; that is, the ratios of the measures of their corresponding sides are equal.

Note that since triangles are polygons, it follows that if two triangles are similar, their corresponding sides are in proportion, that is, the ratios of the measures of their corresponding sides must be equal.

Definition. **The *ratio of similitude* of two similar polygons is the ratio of the measures of any two corresponding sides.**

If polygon $ABCD$ and polygon $A'B'C'D'$ are similar (Fig. 6–10), the ratio of the measures of any two corresponding sides, or the ratio of similitude, is 2:1.

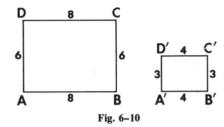

Fig. 6–10

Properties of Similarity

The relationship of similarity of two polygons, like the relationship of congruence of two polygons, gives rise to equations involving the measures of angles and the measures of line segments. Hence, in dealing with the relationship of similarity we may use the following postulates:

THE REFLEXIVE PROPERTY OF SIMILARITY

Postulate 39. **Polygon $ABCD$ ~ polygon $ABCD$.**

THE SYMMETRIC PROPERTY OF SIMILARITY

Postulate 40. **If polygon $ABCD$ ~ polygon $EFGH$, then polygon $EFGH$ ~ polygon $ABCD$.**

THE TRANSITIVE PROPERTY OF SIMILARITY

Postulate 41. **If polygon $ABCD$ ~ polygon $EFGH$, and polygon $EFGH$ ~ polygon $WXYZ$, then polygon $ABCD$ ~ polygon $WXYZ$.**

KEEP IN MIND

1. To prove that angles are congruent, show that they are corresponding angles of similar polygons.
2. To prove that the measures of line segments are in proportion, show that the line segments are corresponding sides of similar polygons.

MODEL PROBLEM

Triangle $ABC \sim$ triangle $A'B'C'$, and $A'C'$ corresponds to AC.

a. Find the ratio of similitude.

b. Find x and y.

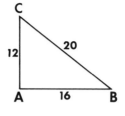

Solution:

a. The ratio of similitude of two similar polygons is the ratio of the measures of any two corresponding sides.

Ratio of similitude $= \dfrac{AC}{A'C'} = \dfrac{12}{6} = \dfrac{2}{1}$.

Answer: 2:1.

b. *Method 1*	*Method 2*
Since the ratio of similitude of $\triangle ABC$ to $\triangle A'B'C'$ is 2:1, each side of $\triangle ABC$ is 2 times as long as its corresponding side in $\triangle A'B'C'$, and each side of $\triangle A'B'C'$ is $\frac{1}{2}$ as long as its corresponding side in $\triangle ABC$. Therefore,	Since the corresponding sides of similar polygons are in proportion,

Method 2

1. $\dfrac{AC}{A'C'} = \dfrac{AB}{A'B'}$ and $\dfrac{AC}{A'C'} = \dfrac{BC}{B'C'}$

2. $\dfrac{12}{6} = \dfrac{16}{x}$ $\dfrac{12}{6} = \dfrac{20}{y}$

3. $12x = 96$ $12y = 120$

4. $x = 8$ $y = 10$

Method 1:

$A'B' = \frac{1}{2}AB$, or $x = \frac{1}{2}(16) = 8$

$B'C' = \frac{1}{2}BC$, or $y = \frac{1}{2}(20) = 10$

Answer: $x = 8$, $y = 10$.

EXERCISES

1. Are two congruent polygons always similar? Why?
2. What is the ratio of similitude of two congruent polygons?
3. Are all similar polygons congruent? Why?
4. What must be the ratio of similitude of two similar polygons in order for them to be congruent polygons?
5. Are all squares similar? Why?
6. Are all rectangles similar? Why?

7. Are all rhombuses similar? Why?

8. Can a quadrilateral be similar to a hexagon? Why?

9. The sides of a triangle measure 4, 8, and 10. If the smallest side of a similar triangle measures 12, find the measures of the remaining sides of this triangle.

10. The sides of a quadrilateral measure 12, 18, 20, and 16. The longest side of a similar quadrilateral measures 5. Find the measures of the remaining sides of this quadrilateral.

11. In two similar triangles, two corresponding sides measure 4 inches and 2 feet. Find the ratio of similitude of the two triangles.

12. Triangle $ABC \sim$ triangle $A'B'C'$, and their ratio of similitude is 1:3. If the measures of the sides of triangle ABC are represented by a, b, and c, represent the measures of the sides of triangle $A'B'C'$.

13. The ratio of similitude of two similar quadrilaterals is 2:1. If the measures of the sides of the larger quadrilateral are represented by w, x, y, and z, represent the measures of the sides of the smaller quadrilateral.

14. Rhombus $ABCD$ has a 60° angle and a side 5 inches in length. Rhombus $A'B'C'D'$ has a 120° angle and a side 10 inches in length. Prove that rhombus $ABCD$ is similar to rhombus $A'B'C'D'$.

15. Prove that any two equiangular triangles are similar.

16. Prove that any two equilateral triangles are similar.

4. Proving Triangles Similar

Since triangles are polygons, we can prove that two triangles are similar by showing that they satisfy the two conditions required in similar polygons. See how this is done in the following discussion:

Consider $\triangle ABC$ and $\triangle A'B'C'$ (Fig. 6-11) in which vertex A corresponds to vertex A', making $\angle A$ and $\angle A'$ a pair of *corresponding angles*, vertex B corresponds to vertex B', making $\angle B$ and $\angle B'$ a pair of *corresponding angles*, and vertex C corresponds to vertex C', making $\angle C$ and $\angle C'$ a pair of *corresponding angles*. Since $m\angle A = 53$ and $m\angle A' = 53$, $\angle A \cong \angle A'$. Since $m\angle B = 37$ and $m\angle B' = 37$, $\angle B \cong \angle B'$. Since $m\angle C = 90$ and $m\angle C' = 90$,

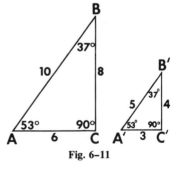

Fig. 6–11

$\angle C \cong \angle C'$. Therefore, all pairs of corresponding angles in $\triangle ABC$ and $\triangle A'B'C'$ are congruent.

The sides of the two triangles whose endpoints are corresponding vertices in the triangle are *corresponding sides* of the triangles. Therefore, in $\triangle ABC$ and $\triangle A'B'C'$, $\overline{AB}$ and $\overline{A'B'}$ are a pair of corresponding sides, $\overline{AC}$ and $\overline{A'C'}$ are a pair of corresponding sides, and $\overline{BC}$ and $\overline{B'C'}$ are a pair of corresponding sides. In each case, the pair of corresponding sides is opposite a pair of corresponding angles. For example, corresponding sides $\overline{AB}$ and $\overline{A'B'}$ are opposite the corresponding angles C and C' respectively.

Notice that if the measures indicated on the sides of triangles ABC and $A'B'C'$ are correct to the nearest integer, then $\dfrac{AB}{A'B'} = \dfrac{10}{5} = \dfrac{2}{1}$, $\dfrac{AC}{A'C'} = \dfrac{6}{3} = \dfrac{2}{1}$, and $\dfrac{BC}{B'C'} = \dfrac{8}{4} = \dfrac{2}{1}$. Thus, $\dfrac{AB}{A'B'} = \dfrac{AC}{A'C'} = \dfrac{BC}{B'C'}$. In other words, the corresponding sides of triangle ABC and triangle $A'B'C'$ are in proportion. Therefore, by the definition of similar polygons, $\triangle ABC \sim \triangle A'B'C'$.

However, there are shorter methods of proving triangles similar. These methods are indicated in the theorems and corollaries that follow. In stating these theorems and corollaries, we will follow the same practice that we employed in stating the congruence theorems. In each case, we will understand that a correspondence exists between the vertices of the two triangles for which the congruences and the proportions stated in the hypothesis are true statements.

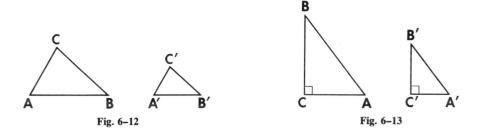

Fig. 6–12   Fig. 6–13

Theorem 88. Two triangles are similar if three angles of one triangle are congruent to three corresponding angles of the other. [a.a.a. ≅ a.a.a.]

[The proof for this theorem appears on pages 608–609.]

In $\triangle ABC$ and $A'B'C'$ (Fig. 6–12), if $\angle A \cong \angle A'$, $\angle B \cong \angle B'$, and $\angle C \cong \angle C'$, then $\triangle ABC \sim \triangle A'B'C'$.

Corollary T88–1. Two triangles are similar if two angles of one triangle are congruent to two corresponding angles of the other. [a.a. ≅ a.a.]

In $\triangle ABC$ and $A'B'C'$ (Fig. 6–12), if $\angle A \cong \angle A'$ and $\angle B \cong \angle B'$, then $\triangle ABC \sim \triangle A'B'C'$.

Corollary T88–2. **Two right triangles are similar if an acute angle of one triangle is congruent to an acute angle of the other.**

In right △*ABC* and *A'B'C'* (Fig. 6–13), if acute ∠*A* ≅ acute ∠*A'*, then right △*ABC* ~ right △*A'B'C'*.

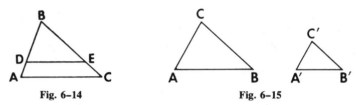

Fig. 6–14   Fig. 6–15

Corollary T88–3. **A line that is parallel to one side of a triangle and intersects the other two sides in different points cuts off a triangle similar to the given triangle.**

In △*ABC* (Fig. 6–14), if $\overleftrightarrow{DE} \parallel \overline{AC}$, then △*DBE* ~ △*ABC*.

Theorem 89. **Two triangles are similar if an angle of one triangle is congruent to an angle of the other and the including sides are in proportion.**

In △*ABC* and *A'B'C'* (Fig. 6–15), if ∠*C* ≅ ∠*C'* and the sides including these angles are in proportion, or $\dfrac{AC}{A'C'} = \dfrac{BC}{B'C'}$, then △*ABC* ~ △*A'B'C'*.

Theorem 90. **Two triangles are similar if their corresponding sides are proportional.**

In △*ABC* and *A'B'C'* (Fig. 6–15), if the corresponding sides are proportional, or $\dfrac{AB}{A'B'} = \dfrac{BC}{B'C'} = \dfrac{CA}{C'A'}$, then △*ABC* ~ △*A'B'C'*.

Methods of Proving Triangles Similar

To prove that two triangles are similar:

1. Use the definitions of similar polygons.

OR

2. Use any one of the preceding three theorems or their corollaries.

MODEL PROBLEM

Given: Lines $\overleftrightarrow{AC}$ and $\overleftrightarrow{BD}$ intersect at *E*. $\overleftrightarrow{AB} \parallel \overleftrightarrow{DC}$.
a. Prove △*ABE* ~ △*CDE*.
b. Write any proportion which would be true in the two triangles.
c. If *DE* = 10, *BE* = 15, and *CE* = 20, find *AE*.

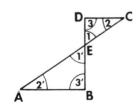

a. Plan: Prove that two angles in $\triangle ABE$ are congruent to two corresponding angles of $\triangle CDE$.

Proof: | *Statements* | *Reasons*
---|---

Statements	*Reasons*
1. $\overleftrightarrow{AC}$ and $\overleftrightarrow{BD}$ are straight lines.	1. Given.
2. $\angle 1$ and $\angle 1'$ are vertical angles.	2. Definition of vertical angles.
3. $\angle 1 \cong \angle 1'$. (a. $\cong$ a.)	3. If two angles are vertical angles, they are congruent.
4. $\overleftrightarrow{AB} \parallel \overleftrightarrow{CD}$.	4. Given.
5. $\angle 2 \cong \angle 2'$. (a. $\cong$ a.)	5. If parallel lines are cut by a transversal, the alternate interior angles are congruent.
6. $\triangle ABE \sim \triangle CDE$.	6. a.a. $\cong$ a.a.

b. Plan: Select pairs of sides which are opposite congruent angles. These sides must be in proportion because corresponding sides of similar triangles are in proportion.

$$\frac{AE \ (\text{opposite } \angle 3')}{CE \ (\text{opposite } \angle 3)} = \frac{BE \ (\text{opposite } \angle 2')}{DE \ (\text{opposite } \angle 2)}$$

c.

1. Since $AE{:}CE = BE{:}DE$, Let $AE = x$.

2. $\qquad x{:}20 = 15{:}10$

3. $\qquad 10x = 300$

4. $\qquad x = 30$

Answer: $AE = 30$.

EXERCISES

1. In triangle ABC, $m\angle A = 40$ and $m\angle B = 30$.
   In triangle EDF, $m\angle D = 30$ and $m\angle E = 40$.
   Is triangle ABC similar to triangle EDF? Why?
2. In triangle RST, $m\angle R = 90$ and $m\angle S = 40$.
   In triangle ZXY, $m\angle X = 40$ and $m\angle Y = 50$.
   Is triangle $RST \sim$ triangle ZXY?
3. In triangle ABC, $AC = 4$, $AB = 5$, and $m\angle A = 40$.
   In triangle RTS, $RT = 10$, $RS = 8$, and $m\angle R = 40$.
   Prove that $\triangle ABC \sim \triangle RTS$.

4. In triangle ABC, $AC = 5$, $AB = 4$, and $BC = 6$. In triangle STR, $ST = 8$, $RT = 12$, and $RS = 10$. Prove that $\triangle ABC \sim \triangle STR$.

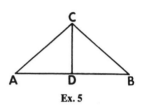

Ex. 5

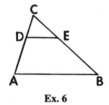

Ex. 6

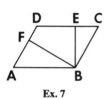

Ex. 7

5. In triangle ABC, $\overline{AC} \cong \overline{CB}$ and $\overline{CD}$ bisects angle C. (*a*) Prove $\triangle ACD \sim \triangle BCD$. (*b*) Write a proportion involving the measures of the sides of these triangles.

6. In triangle ABC, $\overline{DE} \parallel \overline{AB}$. (*a*) Prove that $\triangle ABC \sim \triangle DEC$. (*b*) Write a proportion involving the measures of the sides of these triangles. (*c*) If $CD = 6$, $CA = 18$, and $DE = 2$, find AB.

7. In $\square ABCD$, $\overline{BE} \perp \overline{DC}$, and $\overline{BF} \perp \overline{AD}$. (*a*) Prove $\triangle BAF \sim \triangle BCE$. (*b*) Write a proportion involving the measures of the sides of these triangles. (*c*) If $AB = 16$, $BC = 12$, and $FB = 14$, find EB.

8. In $\triangle ABC$, $\overline{AC} \cong \overline{CB}$, $\overline{PR} \perp \overline{AC}$, $\overline{PS} \perp \overline{BC}$. (*a*) Prove $\triangle APR \sim \triangle BPS$. (*b*) Write a proportion involving the measures of the sides of these triangles. (*c*) If $PR = 6$, $PS = 8$, and $AB = 28$, find AP and PB.

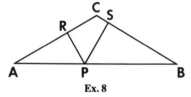

Ex. 8

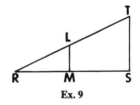

Ex. 9

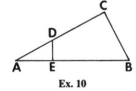

Ex. 10

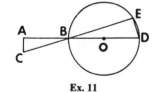

Ex. 11

9. $\overline{TS} \perp \overline{RS}$ and $\overline{LM} \perp \overline{RS}$. (*a*) Prove $\triangle LMR \sim \triangle TSR$. (*b*) Write a proportion involving the measures of the sides of these triangles. (*c*) If $LM = 6$, $TS = 9$, and $MS = 4$, find RM.

10. In triangle ABC, $\overline{BC} \perp \overline{AC}$, and $\overline{DE} \perp \overline{AB}$. (*a*) Prove $\triangle ABC \sim \triangle ADE$. (*b*) Write a proportion involving the measures of the sides of these triangles. (*c*) If $DE = 5$, $AD = 6$, and $AB = 18$, find BC.

11. In circle O, $\overline{BD}$ is a diameter. $\overleftrightarrow{AD}$ and $\overleftrightarrow{CE}$ are straight lines. $\overleftrightarrow{CA} \perp \overleftrightarrow{AD}$. (*a*) Prove $\triangle ABC \sim \triangle EBD$. (*b*) Write a proportion involving the measures of the sides of these triangles. (*c*) If $AC = 6$, $ED = 12$, $BC = x$, and $BD = x + 10$, find BC and BD.

12. In circle O, $\overline{CD}$ is a diameter and $\overleftrightarrow{AC}$ is a tangent. (*a*) Prove $\triangle BCD \sim \triangle CAD$. (*b*) Write a proportion involving the measures of the sides of these triangles. (*c*) If $AB = 18$ and $BD = 32$, find CD.

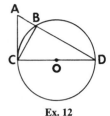

Ex. 12

13. Prove that two equilateral triangles are similar.

14. Prove that in a circle if chords $\overline{AB}$ and $\overline{CD}$ intersect in E, triangle AEC is similar to triangle DEB.

15. Prove that the altitude drawn to the hypotenuse of a right triangle divides the triangle into two similar triangles.

16. In triangle ABC, all of whose angles are acute, altitudes $\overline{BD}$ and $\overline{CE}$ intersect at F. Prove that triangles BEF and CEA are similar.

17. In triangle ABC, $\overline{CD}$ and $\overline{AE}$ are medians intersecting at O. $\overline{DE}$ is drawn. (*a*) Why is $\overline{DE}$ parallel to $\overline{AC}$? (*b*) Prove triangles ACO and EDO similar. (*c*) Write a proportion involving the measures of the sides of these triangles.

18. Prove that two isosceles triangles with congruent vertex angles are similar.

19. Given two isosceles triangles with a base angle of one congruent to a base angle of the other, prove that the triangles are similar.

20. Prove that the line segments which join the midpoints of the three sides of a given triangle form a triangle similar to the given triangle.

21. $\overline{HB}$ and $\overline{HA}$ are secants to circle O. Chords $\overline{EB}$ and $\overline{EC}$ intersect $\overline{AH}$ in F and G respectively. $m\widehat{AB}$: $m\widehat{BC}$: $m\widehat{CD} = 7{:}6{:}1$.

Ex. 21

    a. Letting n equal the number of degrees in $\widehat{CD}$, find in terms of n the number of degrees in $\widehat{BC}$ and $\widehat{AB}$.

    b. Prove that angle E is congruent to angle H.

    c. Prove that triangle GEF is similar to triangle GHC.

    d. If $CH = 20$, $EG = 14$, and $EF = 10$, find GH.

22. In isosceles trapezoid $ABCD$, $\overline{BC} \cong \overline{AD}$. If diagonals $\overline{AC}$ and $\overline{BD}$ intersect at E, prove that $\triangle DEA \sim \triangle CEB$.

23. In circle O, M is the midpoint of $\widehat{RS}$ and a chord is drawn through M meeting chord $\overline{RS}$ at N and the circle at P. Chords $\overline{RM}$ and $\overline{RP}$ are drawn. Prove that $\triangle RPM \sim \triangle NRM$.

24. Two circles O and O' are tangent externally at P. Through P, a line is drawn which intersects circle O at S and circle O' at G. Through P, a second line is drawn which intersects circle O at R and circle O' at H. $\overline{SR}$ and $\overline{HG}$ are drawn. Prove that $\triangle SPR \sim \triangle HPG$. [*Hint:* Through P, draw the common tangent to circles O and O'.]

5. Using Similar Triangles to Prove Proportions Involving Line Segments

To prove that the measures of four line segments are in proportion, show that the line segments are corresponding sides in similar triangles. Try to find two triangles each of which has as sides two of the segments whose measures are mentioned in the proportion. Sometimes the numerators in the proportion are the measures of the sides of one triangle, and the denominators in the proportion are the measures of the sides of the other triangle. At other times, the terms of the first ratio in the proportion are the measures of the sides of one triangle, and the terms of the second ratio are the measures of the sides of the other triangle. When the triangles are selected, mark the angles of the triangles so that the angle opposite one segment involved in the proportion is named $\angle 1$, and the angle opposite the corresponding segment involved in the proportion is named $\angle 1'$. In a similar way, mark the angles opposite the second pair of corresponding segments involved in the proportion $\angle 2$ and $\angle 2'$. Mark the third pair of angles in the triangles $\angle 3$ and $\angle 3'$. Use any proper method to prove the triangles similar.

MODEL PROBLEM

In isosceles triangle ABC, $\overline{AB} \cong \overline{AC}$. $\overline{AF}$ is the altitude upon $\overline{BC}$. Through D, which is a point on $\overline{AB}$, a perpendicular to $\overline{AB}$ is drawn which meets $\overline{BC}$, extended if necessary, at P. Prove $FC : DB = AC : PB$.

Given: $\triangle ABC$ with $\overline{AB} \cong \overline{AC}$.
          $\overline{PD} \perp \overline{AB}$.
          $\overline{AF} \perp \overline{BC}$.

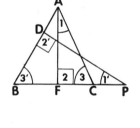

To prove: $\overset{\triangle FCA}{\dfrac{FC}{DB} = \dfrac{AC}{PB}}_{\triangle DBP}$

Plan: $\overline{FC}$ and $\overline{AC}$ are sides of $\triangle FCA$. $\overline{DB}$ and $\overline{PB}$ are sides of $\triangle DBP$. Mark the angles of $\triangle FCA$, $\angle 1$, $\angle 2$, and $\angle 3$. Mark the corresponding angles of $\triangle DBP$, $\angle 1'$, $\angle 2'$, and $\angle 3'$. Prove the triangles similar by proving two pairs of corresponding angles congruent.

Proof: Statements	Reasons
1. $\overline{AB} \cong \overline{AC}$.	1. Given.
2. $\angle 3 \cong \angle 3'$. (a. $\cong$ a.)	2. If two sides of a triangle are congruent, the angles opposite these sides are congruent.
3. $\overline{AF} \perp \overline{BC}, \overline{PD} \perp \overline{AB}$.	3. Given.
4. $\angle 2$ and $\angle 2'$ are right angles.	4. Perpendicular lines intersect forming right angles.
5. $\angle 2 \cong \angle 2'$. (a. $\cong$ a.)	5. All right angles are congruent.
6. $\triangle FCA \sim \triangle DBP$.	6. a.a. $\cong$ a.a.
7. $\dfrac{FC \text{ (opp. } \angle 1)}{DB \text{ (opp. } \angle 1')} = \dfrac{AC \text{ (opp. } \angle 2)}{PB \text{ (opp. } \angle 2')}$.	7. Corresponding sides of similar triangles are in proportion.

EXERCISES

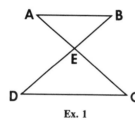

Ex. 1

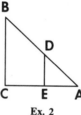

Ex. 2

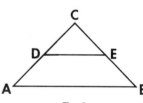

Ex. 3

1. $\overline{AB}$ is parallel to $\overline{DC}$. Prove: $\dfrac{AE}{CE} = \dfrac{BE}{DE}$.

2. In right $\triangle ABC$, $m\angle C = 90$ and $\overline{DE} \perp \overline{CA}$. Prove: $\dfrac{AD}{AB} = \dfrac{DE}{BC}$.

3. In $\triangle ABC$, D is the midpoint of $\overline{AC}$ and E is the midpoint of $\overline{BC}$. Prove: $CD:CA = DE:AB$.

Exercises 4–6 on the next page refer to the following figures:

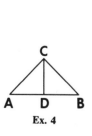

Ex. 4

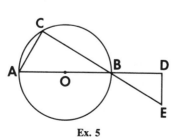

Ex. 5

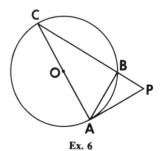

Ex. 6

4. In right triangle ABC, $m\angle C = 90$ and $\overline{CD} \perp \overline{AB}$. Prove: $AB{:}AC = AC{:}AD$.

5. In circle O, $\overline{AB}$ is a diameter. $\overline{AB}$ is extended through B to D. $\overline{ED} \perp \overline{AD}$. $\overleftrightarrow{CBE}$ is a line. Prove: $AB{:}BC = EB{:}BD$.

6. In circle O, $\overline{PA}$ is a tangent and $\overline{PC}$ is a secant. Prove that AP is the mean proportional between PC and PB.

7. In triangle ABC, altitudes $\overline{CE}$ and $\overline{BD}$ intersect at F. Prove that $AB{:}AC = BD{:}CE$.

8. In triangle ABC, D is a point on $\overline{AB}$ and E is a point on $\overline{AC}$. $\overline{DE}$ is parallel to $\overline{BC}$. Prove that $AD{:}AB = DE{:}BC$.

9. Prove that the diagonals of a trapezoid divide each other proportionally.

10. In a circle, $\overline{AB}$ is a diameter and $\overline{BC}$ is a tangent. $\overline{AC}$ intersects the circle at D. Prove that $AD{:}AB = AB{:}AC$.

11. In triangle ABC, medians $\overline{BD}$ and $\overline{AE}$ intersect in F.
    a. Prove that $\overline{DE}$ is parallel to $\overline{AB}$.
    b. Prove that $ED{:}AB = EF{:}AF$.
    c. Prove that $DF{:}BF = EF{:}AF$.
    d. Find the value of the ratio $ED{:}AB$.
    e. Find the value of the ratio $DF{:}BF$.
    f. What fractional part of BD is BF?
    g. What fractional part of AE is FE?

12. In right triangle ABC, $\overline{CD}$ is the altitude to the hypotenuse $\overline{AB}$. Prove that BC is the mean proportional between AB and BD.

13. Triangle ABC is inscribed in circle O. $\overline{AF}$ is the altitude on $\overline{BC}$. $\overline{AD}$ is a diameter of the circle. Prove that $AC{:}AF = AD{:}AB$.

14. Prove that the measures of a pair of corresponding altitudes of similar triangles have the same ratio as the measures of a pair of corresponding sides.

15. *Prove:* In two similar triangles, the measures of the bisectors of a pair of corresponding angles have the same ratio as the measures of a pair of corresponding sides.

16. $ABCD$ is a parallelogram with side $\overline{BC}$ extended through C to any point E. $\overline{AE}$ is drawn intersecting $\overline{DC}$ in F. Prove that $CF{:}DF = CE{:}CB$.

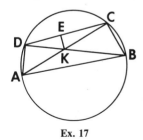

Ex. 17

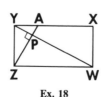

Ex. 18

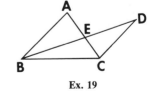

Ex. 19

17. $ABCD$ is a quadrilateral inscribed in a circle. $\overline{AB}$ is a diameter, and diagonals $\overline{AC}$ and $\overline{DB}$ intersect at K. $\overline{KE}$ is perpendicular to $\overline{DC}$.
    Prove: $\dfrac{AB}{DK} = \dfrac{AC}{DE}$.

18. Given rectangle $WXYZ$ with A a point on $\overline{XY}$ such that $\overline{WY}$ intersects $\overline{ZA}$ at point P and $\overline{WY} \perp \overline{ZA}$.
    Prove: (a) $\triangle WPZ \sim \triangle WZY$ (b) $\triangle WPZ \sim \triangle YPA$ (c) $YP{:}WZ = YA{:}WY$.

19. *Given:* $\angle ABE \cong \angle EBC$, $\overline{CD} \parallel \overline{AB}$.
    Prove: (a) $\overline{BC} \cong \overline{CD}$ (b) $AB{:}CD = AE{:}CE$ (c) $AB{:}BC = AE{:}CE$.

20. $\overline{PA}$ is a tangent to circle O at point A. Secant $\overline{PDC}$ passes through the center of the circle, O, and is perpendicular to chord $\overline{AB}$ at E. Radii $\overline{OA}$ and $\overline{OB}$ are drawn. Prove that $OP{:}OB = PA{:}BE$.

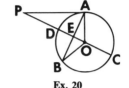

Ex. 20

21. In circle O, diameter $\overline{AB}$ is perpendicular to diameter $\overline{CD}$, and $\overline{AM}$ is any chord intersecting $\overline{CD}$ at P. Line segments $\overline{MB}$ and $\overline{BP}$ are drawn.
    a. Prove that $AP = BP$.
    b. Prove that $OB{:}MA = OP{:}BM$.

22. In circle O, $\overline{AB}$ and $\overline{AC}$ are congruent chords. A chord $\overline{AE}$ intersects chord $\overline{BC}$ in D. Prove that AB is the mean proportional between AE and AD.

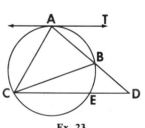

Ex. 23

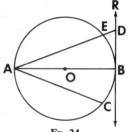

Ex. 24

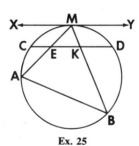

Ex. 25

23. $\overleftrightarrow{AT}$ is tangent to the given circle. $\overline{CE}$ is a chord parallel to $\overleftrightarrow{AT}$, and B is any point on $\widehat{AE}$. $\overline{AC}$, $\overline{BC}$, and $\overline{AB}$ are drawn. $\overline{AB}$ and $\overline{CE}$ are extended to meet at D. Prove that AC is the mean proportional between AB and AD.

24. $\overline{AB}$ is a diameter of circle O, $\overleftrightarrow{RB}$ is a tangent at B, chords $\overline{AE}$ and $\overline{AC}$ are drawn on opposite sides of $\overline{AB}$ such that arc $\widehat{BE}$ is congruent to arc $\widehat{BC}$, and chord $\overline{AE}$ is extended to meet $\overleftrightarrow{RB}$ at D.
    Prove: $AD{:}AB = AB{:}AC$.

25. Triangle MAB is inscribed in a circle. $\overleftrightarrow{XY}$ is tangent to the circle at point

M. Chord $\overline{CD}$ is parallel to $\overset{\leftrightarrow}{XY}$ and intersects $\overline{MA}$ and $\overline{MB}$ at points *E* and *K* respectively.

Prove: $\dfrac{ME}{MB} = \dfrac{MK}{MA}$.

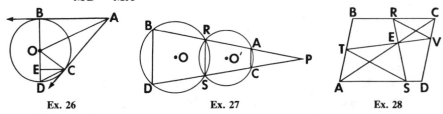

Ex. 26   Ex. 27   Ex. 28

26. $\overset{\leftrightarrow}{AB}$ and $\overset{\leftrightarrow}{AC}$ are tangents to circle *O* at points *B* and *C* respectively. From *C*, a line is drawn perpendicular to diameter $\overline{BD}$ and intersecting $\overline{BD}$ at *E*. Line segments $\overline{AO}, \overline{OC},$ and $\overline{DC}$ are drawn. Prove that: (*a*) $\overline{AO}$ bisects arc $\overset{\frown}{BC}$. (*b*) $\angle BOA \cong \angle EDC$. (*c*) $AB{:}CE = BO{:}ED$.

27. Circles *O* and *O'* intersect at points *R* and *S*. Secants from point *P*, outside circles *O* and *O'*, through *R* and *S* intersect the circles at points *A* and *B*, and *C* and *D* respectively. Chords $\overline{AC}, \overline{RS},$ and $\overline{BD}$ are drawn. (*a*) If the number of degrees contained in $\overset{\frown}{RBD}$ is represented by $2x$, express in terms of *x* the number of degrees contained in $\angle DSR$, $\angle DBR$, $\angle RSC$, and $\angle CAR$. (*b*) Prove that $PA{:}PB = PC{:}PD$.

28. Given parallelogram *ABCD* with *E* a point on diagonal $\overline{AC}$. Lines through *E* intersect $\overline{BC}$ at *R*, $\overline{AD}$ at *S*, $\overline{AB}$ at *T*, and $\overline{CD}$ at *V*. *Prove:* (*a*) $AE{:}CE = TE{:}VE$. (*b*) $AE{:}CE = SE{:}RE$. (*c*) Triangle *TES* is similar to triangle *VER*. (*d*) $\overline{TS}$ is parallel to $\overline{RV}$.

6. Proving That Products Involving Line Segments Are Equal

To prove that the product of the measures of two line segments is equal to the product of the measures of two other line segments:

1. Form a proportion in which the measures of the four line segments appear. Do this by using the theorem "If the product of two numbers (not zero) is equal to the product of two other numbers (not zero), either pair of numbers may be made the means and the other pair the extremes in a proportion."
2. Prove this proportion by the procedure outlined on page 294.
3. Use the theorem "In a proportion, the product of the means is equal to the product of the extremes."

MODEL PROBLEM

Triangle *ABC* is inscribed in a circle. $\overline{BD}$ is the altitude on $\overline{AC}$, and $\overline{BR}$ is a diameter. Prove that $BA \times BC = BR \times BD$.

Given: $\triangle ABC$ is inscribed in circle O.
            $\overline{BD} \perp \overline{AC}$.
            $\overline{BR}$ is a diameter.

To prove: $BA \times BC = BR \times BD$.

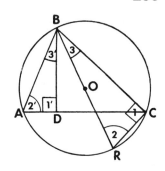

$$\triangle BRC$$

$$\left[\text{If } \frac{BR}{BA} = \frac{BC}{BD} \right]$$

$$\triangle BAD$$

Plan: We can prove that $BA \times BC = BR \times BD$ if we can prove the proportion which we get when we make BR and BD the extremes and BA and BC the means. $BR:BA = BC:BD$. Name the pairs of corresponding angles 1 and 1′, 2 and 2′, 3 and 3′. We can prove this proportion by proving $\triangle BRC \sim \triangle BAD$ by a.a. $\cong$ a.a.

Proof: *Statements*

1. Draw $\overline{RC}$ to form $\triangle BRC$.

2. $\overline{BD} \perp \overline{AC}$, $\overline{BR}$ is a diameter.
3. $\angle 1$ is a right angle.

4. $\angle 1'$ is a right angle.

5. $\angle 1 \cong \angle 1'$ (a. $\cong$ a.)
6. $m\angle 2 = \frac{1}{2}m\widehat{BC}$, $m\angle 2' = \frac{1}{2}m\widehat{BC}$.

7. $m\angle 2 = m\angle 2'$.
8. $\angle 2 \cong \angle 2'$.   (a. $\cong$ a.)
9. $\triangle BRC \sim \triangle BAD$.
10. $\dfrac{BR \ (\text{opp. } \angle 1)}{BA \ (\text{opp. } \angle 1')} = \dfrac{BC \ (\text{opp. } \angle 2)}{BD \ (\text{opp. } \angle 2')}$.

11. $BA \times BC = BR \times BD$.

Reasons

1. One and only one straight line may be drawn between two points.

2. Given.
3. An angle inscribed in a semicircle is a right angle.

4. Perpendicular lines intersect forming right angles.

5. All right angles are congruent.
6. The measure of an inscribed angle is equal to one-half the measure of its intercepted arc.

7. Transitive property of equality.

8. Definition of congruent angles.
9. a.a. $\cong$ a.a
10. Corresponding sides of similar triangles are in proportion.

11. In a proportion, the product of the means is equal to the product of the extremes.

EXERCISES

Exercises 1–3 refer to the figures below.

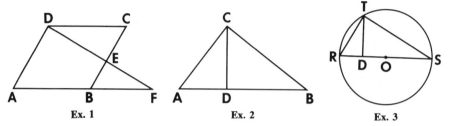

Ex. 1   Ex. 2   Ex. 3

1. If $ABCD$ is a parallelogram, prove that $DE \times BE = FE \times CE$.
2. In right triangle ABC, $\angle C$ is a right angle and $\overline{CD} \perp \overline{AB}$. Prove that $AD \times CB = DC \times AC$.
3. In circle O, $\overline{RS}$ is a diameter, T is a point on $\overset{\frown}{RS}$, and $\overline{TD} \perp \overline{RS}$. Prove that $RS \times RD = (RT)^2$. $[(RT)^2 = RT \times RT]$
4. In circle O, $\overline{PB}$ and $\overline{PD}$ are secants. Prove that $PB \times PA = PD \times PC$.
5. If $\overline{AB}$ is parallel to $\overline{CD}$, and $\overline{AC}$ and $\overline{BD}$ intersect at E, prove that $DE \times AE = BE \times CE$.

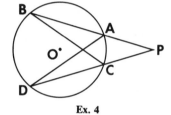

Ex. 4

6. In triangle ABC, altitudes $\overline{CD}$ and $\overline{AE}$ intersect at F. Prove that $FD \times CF = FE \times AF$.
7. In right triangle ABC, angle C is the right angle. From D, a point on a leg $\overline{AC}$, $\overline{DE}$ is drawn perpendicular to $\overline{AB}$. Prove that $AC \times AD = AE \times AB$.
8. In a circle whose center is O, $\overline{AB}$ is a diameter and $\overline{AE}$ a chord. From any point C on chord $\overline{AE}$, $\overline{CD}$ is drawn perpendicular to $\overline{AB}$. Prove that $AB \times AD = AC \times AE$.
9. Triangle ABC is inscribed in a circle. The bisector of angle C intersects side $\overline{AB}$ at D and $\overset{\frown}{AB}$ at E. Prove: $AC \times CB = CD \times EC$.
10. If $\overline{AB}$ is the diameter of a circle, $\overline{AD}$ a chord, and $\overline{DC} \perp \overline{AB}$, prove that $(AD)^2 = AB \times AC$.

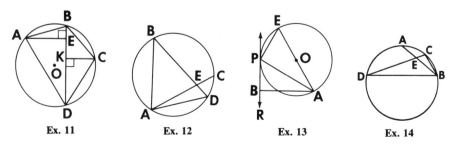

Ex. 11   Ex. 12   Ex. 13   Ex. 14

11. Quadrilateral $ABCD$ is inscribed in circle O. Perpendiculars are drawn to diagonal $\overline{BD}$ from A and C, meeting $\overline{BD}$ at E and K respectively. If $\overset{\frown}{AB}$ is congruent to $\overset{\frown}{BC}$, prove that $ED \times CD = AD \times KD$.

12. B is the midpoint of major arc $\overset{\frown}{AC}$. Chords $\overline{BD}$ and $\overline{AC}$ intersect at E. Chords $\overline{AD}$ and $\overline{AB}$ are drawn. *Prove:* $BD \times BE = (BA)^2$.

13. $\overset{\leftrightarrow}{PR}$ is a tangent, $\overline{PA}$ and $\overline{PE}$ are chords, and $\overline{AE}$ is a diameter of circle O. $\overline{AB}$ is perpendicular to $\overset{\leftrightarrow}{PR}$. *Prove:* $AB \times AE = (AP)^2$.

14. C is the midpoint of arc $\overset{\frown}{AB}$. Chords $\overline{AB}$ and $\overline{CD}$ intersect in E, and chords $\overline{CB}$ and $\overline{BD}$ are drawn. Prove that $CD \times CE = (CB)^2$.

15. In isosceles triangle ABC, $\overline{BA} \cong \overline{AC}$. The bisectors of $\angle B$ and $\angle C$ intersect the congruent sides in D and E respectively. Prove that $AE \times AC = AB \times AD$.

16. In triangle ABC, $\overline{BD}$ bisects angle B and intersects $\overline{AC}$ at D. Through C, a line parallel to $\overline{BD}$ is drawn to meet $\overline{AB}$ extended in E. *Prove:*
    a. Triangle EBC is isosceles.
    b. $AD \times CB = AB \times CD$.

17. In parallelogram $PQRS$, $\overline{QC}$ intersects diagonal $\overline{RP}$ at B, side $\overline{SP}$ at A, and extended side $\overline{RS}$ at C.
    a. Prove that $\triangle APB \sim \triangle QRB$.
    b. Prove that $\triangle QBP \sim \triangle CBR$.
    c. Prove that $(QB)^2 = AB \times BC$.

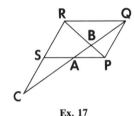

Ex. 17

7. Using Proportions Involving Corresponding Line Segments in Similar Triangles

We have already learned from the definition of similar polygons that if two polygons are similar, their corresponding sides are in proportion. Since triangles are polygons, it follows that:

If two triangles are similar, their corresponding sides are in proportion.

If $\triangle ABC \sim \triangle A'B'C'$ (Fig. 6–16), $\dfrac{a}{a'} = \dfrac{b}{b'} = \dfrac{c}{c'}$. The ratio of the measures of any pair of corresponding sides of the similar triangles, $\dfrac{a}{a'}$ or $\dfrac{b}{b'}$ or $\dfrac{c}{c'}$, is called the *ratio of similitude* of the similar triangles.

Fig. 6–16

Theorem 91. **If two triangles are similar, the measures of corresponding altitudes have the same ratio as the measures of any two corresponding sides.**

In Fig. 6-17, if $\triangle ABC \sim$ $\triangle A'B'C'$, h and h' represent the measures of two corresponding altitudes, and a and a' represent the measures of two corresponding sides, then $\dfrac{h}{h'} = \dfrac{a}{a'}$.

 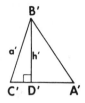

Fig. 6-17

In theorem 91, if the expression "corresponding altitudes" is replaced by "corresponding medians" or by "corresponding angle bisectors," the resulting theorems would also be true. We therefore have the following corollary to theorem 91:

Corollary T91-1. **In two similar triangles, the measures of any two corresponding line segments have the same ratio as the measures of any pair of corresponding sides.**

If $\triangle ABC \sim \triangle A'B'C'$, then:

$$\frac{\text{measure of any line seg. in } \triangle ABC}{\text{measure of corr. line seg. in } \triangle A'B'C'} = \frac{\text{measure of any side in } \triangle ABC}{\text{measure of corr. side in } \triangle A'B'C'}$$

Theorem 92. **The perimeters of two similar triangles have the same ratio as the measures of any pair of corresponding sides.**

In Fig. 6-18, if $\triangle ABC \sim \triangle A'B'C'$, p and p' represent their perimeters, and a and a' represent the measures of a pair of corresponding sides, then $\dfrac{p}{p'} = \dfrac{a}{a'}$.

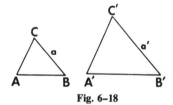

Fig. 6-18

MODEL PROBLEMS

1. The sides of triangle ABC measure 5, 7, and 9. The shortest side of a similar triangle $A'B'C'$ measures 10.
   a. Find the measure of the longest side of triangle $A'B'C'$.
   b. Find the ratio of the measures of a pair of corresponding altitudes in triangles ABC and $A'B'C'$.
   c. Find the perimeter of triangle $A'B'C'$.

Solution:

a. 1. The longest side of $\triangle A'B'C'$ is $\overline{B'C'}$ because it corresponds to $\overline{BC}$, the longest side in $\triangle ABC$.

2. Since $\triangle A'B'C' \sim \triangle ABC$, then

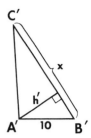

$\dfrac{AB}{A'B'} = \dfrac{BC}{B'C'}$ Let x = the length of $B'C'$.

3. $\dfrac{5}{10} = \dfrac{9}{x}$

4. $5x = 90$

5. $x = 18$

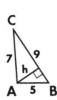

Answer: The longest side of $\triangle A'B'C'$ measures 18.

b. Since $\triangle ABC \sim \triangle A'B'C'$, then $\dfrac{h}{h'} = \dfrac{AB}{A'B'} = \dfrac{5}{10} = \dfrac{1}{2}$.

Answer: $h{:}h' = 1{:}2$

c. 1. Since $\triangle ABC \sim \triangle A'B'C'$, then

$\dfrac{p}{p'} = \dfrac{s}{s'}$ Perimeter of $\triangle ABC = 5 + 7 + 9 = 21$.
Let y = the perimeter of $\triangle A'B'C'$.

2. $\dfrac{21}{y} = \dfrac{5}{10}$

3. $5y = 210$

4. $y = 42$

Answer: The perimeter of $\triangle A'B'C' = 42$.

2. In an isosceles trapezoid, the length of the lower base is 15, the length of the upper base is 5, and the length of each congruent side is 6. How many units must each nonparallel side be extended to form a triangle?

Solution:

1. Since $\overline{DC} \parallel \overline{AB}$, then $\triangle DEC \sim \triangle AEB$ and their corresponding sides are in proportion.

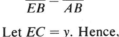

2. $\dfrac{ED}{EA} = \dfrac{DC}{AB}$

    Let $ED = x$. Hence,

    $EA = x + 6$

3. $\dfrac{x}{x+6} = \dfrac{5}{15}$

4. $15x = 5x + 30$

5. $10x = 30$

6. $x = 3$

2. $\dfrac{EC}{EB} = \dfrac{DC}{AB}$

    Let $EC = y$. Hence,

    $EB = y + 6$

3. $\dfrac{y}{y+6} = \dfrac{5}{15}$

4. $15y = 5y + 30$

5. $10y = 30$

6. $y = 3$

Answer: 3.

EXERCISES

1. The lengths of the sides of a triangle are 8, 10, and 12. If the length of the shortest side of a similar triangle is 6, find the length of its longest side.

2. Triangle DEF is similar to triangle $D'E'F'$. $\angle D$ corresponds to $\angle D'$ and $\angle E$ corresponds to $\angle E'$. If $DE = 2x + 2$, $DF = 5x - 7$, $D'E' = 2$, and $D'F' = 3$, find DE and DF.

3. The ratio of similitude in two similar triangles is 3:1. If a side in the larger triangle measures 30, find the measure of the corresponding side in the smaller triangle.

4. A vertical pole 10 ft. high casts a shadow 8 ft. long, and at the same time a nearby tree casts a shadow 40 ft. long. What is the height of the tree?

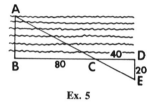

Ex. 5

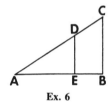

Ex. 6

5. In the figure, $\overline{AB}$ represents the width of a river. $\overline{AE}$ and $\overline{BD}$ intersect at C. $\overline{AB} \perp \overline{BD}$ and $\overline{ED} \perp \overline{BD}$. Find AB, the width of the river.

6. $\overline{DE} \perp \overline{AB}$, and $\overline{CB} \perp \overline{AB}$. If $CB = 40$, $DE = 30$, and $EB = 20$, find AE.

7. A boy 5 ft. tall stands on level ground 6 ft. from a point P which is directly below a light. (a) If the boy's shadow is 3 ft. long, find the height of the light above the ground. (b) If the boy takes a position 2 ft. nearer P, find the length of his shadow.

8. The sides of a triangle are 10, 12, 15. A line segment whose length is 5 is parallel to the longest side of the triangle and has its endpoints on the other two sides of the triangle. Find the shorter segment of side 10.

9. In triangle ABC, a line parallel to $\overline{AB}$ intersects $\overline{AC}$ at D and $\overline{CB}$ at E. If $CD = 6$, $DA = 12$, and AB is 8 less than 4 times DE, find DE and AB.

10. The bases of an isosceles trapezoid are 5 and 10, and each of the non-parallel sides is 4. How many units must each of the nonparallel sides be extended to form a triangle?

11. The bases of a trapezoid are 10 and 15 and the nonparallel sides are 4 and 5. How many units must each of the nonparallel sides be extended to form a triangle?

12. If the lengths of the sides of two similar triangles are in the ratio 5:1, find the ratio of the lengths of a pair of corresponding altitudes.

13. The lengths of two corresponding sides of two similar triangles are 8

and 12. If an altitude of the smaller triangle is 6, find the length of the corresponding altitude of the larger triangle.

14. The lengths of two corresponding altitudes in two similar triangles are 18 and 27. If the length of a side in the larger triangle exceeds the length of the corresponding side of the smaller triangle by 12, find the lengths of these two sides of the triangles.

15. A side of a triangle is 20 inches and the altitude drawn to this side is 12 inches. Find the length of a line segment drawn parallel to the given side, through a point inside the triangle which is 3 inches from the vertex, and which terminates in the other two sides.

16. The bases of a trapezoid are 10 and 40 and the altitude is 6. The non-parallel sides are extended until they intersect. Find the distance between the point of intersection and the shorter base of the trapezoid.

17. The ratio of similitude in two similar triangles is 4:3. If the length of a median in the first triangle is 12, find the length of the corresponding median in the second triangle.

18. In two similar triangles, the ratio of the lengths of two corresponding angle bisectors is 5:3. If the length of a side of the smaller triangle is 21, find the length of the corresponding side of the larger triangle.

19. The ratio of the lengths of the corresponding sides of two similar triangles is 7:4. Find the ratio of the perimeters of the triangles.

20. The sides of a triangle are 7, 9, and 11. Find the perimeter of a similar triangle in which the side corresponding to 7 in the first triangle is 21.

21. Corresponding altitudes of two similar triangles are 9 and 6. If the perimeter of the larger triangle is 24, what is the perimeter of the smaller triangle?

22. In two similar triangles, the ratio of the lengths of two corresponding sides is 5:8. If the perimeter of the larger triangle is 10 less than twice the perimeter of the smaller triangle, find the perimeter of each triangle.

8. Using Proportions Involving Corresponding Line Segments in Similar Polygons

We have already learned from the definition of similar polygons that if polygon $ABCDE \sim$ polygon $A'B'C'D'E'$ (Fig. 6–19), then their corresponding sides are in proportion, or

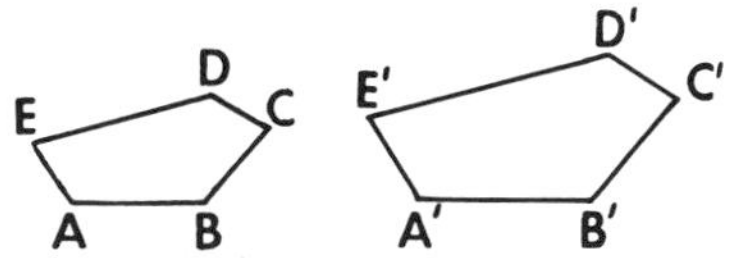

Fig. 6–19

$$\frac{AB}{A'B'} = \frac{BC}{B'C'} = \frac{CD}{C'D'} = \frac{DE}{D'E'} = \frac{EA}{E'A'}$$

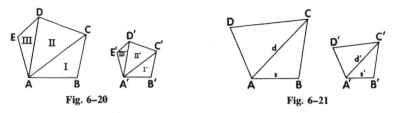

Fig. 6–20   Fig. 6–21

Theorem 93. **Similar polygons may be divided, by drawing the diagonals from a pair of corresponding vertices, into triangles so that the corresponding triangles are similar.**

In Fig. 6–20, if polygon $ABCDE \sim$ polygon $A'B'C'D'E'$, then:
$$\triangle I \sim \triangle I', \triangle II \sim \triangle II', \triangle III \sim \triangle III'$$

Corollary T93–1. **If two polygons are similar, the ratio of the lengths of two corresponding diagonals is equal to the ratio of the lengths of any two corresponding sides.**

In Fig. 6–21, if polygon $ABCD \sim$ polygon $A'B'C'D'$, then $\dfrac{d}{d'} = \dfrac{s}{s'}$.

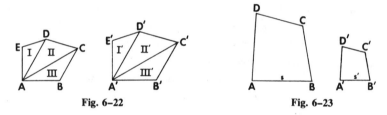

Fig. 6–22   Fig. 6–23

Theorem 94. **Two polygons are similar if they are composed of the same number of triangles similar each to each and similarly placed.**

In Fig. 6–22, if $\triangle I \sim \triangle I'$, $\triangle II \sim \triangle II'$, $\triangle III \sim \triangle III'$, and all pairs of $\triangle$ are similarly placed, then polygon $ABCDE \sim$ polygon $A'B'C'D'E'$.

Theorem 95. **The perimeters of two similar polygons have the same ratio as the measures of any pair of corresponding sides.**

In Fig. 6–23, if polygon $ABCD \sim$ polygon $A'B'C'D'$, and p and p' represent their perimeters, and s and s' represent the measures of a pair of corresponding sides, then $\dfrac{p}{p'} = \dfrac{s}{s'}$.

Corollary T95–1. **The perimeters of two similar polygons have the same ratio as the measures of any pair of corresponding line segments.**

If p and p' represent the perimeters of two similar polygons and l and l' represent the measures of any pair of corresponding line segments of these polygons, then $\dfrac{p}{p'} = \dfrac{l}{l'}$.

MODEL PROBLEM

The lengths of two corresponding sides of two similar polygons are 4 and 7. If the perimeter of the smaller polygon is 20, find the perimeter of the larger polygon.

Solution:

1. Since the polygons are similar, then

$$\frac{p}{p'} = \frac{s}{s'} \qquad s = 4, s' = 7, p = 20.$$
$$\text{Let } p' = x.$$

2. $\dfrac{20}{x} = \dfrac{4}{7}$

3. $4x = 140$

4. $x = 35$

Answer: The perimeter of the larger polygon is 35.

EXERCISES

1. The lengths of two corresponding sides of two similar polygons are 5 and 20. Find the ratio of similitude of the two polygons.

2. Two corresponding diagonals of two similar polygons are 4 and 8. Find the ratio of similitude of the two polygons.

3. The ratio of similitude of two similar polygons is 3:4, and a diagonal of the larger polygon is 20. Find the length of the corresponding diagonal in the smaller polygon.

4. Two corresponding sides of two similar polygons are 8 and 12. Find the ratio of their perimeters.

5. Two corresponding sides of two similar polygons are 9 and 12. If the perimeter of the larger polygon is 72, find the perimeter of the smaller polygon.

6. The perimeter and side of a polygon are 30 and 6 respectively. Find the length of the corresponding side of a similar polygon whose perimeter is 20.

7. Two corresponding sides of two similar polygons are 14 and 7. If the perimeter of the smaller polygon is 23 less than the perimeter of the larger polygon, find the perimeter of the larger polygon.

8. Two corresponding diagonals of two similar polygons are in the ratio 3 to 1. If the perimeter of the larger polygon exceeds the perimeter of the smaller polygon by 48, find the perimeter of the smaller polygon.

9. Two Chords Intersecting Inside a Circle

Theorem 96. If two chords intersect inside a circle, the product of the measures of the segments of one chord is equal to the product of the measures of the segments of the other.

If chords $\overline{AB}$ and $\overline{CD}$ intersect at E (Fig. 6–24), the product of the measures of the segments of chord $\overline{AB}$, $AE \times EB$, is equal to the product of the measures of the segments of chord $\overline{CD}$, $CE \times ED$, or:
$$AE \times EB = CE \times ED$$

Fig. 6-24

MODEL PROBLEMS

1. In circle O, chords $\overline{AB}$ and $\overline{CD}$ intersect at E. If $AE = 6$, $EB = 8$, and $CE = 12$, find ED.

Solution:

1. $AE \times EB = CE \times ED$ Let $ED = x$.

2. $6 \times 8 = 12x$

3. $48 = 12x$

4. $4 = x$

Answer: ED = 4.

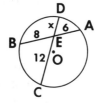

2. In circle O, chord $\overline{CD}$ is bisected at S by chord $\overline{EF}$. If $ES = 16$ and $SF = 4$, find the length of chord $\overline{CD}$.

Solution:

1. Since $\overline{EF}$ bisects $\overline{CD}$, $\overline{CS} \cong \overline{SD}$, and $CS = SD$.

2. $CS \times SD = ES \times SF$ Let x = the length of

3. $(x)(x) = (16)(4)$ $\overline{CS}$ and the length of

4. $x^2 = 64$ $\overline{SD}$.

5. $x = 8$

6. $CD = 8 + 8 = 16$

Answer: CD = 16.

3. In circle O, the length of the chord of a minor arc is 8. The height of the arc (the length of the line segment joining the midpoint of the arc to the midpoint of its chord) is 2. Find the length of the radius of the circle.

Solution:

1. Since $\overline{CD}$ is the perpendicular bisector of $\overline{AB}$, when $\overline{CD}$ is extended it will pass through the center of the circle, O.

2. Since $AB = 8$ and $AD = DB$, $AD = 4$ and $DB = 4$.

3. $AD \times DB = CD \times DE$ Let $DE = x$.

4. $4 \times 4 = 2x$

5. $16 = 2x$

6. $x = 8$

7. The length of diameter $\overline{CE} = 2 + x = 2 + 8 = 10$.

8. The length of radius $\overline{OE} = \frac{1}{2}CE = \frac{1}{2}(10) = 5$.

Answer: The length of the radius is 5.

EXERCISES

1. Two chords intersect inside a circle. The segments of one chord measure 8 and 3. If one segment of the second chord measures 6, then the measure of the other segment is _____ .

2. Chords $\overline{AB}$ and $\overline{CD}$ intersect inside a circle at point E. $AE = 4$, $CE = 3$, and $ED = 8$. Find EB.

3. A diameter of a circle is perpendicular to a chord whose length is 14 inches. If the length of the shorter segment of the diameter is 4 inches, find the length of the longer segment of the diameter.

4. Chords $\overline{AB}$ and $\overline{CD}$ intersect inside circle O at point E. If $AE = 9\frac{3}{5}$, $EB = 1\frac{1}{4}$, and $DE = 3$, find EC.

5. Chords $\overline{AB}$ and $\overline{CE}$ intersect inside a circle at D. If $AD = a$, $DB = b$, and $CD = c$, express DE in terms of a, b, and c.

6. In circle O, chord $\overline{AB}$ bisects chord $\overline{CD}$ at E. If $AE = 16$ and $EB = 4$, find the length of $\overline{CE}$.

7. Chords $\overline{AB}$ and $\overline{CD}$ intersect inside a circle at point E. If $CD = 9$, $ED = 8$, and AE is twice EB, find EB.

8. Chords $\overline{AB}$ and $\overline{CD}$ intersect inside a circle at point E. If $AE = 25$, $EB = 8$, and the ratio of $CE:ED$ is 1:2, find CD.

9. A chord of a circle is perpendicular to a diameter of the circle and divides the diameter into segments which are 2 inches and 18 inches in length. Find the length of the chord.

10. Point P is a distance of 6 from the center of a circle whose radius is 10; the product of the lengths of the segments of any chord drawn through P is _____ .

11. Point P is 3 inches from the center of a circle whose radius is 5 inches. (*a*) Find the length of the shortest chord that can be drawn through P. (*b*) Find the length of the longest chord which can be drawn through P.

12. In a circle, chord $\overline{AB}$, which is 12 in. in length, is drawn. The height of minor arc $\overset{\frown}{AB}$ is 3 in. Find the length of the radius of the circle.

13. In a circle, chord $\overline{CD}$, which is 16 in. in length, is drawn. The center of minor arc $\overset{\frown}{CD}$ is joined to the midpoint of chord $\overline{CD}$ by a line segment 4 in. in length. Find the length of the radius of the circle.

14. Chords $\overline{AB}$ and $\overline{CD}$ intersect inside a circle at point E. $\overline{AE}$ measures 4 in., $\overline{DE}$ measures 3 in., and $\overline{EB}$ measures 4 inches shorter than $\overline{CE}$. (*a*) If the length of $\overline{CE}$ is represented by x, write an equation that can be used to find x. (*b*) Find the length of the shorter chord.

15. In a circle, chords $\overline{AB}$ and $\overline{CD}$ intersect in E. If $CE = 6$, $ED = 4$, $AE = x + 3$, and $EB = x - 2$, find AE, EB, and AB.

16. In a circle, chords $\overline{AB}$ and $\overline{CD}$ intersect at E. $\overline{DE}$ measures 12 in., $\overline{CE}$ measures 8 in., and AE exceeds BE by 20. (*a*) If the length of $\overline{BE}$ is represented by x, write an equation which can be used to find x. (*b*) Solve this equation for x. (*c*) Find the length of chord $\overline{AB}$.

17. In a given circle, chords $\overline{AB}$ and $\overline{CD}$ are drawn so that chord $\overline{AB}$ bisects chord $\overline{CD}$. Prove that the measure of each segment of chord $\overline{CD}$ is the mean proportional between the measures of the segments of chord $\overline{AB}$.

18. Prove that the product of the measures of the segments of the chords drawn through a point which is b inches from the center of a circle whose radius measures r inches long is constant.

10. Secants and Tangents Drawn to a Circle From an Outside Point

Definition. The *distance from a point to a circle* is the shortest distance from the given point to a point of intersection of the circle with the line which passes through the given point and the center of the circle.

In Fig. 6–25, if point P is outside circle O, and if when $\overline{PO}$ is drawn it intersects the circle at B, then the distance from P to B is the distance from point P to circle O.

Similarly, if point P' is inside circle O, the distance from P' to B' is the distance from point P' to circle O.

Fig. 6–25

If $\overleftrightarrow{PB}$ is a secant to circle O from outside point P (Fig. 6–26), then we will also refer to $\overline{PB}$ as a secant to circle O from point P. Then PB, which is the distance from P to the farther point of intersection B, is called the *length of the secant*. PA, which is the distance from P to the nearer point of intersection A, is called the *length of the external segment of the secant*. AB, which is the distance between the two points of intersection

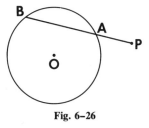

Fig. 6–26

A and B, is called the *length of the internal segment of the secant*.

Theorem 97. If from a point outside a circle two secants are drawn to the circle, the product of the length of one secant and the length of its external segment is equal to the product of the length of the other secant and the length of its external segment.

If $\overline{PB}$ and $\overline{PD}$ are secants to the circle (Fig. 6–27), the product of the length of secant $\overline{PB}$ and the length of its external segment $\overline{PA}$, $PB \times PA$, is equal to the product of the length of secant $\overline{PD}$ and the length of its external segment $\overline{PC}$, $PD \times PC$, or $PB \times PA = PD \times PC$.

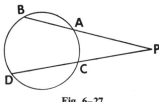

Fig. 6–27

Theorem 98. If from a point outside a circle a tangent and a secant are drawn to the circle, the length of the tangent is the mean proportional between the length of the secant and the length of its external segment.

If tangent $\overline{PA}$ and secant $\overline{PC}$ are drawn to the circle (Fig. 6–28), then the length of tangent $\overline{PA}$ is the mean proportional between the length of secant $\overline{PC}$ and the length of its external segment $\overline{PB}$, or $\dfrac{PB}{PA} = \dfrac{PA}{PC}$, or

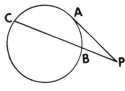

Fig. 6–28

$(PA)^2 = PB \times PC$.

MODEL PROBLEMS

1. $\overline{PB}$ and $\overline{PD}$, which are secants drawn to circle O, intersect the circle in points A and C respectively. If $PA = 4$, $AB = 5$, and $PD = 12$, find PC.

Solution:

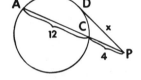

1. $PB \times PA = PD \times PC$ Let $x = PC$.

2. $9 \times 4 = 12x$

3. $36 = 12x$

4. $3 = x$

Answer: PC = 3.

2. From a point outside a circle, a tangent and a secant are drawn to the circle. The point at which the secant intersects the circle divides the secant into an external segment of length 4 and an internal segment of length 12. Find the length of the tangent.

Solution:

1. $PA{:}PD = PD{:}PC$ Let $x = PD$, the

2. $16{:}x = x{:}4$ length of the tangent.

3. $x^2 = 64$

4. $x = 8$

Answer: PD = 8.

3. The length of a radius of circle O is 4. From a point P outside circle O, tangent $\overline{PA}$ is drawn. If the length of $\overline{PA}$ is 3, find the distance from P to the circle.

Solution:

1. PB is the distance from P to the circle.

2. $PC{:}PA = PA{:}PB$ Let $x = PB$.

3. $(x + 8){:}3 = 3{:}x$ Then $x + 8 = PC$.

4. $x(x + 8) = 3 \times 3$

5. $x^2 + 8x = 9$

6. $x^2 + 8x - 9 = 0$

7. $(x - 1)(x + 9) = 0$

8. $x - 1 = 0 \mid x + 9 = 0$

9. $\;\;\;\;x = 1 \mid \;\;\;\; x = -9$ Reject the negative value.

Answer: PB = 1.

EXERCISES

1. Two secants are drawn to a circle from an outside point. The length of one secant is 20 and the length of its external segment is 5. If the length of the other secant is 25, find the length of its external segment.

2. Two secants are drawn to a circle from an outside point. The external segment of the first secant is 4 and its internal segment is 8. Find the length of the second secant if its external segment is 6.

3. From point P outside circle O, tangent $\overline{PD}$ and secant $\overline{PA}$ are drawn. Secant $\overline{PA}$ intersects the circle at C. If $PD = 8$ and $PC = 4$, find the length of secant $\overline{PA}$.

4. A tangent and a secant are drawn to a circle from a point outside the circle. If the tangent is 14 in. long and the secant is 28 in. long, the length of the external segment of the secant is _____ in.

5. If the length of a secant to a circle from an external point is 9 and the length of its external segment is 4, the length of the tangent from that point is _____.

6. A tangent and a secant are drawn to a circle from the same outside point. If the length of the external segment of the secant is 3 and the length of the internal segment is 7, find the length of the tangent.

7. A tangent and a secant are drawn to a circle from the same external point. If the length of the tangent is 10 and the length of the external segment of the secant is 4, find the length of the internal segment of the secant.

8. From point P outside a circle, tangent $\overline{PD}$ and secant $\overline{PA}$ are drawn. Secant $\overline{PA}$ intersects the circle at C. $PD = 8$ and the length of the secant is four times the length of its external segment. Find the length of the secant.

9. From point P outside a circle, tangent $\overline{PD}$ and secant $\overline{PA}$ are drawn. Secant $\overline{PA}$ intersects the circle at C. If $PD = a$ and $PC = b$, express PA in terms of a and b.

10. The diameter of a circle is 15 inches. If this diameter is extended 5 inches beyond the circle to point A, find the number of inches in the length of a tangent to the circle from point A.

11. In the circle shown, $\overline{AB}$ is a diameter, $\overline{PC}$ is a tangent, and $\overline{PBA}$ is a secant. If $AP = 9$ and $CP = 6$, find the number of units in the diameter of the circle.

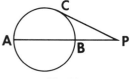

Ex. 11

12. The length of a tangent drawn from a point 3 inches from a circle the length of whose radius is 12 inches is _____ inches.

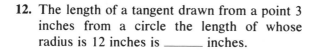

13. Point P is 15 in. from the center of a circle the length of whose radius is 9 in. Find the length of the tangent drawn from point P to the circle.

14. A tangent and a secant are drawn to a circle from an external point. The length of the tangent is 4 inches. If the length of the internal segment of the secant is 6 inches, find the length of its external segment.

15. A tangent and a secant are drawn to a circle from an external point. The length of the tangent is represented by $3x$. The length of the external segment of the secant is represented by $x + 5$ and the length of its internal segment by $8x - 23$. Find the length of the tangent and the length of the secant.

16. Diameter $\overline{AB}$ of circle O is 21 inches in length. $\overline{AB}$ is extended through B to a point C and tangent $\overline{CD}$ is drawn, meeting the circle at D. $\overline{CD}$ is 6 inches longer than $\overline{BC}$.

   a. Let x represent the length of $\overline{BC}$, and express CD and CA in terms of x.

   b. Express as an equation involving the variable x the relationship that exists among BC, CA, and CD.

   c. Find the length of $\overline{BC}$ by solving the equation obtained in part *b*.

17. *Prove:* If two circles intersect in two points, the lengths of tangents to these circles drawn from any point on the line containing the common chord are equal.

18. $\overline{MN}$ is a diameter of a circle whose center is O. $\overline{OR}$ is a radius perpendicular to $\overline{MN}$. S is a point on radius $\overline{ON}$. $\overline{RS}$ is drawn and extended to meet the circle at W. At W, a tangent is drawn to the circle which meets $\overline{MN}$ extended at T. (*a*) Show that angle RWT and angle WSN are congruent. (*b*) If $TM = 25$ and $TS = 10$, find the length of the radius of the circle.

11. Proportions in the Right Triangle

Projection of a Point or of a Line Segment on a Line

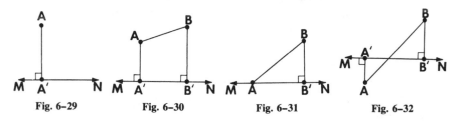

Fig. 6–29   Fig. 6–30   Fig. 6–31   Fig. 6–32

Definition. The *projection of a given point on a given line* is the foot of the perpendicular drawn from the given point to the given line.

In Fig. 6–29, point A' is the projection of point A on line $\overleftrightarrow{MN}$.

Definition. **The** *projection of a segment on a given line*, **when the segment is not perpendicular to the line, is the segment whose endpoints are the projections of the endpoints of the given line segment on the given line.**

In Fig. 6–30, $\overline{A'B'}$ is the projection of $\overline{AB}$ on $\overleftrightarrow{MN}$.
In Fig. 6–31, $\overline{AB'}$ is the projection of $\overline{AB}$ on $\overleftrightarrow{MN}$.
In Fig. 6–32, $\overline{A'B'}$ is the projection of $\overline{AB}$ on $\overleftrightarrow{MN}$.

NOTE. When the segment is perpendicular to the given line, the projection of the segment on the given line is a point.

Proportions in the Right Triangle

Theorem 99. **If the altitude is drawn to the hypotenuse of a right triangle,**

a. **the two triangles thus formed are similar to the given triangle and similar to each other.**

[The proof for this theorem appears on pages 609–610.]

In Fig. 6–33, if ABC is a right triangle and $\overline{CD} \perp$ hypotenuse $\overline{AB}$, then $\triangle ACD \sim \triangle ABC$, $\triangle CBD \sim \triangle ABC$, $\triangle ACD \sim \triangle CBD$.

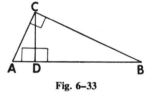

Fig. 6–33

b. **the length of the altitude is the mean proportional between the lengths of the segments of the hypotenuse.**

In Fig. 6–33, the length of altitude $\overline{CD}$ is the mean proportional between the lengths of $\overline{AD}$ and $\overline{DB}$, the segments of hypotenuse $\overline{AB}$, or $AD{:}CD = CD{:}DB$.

c. **the length of each leg of the given triangle is the mean proportional between the length of the whole hypotenuse and the length of the projection of that leg on the hypotenuse.**

[The proof for this theorem appears on pages 609–610.]

In Fig. 6–33, the length of leg $\overline{AC}$ is the mean proportional between the length of the hypotenuse $\overline{AB}$ and the length of $\overline{AD}$, the projection of leg $\overline{AC}$ on hypotenuse $\overline{AB}$, or $AB{:}AC = AC{:}AD$.

Also, the length of leg $\overline{BC}$ is the mean proportional between the length of hypotenuse $\overline{AB}$ and the length of $\overline{BD}$, the projection of leg $\overline{BC}$ on hypotenuse $\overline{AB}$, or $AB{:}BC = BC{:}BD$.

MODEL PROBLEMS

1. In right triangle ABC, altitude $\overline{CD}$ is drawn on hypotenuse $\overline{AB}$. If $AD = 6$ and $DB = 24$, find   *(a)* CD and   *(b)* AC.

[The solution is given on the next page.]

Solution: Since $\overline{CD} \perp$ hypotenuse $\overline{AB}$ in right triangle ABC,

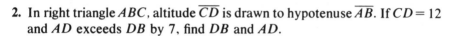

a. 1. $\dfrac{AD}{CD} = \dfrac{CD}{DB}$	*b.* 1. $\dfrac{AD}{AC} = \dfrac{AC}{AB}$
Let $x =$ length of $\overline{CD}$.	Let $y =$ length of $\overline{AC}$.
2. $\dfrac{6}{x} = \dfrac{x}{24}$	2. $\dfrac{6}{y} = \dfrac{y}{30}$
3. $x^2 = 144$	3. $y^2 = 180$
4. $x = 12$	4. $y = \sqrt{180} = \sqrt{36} \cdot \sqrt{5} = 6\sqrt{5}$
Answer: $CD = 12$.	*Answer:* $AC = 6\sqrt{5}$.

2. In right triangle ABC, altitude $\overline{CD}$ is drawn to hypotenuse $\overline{AB}$. If $CD = 12$ and AD exceeds DB by 7, find DB and AD.

Solution:

1. Since $\overline{CD} \perp$ hypotenuse $\overline{AB}$ in right triangle ABC,

$\dfrac{AD}{CD} = \dfrac{CD}{DB}$.   Let $x =$ the length of $\overline{DB}$.
Then $x + 7 =$ the length of $\overline{AD}$.

2. $\qquad\qquad \dfrac{x + 7}{12} = \dfrac{12}{x}$

3. $\qquad\qquad x(x + 7) = 12 \times 12$

4. $\qquad\qquad x^2 + 7x = 144$

5. $\qquad\quad x^2 + 7x - 144 = 0$

6. $\qquad (x - 9)(x + 16) = 0$

7. $x - 9 = 0 \quad\mid\quad x + 16 = 0$
8. $\qquad x = 9 \quad\mid\quad x = -16$ Reject the negative value.

9. $x + 7 = 9 + 7 = 16$.

Answer: $DB = 9, AD = 16$.

EXERCISES

1. The altitude upon the hypotenuse of a right triangle divides the hypotenuse into segments of lengths 3 and 12. Find the length of the altitude.

2. The altitude to the hypotenuse of a right triangle divides the hypotenuse into segments of lengths 2 and 5. Find the length of the altitude.

3. In right triangle ABC, altitude $\overline{CD}$ is drawn on hypotenuse $\overline{AB}$. If $CD = 6$ and $AD = 3$, find DB.

4. In right triangle ABC, altitude $\overline{CD}$ is drawn on hypotenuse $\overline{AB}$. If $DB = 5$ and $CD = 10$, find AB.

5. In triangle ABC, angle C is a right angle and $\overline{CD}$ is the altitude on $\overline{AB}$. If $AC = 6$ and $AB = 9$, find AD.

6. In right triangle ABC, the right angle is at C and $\overline{CD}$ is the altitude on $\overline{AB}$. If $AD = 3$ and $DB = 9$, find AC.

7. In a right triangle whose hypotenuse measures 50, the shorter leg measures 30. Find the measure of the projection of the shorter leg on the hypotenuse.

8. In a right triangle whose hypotenuse measures 10, the projection of the longer leg on the hypotenuse measures 6.4. Find the measure of the longer leg.

9. The segments made by the altitude on the hypotenuse of right triangle ABC measure 4 and 5. Find the measure of the shorter leg of triangle ABC.

10. The altitude drawn to the hypotenuse of a right triangle is 8 inches long. If the lengths of the segments of the hypotenuse are represented by x and $4x$, find the number of inches in the smaller segment.

11. If the altitude to the hypotenuse of a right triangle measures 8, the segments of the hypotenuse formed by the altitude may measure   (1) 8 and 12   (2) 2 and 32   (3) 3 and 24   (4) 6 and 8.

12. ABC is a right triangle with $\overline{CD}$ the altitude on hypotenuse $\overline{AB}$. If $AC = 20$ and $AB = 25$, find AD, CD, and BC.

13. In right triangle ABC, $\overline{CD}$ is the altitude drawn to hypotenuse $\overline{AB}$. If $CD = 6$, $AD = 3$, and $DB = 5x - 3$, find x.

14. $\overline{CD}$ is the altitude on hypotenuse $\overline{AB}$ of right triangle ABC. $AC = 12$ and $AD = 6$. If BD is represented by x, write an equation that can be used to find x. Solve this equation for x.

15. In right triangle ABC, $\overline{CD}$, the altitude to hypotenuse $\overline{AB}$, measures 3. If DB exceeds AD by 8, find AD and DB.

16. $\overline{BD}$ is the altitude on hypotenuse $\overline{AC}$ of right triangle ABC. $BD = 4$ and $AC = 10$. If CD, the length of the shorter segment of $\overline{AC}$, is represented by x, write an equation which could be used to find x. Solve this equation for x, and find CD and AD.

17. Given right triangle ABC with hypotenuse $\overline{AB}$ and with $\overline{CD}$ the altitude to hypotenuse $\overline{AB}$. $AD = 21$ and $CB = 10$. [Leave irrational answers in radical form.]
   a. Represent DB by x and write an equation that can be used to find x.
   b. Solve for x the equation written in answer to *a*.
   c. Find the length of $\overline{CD}$.

12. The Pythagorean Theorem and Its Applications

Theorem 100. **In a right triangle, the square of the length of the hypotenuse is equal to the sum of the squares of the lengths of the legs.**

[The proof for this theorem appears on page 611.]

In right triangle ABC (Fig. 6–34), the length of whose hypotenuse is c and the lengths of whose legs are a and b,

(hypotenuse)^2 = (one leg)^2 + (the other leg)^2, or
$$c^2 = a^2 + b^2$$

This relationship is known as the *Theorem of Pythagoras.*

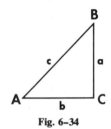

Fig. 6–34

Pythagorean Triples

Let us find the length of the hypotenuse of a right triangle whose legs measure 3 and 4. (See Fig. 6–35.)

1. $c^2 = a^2 + b^2$
2. $c^2 = (3)^2 + (4)^2$
3. $c^2 = 9 + 16$
4. $c^2 = 25$
5. $c = 5$

The length of the hypotenuse is 5.

When three integers are so related that the sum of the squares of two of them is equal to the square of the third, the set of three integers is called a *Pythagorean triple.* For example, (3, 4, 5) is called a Pythagorean triple because the numbers 3, 4, and 5 satisfy the relation $a^2 + b^2 = c^2$.

If each number in the triple (3, 4, 5) is doubled, we get the triple (2×3, 2×4, 2×5), or (6, 8, 10). A triangle whose sides are 6, 8, and 10 is similar to a triangle whose sides are 3, 4, and 5 because the corresponding sides of the two triangles are in proportion. Since the triangle whose sides are 3, 4, and 5 is a right triangle, the triangle whose sides are 6, 8, and 10 is also a right triangle. Therefore, (6, 8, 10) is also a Pythagorean triple.

Similarly, (3×3, 3×4, 3×5), or (9, 12, 15), is a Pythagorean triple. Also, (4×3, 4×4, 4×5), or (12, 16, 20), is a Pythagorean triple.

In general, if (3, 4, 5) is a Pythagorean triple, then ($3x$, $4x$, $5x$) is also a Pythagorean triple when x is a positive number.

If we wish to find the hypotenuse of a right triangle whose legs are 30 and 40, we can get the result quickly if we realize that $30 = 10 \times 3$ and $40 = 10 \times 4$. The hypotenuse must be the third number in the Pythagorean triple, 10×5, or 50.

Other examples of Pythagorean triples that occur frequently are:

(5, 12, 13) or, in general, $(5x, 12x, 13x)$, x being a positive integer, and
(8, 15, 17) or, in general, $(8x, 15x, 17x)$, x being a positive integer

With a knowledge of these Pythagorean triples, we can solve some right triangle problems mentally without writing out a lengthy algebraic solution.

KEEP IN MIND

> If the lengths of two sides of a right triangle are known, the length of the third side can always be found by using the Pythagorean Theorem.

MODEL PROBLEMS

1. In a right triangle the length of whose hypotenuse is 20, the length of one leg is 16. Find the length of the other leg.

   Solution:

   1. $a^2 + b^2 = c^2$

   2. $a^2 + (16)^2 = (20)^2$

   3. $a^2 + 256 = 400$

   4. $a^2 = 144$

   5. $a = 12$

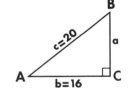

   Answer: The length of the other leg is 12.

   NOTE. If we notice that the hypotenuse, 20, is 4×5 and one leg, 16, is 4×4, then the other leg must be 4×3, or 12, in order to complete the Pythagorean triple $(3x, 4x, 5x)$, x being 4.

2. Find the length of the diagonal of a rectangle whose sides are $\sqrt{5}$ inches and 2 inches respectively.

   Solution: Let $x =$ the length of the diagonal.

   1. Since $\triangle ABC$ is a right triangle whose hypotenuse is x,

   $$x^2 = (2)^2 + (\sqrt{5})^2 \qquad (\sqrt{5})^2 = \sqrt{5} \cdot \sqrt{5} = \sqrt{25} = 5.$$

   [The solution continues on the next page.]

2. $x^2 = 4 + 5$

3. $x^2 = 9$

4. $x = 3$

Answer: The length of the diagonal of the rectangle is 3 inches.

3. In an isosceles triangle, the length of each of the congruent sides is 10 and the length of the base is 12. Find the length of the altitude drawn to the base.

Solution: In isosceles triangle ABC, altitude $\overline{BD} \perp \overline{AC}$, and $\overline{BD}$ bisects $\overline{AC}$. Therefore, $\triangle BDC$ is a right triangle and $DC = 6$. Let $x =$ the length of altitude $\overline{BD}$.

1. $(x)^2 + (6)^2 = (10)^2$

2. $x^2 + 36 = 100$

3. $x^2 = 64$

4. $x = 8$

Answer: The length of the altitude drawn to the base is 8.

4. The lengths of the diagonals of a rhombus are 30 and 40. Find the perimeter of the rhombus.

Solution: Since the diagonals of a rhombus are perpendicular to each other and bisect each other, $\triangle AEB$ is a right triangle in which $EB = \frac{1}{2}(30)$, or 15, and $AE = \frac{1}{2}(40)$, or 20.

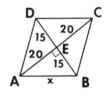

Let $x =$ the length of hypotenuse $\overline{AB}$.

1. $x^2 = (20)^2 + (15)^2$

2. $x^2 = 400 + 225$

3. $x^2 = 625$

4. $x = 25$

5. Since the four sides of a rhombus are equal in length, the perimeter $= 4 \times 25$, or 100.

Answer: The perimeter of the rhombus is 100.

5. A chord 16 inches long is 6 inches from the center of a circle. Find the length of the radius of the circle.

Solution: Since the distance of a chord from the center of a circle is measured on a line which is perpendicular to the chord and which passes through the center of the circle, $\overleftrightarrow{OC} \perp \overline{AB}$ and $\triangle OCB$ is a right triangle. $\overline{OC}$ bisects $\overline{AB}$. Therefore, $CB = \frac{1}{2}(16) = 8$.

Let r = the length of radius $\overline{OB}$.

1. $(r)^2 = (6)^2 + (8)^2$

2. $r^2 = 36 + 64$

3. $r^2 = 100$

4. $r = 10$

Answer: The length of the radius of the circle is 10 inches.

EXERCISES

In the following exercises, all irrational answers may be left in radical form:

In 1–20, use the information that is marked on the figure to find the value of x.

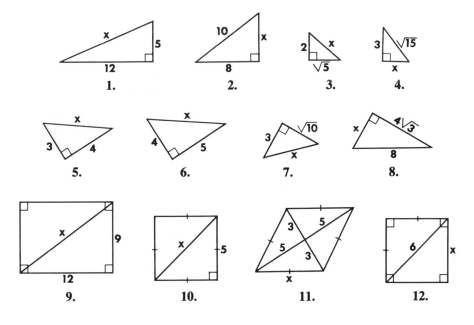

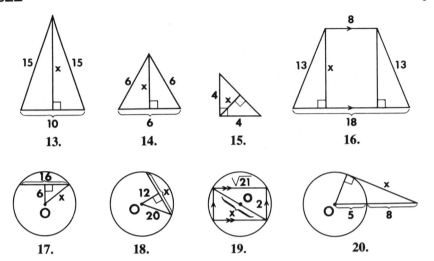

13. **14.** **15.** **16.**

17. **18.** **19.** **20.**

21. Find the length of the hypotenuse of a right triangle whose legs measure 9 and 12.

22. Find the measure of the hypotenuse of a right triangle whose legs measure 5 in. and 3 in.

23. The length of the hypotenuse of a right triangle is 2.5 and the length of one leg is 1.5. Find the length of the other leg.

24. The legs of a right triangle measure 3 in. and 4 in. One leg of another right triangle measures 4 in. and its hypotenuse measures 5 in. (*a*) Are the triangles congruent? (*b*) Why?

25. Find the measure of the diagonal of a rectangle whose sides measure 15 in. and 8 in.

26. If the length of the diagonal of a rectangle is 26 and the length of its base is 24, find the length of the altitude of the rectangle.

27. Find the length of the diagonal of a square whose side is 6 in. in length.

28. Find the length of the side of the rhombus whose diagonals measure 8 and 6.

29. The lengths of the diagonals of a rhombus are 16 and 12. Find the perimeter of the rhombus.

30. Find the length of the side of a square inscribed in a circle whose diameter measures 6.

31. In a circle whose diameter is $\overline{AB}$, chords $\overline{AC}$ and $\overline{BC}$ are drawn. If AB is 6 inches and AC is 3 inches, find in radical form the number of inches in the length of chord $\overline{BC}$.

32. The legs of a right triangle measure 6 inches and 8 inches. Find the number of inches in the length of the radius of the circumscribed circle.

33. Two radii of a circle, $\overline{OA}$ and $\overline{OB}$, are perpendicular to each other and chord $\overline{AB}$ is drawn. If AB is 6, the length of the radius of the circle is
    (1) 3   (2) 6   (3) $3\sqrt{2}$ (4) $6\sqrt{2}$

34. In a circle whose radius measures 5 in., a chord is drawn perpendicular to a diameter and at a distance of 3 in. from the center. Find the length of the chord in inches.

35. The radius of a circle measures 13 in. and a chord of this circle measures 10 in. Find the distance of this chord from the center of the circle.

36. A chord 12 in. long is 8 in. from the center of a circle. Find the length of the diameter of the circle.

37. A chord 24 in. long is 5 in. from the center of a circle. Find the length of a chord which is 12 in. from the center of the circle.

38. A point is 15 in. from the center of a circle the length of whose radius is 9 in. Find the length of the tangent drawn from this point to the circle.

39. Find the length of the radius of a circle circumscribed about a rectangle whose base measures 6 and whose altitude measures 8.

40. The lengths of the radii of two concentric circles are 13 in. and 5 in. Find the length of a chord of the larger circle which is tangent to the smaller circle.

41. A point P on the circumference of a circle is joined by line segments to the ends of diameter $\overline{CD}$. If $PC = 12$ and $PD = 16$, find the length of the radius of the circle.

42. The congruent sides of an isosceles triangle are each 15 in. and the base is 24 in. Find the length of the altitude drawn to the base.

43. In triangle ABC, $m\angle C = 90$, $\overline{CM}$ is the median to $\overline{AB}$, and $\overline{MD}$ is perpendicular to $\overline{CB}$. If $CM = 10$ and $MD = 8$, find the perimeter of triangle ABC.

44. In an isosceles trapezoid, the lengths of the bases are 14 and 30 and the length of each of the nonparallel sides is 10. Find the length of the altitude of the trapezoid.

45. In the isosceles trapezoid $ABCD$, angle A contains 45°, the longer base measures 17, and the shorter base measures 7. Find the length of the diagonal $\overline{BD}$.

46. ABC is a right triangle with $\overline{CD}$ the altitude on hypotenuse $\overline{AB}$. If $AC = 20$ and $CD = 12$, find AD.

47. $\overline{AB}$ is a common external tangent to nonintersecting circles O and O', point A being on circle O' and point B being on circle O. $OO' = 17$, $O'A = 10$, and $OB = 2$. Find AB. [*Hint:* Draw $\overline{OE} \perp \overline{O'A}$.]

48. In right triangle ABD, the length of leg $\overline{AB}$ is 12 and the length of hypotenuse $\overline{AD}$ is 15. C is a point on $\overline{DB}$. The length of $\overline{AC}$ is 13. Find the length of $\overline{DC}$.

49. In right triangle ABC, the length of leg $\overline{CB}$ is 8 and hypotenuse $\overline{AB}$ is 4 inches longer than leg $\overline{AC}$. (*a*) If the length of $\overline{AC}$ is represented by x, write an equation which can be used to find x. (*b*) Find AC and AB.

50. In right triangle ABC, the length of hypotenuse $\overline{AC}$ is 5 inches. If BC is 1 inch more than AB, find AB and BC.

51. In parallelogram $ABCD$, diagonals $\overline{AC}$ and $\overline{BD}$ intersect at E. $BC = 26$, $BE = 5x - 5$, $DE = 3x + 1$, $AE = 2y + 2$, and $CE = 4y - 20$. (*a*) Find x and y. (*b*) Show that parallelogram $ABCD$ is a rhombus.

52. $ABCD$ is a rectangle in which $AB = 32$ and $AD = 24$. $\overline{AE} \cong \overline{CF}$, and $\overline{BE} \cong \overline{ED}$. (*a*) Prove $EDFB$ is a rhombus. (*b*) Find DB. (*c*) If AE is represented by x, express ED in terms of x. [*Hint:* Use the relationship $\overline{BE} \cong \overline{ED}$.] (*d*) Find x. (*e*) Find EF.

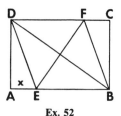

Ex. 52

13. The Converse of the Pythagorean Theorem

Theorem 101. **If the square of the length of one side of a triangle is equal to the sum of the squares of the lengths of the other two sides, then the triangle is a right triangle.**

In triangle ABC (Fig. 6–36), if a, b, and c represent the lengths of the sides, and if $c^2 = a^2 + b^2$, then triangle ABC is a right triangle, angle C being the right angle.

Theorem 101, which is the converse of the Pythagorean Theorem, can be used to determine whether a triangle is a right triangle.

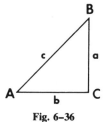

Fig. 6–36

MODEL PROBLEM

The lengths of the sides of a triangle are 8, 15, 17. Show that the triangle is a right triangle.

Solution: Let $c = 17$, the longest side of the triangle, $a = 8$, and $b = 15$.

Then $c^2 = (17)^2 = 289$.
Also, $a^2 + b^2 = (8)^2 + (15)^2 = 64 + 225 = 289$.
Since $(17)^2 = (8)^2 + (15)^2$, the triangle is a right triangle.

EXERCISES

In 1–6, show that the triangle the measures of whose sides are given is a right triangle.

1. 15, 20, 25   **2.** 36, 48, 60   **3.** 16, 30, 34
4. $\sqrt{5}$, $\sqrt{5}$, $\sqrt{10}$ **5.** 9, $\sqrt{19}$, 10   **6.** 4, 8, $4\sqrt{3}$

7. In a parallelogram, the lengths of two adjacent sides are 21 and 28. If the length of a diagonal of the parallelogram is 35, show that the parallelogram is a rectangle.

8. If each side of a rhombus is 3 and a diagonal is $3\sqrt{2}$, show that the rhombus is a square.

9. In circle O, the length of the radius $\overline{OA}$ is 4, $AP = \sqrt{20}$, and $OP = 6$. Show that $\overleftrightarrow{PA}$ is tangent to circle O.

Ex. 9

14. The 30°–60° Right Triangle

In right triangle ABC (Fig. 6–37), $m\angle A = 30$, $m\angle B = 60$, $m\angle C = 90$. In such a triangle, the following relationships can be proved:

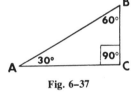

Fig. 6–37

1. The length of $\overline{BC}$, the leg opposite the 30° angle, is equal to one-half the length of the hypotenuse, $\overline{AB}$. $BC = \frac{1}{2}AB$.

2. The length of $\overline{AC}$, the leg opposite the 60° angle, is equal to one-half the length of the hypotenuse $\overline{AB}$, times $\sqrt{3}$. $AC = \frac{1}{2}AB\sqrt{3}$.

3. The length of the longer leg $\overline{AC}$ is equal to the length of the shorter leg $\overline{BC}$, times $\sqrt{3}$. $AC = BC\sqrt{3}$.

4. The length of the shorter leg $\overline{BC}$ is equal to the length of the longer leg $\overline{AC}$, divided by $\sqrt{3}$. $BC = \dfrac{AC}{\sqrt{3}}$.

5. The ratio of the length of the shorter leg $\overline{BC}$ to the length of the hypotenuse $\overline{AB}$ is 1:2. $BC:AB = 1:2$.

Since an altitude of an equilateral triangle divides the triangle into two 30°–60° right triangles (Fig. 6–38), the following relationship in an equilateral triangle can also be proved:

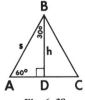

Fig. 6–38

6. The length of the altitude, h, is equal to one-half the length of the side, s, times $\sqrt{3}$. $h = \dfrac{s}{2}\sqrt{3}$.

MODEL PROBLEMS

1. In a circle, angle ABC, which is formed by diameter $\overline{AB}$ and chord $\overline{BC}$, contains 30°. If the length of the diameter of the circle is 20, find the length of chord $\overline{AC}$, and find the length of chord $\overline{BC}$ in radical form.

Solution:

1. Since $\overline{AB}$ is a diameter, $m\angle C = 90$.

2. $m\angle B = 30$ and $m\angle A = 60$.

3. $AC = \frac{1}{2}AB = \frac{1}{2}(20) = 10$.

4. $BC = \frac{1}{2}AB\sqrt{3} = \frac{1}{2}(20)\sqrt{3} = 10\sqrt{3}$.

Answer: $AC = 10$, $BC = 10\sqrt{3}$.

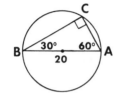

2. In triangle ABC, $m\angle A = 30$, $m\angle B = 60$, $m\angle C = 90$, $\overline{AC}$ measures 6 inches. Find BC to the *nearest tenth of an inch*.

Solution:

Method 1	*Method 2*
BC, the length of the leg opposite the 30° angle, is equal to one-half of AB, the length of the hypotenuse.	The length of the leg opposite the 30° angle is equal to the length of the leg opposite the 60° angle divided by $\sqrt{3}$.

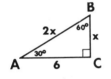

Method 1

1. Let x = the length of $\overline{BC}$.

2. Then $2x$ = the length of $\overline{AB}$.

3. $(2x)^2 = (x)^2 + (6)^2$

4. $4x^2 = x^2 + 36$

5. $3x^2 = 36$

6. $x^2 = 12$

7. $x = \sqrt{12}$

8. $x = \sqrt{4} \cdot \sqrt{3}$

9. $x = 2\sqrt{3}$

   [Use $\sqrt{3} = 1.73$.]

10. $x = 2(1.73) = 3.46$

11. $x = 3.5$

Method 2

1. $BC = \dfrac{AC}{\sqrt{3}}$

2. $BC = \dfrac{6}{\sqrt{3}}$

3. $BC = \dfrac{6}{\sqrt{3}} \cdot \dfrac{\sqrt{3}}{\sqrt{3}}$

4. $BC = \dfrac{6\sqrt{3}}{3}$

5. $BC = 2\sqrt{3}$

6. $BC = 2(1.73) = 3.46$

7. $BC = 3.5$

Answer: $BC = 3.5$ in. to the nearest tenth of an inch.

3. Find in radical form the length of the altitude of an equilateral triangle whose side measures 12 inches.

Solution:

Method 1	*Method 2*	
In an equilateral triangle, the length of the altitude, h, is equal to one-half the length of the side, s, times $\sqrt{3}$.	Draw altitude $\overline{CD}$, which bisects base $\overline{AB}$. Let $h =$ the length of the altitude. In right triangle CDB,	

Method 1	*Method 2*
1. $h = \frac{1}{2}s\sqrt{3} \quad s = 12$	1. $(h)^2 + (6)^2 = (12)^2$
2. $h = \frac{1}{2}(12)\sqrt{3}$	2. $\quad h^2 + 36 = 144$
3. $h = 6\sqrt{3}$	3. $\quad\quad h^2 = 108$
	4. $\quad h = \sqrt{108} = \sqrt{36} \cdot \sqrt{3} = 6\sqrt{3}$

Answer: Length of the altitude $= 6\sqrt{3}$ inches.

EXERCISES

In the following exercises, an irrational answer may be left in radical form unless otherwise indicated:

1. In right triangle ABC, $m\angle A = 30$, $m\angle B = 60$, $m\angle C = 90$. Find BC and AC when AB is:
  a. 6   *b.* 10   *c.* 5   *d.* $8\sqrt{3}$ *e.* $4x$

2. In right triangle ABC, $m\angle A = 30$, $m\angle B = 60$, $m\angle C = 90$. Find AB and AC when BC is:
  a. 4   *b.* 8   *c.* 3.5   *d.* $4\sqrt{3}$ *e.* $2x$

3. In right triangle ABC, $m\angle A = 30$, $m\angle B = 60$, $m\angle C = 90$. Find BC and AB when AC is:
  a. $4\sqrt{3}$ *b.* $7\sqrt{3}$ *c.* $2.5\sqrt{3}$ *d.* $x\sqrt{3}$

4. In triangle ABC, $m\angle B = 30$ and $AB = 6$. Find the length of the altitude $\overline{AD}$ upon side $\overline{BC}$.

5. Two sides of a triangle are 10 and 14 and the angle included between these sides measures $30°$. Find the length of the altitude on the side whose length is 14.

6. $\overline{AB}$ intersects $\overleftrightarrow{LM}$ at A. If $m\angle MAB = 60$, find the length of the projection of $\overline{AB}$ on $\overleftrightarrow{LM}$ when AB is:
  a. 4   *b.* 8   *c.* 7   *d.* $2\sqrt{3}$ *e.* $2x$

7. $\overleftrightarrow{CD}$ intersects $\overleftrightarrow{AB}$ at C. If $m\angle BCD = 30$, find the length of the projection of $\overline{CD}$ on $\overleftrightarrow{AB}$ when CD is:

    a. 6   *b.* 14   *c.* 9   *d.* 13   *e.* 7*c*

8. In a right triangle, the measure of one acute angle is double the measure of the other acute angle. If the length of the shorter leg of the triangle is 3, find the length of the hypotenuse.

9. The measures of the angles of a triangle are in the ratio 1:2:3. The length of the shortest side of the triangle is 4. Find the length of the longest side.

10. Angle ABC formed by diameter $\overline{AB}$ and chord $\overline{BC}$ of a circle contains 30°. If the length of the diameter of the circle is 10, find the length of chord $\overline{AC}$.

11. The measure of one acute angle of a right triangle is double the measure of the other. The length of the longer leg is $5\sqrt{3}$. Find the length of the hypotenuse.

12. If one angle of a right triangle measures 60 and the length of the hypotenuse is 8, find the length of the side opposite the 60° angle, correct to the *nearest tenth.*

13. In a parallelogram, two adjacent sides whose lengths are 6 in. and 16 in. include an angle of 60°. Find the length of the shorter diagonal.

14. The angle formed by two tangents drawn to a circle from an outside point measures 60. If the length of the radius of the circle is 8 in., find the length of each tangent.

15. In an isosceles triangle ABC, the vertex angle C measures 120 and the length of $\overline{AC}$ is 8. (*a*) Find the length of the altitude on $\overline{AB}$. (*b*) Find AB to the *nearest integer.*

16. In a triangle, two adjacent sides which are 8 in. and 15 in. include an angle of 60°. Find the length of the third side.

17. In a rhombus which contains an angle of 60°, the length of each side is 10 in. Find the length of each diagonal.

18. In right triangle ABC, $m\angle C = 90$ and $m\angle ABC = 30$. D is a point on $\overline{CB}$. If $DB = 50$ and $m\angle ADC = 60$, find AC.

19. *Prove:* In a 30°–60° right triangle, the length of the side opposite the 30° angle is equal to one-half the length of the hypotenuse. [*Hint:* Start with equilateral triangle ABC and draw the bisector of $\angle ACB$.]

20. *Prove:* In a 30°–60° right triangle, the length of the side opposite the 60° angle is equal to one-half the length of the hypotenuse times $\sqrt{3}$. [*Hint:* Start with right triangle ABC in which $m\angle A = 30$ and $m\angle B = 60$. Represent the length of $\overline{AB}$ by h and the length of $\overline{BC}$ by $\frac{1}{2}h$. Then $(x)^2 + (\frac{1}{2}h)^2 = (h)^2$.]

21. Find the length of the altitude of an equilateral triangle the length of whose side is:

    a. 2   *b.* 4   *c.* 8   *d.* 10   *e.* 5   *f.* 9

22. Find the length of the side of an equilateral triangle the length of whose altitude is:

    a. $3\sqrt{3}$ *b.* $4\sqrt{3}$ *c.* $6\sqrt{3}$ *d.* $\sqrt{3}$ *e.* $3.5\sqrt{3}$ *f.* $\frac{5}{2}\sqrt{3}$

23. *Prove:* In an equilateral triangle, the length of an altitude is equal to one-half the length of a side times $\sqrt{3}$. [*Hint:* Use one of the 30°–60° right triangle relationships.]

15. The Isosceles Right Triangle

Fig. 6–39

In right triangle ABC (Fig. 6–39), $m\angle A = 45$, $m\angle B = 45$, $m\angle C = 90$. In such a triangle, which is an isosceles right triangle, the following relationships can be proved:

1. The lengths of the legs, $\overline{AC}$ and $\overline{BC}$, are equal. $AC = BC$.
2. The length of the hypotenuse, h, is equal to the length of the leg, L, times $\sqrt{2}$. $h = L\sqrt{2}$.
3. The length of a leg, L, is equal to one-half the length of the hypotenuse, h, times $\sqrt{2}$. $L = \frac{1}{2}h\sqrt{2}$.

Fig. 6–40

Since a diagonal divides a square into two isosceles right triangles (Fig. 6–40), the following relationships can also be proved:

4. The length of the diagonal, d, is equal to the length of the side, s, times $\sqrt{2}$. $d = s\sqrt{2}$.
5. The length of the side, s, is equal to one-half the length of the diagonal, d, times $\sqrt{2}$. $s = \frac{1}{2}d\sqrt{2}$.

MODEL PROBLEMS

1. Find in radical form the length of the hypotenuse of an isosceles right triangle, each of whose legs is 4 units long.

Solution:

Method 1	*Method 2*
In an isosceles right triangle, the length of the hypotenuse is equal to the length of a leg times $\sqrt{2}$.	In right $\triangle ABC$,
	1. $h^2 = (4)^2 + (4)^2$
1. $h = L\sqrt{2}$ $L = 4$.	2. $h^2 = 16 + 16$
	3. $h^2 = 32$
2. $h = 4\sqrt{2}$	4. $h = \sqrt{32} = \sqrt{16} \cdot \sqrt{2}$ $= 4\sqrt{2}$

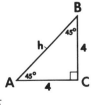

Answer: The length of the hypotenuse is $4\sqrt{2}$.

2. The lengths of the bases of an isosceles trapezoid are 8 and 14, and each of the base angles measures 45°. Find the length of the altitude of the trapezoid.

Solution:

1. Draw altitudes $\overline{DE}$ and $\overline{CF}$.

2. *DCFE* is a rectangle.

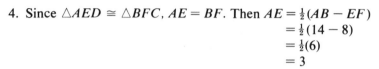

3. $DC = EF = 8$.

4. Since $\triangle AED \cong \triangle BFC$, $AE = BF$. Then $AE = \frac{1}{2}(AB - EF)$
$$= \frac{1}{2}(14 - 8)$$
$$= \frac{1}{2}(6)$$
$$= 3$$

5. Since $\triangle AED$ is a 45°–45°–90° triangle, $AE = DE = 3$.

Answer: The length of the altitude is 3.

3. Find to the nearest tenth of an inch the length of a side of a square whose diagonal measures 8 inches.

Solution:

Method 1	*Method* 2

Method 1

In a square, the length of a side is equal to one-half the length of a diagonal times $\sqrt{2}$.

1. $s = \frac{1}{2}d\sqrt{2}$ $d = 8$.

2. $s = \frac{1}{2}(8)\sqrt{2}$

3. $s = 4\sqrt{2}$
   [Use $\sqrt{2} = 1.41$.]

4. $s = 4(1.41) = 5.64$

5. $s = 5.6$

Method 2

Let $s =$ the length of a side of the square.
In right $\triangle ABC$,

1. $s^2 + s^2 = 8^2$

2. $2s^2 = 64$

3. $s^2 = 32$

4. $s = \sqrt{32} = \sqrt{16} \cdot \sqrt{2} = 4\sqrt{2}$
              [Use $\sqrt{2} = 1.41$.]

5. $s = 4(1.41) = 5.64$

6. $s = 5.6$

Answer: The length of a side of the square is 5.6 inches, to the nearest tenth of an inch.

EXERCISES

In the following exercises, an irrational answer may be left in radical form unless otherwise indicated:

1. In right triangle ABC, $m\angle A = 45$ and $m\angle B = 45$. Find AC and AB when BC is:

   a. 6   *b.* 8   *c.* 12   *d.* 5   *e.* 4x

2. In right triangle ABC, $m\angle A = 45$ and $m\angle B = 45$. Find BC and AC when AB is:

   a. 6   *b.* 8   *c.* 5   *d.* $4\sqrt{2}$ *e.* 2x

3. The length of a leg of an isosceles right triangle is 4. Find the length of the hypotenuse to the *nearest tenth*.

4. In an isosceles right triangle, the length of one leg is 10. Express in radical form the length of the altitude upon the hypotenuse.

5. $\overline{AB}$ intersects $\overleftrightarrow{LM}$ at A. If $m\angle MAB = 45$, find the length of the projection of $\overline{AB}$ on $\overleftrightarrow{LM}$ when AB is:

   a. 4   *b.* 12   *c.* 3   *d.* $6\sqrt{2}$ *e.* 4x

6. The lengths of the bases of an isosceles trapezoid are 7 and 15. Each leg makes an angle of 45° with the longer base. Find the length of the altitude of the trapezoid.

7. The bases of an isosceles trapezoid are 9 and 15, and each base angle contains 45°. Find the length of the altitude of the trapezoid.

8. *Prove:* In an isosceles right triangle, the length of the hypotenuse is equal to the length of a leg times $\sqrt{2}$.

9. *Prove:* In an isosceles right triangle, the length of a leg is equal to one-half the length of the hypotenuse times $\sqrt{2}$.

10. Find the length of the diagonal of a square whose side is:

    a. 2   *b.* 8   *c.* 5   *d.* 9   *e.* $4\sqrt{2}$ *f.* $3\sqrt{2}$ *g.* 6x

11. Find the length of the side of a square whose diagonal is:

    a. 4   *b.* 6   *c.* 3   *d.* 5   *e.* $6\sqrt{2}$ *f.* 2x   *g.* $4a\sqrt{2}$

12. Find to the *nearest tenth of an inch* the length of the diagonal of a square whose side is 3 inches in length.

13. Find to the *nearest tenth of an inch* the length of the side of a square whose diagonal is 10 inches in length.

14. *Prove:* The length of the diagonal of a square is equal to the length of the side of the square times $\sqrt{2}$.

15. *Prove:* The length of the side of a square is equal to one-half the length of the diagonal of the square times $\sqrt{2}$.

16. Trigonometry of the Right Triangle

The word *trigonometry*, which comes from the Greek, means "measurement of triangles." In this branch of mathematics, we will study relationships among the measures of the sides and angles of triangles.

Direct and Indirect Measurement

Many mathematical problems involve the measurement of line segments and angles. Sometimes we can conveniently make a *direct measurement* of a segment or an angle by applying the unit of measure to it. The number of times the unit of measure is contained in the segment or angle represents the measure of the segment or angle.

However, in many situations, it is inconvenient or impossible to apply the unit of measure directly to the object being measured; for example, we cannot measure directly the height of a tall tree or building, the width of a river, or the distance to the sun. In such cases, we resort to methods of *indirect measurement*.

When we use indirect measurement to discover the length of a line segment, for example, we first measure directly segments and angles which can be conveniently measured. Then we compute the length of the segment we wish to measure by using a formula or mathematical relationship which relates the length of that segment with the measurements which were made directly. When we worked with similar figures and the Pythagorean Theorem, we used indirect measurement.

In our study of trigonometry of the right triangle, we will discover new relationships which will provide additional methods for measuring segments and angles indirectly. Engineers, surveyors, physicists, and astronomers frequently use these trigonometric methods in their work.

17. The Tangent Ratio

Each of the triangles in Fig. 6–41 represents a right triangle in which there is a 31° angle. In each figure, the lengths of the leg opposite the 31° angle and the leg adjacent to the 31° angle are shown. In each triangle, let us find the ratio of the length of the leg opposite the 31° angle to the length of the leg adjacent to the 31° angle. Note that in each triangle the indicated linear measures are given correct to the nearest integer.

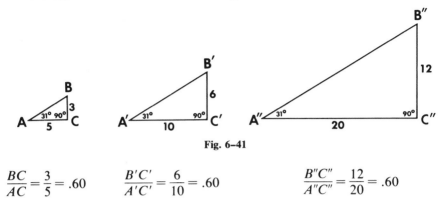

Fig. 6–41

$$\frac{BC}{AC} = \frac{3}{5} = .60 \qquad \frac{B'C'}{A'C'} = \frac{6}{10} = .60 \qquad \frac{B''C''}{A''C''} = \frac{12}{20} = .60$$

Notice that in all three cases, the ratio,

$$\frac{\text{length of the leg opposite the } 31° \text{ angle}}{\text{length of the leg adjacent to the } 31° \text{ angle}} = .60, \text{ a constant}$$

We might have expected that the three ratios $\frac{BC}{AC}$, $\frac{B'C'}{A'C'}$, and $\frac{B''C''}{A''C''}$ would be equal because the right triangles ABC, $A'B'C'$, and $A''B''C''$, each of which contains an angle of $31°$, are similar, and the ratios of the lengths of corresponding sides in these similar triangles must be equal.

In fact, in all right triangles which contain an angle of $31°$, the value of the ratio $\frac{\text{length of the leg opposite the } 31° \text{ angle}}{\text{length of the leg adjacent to the } 31° \text{ angle}}$ is constant (approximately .60), no matter what the size of the triangle.

What we have shown to be true for a $31°$ angle would also be true for any other acute angle in a right triangle. In general, in every right triangle having an acute angle whose measure is a particular number of degrees, the ratio of the length of the leg opposite the acute angle to the length of the leg adjacent to the acute angle is constant. This is true because every right triangle containing an acute angle whose measure is a given number of degrees is similar to every other right triangle containing an acute angle whose measure is the same number of degrees. For different acute angles, the ratio is a different constant.

In Fig. 6–42, in which $\angle C$, $\angle C'$, and $\angle C''$ are right angles, we can see that $\triangle ABC \sim \triangle AB'C' \sim \triangle AB''C''$. Therefore, by using the definition of similar polygons, it follows that:

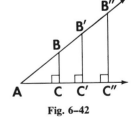

$$\frac{BC}{AC} = \frac{B'C'}{AC'} = \frac{B''C''}{AC''} = \text{a constant ratio for } \angle A.$$

This ratio is called the *tangent of the angle*.

Fig. 6–42

Definition. The *tangent of an acute angle of a right triangle* is the ratio of the length of the leg opposite the acute angle to the length of the leg adjacent to the acute angle.

In right triangle ABC (Fig. 6–43), with $m\angle C = 90$, the definition of the *tangent of angle A*, abbreviated "tan A," is:

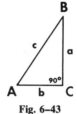

$$\tan A = \frac{\text{length of leg opposite } \angle A}{\text{length of leg adjacent to } \angle A} = \frac{BC}{AC} = \frac{a}{b}$$

Fig. 6–43

The Table of Tangents

As the measure of angle A changes, the tangent ratio for angle A also changes. The tangent ratio for angle A depends upon the measure of angle A, not upon the size of the right triangle which contains angle A. Mathematicians have constructed a table of tangent ratios for all acute angles whose measures are between 0 and 90. This table, which is called a table of trigonometric functions, is found on page 748 in the fourth column.

To find tan 28° from this table, for example, first look in the column headed "Angle" for the angle 28°. Then, in the column headed "Tangent," on the same horizontal line as 28°, find the number .5317. Thus, tan 28° = .5317 to the *nearest ten-thousandth*.

The table may also be used to find an angle when its tangent ratio is known. Thus, if tan A = 1.5399, we see from the table that angle A must contain 57°.

Sometimes the value of the tangent of an angle is not in the table. In such a case, we can estimate the measure of the angle to the *nearest degree*. For example, suppose we wish to find the measure of angle A when tan A = .5000. This value is not in the table of tangent ratios. In the table, we can find the tangent ratio which is just larger than .5000 and the tangent ratio which is just smaller than .5000, and we can then discover to which of these two ratios .5000 is closer.

Angle	Tangent	Difference
27°	.5095	.0095
A	.5000	.0123
26°	.4877	

Since .0095 is less than .0123, then .5000 is closer to .5095 than it is to .4877. Hence, the measure of angle A is closer to 27 than it is to 26. We now know that angle A contains 27° to the *nearest degree*.

EXERCISES

In 1–4, represent the tangent of each acute angle.

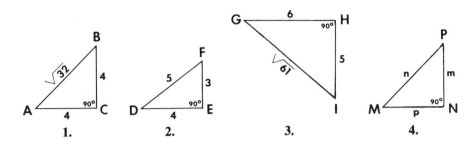

| **1.** | **2.** | **3.** | **4.** |

5. In triangle ABC, $m\angle C = 90$, $AC = 6$, and $AB = 10$. Find tan A.

6. In triangle RST, $m\angle T = 90$, $RS = 13$, and $ST = 12$. Find tan S.

Using the table on page 748, find each of the following:

7. tan 10°   **8.** tan 30°   **9.** tan 70°   **10.** tan 45°

11. tan 1°   **12.** tan 89°   **13.** tan 36°   **14.** tan 60°

Using the table on page 748, find the measure of angle A if:

15. tan A = .0875   **16.** tan A = .3640   **17.** tan A = .5543

18. tan A = 1.0000   **19.** tan A = 2.0503   **20.** tan A = 3.0777

Using the table on page 748, find the measure of angle A to the *nearest degree* if:

21. tan A = .3754   **22.** tan A = .7654   **23.** tan A = 1.8000

24. tan A = .3500   **25.** tan A = .1450   **26.** tan A = 2.9850

27. Does the tangent of an angle increase or decrease as the measure of the angle varies from 1 to 89?

28. *a.* Use the table on page 748 to discover whether tan 40° is twice tan 20°.

   b. If the measure of an angle is doubled, is the tangent of the angle also doubled?

29. In triangle ABC, $m\angle C = 90$, $AC = 6$, and $BC = 6$.   (*a*) Find tan A. (*b*) Find the measure of angle A.

30. In triangle RST, $m\angle S = 90$, $TS = 4$, and $RS = 3$.   (*a*) Find tan T to the *nearest ten-thousandth*.   (*b*) Find the measure of angle T to the *nearest degree*.

31. In triangle ABC, $m\angle C = 90$, $AC = 5$, and $BC = 12$.   (*a*) Find tan B to the *nearest ten-thousandth*.   (*b*) Find the degree measure of angle B to the *nearest degree*.

Angle of Elevation and Angle of Depression

In Fig. 6–44, if a person using a telescope or some similar instrument wishes to sight the top of the telephone pole above him, he must elevate (tilt upward) the instrument from a horizontal position. The line $\overset{\leftrightarrow}{OT}$ passing through the eye of the observer, O, and the top of the pole, T, is called the *line of sight*. The angle determined by the rays which are part of the horizontal line and the line of sight, $\angle AOT$, is called the *angle of elevation* of the top of the pole, T, from point O. (The horizontal line and the line of sight must be in the same vertical plane.)

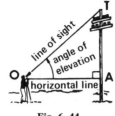

Fig. 6–44

In Fig. 6–45, if a person using a telescope or some similar instrument wishes to sight the boat below him, he must depress (tilt downward) the instrument from a horizontal position. The line $\overset{\leftrightarrow}{OB}$ passing through the eye of the observer, O, and the boat, B, is called the *line of sight*. The angle determined by the rays which are part of the horizontal line and the line of sight, $\angle HOB$, is called the *angle of depression* of the boat, B, from point O. (The horizontal line and the line of sight must be in the same vertical plane.)

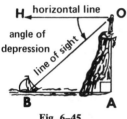

Fig. 6–45

In Fig. 6–45, if we find the measure of the angle of elevation of O from B, $\angle OBA$, and also find the measure of the angle of depression of B from O, $\angle HOB$, we discover that both angles contain the same number of degrees. We therefore say that the angle of elevation of O from B is congruent to the angle of depression of B from O. Note that this must be so because $\overset{\leftrightarrow}{HO}$ is parallel to $\overset{\leftrightarrow}{AB}$, making the alternate interior angles, $\angle HOB$ and $\angle ABO$, congruent.

Using the Tangent Ratio to Solve Problems

To solve problems by use of the tangent ratio, proceed as follows:

1. Make an approximate scale drawing which contains the line segments and angles given in the problem and those to be found.
2. Select a right triangle in which either (*a*) the measures of two legs are given (known) and the measure of an acute angle is to be found or (*b*) the measures of one leg and an acute angle are given (known) and the measure of the other leg is to be found.
3. Write the formula for the tangent of the acute angle mentioned in step 2, and then substitute in the formula the values given in the problem.
4. Solve the resulting equation.

MODEL PROBLEMS

1. At a point on the ground 40 feet from the foot of a tree, the angle of elevation of the top of the tree contains 42°. Find the height of the tree to the *nearest foot*.

Solution: Since the segments mentioned in the problem are legs of a right triangle opposite and adjacent to the given acute angle, use the tangent ratio.

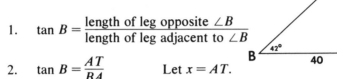

1. $\tan B = \dfrac{\text{length of leg opposite } \angle B}{\text{length of leg adjacent to } \angle B}$

2. $\tan B = \dfrac{AT}{BA}$ Let $x = AT$.

3. $\tan 42° = \dfrac{x}{40}$ In the table on page 748, $\tan 42° = .9004$.

4. $.9004 = \dfrac{x}{40}$

5. $x = 40(.9004)$ M_{40} [Multiply both members of the equation by 40.]

6. $x = 36.016$

Answer: The height of the tree is 36 feet to the nearest foot.

2. From the top of a lighthouse 160 feet above sea level, the angle of depression of a boat at sea contains 35°. Find to the *nearest foot* the distance from the boat to the foot of the lighthouse.

Solution: The angle of depression, $\angle HLB$, is not inside right triangle BAL. To find the measure of $\angle BLA$, which is inside triangle BAL, subtract $m\angle HLB$ from 90. $90 - 35 = 55$. Since the segments mentioned in the problem are legs of right triangle BAL opposite and adjacent to $\angle BLA$, use the tangent ratio.

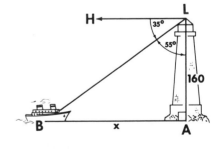

[The solution continues on the next page.]

1. $\tan \angle BLA = \dfrac{\text{length of leg opposite } \angle BLA}{\text{length of leg adjacent to } \angle BLA}$

2. $\tan \angle BLA = \dfrac{BA}{LA}$ Let $x = BA$

3. $\tan 55° = \dfrac{x}{160}$ In the table on page 748,
    $\tan 55° = 1.4281$.

4. $1.4281 = \dfrac{x}{160}$

5. $x = 160(1.4281)$ $\mathbf{M}_{160}$

6. $x = 228.496$

Answer: 228 feet.

3. A ladder which is leaning against a building makes an angle of 75° with the ground. If the top of the ladder reaches a point which is 20 feet above the ground, find to the *nearest foot* the distance from the foot of the ladder to the foot of the building.

Solution:

Method 1	*Method 2*

Method 1

1. $\tan A = \dfrac{BC}{AC}$

    Let $x = AC$.

2. $\tan 75° = \dfrac{20}{x}$

3. $3.7321 = \dfrac{20}{x}$

4. $3.7321x = 20$

5. $x = \dfrac{20}{3.7321}$

6. $x = 5.3$

Answer: 5 feet.

Method 2

1. Find $m\angle B$,
    $m\angle B = 90 - 75 = 15.$

2. $\tan B = \dfrac{AC}{BC}$

    Let $x = AC$.

3. $\tan 15° = \dfrac{x}{20}$

4. $.2679 = \dfrac{x}{20}$

5. $x = 20(.2679)$

6. $x = 5.3580$

NOTE. In method 1, since the unknown was the measure of the leg adjacent to $\angle A$, the solution required the inconvenient long division $\dfrac{20}{3.7321}$. In method 2, however, when we used the other acute angle, $\angle B$, the unknown was the measure of the leg opposite $\angle B$; and the solution required the convenient multiplication 20(.2679).

4. Find to the *nearest degree* the measure of the angle of elevation of the sun when a vertical pole 6 feet high casts a shadow 8 feet long.

Solution: The angle of elevation of the sun is the same as $\angle A$, the angle of elevation of the top of the pole from A. Since the segments mentioned in the problem are legs of a right triangle opposite and adjacent to $\angle A$, use the tangent ratio.

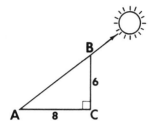

1. $\tan A = \dfrac{\text{length of leg opposite } \angle A}{\text{length of leg adjacent to } \angle A}$

2. $\tan A = \dfrac{BC}{AC} = \dfrac{6}{8}$ Express $\dfrac{6}{8}$ as the decimal .7500.

3. $\tan A = .7500$ In the table on page 748, $\tan 36° = .7265$ and
4. $m\angle A = 37$ $\tan 37° = .7536$. Since .7500 is closer to .7536 than it is to .7265, $m\angle A$ is closer to 37.

Answer: 37° to the nearest degree.

EXERCISES

In 1–8, in the given triangle, find the length of the side marked x to the *nearest foot* or the number of degrees contained in the angle marked x to the *nearest degree*.

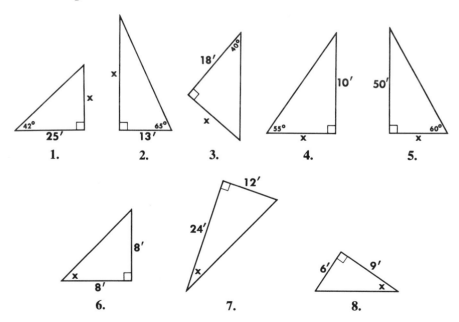

9. At a point on the ground 50 feet from the foot of a tree, the angle of elevation of the top of the tree contains 48°. Find the height of the tree to the *nearest foot*.

10. A ladder is leaning against a wall. The foot of the ladder is 6.5 feet from the wall. The ladder makes an angle of 74° with the level ground. How high on the wall does the ladder reach? Round off the answer to the *nearest tenth of a foot*.

11. A boy visiting New York City views the Empire State Building from a point on the ground, *A*, which is 940 feet from the foot, *C*, of the building. The angle of elevation of the top, *B*, of the building as seen by the boy contains 53°. Find the height of the building to the *nearest foot*.

12. Find to the *nearest foot* the height of a vertical post if its shadow is 18 feet long when the angle of elevation of the sun contains 38°.

13. From the top of a lighthouse 160 feet high, the angle of depression of a boat out at sea is an angle of 24°. Find to the *nearest foot* the distance from the boat to the foot of the lighthouse, the foot of the lighthouse being at sea level.

14. From the top of a tower 80 feet high, the angle of depression of an object on the ground contains 38°. Find to the *nearest foot* the distance from the object to the foot of the tower.

15. Find to the *nearest degree* the measure of the angle of elevation of the sun when a boy 5 feet high casts a shadow 5 feet long.

16. Find to the *nearest degree* the measure of the angle of elevation of the sun when a vertical post 15 feet high casts a shadow 20 feet long.

17. A ladder leans against a building. The top of the ladder reaches a point on the building which is 18 feet above the ground. The foot of the ladder is 7 feet from the building. Find to the *nearest degree* the measure of the angle which the ladder makes with the level ground.

18. The Sine Ratio

Since the tangent ratio involves the two legs of a right triangle, it is not directly useful in solving problems in which the hypotenuse, a leg, and an acute angle are involved. In a case where two of these three parts of a right triangle are given and the third part is to be found, ratios other than the tangent ratio can be more useful.

If we refer to Fig. 6–42 on page 333, we can see that since $\triangle ABC \sim \triangle AB'C' \sim \triangle AB''C''$, it also follows that:

$$\frac{BC}{AB} = \frac{B'C'}{AB'} = \frac{B''C''}{AB''} = \text{a constant ratio for } \angle A.$$

This ratio is called the *sine of the angle*.

Definition. The *sine of an acute angle of a right triangle* is the ratio of the length of the leg opposite the acute angle to the length of the hypotenuse.

In right triangle ABC (Fig. 6–46), with $m\angle C = 90$, the definition of the *sine of angle A*, abbreviated "sin A," is:

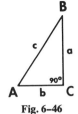

$$\sin A = \frac{\text{length of leg opposite } \angle A}{\text{length of hypotenuse}} = \frac{BC}{AB} = \frac{a}{c}$$

Fig. 6–46

The Table of Sines

As the measure of angle A changes, the sine ratio for angle A also changes. The sine ratio for angle A depends upon the measure of angle A, not upon the size of the right triangle which contains angle A. The table of sine ratios which mathematicians have constructed for all acute angles whose measures are between 0 and 90 is found on page 748 in the second column.

If we use this table as we did when we studied the tangent ratio, we can obtain the following results:

1. $\sin 25° = .4226$.
2. If $\sin A = .7660$, angle A contains $50°$.
3. If $\sin A = .2500$, angle A contains $14°$ to the *nearest degree* because .2500 is closer to .2419, which is sin $14°$, than it is to .2588, which is sin $15°$.

EXERCISES

In 1–4, represent the sine of each acute angle.

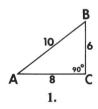
1.

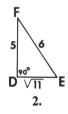
2.

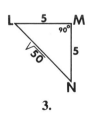
3.

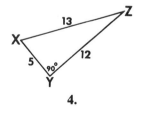
4.

5. In triangle ABC, $m\angle C = 90$, $AC = 4$, and $BC = 3$. Find sin A.

6. In triangle RST, $m\angle S = 90$, $RS = 5$, and $ST = 12$. Find sin T.

Using the table on page 748, find each of the following:

7. sin 18°   **8.** sin 42°   **9.** sin 58°   **10.** sin 76°

11. sin 1°   **12.** sin 89°   **13.** sin 35°   **14.** sin 68°

Using the table on page 748, find the measure of angle *A* if:

15. sin *A* = .1908   **16.** sin *A* = .8387   **17.** sin *A* = .6561

18. sin *A* = .3420   **19.** sin *A* = .7071   **20.** sin *A* = .9962

Using the table on page 748, find the degree measure of angle *A* to the *nearest degree* if:

21. sin *A* = .1900   **22.** sin *A* = .8740   **23.** sin *A* = .5800

24. sin *A* = .9725   **25.** sin *A* = .1275   **26.** sin *A* = .8695

27. Does the sine of an angle increase or decrease as the measure of the angle varies from 1 through 89?

28. *a.* Use the table on page 748 to discover whether sin 50° is twice sin 25°.

   b. If the measure of an angle is doubled, is the sine of the angle also doubled?

29. In triangle *ABC*, *m∠C* = 90, *BC* = 20, and *BA* = 40.   (*a*) Find sin *A* to the *nearest ten-thousandth*.   (*b*) Find the measure of angle *A*.

30. In triangle *ABC*, *m∠C* = 90, *AC* = 5, and *BC* = 12.   (*a*) Find sin *B* to the *nearest ten-thousandth*.   (*b*) Find the degree measure of angle *B* to the *nearest degree*.

31. Why must the sine of an acute angle be less than 1?

Using the Sine Ratio to Solve Problems

When the hypotenuse, a leg, and an acute angle of a right triangle are involved in a problem, with the measures of any two of these three parts given (known), the use of the sine ratio will help us to find the measure of the unknown third part. We proceed as we did when we were using the tangent ratio.

MODEL PROBLEMS

1. A boy who is flying a kite lets out 300 feet of string which makes an angle of 38° with the ground. Assuming that the string is straight, how high above the ground is the kite? Give your answer correct to the *nearest foot*.

> *Solution:* Since the segments mentioned in the problem are the leg opposite the acute angle and the hypotenuse of a right triangle, use the sine ratio.

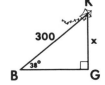

$$\text{1.} \quad \sin B = \frac{\text{length of leg opposite } \angle B}{\text{length of hypotenuse}}$$

2. $\sin B = \dfrac{KG}{KB}$ Let $x = KG$.

3. $\sin 38° = \dfrac{x}{300}$ In the table on page 748, $\sin 38° = .6157$.

4. $.6157 = \dfrac{x}{300}$

5. $x = 300(.6157)$ $\mathbf{M_{300}}$

6. $x = 184.71$

Answer: 185 feet to the nearest foot.

2. A road is inclined 8° to the horizontal. Find to the *nearest hundred feet* the distance one must drive up this road to increase one's altitude 1000 feet.

Solution: Since the segments mentioned in the problem are the leg opposite the acute angle and the hypotenuse of a right triangle, use the sine ratio.

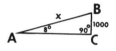

1. $\sin A = \dfrac{\text{length of leg opposite } \angle A}{\text{length of hypotenuse}}$

2. $\sin A = \dfrac{BC}{AB}$ Let $x = AB$.

3. $\sin 8° = \dfrac{1000}{x}$ In the table on page 748, $\sin 8° = .1392$.

4. $.1392 = \dfrac{1000}{x}$

5. $.1392x = 1000$ $\mathbf{M_x}$

6. $x = \dfrac{1000}{.1392}$ $\mathbf{D_{.1392}}$

7. $x = 7184$

Answer: 7200 feet correct to the nearest hundred feet.

3. A ladder 25 feet long leans against a building and reaches a point 23.5 feet above the ground. Find to the *nearest degree* the angle which the ladder makes with the ground.

[The solution is given on the next page.]

Solution: Since the given segments are the hypotenuse of a right triangle and the leg opposite the acute angle to be found, use the sine ratio.

1. $\sin A = \dfrac{\text{length of leg opposite } \angle A}{\text{length of hypotenuse}}$

2. $\sin A = \dfrac{23.5}{25}$ Express $\dfrac{23.5}{25}$ as the decimal .9400.

3. $\sin A = .9400$ In the table on page 748:

4. $m\angle A = 70$ $\sin 70° = .9397$, $\sin 71° = .9455$. Since .9400 is closer to .9397 than it is to .9455, $m\angle A$ is closer to 70.

Answer: 70° to the nearest degree.

EXERCISES

In 1–8, in the given right triangles, find the length of the side marked x to the *nearest foot* or the number of degrees contained in the angle marked x to the *nearest degree.*

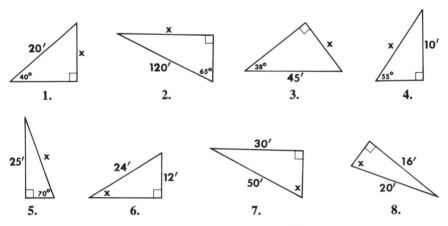

9. A wooden beam 24 feet long leans against a wall and makes an angle of 71° with the ground. Find to the *nearest foot* how high up the wall the beam reaches.

10. A boy who is flying a kite lets out 300 feet of string which makes an angle of 52° with the ground. Assuming that the string is stretched taut, find to the *nearest foot* how high the kite is above the ground.

11. A straight road to the top of a hill is 2500 feet long and makes an angle of 12° with the horizontal. Find the height of the hill to the *nearest hundred feet*.

12. A ladder which leans against a building makes an angle of 75° with the ground and reaches a point on the building 20 feet above the ground. Find to the *nearest foot* the length of the ladder.

13. From an airplane which is flying at an altitude of 3000 feet, the angle of depression of an airport ground signal is an angle of 27°. Find to the *nearest hundred feet* the distance between the airplane and the airport signal.

14. An airplane climbs at an angle of 11° with the ground. Find to the *nearest hundred feet* the distance it has traveled when it has attained an altitude of 400 feet.

15. A 20-foot pole which is leaning against a wall reaches a point 18 feet above the ground. Find to the *nearest degree* the number of degrees contained in the angle which the pole makes with the ground.

16. In order to reach the top of a hill which is 250 feet high, one must travel 2000 feet up a straight road which leads to the top. Find to the *nearest degree* the number of degrees contained in the angle which the road makes with the horizontal.

17. After takeoff, a plane flies in a straight line for a distance of 4000 feet in order to gain an altitude of 800 feet. Find to the *nearest degree* the number of degrees contained in the angle which the rising plane makes with the ground.

19. The Cosine Ratio

A third important ratio in a right triangle involves the length of the leg adjacent to one of the acute angles of the triangle and the length of the hypotenuse.

If we refer again to Fig. 6–42 on page 333, we can see that since $\triangle ABC \sim \triangle AB'C' \sim \triangle AB''C''$, it also follows that:

$$\frac{AC}{AB} = \frac{AC'}{AB'} = \frac{AC''}{AB''} = \text{a constant ratio for } \angle A.$$

This ratio is called the *cosine of the angle.*

Definition. **The *cosine of an acute angle of a right triangle* is the ratio of the length of the leg adjacent to the acute angle to the length of the hypotenuse.**

In right triangle ABC (Fig. 6–47), with $m\angle C = 90$, the definition of the *cosine of angle A*, abbreviated "cos A," is:

$$\cos A = \frac{\text{length of leg adjacent to } \angle A}{\text{length of hypotenuse}} = \frac{AC}{AB} = \frac{b}{c}$$

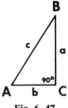

Fig. 6–47

The Table of Cosines

As angle A changes, the cosine ratio for angle A also changes. The cosine ratio for angle A depends upon the measure of angle A, not upon the size of the right triangle which contains angle A. The table of cosine ratios which mathematicians have constructed for all acute angles whose measures are between 0 and 90 is found on page 748 in the third column.

If we use this table as we did when we studied the tangent ratio and the sine ratio, we can obtain the following results:

1. $\cos 55° = .5736$.
2. If $\cos A = .9063$, angle A contains 25°.
3. If $\cos A = .3300$, angle A contains 71° to the *nearest degree* because .3300 is closer to .3256, which is cos 71°, than it is to .3420, which is cos 70°.

EXERCISES

In 1–4, represent the cosine of each acute angle.

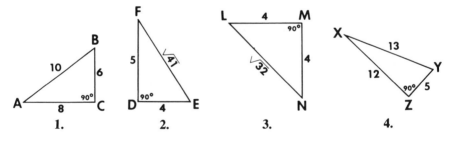

1.   **2.**   **3.**   **4.**

5. In triangle ABC, $m\angle C = 90$, $AC = 4$, and $BC = 3$. Find cos A.
6. In triangle RST, $m\angle S = 90$, $RS = 5$, and $ST = 12$. Find cos T.

Using the table on page 748, find the following:

7. cos 21°	**8.** cos 35°	**9.** cos 40°	**10.** cos 45°
11. cos 59°	**12.** cos 67°	**13.** cos 74°	**14.** cos 88°

Using the table on page 748, find the measure of angle A if:

15. $\cos A = .9397$ **16.** $\cos A = .6428$ **17.** $\cos A = .3584$

18. $\cos A = .8910$ **19.** $\cos A = .9986$ **20.** $\cos A = .0698$

Using the table on page 748, find the degree measure of angle A to the *nearest degree* if:

21. $\cos A = .9750$ **22.** $\cos A = .8545$ **23.** $\cos A = .6000$

24. $\cos A = .5934$ **25.** $\cos A = .2968$ **26.** $\cos A = .1250$

27. Does the cosine of an angle increase or decrease as the measure of the angle varies from 1 through 89?

28. *a.* Use the table on page 748 to discover whether $\cos 80°$ is twice $\cos 40°$.

      b. If the measure of an angle is doubled, is the cosine of the angle also doubled?

29. In triangle ABC, $m\angle C = 90$, $AC = 40$, and $AB = 80$.   (*a*) Find $\cos A$ to the *nearest ten-thousandth*.   (*b*) Find the measure of angle A.

30. In triangle ABC, $m\angle C = 90$, $AC = 12$, and $BC = 5$.   (*a*) Find $\cos B$ to the *nearest ten-thousandth*.   (*b*) Find the degree measure of angle B to the *nearest degree*.

31. Why must the cosine of an acute angle be less than 1?

Using the Cosine Ratio to Solve Problems

When the leg adjacent to an acute angle in a right triangle and the hypotenuse of the right triangle are involved in a problem, the use of the cosine ratio will help us find the length of one of these sides when the length of the other side and the measure of the acute angle are given. We proceed as we did when we were using the tangent ratio or the sine ratio.

MODEL PROBLEMS

1. A plane took off from a field and rose at an angle of $8°$ with the horizontal ground. Find to the *nearest ten feet* the horizontal distance the plane had covered when it had flown 2000 feet.

     Solution: Since the segments mentioned in the problem are the leg adjacent to an acute angle of a right triangle and the hypotenuse of the triangle, use the cosine ratio.

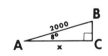

         [The solution continues on the next page.]

1. $\cos A = \dfrac{\text{length of leg adjacent to } \angle A}{\text{length of hypotenuse}}$

2. $\cos A = \dfrac{AC}{AB}$ Let $x = AC$.

3. $\cos 8° = \dfrac{x}{2000}$ In the table on page 748, $\cos 8° = .9903$.

4. $.9903 = \dfrac{x}{2000}$

5. $x = 2000(.9903)$ M_{2000}

6. $x = 1980.6$

Answer: 1980 feet correct to the nearest ten feet.

2. A guy wire reaches from the top of a pole to a stake in the ground. The stake is 10 feet from the foot of the pole. The wire makes an angle of 65° with the ground. Find to the *nearest foot* the length of the wire.

Solution: Since the segments mentioned in the problem are the leg adjacent to the acute angle and the hypotenuse of a right triangle, use the cosine ratio.

1. $\cos S = \dfrac{\text{length of leg adjacent to } \angle S}{\text{length of hypotenuse}}$

2. $\cos S = \dfrac{BS}{ST}$ Let $x = ST$.

3. $\cos 65° = \dfrac{10}{x}$ In the table on page 748, $\cos 65° = .4226$.

4. $.4226 = \dfrac{10}{x}$

5. $.4226x = 10$ M_x

6. $x = \dfrac{10}{.4226}$ $D_{.4226}$

7. $x = 23.6$

Answer: 24 feet correct to the nearest foot.

EXERCISES

In 1–8, in the given right triangles, find the length of the side marked *x* to the *nearest foot* or the number of degrees contained in the angle marked *x* to the *nearest degree.*

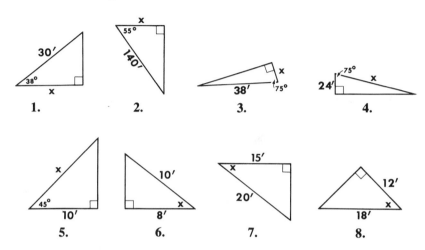

1.   2.   3.   4.

5.   6.   7.   8.

9. A 20-foot ladder leans against a building and makes an angle of 72° with the ground. Find to the *nearest foot* the distance between the foot of the ladder and the building.

10. A man walked 2500 feet along a straight road which is inclined 12° to the horizontal. Find to the *nearest foot* the horizontal distance traveled by the man.

11. A guy wire attached to the top of a pole reaches a stake in the ground 20 feet from the foot of the pole and makes an angle of 58° with the ground. Find to the *nearest foot* the length of the guy wire.

12. An airplane rises at an angle of 14° with the ground. Find to the *nearest ten feet* the distance it has flown when it has covered a horizontal distance of 1500 feet.

13. Henry is flying a kite. The kite string makes an angle of 43° with the ground. If Henry is standing 100 feet from a point on the ground directly below the kite, find to the *nearest foot* the length of the kite string.

14. A 30-foot steel girder is leaning against a wall. The foot of the girder is 20 feet from the wall. Find to the *nearest degree* the number of degrees contained in the angle which the girder makes with the ground.

15. A plane took off from an airport. When the plane had flown 4000 feet in the direction in which it had taken off, it had covered a horizontal distance of 3900 feet. Find to the *nearest degree* the number of degrees contained in the angle at which the plane rose from the ground.

16. A 40-ft. ladder which is leaning against a wall reaches the wall at a point 36 ft. from the ground. Find to the *nearest degree* the number of degrees contained in the angle which the ladder makes with the wall.

20. Using All Three Trigonometric Ratios

When solving a problem using trigonometry, first make a drawing showing the segments and angles whose measures are given, and the segments and angles whose measures are to be found. Then, in a right triangle, use the proper trigonometric ratios which relate the measures to be found with the measures that are given.

KEEP IN MIND

$$\tan A = \frac{\text{length of leg opposite } \angle A}{\text{length of leg adjacent to } \angle A} = \frac{a}{b}$$

$$\sin A = \frac{\text{length of leg opposite } \angle A}{\text{length of hypotenuse}} = \frac{a}{c}$$

$$\cos A = \frac{\text{length of leg adjacent to } \angle A}{\text{length of hypotenuse}} = \frac{b}{c}$$

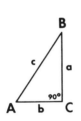

MODEL PROBLEMS

1. *Given:* In isosceles triangle ABC, $AC = CB = 20$ and $m\angle A = m\angle B = 68$. $\overline{CD}$ is an altitude.

   To find: a. Length of altitude $\overline{CD}$ to the *nearest tenth*.

   b. Length of $\overline{AB}$ to the *nearest tenth*.

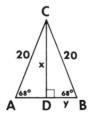

a.

1. In rt. $\triangle BDC$, $\sin B = \dfrac{CD}{CB}$

2. Let $x = CD$. $\sin 68° = \dfrac{x}{20}$

3. $\qquad\qquad .9272 = \dfrac{x}{20}$

4. $\qquad\qquad x = 20(.9272)$

5. $\qquad\qquad x = 18.5440$

6. $\qquad\qquad x = 18.5$

Answer: $CD = 18.5$ to the nearest tenth.

b.

Since the altitude drawn to the base of an isosceles triangle bisects the base, $AB = 2DB$. Therefore, we will find DB in triangle BDC and double it to find AB.

1. In rt. $\triangle BDC$, $\cos B = \dfrac{DB}{CB}$

2. Let $y = DB$. $\cos 68° = \dfrac{y}{20}$

3. $\qquad\qquad .3746 = \dfrac{y}{20}$

4. $\qquad\qquad y = 20(.3746)$

5. $\qquad\qquad y = 7.4920$

6. $\qquad AB = 2y = 2(7.4920)$

7. $\qquad AB = 14.9840$

8. $\qquad AB = 15.0$

Answer: $AB = 15.0$ to the nearest tenth.

2. The diagonals of a rhombus are 10 and 24. Find, to the *nearest degree,* the number of degrees contained in the angles of the rhombus.

Given: Rhombus $ABCD$.
$BD = 10$.
$AC = 24$.

To find: $m\angle A$, $m\angle B$, $m\angle C$, $m\angle D$.

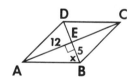

Solution: Since the diagonals of a rhombus are perpendicular to each other and bisect each other, $\angle AEB$ is a right angle, $EB = \frac{1}{2}(DB) = \frac{1}{2}(10) = 5$, and $AE = \frac{1}{2}(AC) = \frac{1}{2}(24) = 12$.

Since in rhombus $ABCD$, diagonal $\overline{DB}$ bisects $\angle ABC$, then $m\angle ABC = 2(m\angle ABE)$. Therefore, we will find the measure of $\angle ABE$ in right triangle AEB and multiply the result by 2 to find $m\angle ABC$. Let us represent the measure of $\angle ABE$ by x.

[The solution continues on the next page.]

1. In rt. $\triangle AEB$, $\tan x = \dfrac{\text{length of leg opposite } \angle ABE}{\text{length of leg adjacent to } \angle ABE}$

2. $\tan x = \frac{12}{5}$ Express $\frac{12}{5}$ as the decimal
                                                         2.4000.

3. $\tan x = 2.4000$ In the table on page 748,
                                                         $\tan 67° = 2.3559$, $\tan 68° =$
4. $x = 67$ 2.4751. Since 2.4000 is
5. $m\angle ABC = 2x = 2(67) = 134$ closer to 2.3559 than it is to
                                                         2.4751, x is closer to 67.

    Since the consecutive angles of a rhombus are supplementary, $\angle BCD$ is supplementary to $\angle ABC$. Therefore, $m\angle BCD = 180 - 134 = 46$.

    Since the opposite angles of a rhombus are congruent, $m\angle CDA = m\angle ABC = 134$ and $m\angle DAB = m\angle BCD = 46$.

Answer: The angles of the rhombus contain 46°, 134°, 46°, 134°.

EXERCISES

    Exercises 1–7 refer to rt. $\triangle ABC$. Name the ratio that can be used to find:

1. the measure of side a when the measures of angle A and side c are given.
2. the measure of side b when the measures of angle A and side c are given.
3. the measure of side c when the measures of side a and angle A are given.

Ex. 1–7

4. the measure of side b when the measures of side a and angle B are given.
5. the measure of angle A when the measures of side a and side b are given.
6. the measure of angle B when the measures of side a and side c are given.
7. the measure of side a when the measures of side b and angle A are given.

    Exercises 8–13 refer to $\triangle RST$. In each exercise, give the value of the ratio as a fraction.

8. $\sin R$ 9. $\tan T$ 10. $\sin T$
11. $\cos R$ 12. $\cos T$ 13. $\tan R$

Ex. 8–13

    In 14–21, in the given right triangles, find the length of the side marked x to the *nearest foot* or the number of degrees contained in the angle marked x to the *nearest degree*.

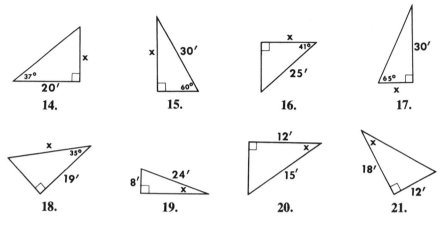

14.   **15.**   **16.**   **17.**

18.   **19.**   **20.**   **21.**

22. If $\cos A = \sin 30°$, angle A contains _____ degrees.

23. Diameter $\overline{AB}$ of a circle is 13 and chord $\overline{AC}$ is 12. Chord $\overline{CB}$ is drawn. Find the value of $\sin B$.

24. If in right triangle ACB $m\angle C = 90$, $m\angle A = 66$, and $AC = 100$, then BC to the *nearest integer* is _____.

25. In right triangle ABC, $m\angle C = 90$, $m\angle B = 28$, and $BC = 30$ ft. Find AB to the *nearest foot*.

26. In triangle ABC, $m\angle C = 90$, $\tan A = .7$, and $AC = 40$. Find BC.

27. In triangle ABC, $m\angle A = 42$, $AB = 14$, and $\overline{BD}$ is the altitude to $\overline{AC}$. Find BD to the *nearest tenth*.

28. In triangle ABC, $\overline{AC} \cong \overline{BC}$, $m\angle A = 50$, and $AB = 30$. Find to the *nearest tenth* the length of the altitude from vertex C.

29. ABC is an isosceles triangle with $\overline{AB} \cong \overline{AC}$. If angle B contains 35° and $BC = 20$, the altitude upon $\overline{BC}$ to the *nearest integer* is _____.

30. The longer side of a rectangle is 10 and a diagonal makes an angle of 27° with this side. Find to the *nearest integer* the shorter side of the rectangle.

31. At a point on the ground 100 feet from the foot of a flagpole, the angle of elevation of the top of the pole contains 31°. The height of the flagpole to the *nearest foot* is _____.

32. Find to the *nearest foot* the height of a church spire that casts a shadow of 50 feet when the angle of elevation of the sun contains 68°.

33. From the top of a lighthouse 190 feet high, the angle of depression of a boat out at sea contains 34°. Find to the *nearest foot* the distance from the boat to the foot of the lighthouse, the foot of the lighthouse being at sea level.

34. In triangle ABC, $m\angle C = 90$, $AB = 30$, and $BC = 15$. How many degrees are contained in angle A?

35. The legs of a right triangle are 3 and 4. Find the degree measure of the smallest angle of this triangle to the *nearest degree*.

36. The length of the hypotenuse $\overline{AB}$ of right triangle ABC is twice the length of leg $\overline{BC}$. Find the number of degrees in angle ABC.

37. In rectangle $ABCD$, diagonal $\overline{AC}$ is 11 and side $\overline{AB}$ is 7. Find the degree measure of angle CAB to the *nearest degree*.

38. Find to the *nearest degree* the degree measure of the angle of elevation of the sun if a post 5 feet high casts a shadow 10 feet long.

39. $\overline{CD}$ is the altitude on the hypotenuse of right triangle ABC. $AB = 25$ and $AC = 20$. Find the length of segment $\overline{BD}$, the length of altitude $\overline{CD}$, and the degree measure of angle B to the *nearest degree*.

40. The longer diagonal of a rhombus is 24 ft. and the shorter diagonal is 10 ft. (*a*) Find the perimeter of the rhombus. (*b*) Find to the *nearest degree* the degree measure of the angle which the longer diagonal makes with a side of the rhombus.

41. The altitude on the hypotenuse of a right triangle divides the hypotenuse into segments whose measures are 9 and 4. Find to the *nearest degree* the degree measure of the smaller acute angle of the original triangle.

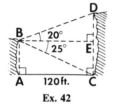

Ex. 42

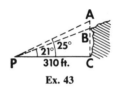

Ex. 43

42. $\overline{AB}$ and $\overline{CD}$ represent cliffs on opposite sides of a river 120 feet wide. From B, the angle of elevation of D contains 20° and the angle of depression of C contains 25°. Find to the *nearest foot:* (*a*) the height of the cliff represented by $\overline{AB}$. (*b*) the height of the cliff represented by $\overline{CD}$.

43. In the diagram, P represents a point 310 feet from the foot of a vertical cliff $\overline{BC}$. $\overline{AB}$ represents a flagpole standing on the edge of the cliff. At P, the angle of elevation of B contains 21° and the angle of elevation of A contains 25°. Find to the *nearest foot:* (*a*) the distance AC. (*b*) AB, which represents the length of the flagpole.

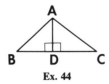

Ex. 44

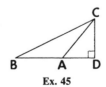

Ex. 45

44. In triangle ABC, $AB = 30$ feet, $m\angle B = 42$, $m\angle C = 36$, and $\overline{AD}$ is an altitude. (*a*) Find to the *nearest foot* the length of $\overline{AD}$. (*b*) Using the result obtained in part *a*, find to the *nearest foot* the length of $\overline{DC}$.

45. CD represents the height of a building. $AD = 85$ ft. and $m\angle D = 90$. At A, the angle of elevation of the top of the building, $\angle CAD$ contains 49°. At B, the angle of elevation of the top of the building, $\angle CBD$, contains 26°. (*a*) Find the height of the building, CD, to the *nearest foot*. (*b*) Find CB, the distance from the top of the building to B, to the *nearest foot*.

46. Angle D in quadrilateral $ABCD$ is a right angle, and diagonal $\overline{AC}$ is perpendicular to $\overline{BC}$. $BC = 20$, $m\angle B = 35$, and $m\angle DAC = 65$. (*a*) Find AC to the *nearest integer*. (*b*) Using the result obtained in answer to *a*, find DC to the *nearest integer*.

47. The diagonals of a rectangle are each 22 and intersect at an angle of 110°. Find to the *nearest integer* the sides of the rectangle.

48. In rhombus $ABCD$, the measure of diagonal $\overline{AC}$ is 80 and $m\angle BAC = 42$. (*a*) Find the length of a side of the rhombus to the *nearest integer*. (*b*) Find the length of an altitude of the rhombus to the *nearest integer*.

49. In circle O, chord $\overline{AC}$ forms an angle of 37° with diameter $\overline{AB}$. If the length of $\overline{AB}$ is 20 inches, find to the *nearest inch:* (*a*) the length of the chord $\overline{BC}$. (*b*) the distance from the center of the circle to chord $\overline{AC}$.

50. A circle is inscribed in a regular pentagon. If a side of the pentagon measures 50, find to the *nearest integer* the length of the radius of the circle.

51. $\overline{PA}$ and $\overline{PB}$ are tangents to circle O and intersect at an angle of 60°. Radius $\overline{OA}$ is 8 inches long. Find to the *nearest inch* the length of $\overline{AP}$.

52. In right triangle ABC, the length of hypotenuse $\overline{AB}$ is 100 and $m\angle A = 18$. (*a*) Find AC and BC to the *nearest integer*. (*b*) Show that the results obtained in answer to *a* are approximately correct by using the relationship $(AB)^2 = (AC)^2 + (BC)^2$.

21. Completion Exercises

Write a word or expression that, when inserted in the blank, will make the resulting statement true.

1. If two polygons are congruent, they must be _____.

2. Two polygons are similar if their corresponding angles are congruent and the ratios of their corresponding sides are _____.

3. The segments of one of two chords intersecting within a circle measure r and s. If the length of one segment of the other chord is m, the length of the other segment of that chord in terms of r, s, and m is _____.

4. If two triangles are similar, their corresponding _____ are congruent.

5. If the measure of one acute angle of a right triangle is 30, the ratio of the length of the shorter leg to the length of the hypotenuse is _____.

6. In a right triangle, the cosine of an acute angle is the ratio of the length of the _____ side to the length of the hypotenuse.

7. Triangle ABC is a right triangle with its right angle at C, and E is any point on side $\overline{AC}$. Segment $\overline{ED}$ is perpendicular to $\overline{AB}$ at D. Complete the proportion $DE:CB = DA:$_____.

8. The formula for the length of the diagonal of a square, d, in terms of the length of its side, s, is $d =$ _____.

9. If the length of the hypotenuse of a right triangle is twice the length of the shorter leg, the smallest angle of the triangle contains _____ degrees.

10. The formula for the length of the altitude of an equilateral triangle, h, in terms of the length of its side, s, is $h =$ _____.

11. The line segment whose endpoints are the midpoints of two sides of a triangle is _____ to the third side.

12. The perimeters of two _____ polygons are to each other as the lengths of any pair of corresponding sides.

13. Two secants are drawn to a circle from an outside point. The length of the first secant is a and the length of its external segment is b. If the length of the second secant is c, the length of its external segment in terms of a, b, and c is _____.

14. In trapezoid $ABCD$ with bases $\overline{AB}$ and $\overline{DC}$, diagonals $\overline{AC}$ and $\overline{BD}$ intersect at E. Triangle DEC is similar to triangle _____.

15. In triangle ABC, E is the midpoint of $\overline{AC}$ and D is the midpoint of $\overline{BC}$. The ratio of $ED:AB$ is _____.

16. In right triangle ABC, $\overline{BD}$ is the altitude to the hypotenuse $\overline{AC}$. Triangle ABD is similar to triangle _____.

17. In a right triangle whose acute angles contain 30° and 60°, if the length of the side opposite the 30° angle is m, then the length of the side opposite the 60° angle is _____.

18. In an isosceles right triangle, if the length of each of the congruent sides is represented by a, then the length of the hypotenuse is represented by _____.

19. If the sides of a triangle measure 10, 24, and 26, it is a(an) _____ triangle.

20. In $\triangle ABC$, D, E, and F are the midpoints of sides $\overline{AB}$, $\overline{BC}$, and $\overline{CA}$ respectively. If $\overline{DE}$,. $\overline{EF}$ and $\overline{FD}$ are drawn, then $\triangle EFD$ is _____ to $\triangle ABC$.

22. True-False Exercises

If the statement is always true, write *true;* if the statement is not always true, write *false*.

1. If the angles of one polygon are congruent respectively to the angles of a second polygon, the polygons are similar.
2. Isosceles right triangles are similar.
3. If the lengths of the sides of two polygons are in proportion, the polygons are similar.
4. The diagonals of a trapezoid divide each other proportionally.
5. A line which contains the midpoints of two sides of a triangle cuts off a triangle similar to the given triangle.
6. The bisector of an angle of a triangle divides the triangle into two similar triangles.
7. If the acute angles of a right triangle measure 30° and 60°, the lengths of the legs opposite these angles are in the ratio 1:2.
8. Isosceles triangles are similar if their vertex angles are congruent.
9. If the measure of acute angle A is twice the measure of acute angle B, then sin A is twice sin B.
10. As the measure of an acute angle increases, the cosine of the angle increases.
11. The length of the hypotenuse of an isosceles right triangle is equal to the length of a leg multiplied by $\sqrt{2}$.
12. If an angle of a rhombus measures 60°, the shorter diagonal is congruent to a side of the rhombus.
13. If the altitude is drawn to the hypotenuse of a right triangle, the length of a leg is the mean proportional between the lengths of the segments of the hypotenuse.
14. If a set of chords is drawn through a point inside a circle, the product of the lengths of the segments of each chord is constant.
15. If the length of each side of a triangle is tripled, the measure of each angle is also tripled.
16. Congruent triangles are similar.
17. The lengths of two corresponding altitudes in two similar triangles have the same ratio as the lengths of any pair of corresponding sides.

18. In right triangle ABC if $\overline{CD}$ is the altitude upon hypotenuse $\overline{AB}$, then $(CD)^2 = AD \times DB$.
19. If $\overline{CD}$ is a diameter of a circle and B is any point on the circle, then $(CB)^2 + (BD)^2 = (CD)^2$.
20. If, from point P outside a circle, tangent $\overline{PA}$ and secant $\overline{PD}$, which intersects the circle at C, are drawn, then $(PA)^2 = PC \times CD$.

23. "Always, Sometimes, Never" Exercises

If the blank space in each of the following exercises is replaced by the word *always, sometimes,* or *never*, the resulting statement will be true. Select the word which will correctly complete each statement.

1. If the angles of one polygon are respectively congruent to the angles of another polygon, the polygons are _____ similar.
2. Congruent polygons are _____ similar.
3. Similar triangles are _____ congruent triangles.
4. If in two polygons, the lengths of corresponding sides are in proportion, the polygons are _____ similar.
5. $\overline{DE}$ and $\overline{D'E'}$ are bases of isosceles triangles DEF and $D'E'F'$. If $DE:D'E' = DF:D'F'$, the triangles are _____ similar.
6. The length of side $\overline{AB}$ of triangle ABC is 16, and a line intersects sides $\overline{AC}$ and $\overline{BC}$ in D and E respectively. If DE equals 8, then $\overline{DE}$ is _____ parallel to $\overline{AB}$.
7. If two chords of a circle intersect, the product of the lengths of the segments of one chord is _____ equal to the product of the lengths of the segments of the other chord.
8. The sine of an angle is _____ equal to the cosine of that angle.
9. If a vertex angle of one isosceles triangle is congruent to the corresponding angle of another isosceles triangle, the two triangles are _____ similar.
10. A median in a triangle _____ divides the triangle into two similar triangles.
11. If two angles of a triangle measure 30° and 60°, the length of the side opposite the 60° angle is _____ twice the length of the side opposite the 30° angle.
12. The sine of an acute angle _____ equals the cosine of the complementary angle.
13. As the measure of an acute angle increases, the tangent of the angle _____ decreases.

14. The diagonals $\overline{AC}$ and $\overline{BD}$ of quadrilateral $ABCD$ inscribed in a circle intersect at E. Triangle AED is _____ similar to triangle BEC.

15. In a right triangle, the length of the altitude drawn to the hypotenuse is _____ the mean proportional between the lengths of the segments of the hypotenuse.

16. A rhombus whose side measures 8 inches _____ has a diagonal 16 inches long.

17. If the lengths of two sides of a triangle are proportional to the lengths of two sides of another triangle, the triangles are _____ similar.

18. If the sides of one triangle are parallel to the sides of another triangle, the triangles are _____ similar.

19. A diagonal of a rhombus is _____ congruent to a side of the rhombus.

20. Two right triangles are _____ similar if the lengths of the legs of one triangle are proportional to the lengths of the legs of the other triangle.

24. Multiple-Choice Exercises

Write the letter preceding the word or expression that best completes the statement.

1. Two figures must be similar if they are (*a*) rectangles (*b*) equilateral triangles (*c*) rhombuses.

2. If altitude $\overline{CD}$ is drawn upon the hypotenuse $\overline{AB}$ of right triangle ABC, then $(AC)^2$ equals (*a*) $CB \times DB$ (*b*) $AB \times AD$ (*c*) $DB \times AD$.

3. If in right triangle ABC, $\overline{AB}$ is the hypotenuse and $\overline{CD}$ is the altitude to the hypotenuse, then (*a*) $(CD)^2 = AD \times DB$ (*b*) $(CD)^2 = AB \times AD$ (*c*) $(CD)^2 = AC \times CB$.

4. If the lengths of the segments of one of two chords intersecting within a circle are represented by r and s and the lengths of the segments of the other chord are represented by v and w, then (*a*) $r \times s = v \times w$ (*b*) $r + s = v + w$ (*c*) $\dfrac{r}{s} = \dfrac{v}{w}$.

5. If from a point outside a circle a tangent and a secant are drawn to the circle, the length of the tangent is the mean proportional between (*a*) the length of the whole secant and the length of its internal segment (*b*) the lengths of the external and internal segments of the secant (*c*) the length of the whole secant and the length of its external segment.

6. If in right triangle ABC $m\angle A = 30$ and $m\angle B = 60$, then (*a*) $AC = 2BC$ (*b*) $AC = \frac{1}{2}AB$ (*c*) $AC = BC\sqrt{3}$.

7. If the altitude $\overline{CD}$ is drawn to the hypotenuse $\overline{AB}$ of right triangle ABC, then AC is the mean proportional between (*a*) AD and DB (*b*) AB and AD (*c*) AB and BC.

8. The length of the diagonal of a square, d, is equal to the length of a side, s, multiplied by   (*a*) $\sqrt{2}$ (*b*) $\sqrt{3}$ (*c*) 2.

9. If the length of each side of a triangle is multiplied by 2, then the measure of each angle   (*a*) is multiplied by 2   (*b*) is multiplied by 4   (*c*) remains unchanged.

10. Two chords intersect inside a circle. The lengths of the segments of one chord are 6 and 12, and the lengths of the segments of the other chord are represented by x and $x + 1$. An equation that can be used to find x is   (*a*) $\dfrac{x+1}{x} = \dfrac{6}{12}$ (*b*) $2x + 1 = 18$ (*c*) $x^2 + x = 72$.

11. If an altitude of an equilateral triangle is $5\sqrt{3}$, the length of a side is   (*a*) 10 (*b*) 5 (*c*) $10\sqrt{3}$.

12. The acute angles of a right triangle contain 30° and 60° respectively. The lengths of the legs of the triangle are in the ratio   (*a*) 1:2 (*b*) 1:$\sqrt{2}$ (*c*) 1:$\sqrt{3}$.

13. A tangent and a secant are drawn to a circle from an external point. The external segment of the secant is 6 and the internal segment is 5. The length of the tangent is   (*a*) $\sqrt{30}$ (*b*) $\sqrt{55}$ (*c*) $\sqrt{66}$.

14. If the lengths of the sides of a triangle are 3, 4, and 5 respectively, the value of the sine of the smallest angle is   (*a*) $\frac{3}{5}$ (*b*) $\frac{3}{4}$ (*c*) $\frac{4}{5}$.

15. In triangle ABC, $m\angle C = 90$. If $AB = 15$ and $AC = 12$, which of the following statements is *not* true?   (*a*) $\tan A = \frac{3}{4}$ (*b*) $\sin B < 1$ (*c*) $\tan B < 1$.

16. If in triangle ABC, $\overline{CD}$ is the altitude upon $\overline{AB}$, then CD equals   (*a*) $AD \times \sin A$ (*b*) $AD \times \cos A$ (*c*) $AD \times \tan A$.

17. If the three sides of a triangle measure 21, 28, and 35, the triangle is   (*a*) right (*b*) obtuse (*c*) acute.

18. In an isosceles triangle whose vertex angle contains 72°, if the length of the altitude drawn to the base is m, then the length of the base of the triangle is   (*a*) $2m \cos 36°$ (*b*) $2m \sin 36°$ (*c*) $2m \tan 36°$.

19. If in triangle ABC, $\overline{BD}$ is the altitude upon $\overline{AC}$, then AD equals   (*a*) $AB \times \sin A$ (*b*) $AB \times \tan A$ (*c*) $AB \times \cos A$.

20. If the ratio of the lengths of a pair of corresponding sides in two similar triangles is 4:1, the ratio of the lengths of a pair of corresponding altitudes is   (*a*) 2:1 (*b*) 4:1 (*c*) 16:1.

25. Construction Exercises

The basic constructions involved in the following exercises, which are to be done with straightedge and compasses, appear in chapter 14, which begins on page 617.

1. Divide line segment $\overline{AB}$ into two parts whose lengths shall be proportional to the lengths of the two given segments m and n.

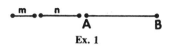

Ex. 1

2. Construct the fourth proportional to the three line segments a, b, and c.

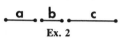

Ex. 2

3. Given the line segments a, b, and c, construct line segment x such that $a:b = c:x$.

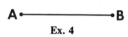

Ex. 3

4. Divide line segment $\overline{AB}$ into three parts that are equal in length.

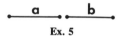

Ex. 4

5. Construct the mean proportional between line segments a and b.

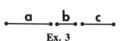

Ex. 5

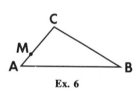

Ex. 6

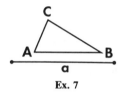

Ex. 7

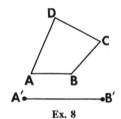

Ex. 8

6. Through point M, construct a line which will divide sides $\overline{AC}$ and $\overline{BC}$ of triangle ABC proportionally.

7. On line segment a corresponding to side $\overline{AB}$ of triangle ABC, construct a triangle similar to triangle ABC.

8. On line segment $\overline{A'B'}$ corresponding to side $\overline{AB}$ in polygon $ABCD$, construct a polygon similar to polygon $ABCD$.

9. If a, b, and c are given line segments, construct a line segment x such that:

    a. $a:b = x:c$ *b.* $a:x = c:b$ *c.* $x:a = b:c$ *d.* $a:2b = c:x$

10. If a, b, and c are given line segments, construct a line segment x such that:

    a. $x = \dfrac{ab}{c}$ *b.* $x = \dfrac{ac}{b}$ *c.* $x = \dfrac{2bc}{a}$ *d.* $x = \dfrac{2ab}{3c}$

11. If a and b are given line segments, construct a line segment x such that:

    a. $x = \dfrac{a^2}{b}$ *b.* $x = \dfrac{b^2}{a}$ *c.* $x = \dfrac{2a^2}{b}$ *d.* $x = \dfrac{b^2}{3a}$

12. Divide a given line segment $\overline{AB}$ into two segments whose lengths are in the ratio:

    a. 1:2   *b.* 1:3   *c.* 2:3   *d.* 3:4

13. Divide a given line segment $\overline{AB}$ into three segments whose lengths are in the ratio 1:3:4.

14. If a and b are given line segments, construct line segment x such that:
    a. $a{:}x = x{:}b$ b. $2a{:}x = x{:}b$ c. $x = \sqrt{ab}$ d. $x = \sqrt{3ab}$

15. The diagram shows the division of given line segment $\overline{AB}$ into two segments whose lengths are in the ratio $r{:}s$.

    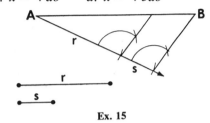
    Ex. 15

    Which statement, a, b, or c, is used to prove that the construction is correct?
    a. A line that divides two sides of a triangle proportionally is parallel to the third side.
    b. If a line is drawn which intersects two sides of a triangle in two different points and is parallel to the third side, the line divides those sides proportionally.
    c. If two triangles are similar, the lengths of their corresponding sides are in proportion.

16. The diagram shows the construction of the fourth proportional to three given line segments, r, s, and t. Which statement, a, b, or c, is used to prove that the construction is correct?

    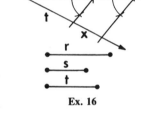
    Ex. 16

    a. If two triangles are similar, the corresponding sides are in proportion.
    b. If a line divides two sides of a triangle proportionally, the line is parallel to the third side.
    c. If a line is parallel to one side of a triangle and intersects the other two sides in two different points, the line divides the other two sides proportionally.

17. The diagram shows the construction of a triangle similar to a given triangle on a given line segment as a base. Which statement, a, b, or c, is used to prove that the construction is correct?

    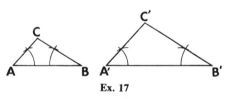
    Ex. 17

    a. If two triangles are congruent, they are similar.
    b. Two triangles are similar if two angles of one are congruent respectively to two angles of the other.
    c. If two triangles are similar, the angles of one triangle are congruent to the corresponding angles of the other.

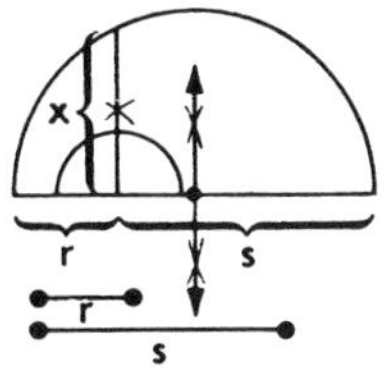

18. The diagram shows the construction of the mean proportional between two given line segments. Which statement, *a*, *b*, or *c*, is used to prove that the construction is correct?

Ex. 18

a. The length of the altitude drawn to the hypotenuse of a right triangle is the mean proportional between the lengths of the segments of the hypotenuse.

b. If from any point on the arc of a chord a line segment is drawn perpendicular to the chord and terminating in the chord, the length of the perpendicular is the mean proportional between the lengths of the segments of the chord.

c. The length of a leg of a right triangle is the mean proportional between the length of the hypotenuse and the length of the projection of the leg on the hypotenuse.

CHAPTER VII

Areas of Polygons

In earlier mathematics courses, you have no doubt learned how to compute the areas of some geometric figures by using special formulas. Hence, you have some understanding of the meaning of the word *area*. In this chapter, we will make a formal study of areas as part of our deductive system.

1. Understanding the Meaning of Area

We have learned that every simple closed polygon has an interior region. The points of the interior region are not points of the polygon. The term *polygonal region* is used to refer to the union of the polygon and its interior. In Fig. 7–1 are pictured polygon $ABCD$ and polygonal region $ABCD$.

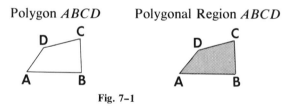

Polygon $ABCD$ Polygonal Region $ABCD$

Fig. 7–1

When we measure a line segment, we determine a number which results from discovering how many times a certain unit length is contained in the line segment. If the length of a line segment is 7 when the unit of measure is the inch, the line segment contains the linear unit, the inch, 7 times.

When we measure an angle, we determine a number which results from discovering how many times a certain unit angle is contained in the angle. If the measure of an angle is 30 when the unit of measure is the degree, the angle contains the unit angle, the degree, 30 times.

Similarly, to measure the area of a polygonal region, we determine a number which results from discovering how many times a certain unit of area is contained in the region. There are many such possible units of measure. However, you know from past experience that the *unit square* is a convenient unit to use for measuring the size of a polygonal region. If we first select a unit of length and then draw a square whose side is that unit (Fig. 7–2), the area of the square is a unit of area. For example, if the length of a side of the unit square is 1 inch, the area

unit of length

1

unit of area

1

1

Fig. 7–2

of the square is a unit of area called a *square inch.* If the measure of the area of a polygonal region is 100 when the unit of measure is a square the length of each of whose sides is 1 inch, the polygonal region contains the area unit, the square inch, 100 times.

Definition. The **area of a polygonal region is the number of area units contained within the region.**

In the future, in order to simplify the language that we use to express ourselves, we shall talk about *finding the area of a polygon* rather than the area of a polygonal region. For example, we shall be finding the area of a triangle rather than the area of a triangular region.

From your experience with congruent triangles, the following postulate should be reasonable to you.

Postulate 42. **If two triangles are congruent, they have the same area.**

In Fig. 7–3, if $\triangle ABC \cong \triangle A'B'C'$, then the area of $\triangle ABC$ = area of $\triangle A'B'C'$.

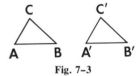

Fig. 7–3

Addition and Subtraction of Areas

Postulate 43. **If a polygon which encloses a region is separated into several polygons which do not overlap, its area is the sum of the areas of these polygons. (Area-Addition Postulate)**

In Fig. 7–4, $\overline{AC}$ separates polygon $ABCD$ into the two triangles ABC and $CDA,$ which do not overlap. Hence, area of polygon $ABCD$ = area of $\triangle ABC$ + area of $\triangle CDA$. It follows from this statement that:

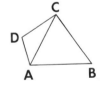

Fig. 7–4

1. Area of polygon $ABCD$ − area of $\triangle ABC$ = area of $\triangle CDA$.
2. Area of polygon $ABCD$ − area of $\triangle CDA$ = area of $\triangle ABC$.

It is often difficult or impossible to find the area of a polygon by counting the number of units of area it contains. For this reason, mathematicians have developed formulas which can be used conveniently to find the areas of familiar geometric figures. We shall soon study some of these formulas.

EXERCISES

In 1–10, answer *yes* or *no.*

1. Does every polygon have an area?
2. Does an angle have an area?
3. Does a line segment have an area?
4. Can a triangle have an area of 10 inches?

5. If two triangles are congruent, must they have the same area?
6. If two triangles have the same area, must they be congruent?
7. If two triangles do not have the same area, can they be congruent?
8. Can a triangle and a square have the same area?
9. Does the diagonal of a parallelogram divide it into two triangles whose areas are equal?
10. Must a plane figure be a polygon in order to have an area?
11. A square each of whose sides is 1 inch long is contained in a rectangle exactly fifty times. Find the area of the rectangle.
12. If the diagonals of a square are drawn, what is the relationship of the areas of the four triangles that are formed?
13. If two equilateral triangles have equal perimeters, what is the relationship of their areas?

2. Finding the Area of a Rectangle

Fig. 7–5 represents a rectangle the length of whose base is 6 inches and whose altitude is 3 inches. The horizontal and vertical segments shown form unit areas of 1 square inch. By counting the number of unit squares contained in the rectangle, we find that the area enclosed in the rectangle is 18 square inches. Notice,

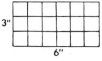

Fig. 7–5

too, that the rectangle contains 3 rows of squares, every row containing 6 squares, each of which is 1 square inch. Therefore, the area of the rectangle is 3 × 6, or 18 square inches.

The preceding example illustrates the reasonableness of accepting the following postulate, provided that the length of the base and the length of the altitude of a rectangle are expressed in the same linear unit:

Postulate 44. **The area of a rectangle is equal to the product of the length of its base and the length of its altitude.**

In Fig. 7–6, the area, A, of rectangle $ABCD$, the length of whose base is represented by b and the length of whose altitude is represented by h, is given by the formula $A = bh$.

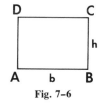

Fig. 7–6

NOTE. In the statement of postulate 44, we might have talked about the "base" and the "altitude" of the rectangle rather than the "length of the base" and the "length of the altitude." From time to time, we will use this simplified language. Remember that "base" and "altitude" refer to lengths which we know are numbers.

We will also use simplified language when we deal with other types of quadrilaterals and with triangles. For example, instead of saying that the length of the base of a parallelogram is 10 feet and the length of the altitude drawn to that base is 4 feet, we may simply say that the base of the parallelogram is 10 feet and the altitude drawn to that base is 4 feet.

MODEL PROBLEMS

1. Find the area of a rectangle whose base is $1\frac{1}{2}$ feet and whose altitude is 6 inches.

   Solution: Since the base and the altitude of the rectangle are expressed in terms of different linear units, we must first convert them to the same linear unit before finding the area. We can convert either $1\frac{1}{2}$ feet to 18 inches or 6 inches to $\frac{1}{2}$ foot.

Method 1	*Method 2*
1. $A = bh$ $b = 18$ in., $h = 6$ in.	1. $A = bh$ $b = 1\frac{1}{2}$ ft., $h = \frac{1}{2}$ ft.
2. $A = 18 \times 6$	2. $A = 1\frac{1}{2} \times \frac{1}{2}$
3. $A = 108$	3. $A = \frac{3}{2} \times \frac{1}{2} = \frac{3}{4}$
Answer: 108 sq. in.	*Answer:* $\frac{3}{4}$ sq. ft.

   NOTE. Unless otherwise stated, in area problems in which measurements are given in terms of a variable such as x, we will assume that all linear measurements were made with the same linear unit and all area measurements were made with the corresponding area unit.

2. A rectangle is inscribed in a circle whose radius is 5 inches. If the base of the rectangle is 8 inches, find the area of the rectangle.

   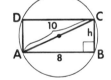

   Solution: Let the length of altitude $\overline{BC} = h$.

   1. In rt. $\triangle ABC$, $(h)^2 + (8)^2 = (10)^2$

   2. $\qquad\qquad\qquad h^2 + 64 = 100$

   3. $\qquad\qquad\qquad\quad h^2 = 36$

   4. $\qquad\qquad\qquad\quad\, h = 6$

   5. Area $= bh$

   6. $\quad A = 8 \times 6$

   7. $\quad A = 48$

   Answer: 48 sq. in.

EXERCISES

1. In each part, find the area of the rectangle whose dimensions are given.
   a. $b = 10$ in., $h = 9$ in.
   b. $b = 5$ ft., $h = 8.4$ ft.
   c. $b = 12$ in., $h = 5\frac{1}{2}$ ft.
   d. $b = 28$ in., $h = 7\frac{3}{4}$ in.
   e. $b = 2$ ft., $h = 6$ in.
   f. $b = 6\frac{1}{3}$ ft., $h = 1\frac{1}{2}$ ft.

2. The base of rectangle I is 18 in. and its altitude is 16 in. The base of rectangle II is 18 in. and its altitude is 4 in. Find the ratio of the areas of the two rectangles.

3. Find the base of a rectangle whose area is 48 sq. in. and whose altitude is 4 in.

4. The dimensions of a rectangular living room are 13 feet by 20 feet. How many square feet of carpet are needed to cover the whole floor?

5. How many tiles, each of which is 1 sq. ft., are needed to cover the floor of a pool which is 40 ft. wide and 80 ft. long?

6. Which rectangle has the greater area: one which is 12 ft. by 9 ft. or one which is 10 ft. by 11 ft.?

7. The perimeter of a rectangle is 30 ft. Find the area of the rectangle if one of its sides is   (a) 4 ft.   (b) 8 ft.   (c) 36 in.   (d) $2\frac{1}{2}$ ft.

8. A diagonal of a rectangle is 10 in. and the base is 6 in. Find the area of the rectangle.

9. A rectangle is inscribed in a circle whose diameter is 13 in. If one side of the rectangle is 5 in., find the area of the rectangle.

10. The base and the altitude of rectangle $PQRS$ are double those of rectangle $ABCD$. The area of $PQRS$, compared with the area of $ABCD$, is   (1) the same   (2) twice as great   (3) four times as great   (4) eight times as great.

11. If the base and the altitude of a rectangle are both tripled, the ratio of the area of the original rectangle to the area of the enlarged rectangle is   (1) 1:3   (2) 1:6   (3) 1:9   (4) 1:18.

12. If the area of a rectangle is to remain constant, what change must take place in the altitude when the base is   (a) multiplied by 4   (b) divided by 5   (c) increased by 50%   (d) decreased by 50%.

13. Express, in terms of x, the areas of the rectangles which have the following dimensions:
   a. $b = 3x, h = 4x$
   b. $b = 7, h = 2x - 3$
   c. $b = 3x, h = 3x + 1$
   d. $b = x + 6, h = x - 2$

14. In a rectangle whose area is 35, the base is 5 and the altitude is $3x + 1$.   (a) Find the value of x.   (b) Find the altitude of the rectangle.

15. In a rectangle whose area is 300, the base and altitude are in the ratio 3:4. Find the dimensions of the rectangle.

16. The area of a rectangle is 56. If its base is represented by $x + 5$ and its height by $x - 5$, find its dimensions.

17. In a rectangle whose area is 15, the base is 1 less than twice the altitude. Find its dimensions.

18. A rectangle whose base is twice as large as its altitude is inscribed in a circle whose radius is 5. Find the area of the rectangle.

19. The perimeter of a rectangle is P and its altitude is H. (*a*) Express its base B in terms of P and H. (*b*) Express its area in terms of P and H. (*c*) State whether the following statement is *true* or *false:* All rectangles which have equal perimeters have equal areas.

20. The base of a rectangle is represented by x and the perimeter is 20. (*a*) Represent the altitude of the rectangle in terms of x. (*b*) Represent the area of the rectangle in terms of x.

21. Find the dimensions of a rectangle whose area is 20 sq. ft. and whose perimeter is 18 ft.

22. The base of a rectangle is 10 in. A diagonal of the rectangle makes an angle of 32° with the base of the rectangle. (*a*) Find the altitude of the rectangle to the *nearest tenth of an inch*. (*b*) Find the area of the rectangle to the *nearest square inch*.

23. Find the area of a rectangle whose diagonal is 50 if the angle which the diagonal makes with the base measures: [Answers may be left in radical form.]   *a*. 30°   *b*. 45°   *c*. 60°

24. In rectangle $ABCD$, $\overline{AB}$ is the base, and $\overline{BD}$ is a diagonal whose length is 8 in. The perpendicular line drawn from C to $\overline{BD}$ meets $\overline{BD}$ at E. If $\overline{BE} \cong \overline{ED}$: (*a*) Find DC and CB. (*b*) Show that rectangle $ABCD$ is a square. (*c*) Find the area of square $ABCD$.

25. Rectangle $ABCD$ has the longer side $\overline{AD}$ as base and diagonal $\overline{AC}$. The perpendicular line drawn from B to $\overline{AC}$ meets $\overline{AC}$ at E. If $BE = 6\sqrt{3}$, and EC exceeds AE by 12: (*a*) Find AE and EC. (*b*) Find the area of rectangle $ABCD$.

3. Finding the Area of a Square

Theorem 102. **The area of a square of side s is equal to the square of s.**

In Fig. 7–7, the area, A, of square $PQRS$, with side s, is given by the formula $A = s^2$.

Corollary T102–1. **The area of a square of diagonal d is equal to one-half the square of d.**

In Fig. 7–7, the area, A, of square $PQRS$, with diagonal d, is given by the formula $A = \frac{1}{2}d^2$.

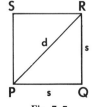

Fig. 7–7

Definition. **Polygons having the same area are called *equivalent polygons.***

NOTE. The symbol that is used to indicate that two triangles are congruent ($\cong$) consists of two parts: $=$ to indicate that the triangles are equal in area; and $\sim$ to indicate that the triangles are similar in shape.

MODEL PROBLEMS

1. Find the area of a square whose perimeter is 20 ft.

Solution:

1. $p = 4s$ $\quad$ $p = 20$.

2. $20 = 4s$

3. $s = 5$

4. $A = s^2 = (5)^2 = 25$

Answer: 25 sq. ft.

2. A rectangle the lengths of whose base and altitude are in the ratio 4:1 is equivalent to a square the length of whose side is 6 inches. Find the dimensions of the rectangle.

Solution: Let $x =$ the altitude of the rectangle in inches.
$\quad\quad\quad$ Then $4x =$ the base of the rectangle in inches.

1. Area of rectangle $= bh$	4. Area of square $= s^2$
2. $\quad\quad\quad A = 4x \cdot x$	5. $\quad\quad\quad A' = (6)^2$
3. $\quad\quad\quad A = 4x^2$	6. $\quad\quad\quad A' = 36$

Since the rectangle and the square are equivalent, their areas are equal.

7. $A = A'$

8. $4x^2 = 36$

9. $x^2 = 9$

10. $x = 3, x = -3$ $\quad$ Reject the negative value.

11. $4x = 12$

Answer: Base of rectangle $= 12$ in., altitude $= 3$ in.

EXERCISES

1. Find the area of a square whose side is:
$\quad a.$ 25 in. $\quad\quad b.$ 13 ft. $\quad\quad c.$ 9 yd. $\quad\quad d.$ $\frac{2}{3}$ ft. $\quad\quad e.$ 7.5 ft.

2. Express, in terms of x, the area of a square whose side is represented by:
    a. x *b.* $2x$ *c.* $x + 2$ *d.* $x - 3$ *e.* $2x + 1$

3. Find the side of a square whose area is:
    a. 144 sq. in.   *b.* 49 sq. ft.   *c.* .81 sq. yd.   *d.* $2\frac{1}{4}$ sq. ft.

4. Find the area of a square whose perimeter is:
    a. 80 in.   *b.* 24 in.   *c.* 32 yd.   *d.* 18 in.   *e.* 9 ft.

5. A baseball diamond is a square 90 ft. on a side. Find the area enclosed by the baselines.

6. Find the area of a square whose diagonal is:
    a. 8   *b.* 12   *c.* 5   *d.* $\sqrt{2}$ *e.* $3\sqrt{2}$ *f.* $4\sqrt{2}$

7. How many square tiles 2 in. by 2 in. are needed to cover a bathroom floor which is 6 ft. by 8 ft.?

8. If the length of each side of a square is tripled, the ratio of the area of the original square to the area of the enlarged square is   (1) 1:3   (2) 1:6   (3) 1:9   (4) 1:18.

9. If the ratio of the area of square $ABCD$ to the area of square $EFGH$ is 16:1, then the ratio of a side of square $ABCD$ to a side of square $EFGH$ is   (1) 16:1   (2) 4:1   (3) 256:1   (4) 64:1.

10. Find the area of a square inscribed in a circle whose diameter is 8.

11. Find the area of a square circumscribed about a circle whose diameter is 20 in.

12. A square is equal in area to a rectangle whose base is 20 and whose altitude is 5. Find a side of the square.

13. Find a side of a square that is equivalent to a rectangle whose base is 4 inches and whose altitude is 3 feet.

14. A rectangle the length of whose base and altitude are in the ratio 5:1 is equivalent to a square whose perimeter is 40 in. Find the length of the base and the length of the altitude of the rectangle.

15. If s represents the length of a side of a square, b and h represent the lengths of the base and altitude of a rectangle, and the square and the rectangle are equivalent, express b in terms of s and h.

16. A square is circumscribed about a circle whose radius is R. Express the area of the square in terms of R.

17. A square is inscribed in a circle whose radius is R. Express the area of the square in terms of R.

18. In the figure, the large rectangle has been divided into a square and three smaller rectangles. If the areas of the square and two of the rectangles are k^2, $4k$, and $8k$ respectively, what is the numerical value of the area of the shaded rectangle?

k^2	8k
4k	

Ex. 18

4. Finding the Area of a Parallelogram

Any side of a parallelogram may be called its *base*. The *altitude* corresponding to this base is a segment which is perpendicular to the line containing this base and which is drawn from any point on the opposite side of the parallelogram.

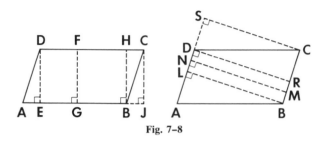

Fig. 7–8

In parallelogram *ABCD*, if $\overline{AB}$ is considered as the base, shown at the left in Fig. 7–8, then any one of the parallel, congruent segments, $\overline{DE}$, $\overline{FG}$, $\overline{HB}$, or $\overline{CJ}$, can be considered a corresponding altitude; if $\overline{AD}$ is considered as the base, shown at the right in Fig. 7–8, then any one of the parallel, congruent segments, $\overline{BL}$, $\overline{MN}$, $\overline{RD}$, or $\overline{CS}$, can be considered a corresponding altitude.

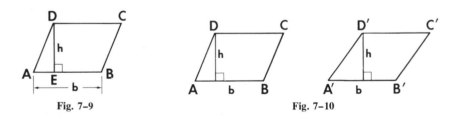

Fig. 7–9   Fig. 7–10

Theorem 103. **The area of a parallelogram is equal to the product of the length of any base and the length of any corresponding altitude.**

[The proof for this theorem appears on pages 612–613.]

In Fig. 7–9, the area, *A*, of parallelogram *ABCD*, the length of whose base is represented by *b* and the length of whose altitude drawn to base *b* is represented by *h*, is given by the formula $A = bh$.

Corollary T103–1. **Parallelograms which have congruent bases and congruent corresponding altitudes are equal in area.**

In Fig. 7–10, parallelograms *ABCD* and *A'B'C'D'*, which have congruent bases and congruent corresponding altitudes, are equal in area.

Corollary T103–2. **The area of a parallelogram is equal to the product of the lengths of two consecutive sides and the sine of their included angle.**

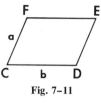

In Fig. 7–11, the area, A, of parallelogram $CDEF$, whose two consecutive sides $\overline{CF}$ and $\overline{CD}$ include angle C, is given by the formula $A = ab \sin C$.

Fig. 7–11

MODEL PROBLEMS

1. Find the area of a parallelogram whose base is 8 ft. and whose altitude is 18 in.

   Solution: Convert 18 in. to $1\frac{1}{2}$ ft.

   1. $A = bh \qquad b = 8$ ft., $h = 1\frac{1}{2}$ ft.

   2. $A = 8 \times 1\frac{1}{2} = 12$

   Answer: 12 sq. ft.

2. The lengths of two consecutive sides of a parallelogram are 10 inches and 15 inches, and these sides include an angle of 63°.
   a. Find to the *nearest tenth of an inch* the length of the altitude drawn to the longer side of the parallelogram.
   b. Find to the *nearest square inch* the area of the parallelogram.

   Solution: Let $h = $ the length of the altitude.

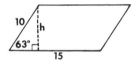

   a. 1. $\sin 63° = \dfrac{h}{10}$

        2. $.8910 = \dfrac{h}{10}$

        3. $\qquad h = 10(.8910)$

        4. $\qquad h = 8.910$

        5. $\qquad h = 8.9$ to the nearest tenth of an inch

   b. 1. $A = bh$

        2. $A = 15(8.9)$

        3. $A = 133.5$

        4. $A = 134$ to the nearest square inch

   Answer: 8.9 in.   *Answer:* 134 sq. in.

3. A parallelogram whose base is represented by $x + 4$ and whose altitude is represented by $x - 1$ is equivalent to a square whose side is 6. Find the base and altitude of the parallelogram.

   [The solution is given on the next page.]

Solution:

1. Area of parallelogram $= bh$.

2. $A = (x + 4)(x - 1)$.

3. Area of square $= s^2$.

4. $A' = 6^2 = 36$.

Since the parallelogram and the square are equivalent, their areas are equal.

5. $\qquad\qquad A = A'$

6. $\qquad (x + 4)(x - 1) = 36$

7. $\qquad x^2 + 3x - 4 = 36$

8. $\qquad x^2 + 3x - 40 = 0$

9. $\qquad (x - 5)(x + 8) = 0$

10. $x - 5 = 0 \quad | \quad x + 8 = 0$

11. $\qquad x = 5 \quad | \qquad x = -8 \qquad$ Reject the negative value.

12. $x + 4 = 5 + 4 = 9$

13. $x - 1 = 5 - 1 = 4$

Answer: Base of parallelogram $= 9$, altitude $= 4$.

EXERCISES

1. If a and b represent the sides of a parallelogram and h represents the altitude on side b, the formula for the area K of the parallelogram is $K = $ _____.

2. Find the area of the parallelogram whose base and altitude have the following measurements:
   a. $b = 8$ in., $h = 12$ in.   b. $b = 7$ ft., $h = 5.3$ ft.
   c. $b = 18$ in., $h = 6\frac{1}{2}$ in.   d. $b = 32$ in., $h = 5\frac{1}{4}$ in.
   e. $b = 4$ ft., $h = 9$ in.   f. $b = 8\frac{1}{2}$ ft., $h = 2\frac{1}{3}$ ft.

3. Two parallelograms have the same base. If their altitudes are in the ratio 4:5, what is the ratio of their areas?

4. Express, in terms of x, the areas of the parallelograms whose bases and altitudes are represented by:
   a. $b = 3x, h = 5$ b. $b = 3x, h = 2x$
   c. $b = x - 3, h = 4$ d. $b = 10, h = 3x + 2$
   e. $b = x - 2, h = x$ f. $b = x + 6, h = x - 3$

5. In a parallelogram whose area is 60, a side is represented by $4x - 4$ and the altitude drawn to that side is 5. Find the value of x and the length of the side represented by $4x - 4$.

6. In a parallelogram, the ratio of a side to the altitude drawn to that side is 2:1. If the area of the parallelogram is 50, find the altitude.

7. In a parallelogram whose area is 36, a side is 5 less than the altitude drawn to that side. Find the altitude.

8. The area of a parallelogram is 30 and a base is 10. Find the altitude drawn to the base.

9. Find the area of a parallelogram if one base angle contains 30° and the measures of the sides including this angle are:
   a. 4 and 8   b. 12 and 20   c. 10 and 5   d. 9 and 8

10. Find the area of a parallelogram if one base angle contains 60° and the measures of the sides including this angle are: [Answers may be left in radical form.]
   a. 8 and 14   b. 18 and 20   c. 6 and 9   d. 13 and 16

11. Find the area of a parallelogram if one base angle contains 45° and the measures of the sides including this angle are: [Answers may be left in radical form.]
   a. 10 and 6   b. 12 and 16   c. 8 and 11   d. 15 and 4

12. Find the area of a parallelogram two of whose consecutive sides are 8 and 20 and include an angle of 150°.

13. Find the area of a parallelogram two of whose adjacent sides are 10 and 6 and include an angle of 120°. [Answer may be left in radical form.]

14. Represent, in terms of x, the area of a parallelogram if one base angle contains 30° and the measures of the sides including this angle are represented by:
   a. 4 and $2x$ b. 6 and $5x$ c. 3 and x d. $4x$ and $2x$

15. Represent, using x, the area of a parallelogram two of whose adjacent sides are represented by 6 and $4x$ and which include an angle of:
   a. 60°   b. 45°   c. 150°   d. 120°   e. 135°

16. A parallelogram is equal in area to a square whose side is 8. If a side of the parallelogram and the altitude drawn to that side are in the ratio 4:1, find the side.

17. In parallelogram $ABCD$, $\overline{AE}$ is perpendicular to $\overline{BC}$, and $\overline{AF}$ is perpendicular to $\overline{CD}$. If $BC = 10$, $CD = 8$, and $AE = 4$, find AF.

18. A parallelogram is equal in area to a rectangle. The altitude of the rectangle is 6 and its diagonal is 10. The ratio of the altitude of the parallelogram to the altitude of the rectangle is 2:1. (a) Find the base of the parallelogram. (b) Select the correct completion for the following statement: The perimeter of the rectangle is (1) greater than the perimeter of the parallelogram (2) equal to the perimeter of the parallelogram (3) smaller than the perimeter of the parallelogram.

19. In parallelogram *ABCD*, angle *A* measures 45, altitude $\overline{DE}$ on base $\overline{AB}$ measures 8, and diagonal $\overline{DB}$ measures 17. (*a*) Find *AE*. (*b*) Find *EB*. (*c*) Find the area of the parallelogram.

20. In each part of this question, find the altitude drawn to the larger side of the parallelogram to the *nearest tenth*. Use this result to find the area of the parallelogram to the *nearest integer*.

    Two adjacent sides of a parallelogram are 8 and 10 and they include an angle of:

    a. 28°   *b*. 35°   *c*. 80°   *d*. 120°   *e*. 150°   *f*. 170°

21. The area of a parallelogram is 72 sq. in. The longer side measures 12 in. and one of the angles of the parallelogram measures 48. Find to the *nearest tenth of an inch* the shorter side of the parallelogram.

22. The base of a parallelogram is 16 and one base angle measures 36. If the area of the parallelogram is 80, find to the *nearest tenth* the side adjacent to the base.

23. In parallelogram *ABCD*, $\overline{DE}$ is an altitude to base $\overline{AB}$, $m\angle A = 67$, *AD* = 13, and *BD* = 20. (*a*) Find *DE* to the *nearest integer*. (*b*) Find *AE* to the *nearest integer*. (*c*) Using the values found in answer to parts *a* and *b*, find *BE* and the area of *ABCD*.

5. Finding the Area of a Triangle

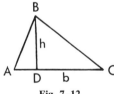

Fig. 7–12

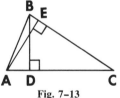

Fig. 7–13

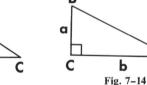

Fig. 7–14

Theorem 104. The area of a triangle is equal to one-half the product of the length of a side and the length of the altitude drawn to that side.

[The proof for this theorem appears on pages 613–614.]

NOTE. Any side of a triangle may be called a *base* of the triangle. For example, in △*ABC* (Fig. 7–13), $\overline{AC}$ may be called a base of △*ABC*. $\overline{BD}$ would then be called the corresponding altitude drawn to the base. Also, $\overline{CB}$ may be called a base of the triangle. Then $\overline{AE}$ would be called the corresponding altitude drawn to the base.

In Fig. 7–12, the area, *A*, of triangle *ABC*, the length of whose base $\overline{AC}$ is represented by *b* and the length of whose altitude $\overline{BD}$ drawn to base $\overline{AC}$ is represented by *h*, is given by the formula $A = \frac{1}{2}bh$.

Corollary T104–1. In any triangle, the product of the length of any side and the length of the altitude drawn to that side is equal to the product of the length of any other side and the length of the altitude drawn to that side.

In triangle ABC (Fig. 7–13), $AC \times BD = BC \times AE$.

Corollary T104–2. The area of a right triangle is equal to one-half the product of the lengths of its two legs.

In right triangle ABC (Fig. 7–14), whose legs are $\overline{BC}$ and $\overline{AC}$, the area, A, is given by the formula $A = \frac{1}{2} \times BC \times AC$, or $A = \frac{1}{2}ab$.

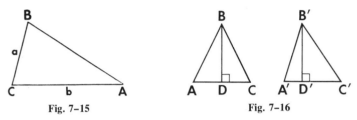

Fig. 7–15   Fig. 7–16

Corollary T104–3. The area of a triangle is equal to one-half the product of the lengths of two consecutive sides and the sine of their included angle.

In Fig. 7–15, the area, A, of triangle ABC, whose two consecutive sides $\overline{AC}$ and $\overline{CB}$ include angle C, is given by the formula $A = \frac{1}{2}ab \sin C$.

Corollary T104–4. Triangles which have congruent bases and congruent altitudes which are drawn to those bases are equal in area.

In Fig. 7–16, triangles ABC and $A'B'C'$, which have congruent bases, $\overline{AC} \cong \overline{A'C'}$, and congruent altitudes, $\overline{BD} \cong \overline{B'D'}$, are equal in area (equivalent), denoted by $\triangle ABC = \triangle A'B'C'$.

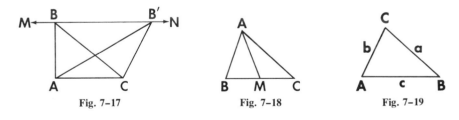

Fig. 7–17   Fig. 7–18   Fig. 7–19

Corollary T104–5. Triangles which have a common base and whose vertices lie on a line parallel to the base are equal in area.

In Fig. 7–17, triangles ABC and $AB'C$, which have $\overline{AC}$ as a common base and whose vertices B and B' lie on line $\overleftrightarrow{MN}$, which is parallel to $\overline{AC}$, are equal in area.

Corollary T104–6. A median drawn to a side of a triangle divides the triangle into two triangles which are equal in area.

In triangle ABC (Fig. 7–18), if $\overline{AM}$ is a median drawn to $\overline{BC}$, then triangle BAM is equal in area to triangle CAM, denoted by $\triangle BAM = \triangle CAM$.

Theorem 105. **The area of a triangle the length of whose three sides are represented by a, b, and c is given by the formula**

$$A = \sqrt{s(s-a)(s-b)(s-c)}$$

[s represents the semi-perimeter: $s = \frac{1}{2}(a + b + c)$.]

In $\triangle ABC$ (Fig. 7–19), $A = \sqrt{s(s-a)(s-b)(s-c)}$. This formula is known as *Heron's formula* or *Hero's formula* for the area of a triangle.

MODEL PROBLEMS

1. In right triangle ABC, $m\angle C = 90$, $AB = 20$ in., and $AC = 16$ in. Find the area of triangle ABC.

    Solution: Consider $\overline{AC}$ as the base of triangle ABC. Since $m\angle C = 90$, $\overline{BC}$ is the altitude to $\overline{AC}$ in triangle ABC. Let $x =$ the length of $\overline{BC}$.

    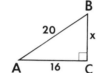

    1. $(x)^2 + (16)^2 = (20)^2$

    2. $x^2 + 256 = 400$

    3. $\qquad x^2 = 144$

    4. $\qquad x = 12$

    5. Area of $\triangle ABC = \frac{1}{2}bh$

    6. Area of $\triangle ABC = \frac{1}{2}(16)(12) = 96$

    Answer: Area of triangle $ABC = 96$ sq. in.

    NOTE. The area of right triangle ABC can also be found by using the corollary "The area of a right triangle is equal to one-half the product of the lengths of its two legs."

2. Find the area of triangle ABC to the *nearest square inch* if $AB = 8$ in., $AC = 4$ in., and $m\angle A = 135$.

    Solution: If $\overline{CA}$ is considered as the base of triangle ABC, the altitude drawn to $\overline{CA}$ extended is BD. Let $h =$ length of $\overline{BD}$.

    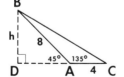

    1. In right triangle BAD, $m\angle BAD = 180 - 135 = 45$.

    2. $h = \frac{1}{2}(\text{hyp.})\sqrt{2}$

    3. $h = \frac{1}{2}(8)\sqrt{2} = 4\sqrt{2}$

    4. Area of $\triangle ABC = \frac{1}{2}bh = \frac{1}{2}(4)(4\sqrt{2})$

5. Area of $\triangle ABC = 8\sqrt{2} = 8(1.4) = 11.2$ [Use $\sqrt{2} = 1.4$.]

Answer: Area of triangle $ABC = 11$ sq. in.

3. In trapezoid $ABCD$, the larger base $\overline{AB}$ measures 24 in., the smaller base $\overline{DC}$ measures 8 in., and altitude $\overline{FG}$ measures 6 in. The nonparallel sides $\overline{AD}$ and $\overline{BC}$ are extended to meet at E.
   a. In triangle DEC, find EF, the measure of the altitude from E to $\overline{DC}$.
   b. Find the area of triangle DEC.

Solution:

a. 1. In trapezoid $ABCD$, $\overline{DC} \parallel \overline{AB}$. $DC = 8$.   Let $EF = x$.

   2. $\triangle DEC \sim \triangle AEB$. $AB = 24$.   Then $EG = x + 6$.
                                                   $FG = 6$.

   3. $\dfrac{\text{length of altitude } \overline{EF}}{\text{length of altitude } \overline{EG}} = \dfrac{\text{length of base } \overline{DC}}{\text{length of base } \overline{AB}}$, or

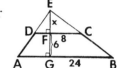

$$\frac{x}{x + 6} = \frac{8}{24}$$

   4. $24x = 8x + 48$

   5. $16x = 48$

   6. $x = 3$

Answer: $EF = 3$ in.

b. 1. Area of $\triangle DEC = \frac{1}{2}bh = \frac{1}{2}DC \times EF$

   2. Area of $\triangle DEC = \frac{1}{2} \times 8 \times 3 = 12$

Answer: Area of $\triangle DEC = 12$ sq. in.

EXERCISES

1. Find the area of a triangle whose base and altitude have the following measures:
   a. $b = 12$ in., $h = 8$ in.   b. $b = 14$ in., $h = 9$ in.
   c. $b = 21$ in., $h = 1\frac{1}{2}$ ft.   d. $b = 7$ ft., $h = 11$ ft.
   e. $b = 3$ ft., $h = 8$ in.   f. $b = 2\frac{1}{2}$ ft., $h = 3\frac{1}{4}$ ft.

2. Express, in terms of x, the areas of the triangles whose bases and altitudes are represented by:
   a. $b = 2x, h = 6$ b. $b = 5x, h = 4x$
   c. $b = 12, h = 5x - 2$ d. $b = 2x + 4, h = 3x$

3. The area of a triangle is 60. If one side of the triangle measures 24, find the length of the altitude drawn to that side.

4. The area of a triangle is 40. If a side of the triangle is represented by $2x + 2$ and the altitude drawn to that side measures 8, find the value of x.

5. The area of a triangle is 12. If the ratio of the length of a side of the triangle to the length of the altitude drawn to that side is 2:3, find the length of the side of the triangle.

6. The area of a triangle is 20. If a side of the triangle measures 3 less than the altitude drawn to that side, find the altitude.

7. Find the area of a right triangle whose legs measure:
   a. 6 and 8   *b.* 12 and 9

8. Find the area of an isosceles right triangle each of whose legs measures 6.

9. If the length of each leg of an isosceles right triangle is represented by L, express the area of the triangle in terms of L.

10. Find the area of an isosceles right triangle whose hypotenuse measures $4\sqrt{2}$.

11. The sides of a triangle have lengths of 3, 4, and 5. Find the area of the triangle.

12. A side of a triangle measures 12 and the altitude to this side measures 4. A second side of the triangle measures 16. Find the altitude drawn to this side.

13. The lengths of the sides of a right triangle measure 5, 12, and 13. Find the length of the altitude drawn to the hypotenuse of the triangle.

14. The bases of two equivalent triangles measure 20 in. and 40 in. Find the ratio of the lengths of the altitudes which are drawn to the given bases of the triangles.

15. In $\triangle ABC$, $\overline{CM}$ is the median drawn to side $\overline{AB}$. If the area of $\triangle ACM$ is 15 sq. in., find the area of $\triangle BCM$.

16. A triangle is equal in area to a square whose side measures 12. If the base of the triangle has a length of 36, find the length of the altitude drawn to this side of the triangle.

17. Find the area of a triangle if one of its angles contains 30° and the sides including this angle measure:
   a. 6 and 10   *b.* 30 and 40   *c.* 20 and 9   *d.* 11 and 8   *e.* 5 and 7

18. Find the area of a triangle if one of its angles contains 60° and the sides including this angle measure: [Answers may be left in radical form.]
   a. 12 and 6   *b.* 20 and 14   *c.* 10 and 9   *d.* 13 and 8   *e.* 3 and 5

19. Find the area of a triangle if one of its angles contains 45° and the sides including this angle measure: [Answers may be left in radical form.]
   a. 8 and 6   *b.* 14 and 12   *c.* 4 and 10   *d.* 11 and 10   *e.* 5 and 9

20. Find the area of a triangle if one of its angles contains 150° and the lengths of the sides including this angle are:
   a. 4 and 6   *b.* 8 and 5   *c.* 7 and 9

21. Find the area of a triangle if one of its angles contains 135° and the sides including this angle measure 6 and 8. [Answers may be left in radical form.]

22. Represent, in terms of x, the area of a triangle if one of its angles contains 30° and the lengths of the sides including this angle are represented by $4x$ and $2x$.

23. Represent, in terms of x, the area of a triangle if two of its sides are represented by 8 and $2x$ and the angle included between these sides contains:
   a. 60°   *b.* 45°   *c.* 150°   *d.* 120°   *e.* 135°

24. Triangle ABC is equal in area to a square whose side measures 4. If $m\angle BAC = 30$ and AB is 4 times AC, find AC and AB.

25. Find the area of an isosceles triangle whose base measures 8 and each of whose congruent sides measures 5.

26. $\overline{AC}$, a diameter of a circle, is 8 inches long and forms an angle of 30° with chord $\overline{AB}$. Find the area of triangle ABC.

27. In triangle ABC, $\overline{AC}$ and $\overline{BC}$ are each 13 and $\overline{AB}$ is 10. (*a*) Find the length of the altitude upon $\overline{AB}$. (*b*) Find the area of triangle ABC. (*c*) Find the length of the altitude from B upon $\overline{AC}$.

28. In circle O, chord $\overline{AB}$ is 16 inches long. C is the midpoint of minor arc $\overset{\frown}{AB}$, and diameter $\overline{CE}$ intersects chord $\overline{AB}$ in D. $\overline{CD}$ is 4 inches long. (*a*) Find the length of $\overline{DE}$. (*b*) Find the length of a diameter of the circle. (*c*) Draw radii $\overline{OA}$ and $\overline{OB}$. Find the area of triangle AOB.

29. The bases of a trapezoid measure 7 and 10 and the altitude measures 6. (*a*) Find the length of the altitude of the triangle formed by the shorter base and the nonparallel sides extended. (*b*) Find the area of the triangle described in *a*.

30. In isosceles trapezoid $ABCD$, the length of base $\overline{AB}$ is 60 feet, the length of base $\overline{CD}$ is 28 feet, and the length of leg $\overline{BC}$ is 20 feet. Legs $\overline{AD}$ and $\overline{BC}$ are extended to intersect in E. Find the area of triangle DEC.

31. In trapezoid $ABCD$, the length of base $\overline{AB}$ is 12 and the length of base $\overline{CD}$ is 4. If diagonal $\overline{AC}$ is drawn, find the ratio of the area of triangle ABC to the area of triangle ACD.

32. Given square $ABCD$ with E, F, G, and H the midpoints of $\overline{AB}$, $\overline{BC}$, $\overline{CD}$, and $\overline{DA}$ respectively.
   a. Prove triangle $EFG \cong$ triangle EHG.
   b. If $AB = 6$, find   (1) the length of $\overline{EF}$ and   (2) the area of $\triangle EFG$.

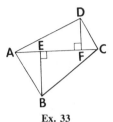

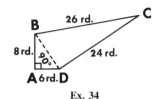

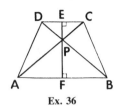

Ex. 33   Ex. 34   Ex. 36

33. To find the area of quadrilateral $ABCD$, diagonal $\overline{AC}$ is drawn, and $\overline{BE}$ and $\overline{DF}$ are drawn perpendicular to $\overline{AC}$. If $AC = 24$ ft., $BE = 12$ ft., and $DF = 9$ ft., find the area of quadrilateral $ABCD$.

34. A plot of land has the form of a quadrilateral whose sides are 8 rods, 26 rods, 24 rods, and 6 rods, as indicated on the accompanying figure. Angle BAD contains $90°$. (*a*) Find the length of diagonal $\overline{BD}$. (*b*) Show that angle BDC is a right angle. (*c*) Find to the *nearest tenth of an acre* the area of the field. [1 acre = 160 sq. rd.]

35. In trapezoid $ABCD$, $\overline{AB}$ is the longer base. Diagonals $\overline{AC}$ and $\overline{BD}$ intersect in E.
    a. Prove: $\triangle AEB \sim \triangle CED$.
    b. If the bases of the trapezoid measure 5 inches and 15 inches, find the ratio of corresponding altitudes of $\triangle CED$ and $\triangle AEB$.
    c. If the altitude of the trapezoid measures 8 inches, find the number of square inches in the area of $\triangle AEB$.

36. In trapezoid $ABCD$, $AB = 20$, $DC = 10$, and altitude $\overline{EF}$ measures 12. (*a*) Using x to represent PE, write an equation which can be used to find PE. (*b*) Solve this equation for x. (*c*) Find the area of triangle DPC and triangle BPA.

37. In trapezoid $ABCD$, $\overline{AB}$ is the lower base. The bisector of angle A intersects $\overline{DC}$ at P. (*a*) Prove that triangle ADP is isosceles. (*b*) If $AD = 8$ and the altitude of the trapezoid measures 6, find the area of triangle ADP.

38. The lengths of the legs of a right triangle are in the ratio 3:4. If the area of the triangle is 54, find the lengths of the three sides of the triangle.

39. In triangle RST, the lengths of sides $\overline{RS}$, $\overline{ST}$, and $\overline{RT}$ are represented by $2x + 9$, $5x - 3$, and $4x$ respectively. The perimeter of triangle RST is 50. (*a*) Find the lengths of the sides of triangle RST. (*b*) Find the area of triangle RST.

40. In each part of this exercise, find the length of the altitude drawn to the larger side to the *nearest tenth*. Use this result to find the area of the triangle to the *nearest integer*.

    Two adjacent sides of a triangle measure 6 and 10 and include an angle of:
    a. 25°   *b.* 37°   *c.* 75°   *d.* 120°   *e.* 150°   *f.* 175°

41. Find to the *nearest square inch* the area of an isosceles triangle whose vertex angle contains 120° and each of whose legs measures 12 inches.

42. In an isosceles triangle, the vertex angle contains 120° and the length of each of the congruent legs is represented by L. Represent the area of the triangle in terms of L.

43. *a.* Given acute $\triangle ABC$ with the sides opposite angles A, B, and C represented by a, b, and c, respectively. Starting with the formula $K = \frac{1}{2}bh$ for the area of $\triangle ABC$, show that $K = \frac{1}{2}ab \sin C$ is also a formula for the area of $\triangle ABC$.

   b. Using the formula $K = \frac{1}{2}ab \sin C$, find the number of degrees contained in angle C if angle C is acute, $a = 40$, $b = 10$, and $K = 100$.

44. In right triangle ABC, the length of hypotenuse $\overline{AB}$ is 13.7 and angle B contains 38°. (*a*) Find AC and BC to the *nearest tenth*. (*b*) Find the area of triangle ABC to the *nearest integer*.

45. In an isosceles triangle, the base is 24 inches and each base angle contains 50°. (*a*) Find to the *nearest tenth of an inch* the altitude drawn upon the base. (*b*) Find the area of the triangle to the *nearest square inch*.

46. The altitude of a triangle is 12 inches, and it divides the vertex angle into two angles containing 20° and 45°. (*a*) Find the lengths of the segments of the base. (*b*) Find to the *nearest square inch* the area of the triangle.

6. Finding the Area of an Equilateral Triangle

All the theorems which involve the area of the general triangle also apply to the equilateral triangle. In addition, the following theorem can be used in finding the area of an equilateral triangle:

Theorem 106. **The area of an equilateral triangle, the length of each of whose sides is represented by s, is given by the formula $A = \dfrac{s^2}{4} \sqrt{3}$.**

MODEL PROBLEMS

1. Find the area of an equilateral triangle whose perimeter is 24.

   Solution:

   1. Perimeter is 24. Therefore, the length of each side is $24 \div 3 = 8$.

   2. $A = \dfrac{s^2}{4} \sqrt{3} = \dfrac{(8)^2}{4} \sqrt{3} = \dfrac{64}{4} \sqrt{3} = 16\sqrt{3}.$

   Answer: Area $= 16\sqrt{3}.$

2. Find the length of a side of an equilateral triangle whose area is $4\sqrt{3}$.

Solution:

1. $A = \dfrac{s^2}{4}\sqrt{3}$

2. $4\sqrt{3} = \dfrac{s^2}{4}\sqrt{3}$

3. $4 = \dfrac{s^2}{4}$ $\mathbf{D}_{\sqrt{3}}$

4. $16 = s^2$ $\mathbf{M}_4$

5. $s = 4$

Answer: Side $= 4$.

3. Find the area of a rhombus one of whose angles contains $60°$ and whose shorter diagonal is 6.

Solution:

1. Since $ABCD$ is a rhombus, $\overline{BA} \cong \overline{AD}$.

2. In $\triangle DAB$, $m\angle A = 60$ and $\overline{BA} \cong \overline{AD}$. Therefore, $m\angle ABD = m\angle BDA = 60$, and $\triangle DAB$ is an equilateral triangle.

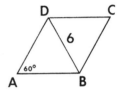

3. Area of $\triangle DAB = \dfrac{s^2}{4}\sqrt{3} = \dfrac{(6)^2}{4}\sqrt{3} = \dfrac{36}{4}\sqrt{3} = 9\sqrt{3}$

4. Since $\overline{BD}$ divides rhombus $ABCD$ into two equivalent triangles, area of rhombus $ABCD = 2 \times$ area of $\triangle DAB = 2(9\sqrt{3}) = 18\sqrt{3}$.

Answer: Area $= 18\sqrt{3}$.

EXERCISES

1. Express the area of an equilateral triangle in terms of the length of its side b.

2. Find the area of an equilateral triangle the length of whose side is: [Answers may be left in radical form.]

  a. 2   *b.* 4   *c.* 6   *d.* 10   *e.* 12   *f.* 20
  g. 3   *h.* 1   *i.* 5   *j.* 9   *k.* 15   *l.* 25

3. Find the area of an equilateral triangle whose perimeter is: [Answers may be left in radical form.]
a. 6   *b.* 12   *c.* 18   *d.* 30   *e.* 15   *f.* 21

4. Find the length of a side of an equilateral triangle whose area is:

a. $9\sqrt{3}$ *b.* $25\sqrt{3}$ *c.* $16\sqrt{3}$ *d.* $100\sqrt{3}$ *e.* $\sqrt{3}$

f. $\frac{9}{4}\sqrt{3}$ *g.* $\frac{25}{4}\sqrt{3}$ *h.* $\frac{49}{4}\sqrt{3}$ *i.* $\frac{81}{4}\sqrt{3}$ *j.* $\frac{\sqrt{3}}{4}$

5. In triangle ABC, the lengths of sides $\overline{AB}$, $\overline{BC}$, and $\overline{CA}$ are represented by $3x - 3$, $x + 7$, and $2x + 2$ respectively. The perimeter of triangle ABC is 36. (*a*) Find the lengths of the sides of triangle ABC. (*b*) Find the area of triangle ABC. [Answer may be left in radical form.]

6. The area of an equilateral triangle is $36\sqrt{3}$. Find the length of the radius of the circle inscribed in this triangle. [Answer may be left in radical form.]

7. Find the area of a rhombus one of whose angles contains 60° and whose shorter diagonal measures:
a. 4   *b.* 8   *c.* 12   *d.* 3   *e.* 5

8. Find the area of a rhombus one of whose angles contains 60° and whose longer diagonal measures 12.

9. The area of a regular hexagon is $96\sqrt{3}$. Find the length of a side of an equilateral triangle whose perimeter is equal to the perimeter of the hexagon.

7. Finding the Area of a Trapezoid

Theorem 107. **The area of a trapezoid is equal to one-half the product of the length of its altitude and the sum of its bases.**

[The proof for this theorem appears on pages 614–615.]

In Fig. 7–20, the area of trapezoid $ABCD$, the lengths of whose bases $\overline{AB}$ and $\overline{DC}$ are represented by b and b' and the length of whose altitude $\overline{DE}$ is represented by h, is given by the formula
$$A = \tfrac{1}{2}h\,(b + b')$$

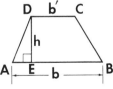

Fig. 7–20

Corollary T107–1. **The area of a trapezoid is equal to the product of the length of its altitude and the length of its median.**

In Fig. 7–21, the area of trapezoid $ABCD$, the length of whose altitude $\overline{DE}$ is represented by h and the length of whose median $\overline{FG}$ is represented by m, is given by the formula $A = h \times m$.

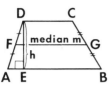

Fig. 7–21

MODEL PROBLEMS

1. Find the area of trapezoid $ABCD$ if the length of $\overline{AB} = 9$ in., the length of $\overline{DC} = 5$ in., and the length of altitude $\overline{DE} = 6$ in.

Solution:

1. $A = \frac{1}{2}h(b + b')$ $b = 9, b' = 5, h = 6.$

2. $A = \frac{1}{2}(6)(9 + 5) = 3(14) = 42$

Answer: Area = 42 sq. in.

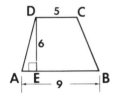

2. The bases of a trapezoid are 12 in. and 20 in. If the area of the trapezoid is 128 sq. in., find the length of its altitude.

Solution:

1. Let $h =$ the length of altitude $\overline{DE}$. $b = 20, b' = 12, A = 128.$

2. $A = \frac{1}{2}h(b + b')$

3. $128 = \frac{1}{2}h(20 + 12)$

4. $128 = \frac{1}{2}h(32)$

5. $128 = 16h$

6. $8 = h$

Answer: Altitude = 8 in.

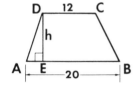

3. In isosceles trapezoid $ABCD$, $\overline{CF}$ and $\overline{DE}$ are altitudes and $m\angle B = 60$. CD exceeds BC by 5. If the perimeter of $ABCD$ is 110, find, in radical form, the area of the trapezoid.

Solution:

1. In right triangle CBF, since $m\angle FBC = 60$, $m\angle BCF = 30$.

2. In 30°–60° right triangle CBF, $BC = 2FB$.

3. Let $FB = x$. Then $BC = 2x$.

4. Therefore, $CD = 2x + 5$.

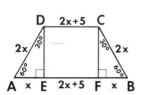

5. Since $DCFE$ is a rectangle, $EF = CD = 2x + 5$.

6. Since $\triangle DAE \cong \triangle CBF$, $AD = BC = 2x$ and $AE = FB = x$.

7. $AE + EF + FB + BC + CD + DA =$ perimeter of $ABCD$

8. $x + 2x + 5 + x + 2x + 2x + 5 + 2x = 110$

9. $10x + 10 = 110$

10. $10x = 100$

11. $x = 10$

12. $CD = 2x + 5 = 2(10) + 5 = 25$, $AB = 4x + 5 = 4(10) + 5 = 45$.

13. In $30°$–$60°$ right triangle CBF, $CF = \frac{1}{2}BC\sqrt{3} = \frac{1}{2}(20)\sqrt{3} = 10\sqrt{3}$.

14. Area of trapezoid $ABCD = \frac{1}{2}h(b + b')$

15. Area of trapezoid $ABCD = \frac{1}{2}(10\sqrt{3})(45 + 25)$
$$= \frac{1}{2}(10\sqrt{3})(70) = \frac{1}{2}(700\sqrt{3}) = 350\sqrt{3}$$

Answer: $350\sqrt{3}$.

EXERCISES

1. The formula for the area A of a trapezoid in terms of its altitude h and its bases b and b' is $A =$ _____.

2. The altitude of a trapezoid is 6 and its bases are 8 and 12. Find the area of the trapezoid.

3. The bases of a trapezoid are 2.4 inches and 5.6 inches and its altitude is 7.0 inches. Find the number of square inches in the area of the trapezoid.

4. The bases of a trapezoid are 8 and 12 and its area is 140. Find its altitude.

5. The area of a trapezoid is 36 and the sum of its bases is 18. Find the length of the altitude.

6. Find the area of a trapezoid whose altitude measures 8 and whose median measures 14.

7. Find the area of a trapezoid whose altitude measures 13 and whose median measures 30.

8. The area of a trapezoid is 72. Its altitude measures 8. Find the lengths of its bases if the larger base is twice the smaller base.

9. The area of a trapezoid is 90 square inches. The altitude measures 6 inches and one base measures 18 inches. Find the number of inches in the length of the other base.

10. The area of a trapezoid is 54 square inches. Its altitude measures 6 in. If the larger base exceeds the smaller base by 2 in., find the lengths of both bases of the trapezoid.

11. If the bases of an isosceles trapezoid are 20 in. and 28 in. respectively and each leg measures 5 in., find the number of square feet in the area of the trapezoid.

12. The congruent sides of an isosceles trapezoid each measure 5 and its altitude measures 4. If the area of the trapezoid is 48, find the lengths of the bases.

13. In trapezoid $ABCD$, the lengths of the bases $\overline{AB}$ and $\overline{DC}$ are 30 and 20, $m\angle A = 30$, and $AD = 8$. Find the area of the trapezoid.

14. In trapezoid $ABCD$, the lengths of the bases $\overline{AB}$ and $\overline{DC}$ are 15 and 11, $m\angle A = 60$, and $AD = 4$. Find the area of the trapezoid. [Answer may be left in radical form.]

15. In trapezoid $ABCD$, the lengths of the bases $\overline{AB}$ and $\overline{DC}$ are 17 and 14, $m\angle A = 45$, and $AD = 6$. Find the area of the trapezoid. [Answer may be left in radical form.]

16. In isosceles trapezoid $ABCD$, the bases are $\overline{AB}$ and $\overline{DC}$. AD is 1 more than twice DC, and AB is 6 more than 4 times DC. (a) If DC is represented by x, represent AD and AB in terms of x. (b) If the perimeter of the trapezoid is 62, find the value of x. (c) Find the length of the altitude of the trapezoid. (d) Find the area of the trapezoid.

17. Find the area of an isosceles trapezoid whose bases are 10 and 26 and whose base angles each contain 60°. [Answer may be left in radical form.]

18. In an isosceles trapezoid, each base angle contains 45° and the bases measure 8 and 24. Find the area of the trapezoid.

19. The measure of the longer base of an isosceles trapezoid exceeds the measure of the shorter base by 6, and each leg measures 5. (a) If the measure of the shorter base is represented by x, express the measure of the longer base in terms of x. (b) Find the measure of the altitude of the trapezoid. (c) If the area of this trapezoid equals 28, find the measure of each base.

20. (a) The longer base of an isosceles trapezoid is 21, its altitude is 6, and one of its angles contains 45°. Find the area of the trapezoid. (b) The length of base $\overline{AD}$ of parallelogram $ABCD$ is represented by x. If angle A contains 30° and if the length of side $\overline{AB}$ is 10, express the area of the parallelogram in terms of x. (c) If the trapezoid and the parallelogram are equal in area, find x.

21. A trapezoid is inscribed in a circle whose radius is 13 inches in length. The bases are 12 inches and 5 inches from the center of the circle and

on opposite sides of the center.   (*a*) Find the lengths of the bases of the trapezoid.   (*b*) Find the area of the trapezoid.

22. In trapezoid $ABCD$, the length of base $\overline{AB}$ is 6 inches and the length of base $\overline{DC}$ is 24 inches. Sides $\overline{DA}$ and $\overline{CB}$ are extended to meet at point G. The altitude of the trapezoid is 6 inches longer than the altitude to side $\overline{AB}$ of triangle GAB.   (*a*) Using x to represent the length of the altitude from G in triangle GAB, represent the length of the corresponding altitude in triangle GDC.   (*b*) Find the length of the altitude of the trapezoid.   (*c*) Find the area of the trapezoid.

23. The base of a triangle measures 30 inches and the altitude drawn to this base measures 15 inches. Find the area of the trapezoid formed by a line parallel to the base and 9 inches from the opposite vertex.

24. Each side of a triangle is 8 inches. A line is drawn parallel to one side of the triangle and forming a trapezoid one of whose nonparallel sides is 6 inches.   (*a*) Find the length of the altitude of the trapezoid.   (*b*) Find to the *nearest square inch* the area of the trapezoid.

25. In trapezoid $ABCD$, the length of base $\overline{BC}$ is to the length of base $\overline{AD}$ as 2 is to 3. Legs $\overline{AB}$ and $\overline{DC}$ are extended to meet at E, and the altitude $\overline{EF}$ of triangle AED intersects $\overline{BC}$ at G. The area of triangle AED is 270 and $EF = 30$.   (*a*) Find AD.   (*b*) Find BC and EG.   (*c*) Find the area of $ABCD$.

26. The diameter $\overline{AB}$ of circle O is a base of the inscribed trapezoid $ABCD$. $m\angle A = 60$ and the length of radius $\overline{OD}$ is 8.   (*a*) Find the length of the altitude of the trapezoid.   (*b*) Find the area of the trapezoid.

27. The area of an equilateral triangle is equal to that of a trapezoid whose bases are 4 and 14 and whose altitude measures $4\sqrt{3}$. Find the length of a side of the triangle.

28. Find the side of an equilateral triangle which is equal in area to an isosceles trapezoid whose bases measure 6 and 10 and each of whose base angles contains 60°.

29. A rectangle and a trapezoid are equal in area. One side of the rectangle is 20 inches and its diagonal is 25 inches. The altitude of the trapezoid is 12 inches and one base is 10 inches longer than the other.   (*a*) Find the area of the rectangle.   (*b*) If x represents the length of the shorter base of the trapezoid, express the area of the trapezoid in terms of x.   (*c*) Find x.

30. $ABCD$ is a trapezoid with bases $\overline{AB}$ and $\overline{DC}$. Diagonals $\overline{CA}$ and $\overline{DB}$ intersect in O. AB is 20, DC is 4, and the area of the trapezoid is 72.   (*a*) Find the altitude of the trapezoid.   (*b*) Find the length of the perpendicular drawn from O to $\overline{AB}$.

31. In the figure, the bases of isosceles trape-
zoid $ABCD$ are $\overline{AB}$ and $\overline{DC}$, with $\overline{AB}$ the
longer base. The length of altitude $\overline{DE}$ is 16,
the length of diagonal $\overline{DB}$ is 34, and $m\angle A =$
45.

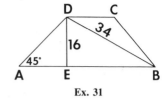

Ex. 31

   a. Find the number of units in the length of
$\overline{AE}, \overline{EB}, \overline{AB}$ and $\overline{DC}$.

   b. Find the number of square units in the
area of trapezoid $ABCD$.

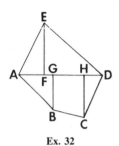

Ex. 32

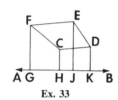

Ex. 33

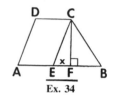

Ex. 34

32. In the figure, $\overline{EF} \perp \overline{AD}$, $\overline{BG} \perp \overline{AD}$, and $\overline{CH} \perp \overline{AD}$. $AF = 7$, $FG = 3$,
$GH = 9, HD = 5, FE = 14, BG = 10, HC = 12$. Find the area of $ABCDE$.

33. In the figure, $\overline{FG} \perp \overleftrightarrow{AB}, \overline{CH} \perp \overleftrightarrow{AB}, \overline{EJ} \perp \overleftrightarrow{AB}$, and $\overline{DK} \perp \overleftrightarrow{AB}$. $GH = 14$,
$HJ = 6, JK = 8, FG = 20, CH = 8, EJ = 22$, and $DK = 10$. Find the area
of $CDEF$.

34. The lengths of the bases $\overline{AB}$ and $\overline{CD}$ of trapezoid $ABCD$ are 24 and 10,
and the lengths of the legs $\overline{AD}$ and $\overline{BC}$ are 13 and 15 respectively. $\overline{CE}$ is
drawn parallel to $\overline{DA}$, and $\overline{CF}$ is perpendicular to $\overline{AB}$. Let EF be represented by x.

   a. Express FB in terms of x.

   b. Using triangles EFC and BFC, write *two* expressions for $(CF)^2$ in
terms of x.

   c. Find the value of x.

   d. Find the area of the trapezoid.

35. The lengths of the bases of an isosceles trapezoid are 8 and 28. One base
angle contains $53°$. (*a*) Find to the *nearest tenth* the length of the
altitude of the trapezoid. (*b*) Find to the *nearest integer* the area of the
trapezoid.

36. In trapezoid $ABCD$, the length of base $\overline{AB} = 23$, the length of base $\overline{DC} =$
17, the length of leg $\overline{AD} = 10$, and $m\angle A = 40$. (*a*) Find to the *nearest
tenth* the length of the altitude of the trapezoid. (*b*) Find to the *nearest
integer* the area of the trapezoid.

37. In the figure, $ABCD$ is a trapezoid in which $\overline{AB} \parallel \overline{DC}$. Diagonal $\overline{CA} \perp$ base $\overline{AB}$. $AB = 28.0$ in., $DC = 12.0$ in., and the measure of the angle included between diagonal $\overline{BD}$ and base $\overline{AB}$ is 24. (a) Find the length of $\overline{AC}$ to the *nearest tenth of an inch.* (b) Find the area of trapezoid $ABCD$ to the *nearest square inch,* using the answer obtained in part a.

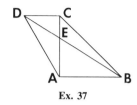

Ex. 37

38. In trapezoid $ABCD$, angle A contains $55°$ and bases $\overline{AB}$ and $\overline{DC}$ are perpendicular to leg $\overline{BC}$. The length of base $\overline{DC}$ is 18 and the length of leg $\overline{AD}$ is 14. (a) Find the length of the altitude of the trapezoid to the *nearest tenth.* (b) Using the answer obtained in part a, find the area of the trapezoid to the *nearest integer.*

8. Finding the Area of a Rhombus

All the theorems which involve the area of the general parallelogram also apply to the rhombus. In addition, the following theorem can be used in finding the area of a rhombus.

Theorem 108. **The area of a rhombus is equal to one-half the product of the lengths of its diagonals.**

In Fig. 7–22, the area of rhombus $ABCD$, the lengths of whose diagonals $\overline{AC}$ and $\overline{BD}$ are represented by d_1 and d_2, is given by the formula $A = \frac{1}{2}d_1d_2$.

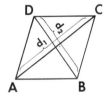

Fig. 7–22

MODEL PROBLEMS

1. Find the area of a rhombus each of whose sides is 10 in. and one of whose diagonals is 16 in.

Solution:

1. Since the diagonals of rhombus $ABCD$ bisect each other at right angles,

   $\overline{AE} \perp \overline{BD}$, and $AE = EC = \frac{1}{2}AC = \frac{1}{2}(16) = 8$

2. In right $\triangle AEB$, let $BE = x$. Thus,

   $x^2 + 8^2 = (10)^2$, $x^2 + 64 = 100$, $x^2 = 36$, $x = 6$. $AB = 10$ in.

   [The solution continues on the next page.]

3. $BD = 2BE = 2(6) = 12$.

4. Area of rhombus $ABCD = \frac{1}{2}d_1d_2 = \frac{1}{2}(16)(12)$ $AC = 16$ in.
$$= 8(12) = 96$$

Answer: Area of rhombus $ABCD = 96$ sq. in.

2. The area of a rhombus is 90 and one diagonal is 10. Find the other diagonal.

Solution:

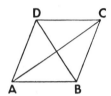

1. $A = \frac{1}{2}d_1d_2$ $A = 90$.

2. $90 = \frac{1}{2}(10)(x)$ Let $BD = d_1 = 10$.

3. $90 = 5x$ Let $AC = d_2 = x$.

4. $18 = x$

Answer: Diagonal $= 18$.

EXERCISES

1. The area, A, of a rhombus in terms of the lengths of its diagonals d and d' is _____ .

2. Find the area of a rhombus whose diagonals measure:
   a. 6 and 8   *b.* 4 and 5   *c.* 25 and 15   *d.* 6.4 and 3.5   *e.* 4 and $4\sqrt{3}$

3. If the diagonals of a rhombus measure 8 and 12, the area of the rhombus is   (*a*) 24   (*b*) 48   (*c*) 96   (*d*) 10.

4. The area of a rhombus is 54 and one of its diagonals measures 12. Find the length of the other diagonal.

5. Find the area of a rhombus whose sides measure 5 and one of whose diagonals measures 8.

6. Find a side of a square equal in area to a rhombus whose diagonals measure 9 and 8.

7. Find the length of the altitude in a rhombus whose area is 320 and whose base is 20.

8. The lengths of the diagonals of a rhombus are represented by n and $n + 3$. Express the area of the rhombus in terms of n.

9. One diagonal of a rhombus is twice as long as the other. If the area of the rhombus is 100 square inches, find the number of inches in the length of the shorter diagonal.

10. The diagonals of a rhombus measure 15 and 20. The rhombus is equal in

area to a trapezoid whose altitude measures 10. If one base of the trapezoid is twice the second base, find the bases of the trapezoid.

11. The perimeter of a rhombus is 40 and one of its diagonals measures 12. Find the area of the rhombus.

12. The perimeter of a rhombus is 52 and one of its diagonals measures 10. Find the area of the rhombus.

13. One angle of a rhombus contains 60° and a side measures 4. Find the area of the rhombus.

14. The shorter diagonal of a rhombus is equal in length to one of its sides. The length of a side of the rhombus is 6 inches. (*a*) Find the length of each diagonal of the rhombus. (*b*) Find the area of the rhombus.

15. If one angle of a rhombus contains 120° and its shorter diagonal measures 8, find its area.

16. The diagonals of a rhombus measure 10 and 24. (*a*) Find the length of a side of the rhombus. (*b*) Find the area of the rhombus. (*c*) Find the length of the altitude of the rhombus.

17. If one side of a rhombus is 25 and the length of the longer diagonal is 40, find: (*a*) the length of the shorter diagonal (*b*) the area of the rhombus (*c*) the length of the altitude.

18. In the figure, *ABCD* is a rhombus. Diagonal $\overline{AC}$ makes an angle of 23° with side $\overline{AB}$, and *AE* = 24.
    a. Find the length of $\overline{EB}$ to the *nearest integer*.
    b. Using the result found in answer to *a*, find the area of the rhombus.
    c. Find the length of $\overline{AB}$ to the *nearest integer*.
    d. Find to the *nearest integer* the length of the altitude of the rhombus from *D* to side $\overline{AB}$.

Ex. 18

19. In rhombus *ABCD*, *m∠A* = 38 and the length of diagonal $\overline{DB}$ = 14.0 inches. (*a*) Find to the *nearest tenth of an inch* the length of diagonal $\overline{AC}$. (*b*) Find to the *nearest square inch* the area of the rhombus. (*c*) Find the length of side $\overline{AD}$ to the *nearest inch*.

20. The lengths of the diagonals of a rhombus are in the ratio 3:4. The area of the rhombus is 96. Find the length of each diagonal and the perimeter of the rhombus.

21. The area of a rhombus is 64 and the length of one diagonal is twice the other. Find the length of the shorter diagonal.

22. The length of the larger diagonal of a rhombus exceeds the length of the smaller diagonal by 2. The area of the rhombus is 40. Find the lengths of the diagonals of the rhombus.

9. Proving Triangles and Polygons Equal in Area

We have learned that two triangles (polygons) are *equivalent* if they are equal in area.

When two triangles (polygons) are congruent (≅), they are both similar (~) and equal in area (=).

> **KEEP IN MIND**
>
> The following corollaries, which we have previously studied, can be helpful in proving triangles, also polygons, equivalent:
>
> 1. A diagonal of a parallelogram divides the parallelogram into two congruent triangles.
> 2. Two triangles are equivalent if they have congruent bases and congruent altitudes.
> 3. Two triangles are equivalent if they have a common base and their vertices lie on a line parallel to the base.
> 4. A median drawn to a side of a triangle divides the triangle into two equivalent triangles.

MODEL PROBLEMS

1. In parallelogram $ABCD$, M is the midpoint of side $\overline{DC}$. Line segment $\overline{AM}$ extended intersects $\overline{BC}$ extended at K.

   a. Prove that triangle ADM is congruent to triangle KCM.

   b. Prove that triangle AKB is equal in area to parallelogram $ABCD$.

   Given: $ABCD$ is a $\square$.
               $\overleftrightarrow{KA}$ and $\overleftrightarrow{KB}$ are straight lines.
               $\overline{DM} \cong \overline{CM}$.

   To prove: (*a*) $\triangle ADM \cong \triangle KCM$.
                   (*b*) Area of $\triangle AKB$ = area of
                    $\square ABCD$.

   a. Plan: Prove that $\triangle ADM \cong \triangle KCM$ by showing that a.s.a. $\cong$ a.s.a.

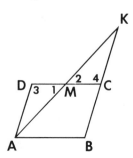

Proof: *Statements*	*Reasons*
1. $ABCD$ is a $\square$.	1. Given.
2. $\overleftrightarrow{KA}$ and $\overleftrightarrow{KB}$ are straight lines.	2. Given.
3. $\angle 1 \cong \angle 2$. (a. $\cong$ a.)	3. If two angles are vertical angles, they are congruent.
4. $\overline{AD} \parallel \overline{BC}$.	4. The opposite sides of a parallelogram are parallel.
5. $\angle 3 \cong \angle 4$. (a. $\cong$ a.)	5. If two parallel lines are cut by a transversal, the alternate interior angles are congruent.
6. $\overline{DM} \cong \overline{CM}$. (s. $\cong$ s.)	6. Given.
7. $\triangle ADM \cong \triangle KCM$.	7. a.s.a. $\cong$ a.s.a.

b. Plan: To prove that the area of $\triangle AKB =$ the area of $\square ABCD$, show that the sum of the areas of quadrilateral $ABCM$ and $\triangle KCM$ is equal to the sum of the areas of quadrilateral $ABCM$ and $\triangle ADM$.

Proof: *Statements*	*Reasons*
1. $\triangle KCM \cong \triangle ADM$.	1. Proved in part *a*.
2. Area of $\triangle KCM =$ area of $\triangle ADM$.	2. If two triangles are congruent, they are equal in area.
3. Area of $ABCM =$ area of $ABCM$.	3. Reflexive property of equality.
4. Area of $\triangle KCM +$ area of $ABCM =$ area of $\triangle ADM +$ area of $ABCM$.	4. Addition property of equality.
5. Area of $\triangle KCM +$ area of $ABCM =$ area of $\triangle AKB$. Area of $\triangle ADM +$ area of $ABCM =$ area of $\square ABCD$.	5. Area-addition postulate.
6. Area of $\triangle AKB =$ area of $\square ABCD$.	6. Substitution postulate.

2. $\overline{AB}$ and $\overline{DC}$ are the bases of trapezoid $ABCD$. Diagonals $\overline{AC}$ and $\overline{BD}$ intersect in E. Prove that triangle ADE is equal in area to triangle CEB.

[Model Problem 2 continues on the next page.]

Given: Trapezoid $ABCD$ with bases $\overline{AB}$ and $\overline{DC}$.

To prove: Area of $\triangle ADE$ = area of $\triangle CEB$.

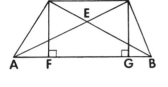

Plan: Prove that the area of $\triangle ADB$ = the area of $\triangle ACB$. Show that the difference between the areas of $\triangle ADB$ and $\triangle AEB$ (area of $\triangle ADB$ − area of $\triangle AEB$) is equal to the difference between the areas of $\triangle ACB$ and $\triangle AEB$ (area of $\triangle ACB$ − area of $\triangle AEB$).

Proof:

Statements	Reasons
1. Draw $\overline{DF} \perp \overline{AB}$ and $\overline{CG} \perp \overline{AB}$.	1. An altitude may be drawn to a side of a triangle.
2. $\overline{AB}$ and $\overline{DC}$ are bases of trapezoid $ABCD$.	2. Given.
3. $\overline{DC} \parallel \overline{AB}$.	3. The bases of a trapezoid are parallel.
4. $DF = CG$, or $\overline{DF} \cong \overline{CG}$.	4. Parallel lines are everywhere equidistant.
5. $\overline{AB} \cong \overline{AB}$.	5. Reflexive property of congruence.
6. Area of $\triangle ADB$ = area of $\triangle ACB$.	6. Two triangles which have congruent bases and congruent altitudes are equal in area.
7. Area of $\triangle AEB$ = area of $\triangle AEB$.	7. Reflexive property of equality.
8. Area of $\triangle ADB$ − area of $\triangle AEB$ = area of $\triangle ACB$ − area of $\triangle AEB$, or	8. Subtraction postulate of equality.
9. Area of $\triangle ADE$ = area of $\triangle CEB$.	9. Substitution postulate.

EXERCISES

1. In parallelogram $ABCD$, diagonals $\overline{AC}$ and $\overline{BD}$ are drawn. Prove that $\triangle ADB$ is equal in area to $\triangle ACB$.

2. In trapezoid $ABCD$, $\overline{AB}$ is the larger base and $\overline{DC}$ is the smaller base. Diagonals $\overline{AC}$ and $\overline{BD}$ are drawn. Prove $\triangle ACD$ is equal in area to $\triangle BCD$.

3. In $\triangle RST$, median $\overline{TN}$ is drawn to side $\overline{RS}$ and median $\overline{RK}$ is drawn to side $\overline{ST}$. Prove that $\triangle RTN$ is equal in area to $\triangle RKS$.

4. In $\triangle ABC$, median $\overline{CD}$ is drawn to side $\overline{AB}$. P is any point on median $\overline{CD}$ between C and D. $\overline{PA}$ and $\overline{PB}$ are drawn. (*a*) *Prove:* area of $\triangle APD$ = area of $\triangle BPD$. (*b*) *Prove:* area of $\triangle APC$ = area of $\triangle BPC$.

5. In $\triangle ABC$, D is the midpoint of $\overline{AB}$ and E is the midpoint of $\overline{AC}$. *Prove:* area of $\triangle CDB$ = area of $\triangle CEB$.

6. In $\triangle ABC$, D is the midpoint of $\overline{AC}$, E is the midpoint of $\overline{BC}$, and F is the midpoint of $\overline{AB}$. Prove that $\triangle DEF$ is equivalent to $\triangle DAF$.

7. The diagonals of a parallelogram intersect in a point forming four triangles. Prove that the four triangles are equal in area.

8. In parallelogram $ABCD$, E is a point on diagonal $\overline{AC}$. Through E, a line is drawn parallel to $\overline{AB}$, intersecting $\overline{AD}$ in F and $\overline{BC}$ in K. Through E, another line is drawn parallel to $\overline{AD}$, intersecting $\overline{AB}$ in G and $\overline{DC}$ in H. (*a*) Prove that triangle HEC is congruent to triangle KCE. (*b*) Prove that the area of quadrilateral $AEHD$ is equal to the area of quadrilateral $AEKB$.

9. In parallelogram $ABCD$, perpendiculars drawn to diagonal $\overline{AC}$ from B and D meet $\overline{AC}$ at points E and K respectively. (*a*) Prove that $\overline{BE} \cong \overline{DK}$. (*b*) A point H is taken on $\overline{AC}$, and $\overline{BH}$ and $\overline{DH}$ are drawn. Prove that triangle ABH is equal in area to triangle ADH.

10. $ABCD$ is a parallelogram. E is the midpoint of diagonal $\overline{BD}$. Through E, a line is drawn intersecting $\overline{BC}$ in F and $\overline{AD}$ in G. Prove: (*a*) Triangle DEG is congruent to triangle BEF. (*b*) The area of quadrilateral $ABEG$ is equal to the area of quadrilateral $CDEF$.

11. In quadrilateral $ABCD$, M is the midpoint of diagonal $\overline{AC}$. $\overline{MB}$ and $\overline{MD}$ are drawn. Prove that $ADMB$ is equal in area to $CDMB$.

12. If diagonal $\overline{AC}$ of quadrilateral $ABCD$ bisects diagonal $\overline{BD}$, prove that $\triangle ABC$ is equal in area to $\triangle ADC$.

13. In parallelogram $ABCD$, P is the point of intersection of diagonals $\overline{AC}$ and $\overline{BD}$. Through P, a line is drawn which intersects $\overline{AB}$ in S and $\overline{CD}$ in R. Prove quadrilateral $ASRD$ is equal in area to quadrilateral $BSRC$.

14. In parallelogram $ABCD$, $\overline{DE} \perp \overline{AB}$ and $\overline{CF} \perp \overline{AB}$ extended through B. Prove that $ABCD$ is equal in area to $DEFC$.

15. In $\triangle RST$, M is any point on $\overline{RT}$ and N is the midpoint of $\overline{ST}$. $\overline{MN}$ is drawn and extended to P so that $\overline{MN} \cong \overline{NP}$. $\overline{PS}$ is drawn. Prove that $\triangle RST$ is equal in area to quadrilateral $MRSP$.

16. In parallelogram $ABCD$, P, any point on $\overline{CD}$, is joined to A and B. Prove that the area of $\triangle ABP$ is one-half the area of parallelogram $ABCD$.

17. From any point P in the base $\overline{AC}$ of triangle ABC, line segments are drawn to R and S, the midpoints of $\overline{AB}$ and $\overline{BC}$ respectively. Perpendiculars from R and S are drawn to $\overline{AC}$, terminating in $\overline{AC}$. (a) Prove that these perpendiculars are congruent. (b) Prove that the area of triangle ARP plus the area of triangle CSP equals one-half the area of triangle ABC.

18. In parallelogram $ABCD$, E is the midpoint of $\overline{AD}$ and F is the midpoint of $\overline{DC}$. If $\overline{BE}$ and $\overline{BF}$ are drawn, prove that $\triangle BAE$ is equal in area to $\triangle BCF$.

19. Given parallelogram $ABCD$ with diagonal $\overline{BD}$. Q is a point on $\overline{AD}$ and R is a point on $\overline{CD}$ such that $AQ{:}QD = CR{:}RD = 2{:}1$.

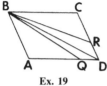

a. Prove that the area of triangle ABQ is $\frac{2}{3}$ of the area of triangle ABD.

b. Prove that line segments $\overline{BQ}$ and $\overline{BR}$ divide the parallelogram into three parts that are equal in area.

Ex. 19

20. $\overline{CD}$ is an altitude of triangle ABC and E is a point on $\overline{CD}$ such that $DE = \frac{1}{3}CD$. Through E, a line parallel to $\overline{AB}$ intersects $\overline{AC}$ in K and $\overline{BC}$ in L. P, the midpoint of $\overline{KL}$, is joined to A, B, and C. Prove that:
(a) area of $\triangle CKP$ = area of $\triangle CPL$ (b) area of $\triangle CAP$ = area of $\triangle CBP$
(c) area of $\triangle ABP = \frac{1}{3}$ of the area of $\triangle ABC$ (d) area of $\triangle PAC$ = area of $\triangle PAB$ = area of $\triangle PBC$.

10. Comparing Areas of Similar Triangles

Theorem 109. **The ratio of the areas of two similar triangles is equal to the ratio of the squares of the lengths of any two corresponding sides.**

In Fig. 7–23, if $\triangle ABC \sim \triangle A'B'C'$ and s and s' are the lengths of a pair of corresponding sides in these triangles, then

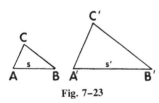

$$\frac{\text{area of } \triangle ABC}{\text{area of } \triangle A'B'C'} = \frac{(s)^2}{(s')^2}, \quad \text{or} \quad \frac{A}{A'} = \frac{(s)^2}{(s')^2}$$

Fig. 7–23

Corollary T109–1. **The ratio of the areas of two similar triangles is equal to the ratio of the squares of the lengths of any two corresponding line segments.**

If $\triangle ABC \sim \triangle A'B'C'$ and l and l' are the lengths of any pair of corresponding line segments in these triangles, then

$$\frac{\text{area of } \triangle ABC}{\text{area of } \triangle A'B'C'} = \frac{(l)^2}{(l')^2}, \quad \text{or} \quad \frac{A}{A'} = \frac{(l)^2}{(l')^2}$$

Corollary T109–2. **The ratio of the areas of two similar triangles is equal to the square of their ratio of similitude.**

If $\triangle ABC \sim \triangle A'B'C'$ and $\dfrac{s}{s'}$ is the ratio of similitude in the two triangles, then

$$\frac{\text{area of } \triangle ABC}{\text{area of } \triangle A'B'C'} = \left(\frac{s}{s'}\right)^2, \quad \text{or} \quad \frac{A}{A'} = \left(\frac{s}{s'}\right)^2$$

MODEL PROBLEMS

1. Triangle $ABC \sim$ triangle $A'B'C'$. If $BC = 4$ and $B'C' = 12$, find the ratio of the areas of the triangles.

Solution:

$$\frac{\text{area of } \triangle ABC}{\text{area of } \triangle A'B'C'} = \frac{(BC)^2}{(B'C')^2} = \frac{(4)^2}{(12)^2} = \frac{16}{144} = \frac{1}{9}$$

Answer: Ratio of the areas of the triangles is 1:9.

2. The areas of two similar triangles are in the ratio of 4:1. The length of a side of the smaller triangle is 5. Find the length of the corresponding side in the larger triangle.

Solution:

| *Method 1* | *Method 2* |

Method 1

1. $\dfrac{A}{A'} = \dfrac{(s)^2}{(s')^2}$ $\qquad \dfrac{A}{A'} = \dfrac{4}{1}$.

2. $\dfrac{4}{1} = \dfrac{s^2}{25}$ $\qquad\qquad s' = 5.$

3. $s^2 = 100$

4. $s = 10$

Method 2

1. If the ratio of the areas is 4:1, the ratio of the lengths of any pair of corresponding sides is 2:1.

2. Since the length of a side in the smaller triangle = 5, the length of the corresponding side in the larger triangle = $2 \times 5 = 10$.

Answer: 10

EXERCISES

1. Find the ratio of the areas of two similar triangles in which the lengths of two corresponding sides are:

   a. $s = 1, s' = 5$ $\qquad\qquad$ *b.* $s = 10, s' = 15$ $\qquad\qquad$ *c.* $s = 9, s' = 3$

2. Find the ratio of the areas of two similar triangles in which the ratio of the lengths of a pair of corresponding lines is:
   a. 4:1   *b.* 9:1   *c.* 7:1   *d.* 4:9   *e.* 3:5

3. The lengths of a pair of corresponding altitudes of two similar triangles are 4 inches and 2 inches. The area of the larger triangle is _____ times the area of the smaller.

4. In two similar triangles, the ratio of similitude is 2:5. Find the ratio of the areas of the two triangles.

5. The ratio of the lengths of a pair of corresponding sides of two similar triangles is 3:1. (*a*) The length of a side in the larger triangle is how many times as large as the length of the corresponding side of the smaller triangle? (*b*) The length of a side of the smaller triangle is what fractional part of the length of the corresponding side in the larger triangle? (*c*) The area of the larger triangle is how many times the area of the smaller triangle? (*d*) The area of the smaller triangle is what fractional part of the area of the larger triangle?

6. Find the ratio of the lengths of a pair of corresponding sides in two similar triangles if the ratio of their areas is:
   a. 1:4   *b.* 1:25   *c.* 9:1   *d.* 4:9   *e.* 25:4

7. The ratio of the areas of two similar triangles is 25:16. (*a*) The area of the larger triangle is how many times the area of the smaller triangle? (*b*) The area of the smaller triangle is what fractional part of the area of the larger triangle? (*c*) The length of a side of the larger triangle is how many times the length of the corresponding side in the smaller triangle? (*d*) The length of a side of the smaller triangle is what fractional part of the length of the corresponding side in the larger triangle?

8. The areas of two similar triangles are in the ratio of 4:9. The length of one side of the smaller triangle is 4. Find the length of the corresponding side of the other triangle.

9. The areas of two similar triangles are in the ratio 9:1. The length of a side of the larger triangle is 12. What is the length of the corresponding side of the smaller triangle?

10. Two triangles are similar, and the area of one is four times the area of the other. The length of one side of the smaller triangle is 12. Find the length of the corresponding side of the larger triangle.

11. Two similar triangles have areas of 16 and 36. The length of a side of the smaller triangle is 8. Find the length of the corresponding side of the larger triangle.

12. The lengths of two corresponding medians of two similar triangles are 10 and 15. If the area of the larger triangle is 81, find the area of the smaller triangle.

13. Two equilateral triangles have sides that measure 8 in. and 12 in. respectively. Find the ratio of the areas of the two triangles.

14. The ratio of the areas of two equilateral triangles is 81 to 25. Find the ratio of the perimeters of the triangles.

15. In trapezoid $ABCD$, the length of base $\overline{AB}$ is 20 in. and the length of base $\overline{DC}$ is 15 in. If the nonparallel sides $\overline{BC}$ and $\overline{AD}$ are extended to meet in E, find the ratio of the area of triangle DEC to the area of triangle AEB.

16. In a circle, chords $\overline{AB}$ and $\overline{CD}$ intersect at E. Chords $\overline{AD}$ and $\overline{BC}$ are drawn. If $DE = 6$ and $BE = 2$, find the ratio of the area of $\triangle AED$ to the area of $\triangle BEC$.

17. *Prove:* A line segment which joins the midpoints of two sides of a triangle cuts off a triangle which is equal in area to one-fourth of the area of the given triangle.

18. Two triangles are similar. The area of the larger triangle exceeds the area of the smaller triangle by 40 square inches. (*a*) If A represents the area of the smaller triangle, represent the area of the larger triangle in terms of A. (*b*) If the ratio of the lengths of a pair of corresponding sides in the triangles is 3:1, write an equation that can be used to find A. (*c*) Find A.

19. The difference between the areas of two similar triangles is 90 square inches. (*a*) If the ratio of the area of the smaller triangle to the area of the larger triangle is 1:4, find the area of each triangle. (*b*) If the length of one side of the smaller triangle is 12 inches, find the length of the corresponding side of the larger triangle.

20. In the figure, $\overline{FG}$ is parallel to $\overline{BC}$. The altitude $\overline{AD}$ of triangle ABC is 6 and BC is 24. The ratio of the area of triangle AFG to the area of triangle ABC is 4:9.

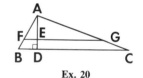

Ex. 20

a. Find the length of $\overline{FG}$.

b. Find the length of the altitude of trapezoid $BCGF$.

21. $ABCD$ is an isosceles trapezoid with $\overline{AB}$ the larger base and $\overline{DC}$ the smaller base. $DC = 8$ and the length of each of the congruent sides, $\overline{AD}$ and $\overline{BC}$, is equal to 5. Sides $\overline{AD}$ and $\overline{BC}$ are extended, intersecting in E and forming isosceles triangles AEB and DEC. The ratio of the area of triangle DEC to the area of triangle AEB is 1:4. (*a*) Find the length of $\overline{DE}$. (*b*) Find the length of the altitude drawn from E to $\overline{AB}$ in triangle AEB. (*c*) Find the area of triangle AEB.

11. Comparing Areas of Similar Polygons

Theorem 110. The ratio of the areas of two similar polygons is equal to the ratio of the squares of the lengths of any two corresponding sides.

In Fig. 7–24, if polygon $TUVWX \sim$ polygon $T'U'V'W'X'$, then

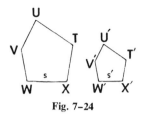

Fig. 7–24

$$\frac{\text{area of polygon } TUVWX}{\text{area of polygon } T'U'V'W'X'} = \frac{(s)^2}{(s')^2},$$

$$\text{or} \quad \frac{A}{A'} = \frac{(s)^2}{(s')^2}$$

Corollary T110–1. **The ratio of the areas of two similar polygons is equal to the ratio of the squares of the lengths of any two corresponding line segments.**

In Fig. 7–24, if polygon $TUVWX \sim$ polygon $T'U'V'W'X'$ and l and l' are the lengths of any pair of corresponding line segments in these polygons, then

$$\frac{\text{area of polygon } TUVWX}{\text{area of polygon } T'U'V'W'X'} = \frac{(l)^2}{(l')^2}, \quad \text{or} \quad \frac{A}{A'} = \frac{(l)^2}{(l')^2}$$

Corollary T110–2. **The ratio of the areas of two similar polygons is equal to the square of their ratio of similitude.**

In Fig. 7–24, if polygon $TUVWX \sim$ polygon $T'U'V'W'X'$ and $\dfrac{s}{s'}$ is the ratio of similitude in the two polygons, then

$$\frac{\text{area of polygon } TUVWX}{\text{area of polygon } T'U'V'W'X'} = \left(\frac{s}{s'}\right)^2, \quad \text{or} \quad \frac{A}{A'} = \left(\frac{s}{s'}\right)^2$$

MODEL PROBLEMS

1. Polygon $WXYZ \sim$ polygon $W'X'Y'Z'$. If $WX = 3$ and $W'X' = 12$, find the ratio of the areas of the two polygons.

Solution:

$$\frac{\text{area of polygon } WXYZ}{\text{area of polygon } W'X'Y'Z'} = \frac{(WX)^2}{(W'X')^2} = \frac{(3)^2}{(12)^2} = \frac{9}{144} = \frac{1}{16}$$

Answer: Ratio of the areas of the two polygons is 1:16.

2. The lengths of two corresponding sides of two similar polygons are 4 and 6. If the area of the smaller polygon is 20, find the area of the larger polygon.

Solution:

| *Method* 1 | *Method* 2 |

1. The ratio of similitude is

Method 1

1. $\dfrac{A}{A'} = \dfrac{(s)^2}{(s')^2}$ $s = 4.$
   $s' = 6.$
   $A = 20.$

2. $\dfrac{20}{x} = \dfrac{(4)^2}{(6)^2}$ Let $x = A'.$

3. $\dfrac{20}{x} = \dfrac{16}{36}$

4. $16x = 720$

5. $x = 45$

Method 2

1. The ratio of similitude is
   $$\dfrac{s}{s'} = \dfrac{4}{6} = \dfrac{2}{3}$$

2. $\dfrac{A}{A'} = \left(\dfrac{s}{s'}\right)^2$

3. $\dfrac{20}{x} = \left(\dfrac{2}{3}\right)^2$

4. $\dfrac{20}{x} = \dfrac{4}{9}$

5. $4x = 180$

6. $x = 45$

Answer: Area of the larger polygon is 45.

EXERCISES

1. Find the ratio of the areas of two similar polygons in which the lengths of two corresponding sides are:
   a. $s = 4$, $s' = 8$ *b.* $s = 8$, $s' = 12$ *c.* $s = 10$, $s' = 5$

2. The length of a side of a polygon is three times as large as the length of the corresponding side of a similar polygon; find the ratio of the areas of the polygons.

3. If two polygons are similar and the length of a side of one is two-thirds of the length of the corresponding side of the other, what is the ratio of the area of the smaller polygon to the area of the larger polygon?

4. If each dimension of a rectangular photograph is doubled to make an enlargement, compare the area of the enlargement with the area of the original photograph.

5. In triangle ABC, D is the midpoint of $\overline{AB}$ and E is the midpoint of $\overline{AC}$. Compare the areas of triangle ADE and triangle ABC.

6. In two similar polygons, the lengths of two corresponding sides are 4 and 20. If the area of the smaller polygon is 60, find the area of the larger one.

7. Find the ratio of the lengths of a pair of corresponding sides in two similar polygons if their areas are:
   a. 25 and 144   *b.* 64 and 400   *c.* 50 and 288   *d.* 108 and 243

8. The areas of two similar polygons are 108 and 192. If the length of a side of the larger polygon is 8, find the length of the corresponding side of the smaller one.

9. If the lengths of two corresponding sides of similar polygons are in the ratio 1:3, then the area of the larger polygon is _____ times the area of the smaller polygon.

10. Find the ratio of the areas of two similar polygons the lengths of whose corresponding sides are in the ratio 2:3.

11. If the ratio of the lengths of two corresponding sides of two similar polygons is 1:2, express the ratio of their areas.

12. If the areas of two similar polygons are in the ratio 4:9, then the lengths of any two corresponding sides of the polygons are in the ratio _____.

13. If each angle of a polygon is kept constant and the length of each side is multiplied by 4, by what number is the area of the polygon multiplied?

14. In two similar polygons, the lengths of two corresponding sides are 4 and 2. If the area of the smaller polygon is 18 less than the area of the larger one, find the area of the larger one.

15. The area of the larger of two similar polygons is 25 times the area of the smaller one. If the length of a side of the larger polygon is 12 more than the length of the corresponding side of the smaller one, find the length of the side of the smaller polygon.

16. Find the ratio of the areas of two similar polygons if the ratio of their perimeters is:
    a. 4:1   *b.* 9:1   *c.* 9:4   *d.* 2:1

17. Find the ratio of the perimeters of two similar polygons if the ratio of their areas is:
    a. 16:1   *b.* 1:4   *c.* 9:25   *d.* 3:1

12. Completion Exercises

Write a word or expression that, when inserted in the blank, will make the resulting statement true.

1. If the base of the rectangle is 10 and the height is represented by $2x$, its area is represented by _____.

2. If a side of a square is represented by $3x$, its area is represented by _____ .

3. If the legs of a right triangle are represented by 5 and $2x$, its area is represented by _____ .

4. If a side of a rhombus is represented by x and an angle of the rhombus contains 30°, its area is represented by _____ .

5. If an altitude of a trapezoid is 8 and the lengths of the bases are represented by x and $x - 4$, its area is represented by _____ .

6. If the perimeter of an equilateral triangle is represented by $6x$, its area is represented by _____ .

7. Two triangles are equal in area if they have congruent altitudes and congruent _____ .

8. Two triangles are equal in area if they have a common base and their vertices lie on a line _____ to the base.

9. A median divides a triangle into two _____ triangles.

10. Areas of rectangles which have congruent altitudes have the same ratio as _____ .

11. The diagonals of a parallelogram divide the parallelogram into four _____ triangles.

12. The base of a triangle is divided into four congruent parts. If each point of division is joined to the opposite vertex, the four triangles thus formed are _____ .

13. If two triangles are similar and the area of one is four times the area of the other, the length of a side of the larger triangle is _____ times the length of the corresponding side of the smaller.

14. If two triangles are similar and the length of a side of one is four times the length of the corresponding side of the other, the area of the larger triangle is _____ times the area of the smaller one.

15. In parallelogram $ABCD$ if diagonals $\overline{AC}$ and $\overline{BD}$ are drawn, triangle ABC is equal in area to triangle _____ .

16. The ratio of the _____ of two similar polygons is equal to the ratio of the squares of the lengths of any two corresponding sides.

17. If a triangle is equal in area to a rectangle and the base of the rectangle is congruent to the base of the triangle, then the length of the altitude of the triangle is _____ times the length of the altitude of the rectangle.

18. If the length of the base of a parallelogram is doubled and the length of the altitude is tripled, the area is multiplied by _____ .

19. The length of side $\overline{AB}$ of $\triangle ABC$ is 5 inches and the length of side $\overline{AC}$ is 6 inches. If the number of degrees contained in angle A varies, then the largest possible area of $\triangle ABC$ is _____ .

20. The diagonals of parallelogram $ABCD$ intersect in point P. Triangles APD and DPC must be _____.

13. True-False Exercises

If the statement is always true, write *true;* if the statement is not always true, write *false*.

1. If two rectangles have equal perimeters, they must have equal areas.
2. The area of a parallelogram whose angles are not right angles is equal to the product of the lengths of two of its consecutive sides.
3. Two parallelograms are always congruent if they have congruent bases and congruent altitudes.
4. The ratio of the areas of two similar triangles is equal to the ratio of the lengths of two corresponding sides.
5. Two equilateral triangles having equal perimeters must have equal areas.
6. An altitude divides a triangle into two triangles which are equal in area.
7. The area of a quadrilateral that has two parallel sides is equal to one-half the product of the sum of the lengths of the two parallel sides and the distance between them.
8. The ratio of the lengths of any two corresponding sides in two similar triangles is equal to the square root of the ratio of the areas.
9. The diagonals of a parallelogram divide it into four equivalent triangles.
10. A diagonal divides a trapezoid into two triangles whose areas have the same ratio as the lengths of the bases of the trapezoid.
11. If the lengths of the diagonals of a rhombus are represented by $4x$ and $6x$, the area is represented by $6x^2$.
12. The areas of rectangles which have congruent bases have the same ratio as the lengths of their altitudes.
13. If the area of a square is represented by $16x^2$, its side is represented by $4x$.
14. If the perimeters of two equilateral quadrilaterals are equal, their areas are equal.
15. If the length of each side of a triangle is doubled, the area of the triangle is doubled.
16. If two parallelograms have their corresponding sides congruent, their areas are equal.
17. If the area of the enlargement of a triangle is nine times the area of the triangle, then the length of a side in the original triangle is one-third the length of the corresponding side in the enlargement.

18. One angle of a rhombus contains 30°. If one of its sides is represented by x, its area is represented by $\frac{1}{2}x^2$.

19. A line segment which joins the midpoints of two sides of a triangle cuts off a triangle whose area is one-fourth the area of the given triangle.

20. If the lengths of two adjacent sides of a parallelogram remain unchanged and the included angle increases from 0° to 90°, the area of the parallelogram increases.

14. "Always, Sometimes, Never" Exercises

If the blank space in each of the following exercises is replaced by the word *always, sometimes,* or *never,* the resulting statement will be true. Select the word which will correctly complete each statement.

1. If two polygons are congruent, they are _____ equal in area.

2. Two rectangles of equal area _____ have unequal perimeters.

3. Triangles that have congruent bases and congruent altitudes are _____ congruent.

4. A diagonal of a parallelogram _____ divides it into two equivalent triangles.

5. If the length of a side of a rhombus none of whose angles is a right angle is represented by x and the length of the side of a square is represented by x, the area of the rhombus is _____ equal to the area of the square.

6. A median of a triangle _____ divides the triangle into two triangles which are equal in area.

7. If the dimensions of a rectangle are doubled, then its area is _____ doubled.

8. The area of a rhombus is _____ equal to one-half the product of the lengths of its diagonals.

9. The ratio of the areas of two triangles having congruent altitudes is _____ equal to the ratio of the lengths of their bases.

10. If the length of the base of one triangle is represented by $2x$ and the length of the base of another triangle is represented by $4x$, the areas of the triangles are _____ equal.

11. If the ratio of the areas of two similar triangles is 1:16, then the length of a side in the larger triangle is _____ 16 times the length of the corresponding side of the smaller triangle.

12. If two equivalent triangles have bases that are not congruent, they _____ have congruent altitudes.

13. Two triangles are _____ equal in area if their corresponding sides are equal in length.

14. If two parallelograms have bases that are unequal in length, their areas are _____ unequal.

15. If two consecutive sides of a rectangle are congruent to two consecutive sides of a parallelogram which is not a rectangle, the area of the rectangle is _____ equal to the area of the parallelogram.

16. A line segment which joins the midpoints of two adjacent sides of a parallelogram _____ cuts off a triangle which is equal in area to one-eighth of the area of the parallelogram.

17. An angle bisector in a scalene triangle _____ divides the triangle into two triangles which are equal in area.

18. A diagonal of a trapezoid _____ divides the trapezoid into two equivalent triangles.

19. If the corresponding sides of two rhombuses are congruent, their areas are _____ equal.

20. If the lengths of two consecutive sides of a parallelogram are unchanged and the measure of the included angle decreases from 90 to 0, then the area of the parallelogram _____ increases.

15. Multiple-Choice Exercises

Write the letter preceding the word or expression that best completes the statement.

1. A median of a triangle divides it into two triangles which are always (*a*) congruent (*b*) similar (*c*) equal in area.

2. The area of a rhombus is equal to (*a*) one-half the sum of the lengths of its diagonals (*b*) one-half the product of the lengths of its diagonals (*c*) the product of the lengths of its diagonals.

3. If the areas of two similar triangles are in the ratio 1:4, then the lengths of any two corresponding sides of these triangles are in the ratio (*a*) 1:4 (*b*) 1:2 (*c*) 1:16.

4. If an angle of a rhombus contains 150° and the length of one side is represented by $2m$, the area is represented by (*a*) $4m^2$ (*b*) $2m^2$ (*c*) $2m$.

5. The diagonals of a parallelogram divide it into four triangles whose common vertex is the intersection of the diagonals. These four triangles are always (*a*) congruent (*b*) similar (*c*) equal in area.

6. If the lengths of the corresponding sides of two similar triangles are in the ratio 1:2, the areas of the two triangles are in the ratio (*a*) 1:4 (*b*) 1:2 (*c*) $1:\sqrt{2}$.

7. Every triangle is divided into two triangles that are equal in area by (*a*) a median   (*b*) the bisector of one of its angles   (*c*) an altitude.

8. A triangle and a parallelogram having the same base are equal in area. The length of the altitude of the triangle is   (*a*) one-fourth the length of the altitude of the parallelogram   (*b*) one-half the length of the altitude of the parallelogram   (*c*) twice the length of the altitude of the parallelogram.

9. If each of the dimensions of a rectangle is multiplied by 3, the area is multiplied by   (*a*) 3   (*b*) 9   (*c*) $\sqrt{3}$.

10. If two adjacent sides of a rectangle are congruent to two adjacent sides of a parallelogram which is not a rectangle, the area of the rectangle is (*a*) greater than the area of the parallelogram   (*b*) equal to the area of the parallelogram   (*c*) smaller than the area of the parallelogram.

11. In two triangles which are equal in area, if the ratio of the lengths of the bases is 2:1, then the ratio of the length of the altitude of the first triangle to the length of the altitude of the second triangle is   (*a*) 2:1   (*b*) 4:1   (*c*) 1:2.

12. If the lengths of two adjacent sides of a triangle are unchanged and the degree measure of the included angle increases from 0 to 90, the area of the triangle   (*a*) increases   (*b*) decreases   (*c*) remains unchanged.

13. If the length of each side of a triangle is multiplied by 2, then the area of the triangle is multiplied by   (*a*) 2   (*b*) 4   (*c*) 6.

14. If the area of a parallelogram is unchanged and the length of the altitude increases, then the length of the base   (*a*) increases   (*b*) decreases (*c*) remains unchanged.

15. If the length of the base of a triangle is doubled and the length of the altitude to the base is halved, then the area of the triangle   (*a*) remains unchanged   (*b*) increases   (*c*) decreases.

16. If two triangles have a common base and their vertices lie on a line parallel to the base, the triangles are always   (*a*) congruent   (*b*) similar (*c*) equivalent.

17. If the area of the larger of two similar triangles is twice the area of the smaller triangle, then the length of each side of the larger triangle is equal to the length of the corresponding side of the smaller triangle multiplied by   (*a*) $\sqrt{2}$ (*b*) 4   (*c*) 2.

18. "The area of a rectangle is equal to the product of the length of its base and the length of its altitude" is   (*a*) a theorem   (*b*) a postulate   (*c*) a corollary.

19. If the length of each diagonal of a square is represented by *d*, then the area of the square is represented by   (*a*) d^2 (*b*) $2d^2$ (*c*) $\frac{1}{2}d^2$.

20. In trapezoid *ABCD*, diagonals $\overline{AC}$ and $\overline{BD}$ intersect at *E*. The length of base $\overline{AB}$ is 20 and the length of base $\overline{DC}$ is 5. The ratio of the area of $\triangle DEC$ to the area of $\triangle AEB$ is   (*a*) 1:2   (*b*) 1:4   (*c*) 1:16.

16. Construction Exercises

An *area-preserving transformation* transforms a given polygon into a polygon which has the same area as the given polygon.

In the following exercises, any transformation that is to be performed is to be an area-preserving transformation. A sample area-preserving transformation is shown in the following boxed problem:

Transform a given triangle ABC into a right triangle one of whose legs will be congruent to $\overline{AB}$.

Solution:

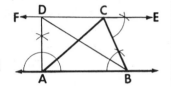

1. Through C, construct $\overleftrightarrow{FE} \parallel \overleftrightarrow{AB}$.
2. At A, construct $\overleftrightarrow{AD} \perp \overleftrightarrow{AB}$.
3. Draw $\overline{DB}$. Triangle BAD is the required right triangle with leg $\overline{AB}$.
4. Since $\triangle ABC$ and BAD have a common base $\overline{AB}$ and their vertices C and D lie on a line parallel to the base, they are equal in area.

---

1. Transform a given triangle ABC whose base is $\overline{BC}$ into an isosceles triangle RBC whose base is also $\overline{BC}$.

2. Transform a given triangle ABC whose base is $\overline{BC}$ into another triangle PBC whose base is $\overline{BC}$ and which has a second side congruent to a given line segment m, the length of m being greater than the length of the altitude from A to side $\overline{BC}$.

3. Transform a given triangle ABC whose base is $\overline{BC}$ into another triangle PBC whose base is $\overline{BC}$ and which has a given angle adjacent to $\overline{BC}$.

4. Transform a given parallelogram $ABCD$ whose base is $\overline{AB}$ into a rectangle whose base is $\overline{AB}$.

5. Transform a given parallelogram $ABCD$ whose base is $\overline{AB}$ into a parallelogram whose base is $\overline{AB}$ and which contains a 30° angle.

6. Transform a given parallelogram $ABCD$ whose base is $\overline{AB}$ into a rhombus whose base is $\overline{AB}$.

7. Transform a given triangle ABC into an equivalent isosceles triangle which will have a given line segment m as its base.

8. Using the diameter $\overline{AB}$ of the semicircle as a base, inscribe in the semicircle a triangle whose area shall be greater than the area of any other triangle that can be inscribed in the semicircle.

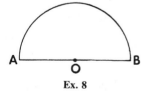

Ex. 8

9. Transform a quadrilateral into a triangle.

10. Transform a parallelogram into a triangle.

11. Transform a rectangle into a triangle.

12. Transform a trapezoid into a triangle.

13. *a.* Transform a quadrilateral into a triangle.
    b. Transform the triangle found in part *a* into an isosceles triangle.

14. Transform a trapezoid into an isosceles triangle.

15. Construct a right triangle equal in area to a given right triangle and having a given line segment *m* as one of its legs.

16. Construct an isosceles triangle which will have a given line segment *m* as its base and which will be equal in area to a given parallelogram *ABCD*.

17. Construct a rectangle which will have a given line segment *m* as its base and which will be equal in area to a given parallelogram *ABCD*.

18. Given a right triangle whose legs are line segments *a* and *b*, transform the triangle into a rectangle whose base is a given line segment *m*.

19. Transform a given rectangle into a square.

20. Transform a given parallelogram into a square.

21. Construct one side of a square whose area will be equal to the area of a given triangle.

22. Construct a square equal in area to twice the area of a given triangle.

23. Construct a square equal in area to one-half the area of a given triangle.

24. It is required to construct a square equal in area to a rhombus whose diagonals are the given line segments of length *d* and *d'*. (*a*) Representing the length of a side of the square by *x*, write an equation showing the relationship between *x*, *d*, and *d'*. (*b*) Construct *x*. (*c*) Construct the required square.

Ex. 24

25. Construct a square equal in area to the sum of the areas of two given squares.

26. Construct a square equal in area to the difference of the areas of two given squares.

27. Construct a triangle similar to two given similar triangles and equal in area to the sum of the areas of the two given triangles.

28. Construct a triangle similar to a given triangle and having twice the area of the given triangle.

CHAPTER VIII

Regular Polygons and the Circle

1. Fundamental Relationships in Regular Polygons

Let us recall some of the things we have already learned about regular polygons.

A polygon is a *regular polygon* if all its sides are congruent and all its angles are congruent, that is, if it is equilateral and equiangular.

In polygon $ABCDEF$ (Fig. 8–1), if $\overline{AB} \cong \overline{BC} \cong \overline{CD} \cong \overline{DE} \cong \overline{EF} \cong \overline{FA}$ and $\angle A \cong \angle B \cong \angle C \cong \angle D \cong \angle E \cong \angle F$, then polygon $ABCDEF$ is a regular polygon.

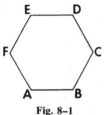

Fig. 8–1

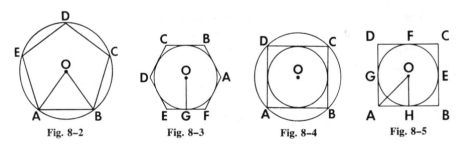

| Fig. 8–2 | Fig. 8–3 | Fig. 8–4 | Fig. 8–5 |

We have learned that a *circle is circumscribed about a polygon* if the circle passes through every vertex of the polygon.

In Fig. 8–2, circle O is circumscribed about polygon $ABCDE$. We also say that polygon $ABCDE$ is *inscribed* in circle O.

Theorem 111. A circle may be circumscribed about any regular polygon.

In Fig. 8–2, if $ABCDE$ is a regular polygon, then a circle whose center is at O can be circumscribed about the polygon.

Definition. A *radius of a regular polygon* is a radius of the circumscribed circle.

In Fig. 8-2, a radius of regular polygon *ABCDE* is $\overline{OA}$. Since radii of the same circle are congruent, the radii of a regular polygon are congruent. Thus, $\overline{OA} \cong \overline{OB}$.

Definition. A *central angle of a regular polygon* is an angle formed by two radii of the polygon drawn to consecutive vertices of the polygon.

In Fig. 8-2, angle *AOB* is a central angle of regular polygon *ABCDE*.

We have learned that a *circle is inscribed in a polygon* if every side of the polygon is tangent to the circle.

In Fig. 8-3, circle *O* is inscribed in polygon *ABCDEF*. We also say that polygon *ABCDEF* is circumscribed about circle *O*.

Theorem 112. A circle may be inscribed in any regular polygon.

In Fig. 8-3, if *ABCDEF* is a regular polygon, then a circle whose center is at *O* can be inscribed in the polygon.

Definition. An *apothem of a regular polygon* is a radius of its inscribed circle.

In regular polygon *ABCDEF* (Fig. 8-3), $\overline{OG}$ is the apothem. Since radii of the same circle are congruent, the apothems of a regular polygon are congruent.

Definition. The *center of a regular polygon* is the common center of the circumscribed and inscribed circles.

In Fig. 8-4, if *O* is the common center of the circles circumscribed about and inscribed in regular polygon *ABCD*, then *O* is the center of regular polygon *ABCD*.

Theorem 113. An apothem of a regular polygon is the perpendicular bisector of the side of the polygon to which it is drawn.

In Fig. 8-5, if $\overline{OH}$ is an apothem of regular polygon *ABCD*, then $\overline{OH}$ is perpendicular to $\overline{AB}$ and $\overline{OH}$ bisects $\overline{AB}$.

Theorem 114. A radius of a regular polygon bisects the angle of the polygon to whose vertex it is drawn.

In Fig. 8-5, $\overline{OA}$, a radius of regular polygon *ABCD*, bisects angle *A*, the angle of the polygon to whose vertex it is drawn.

Theorem 115. The measure of each central angle of a regular polygon of *n* sides is $\dfrac{360}{n}$.

Theorem 116. **The measure of each interior angle of a regular polygon of** *n* sides is $\dfrac{(n-2)180}{n}$.

Theorem 117. **The measure of each exterior angle of a regular polygon of** *n* sides is $\dfrac{360}{n}$.

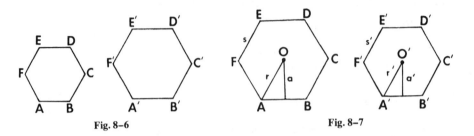

Fig. 8-6   Fig. 8-7

Theorem 118. **Regular polygons of the same number of sides are similar.**

If regular polygon *ABC* . . . and regular polygon *A'B'C'* . . . have the same number of sides, polygon *ABC* . . . ~ polygon *A'B'C'*. . . .

Note that "polygon *ABC* . . ." is used to represent an *n*-gon, which is a polygon with *n* sides.

In Fig. 8–6, for example, regular hexagon *ABCDEF* ~ regular hexagon *A'B'C'D'E'F'*.

Theorem 119. **The ratio of the perimeters of regular polygons of the same number of sides is equal to the ratio of the lengths of their sides, or the ratio of the lengths of their radii, or the ratio of the lengths of their apothems.**

In Fig. 8–7, if regular polygon *ABCDEF* and regular polygon *A'B'C'D'E'F'* have the same number of sides, and their perimeters are represented by *p* and *p'*, then

$$\frac{p}{p'} = \frac{s}{s'} \quad \text{and} \quad \frac{p}{p'} = \frac{r}{r'} \quad \text{and} \quad \frac{p}{p'} = \frac{a}{a'}$$

KEEP IN MIND

In proving theorems and relationships involving regular polygons, it may be helpful to circumscribe a circle about the regular polygon or to inscribe a circle in the regular polygon.

MODEL PROBLEMS

1. If the length of the apothem of a regular pentagon is 5 inches, find the length of the diameter of the circle that is inscribed in the regular pentagon.

Solution:

1. Since the apothem of regular pentagon $ABCDE$ is the radius of the inscribed circle, then $\overline{OF}$, the radius of circle O, is 5 inches in length.

2. The length of the diameter of circle $O = 2 \times OF = 2(5) = 10$.

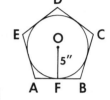

Answer: The length of the diameter of the inscribed circle is 10 inches.

2. For a regular polygon of six sides, find the number of degrees contained in (*a*) each central angle (*b*) each interior angle (*c*) each exterior angle.

Solution:

a. 1. The measure of a central angle of a regular polygon of n sides $= \dfrac{360}{n}$.

   2. $m\angle AOB = \dfrac{360}{6} = 60.$ $n = 6.$

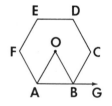

Answer: Each central angle contains 60°.

b. 1. The measure of an interior angle of a regular polygon of n sides $= \dfrac{(n-2)180}{n}$.

   2. The measure of interior angle $BCD = \dfrac{(6-2)180}{6} = \dfrac{4(180)}{6} = 120.$

Answer: Each interior angle contains 120°.

c. 1. The measure of an exterior angle of a regular polygon of n sides $= \dfrac{360}{n}$.

   2. The measure of exterior angle $CBG = \dfrac{360}{6} = 60.$

Answer: Each exterior angle contains 60°.

3. A regular hexagon is inscribed in a circle. If the length of the radius of the circle is 7 in., find the perimeter of the hexagon.

Solution:

1. Since $ABCDEF$ is a regular hexagon, the measure of central $\angle AOB = \dfrac{360}{6} = 60$.

2. Since $\overline{OA} \cong \overline{OB}$, $m\angle OAB = m\angle OBA = 60$.

3. Since $\triangle AOB$ is equiangular, $\triangle AOB$ is also equilateral.

4. Since the length of radius $\overline{OA}$ is 7 in., the length of side $\overline{AB}$ of the regular hexagon is 7 in.

5. Perimeter of regular hexagon $ABCDEF = 6 \times AB = 6 \times 7 = 42$.

Answer: Perimeter of the regular hexagon = 42 inches.

4. In regular polygon $ABCDE$, diagonals $\overline{AC}$ and $\overline{BD}$ intersect at F. *Prove: $AF \times FC = BF \times FD$.*

Given: $ABCDE$ is a regular polygon with diagonals $\overline{AC}$ and $\overline{BD}$ intersecting at F.

To prove: $AF \times FC = BF \times FD$.

Plan: Circumscribe circle O about regular polygon $ABCDE$. Prove that $AF \times FC = BF \times FD$ by showing that the product of the lengths of the segments of chord $\overline{AC}$ equals the product of the lengths of the segments of chord $\overline{BD}$.

Proof:

Statements	Reasons
1. $ABCDE$ is a regular polygon with diagonals $\overline{AC}$ and $\overline{BD}$ intersecting at F.	1. Given.
2. Circumscribe circle O about regular polygon $ABCDE$.	2. A circle may be circumscribed about any regular polygon.
3. In $\odot O, AF \times FC = BF \times FD$.	3. If two chords intersect inside a circle, the product of the lengths of the segments of one chord equals the product of the lengths of the segments of the other chord.

EXERCISES

1. Name the regular polygon that is   (*a*) a triangle   (*b*) a quadrilateral.
2. Is a rectangle a regular polygon? Why?
3. Is a rhombus a regular polygon? Why?
4. Find the measure of each central angle of a regular polygon which has the given number of sides:
   a. 3   *b.* 4   *c.* 5   *d.* 6   *e.* 8   *f.* 10
5. Find the number of degrees contained in each interior angle of a regular:
   a. triangle   *b.* quadrilateral   *c.* hexagon
   d. pentagon   *e.* decagon   *f.* octagon
6. Find the number of degrees contained in each exterior angle of a regular:
   a. quadrilateral   *b.* triangle   *c.* pentagon
   d. hexagon   *e.* octagon   *f.* decagon
7. Can an angle of 50° be a central angle of a regular polygon? Why?
8. Can an angle of 35° be an exterior angle of a regular polygon? Why?
9. If a regular hexagon is inscribed in a circle and a tangent to the circle is drawn at one of the vertices, find the number of degrees contained in the acute angle formed by the tangent and a side of the hexagon.
10. If the length of each side of a regular hexagon is represented by $2x$, represent the perimeter in terms of x.
11. The formula for the perimeter p of a regular polygon in terms of the number of sides n and the length of each side s is $p =$ _____ .
12. A regular hexagon is inscribed in a circle. If the radius of the circle is 4 inches in length, a side of the hexagon is _____ inches in length.
13. A regular hexagon is inscribed in a circle. If the length of the radius of the circle is 2 inches, the perimeter of the hexagon is _____ inches.
14. The perimeter of a regular hexagon is 24. Find the length of the diameter of the circle which circumscribes this hexagon.
15. A regular hexagon is inscribed in a circle. If the length of the radius of the circle is represented by r, represent the perimeter of the hexagon in terms of r.
16. If the length of the apothem of a regular polygon is 8, what is the length of the diameter of the inscribed circle?
17. An equilateral triangle is inscribed in a circle whose radius is 8 in. long. Find the length of its apothem.
18. A square is inscribed in a circle whose radius is 12 in. long. Find the length of its apothem. [Answer may be left in radical form.]
19. A regular hexagon is inscribed in a circle the length of whose radius is 4. Find the length of its apothem. [Answer may be left in radical form.]

20. Find the ratio of the length of the apothem of a square to the length of a side of the square.
21. If the length of an apothem of a regular hexagon is $6\sqrt{3}$, find the length of a side of the hexagon.
22. The length of the apothem of a regular hexagon is represented by $4x\sqrt{3}$. Represent the perimeter of the hexagon in terms of x.
23. Two regular hexagons have perimeters of 60 and 90 inches. Find the ratio of the lengths of their apothems.
24. The ratio of the lengths of the apothems of two regular pentagons is 1:3. The perimeter of the larger polygon is how many times the perimeter of the smaller polygon?
25. *Prove:* If a circle is divided into three congruent arcs, the chords of these arcs form an inscribed regular polygon.
26. *Prove:* The length of a radius of the circle inscribed in an equilateral triangle is one-third the length of an altitude of the triangle.
27. *Prove:* An interior angle of a regular polygon is supplementary to a central angle of the polygon.
28. *Prove:* If two diagonals are drawn from a vertex of a regular pentagon, they trisect the angle at that vertex of the pentagon.
29. $ABCDE$ is a regular pentagon with diagonals $\overline{AC}$, $\overline{AD}$, and $\overline{BD}$ drawn. Prove that triangles ABD and DCA are congruent.
30. *Prove:* In regular hexagon $ABCDEF$, diagonal $\overline{AD}$ is a diameter of the circumscribed circle.
31. *Prove:* In a regular pentagon, if two diagonals intersect in the interior, the longer segment of each diagonal is congruent to a side of the pentagon.
32. *Prove:* If diagonals $\overline{EB}$ and $\overline{AD}$ of regular pentagon $ABCDE$ intersect at F, $FBCD$ is a rhombus.
33. *Prove:* In regular hexagon $ABCDEF$, if diagonals $\overline{AC}$ and $\overline{DF}$ are drawn, quadrilateral $ACDF$ is a rectangle.
34. *Prove:* In regular hexagon $ABCDEF$, if diagonals $\overline{AD}$ and $\overline{CE}$ intersect at G, then $AG \times GD = CG \times GE$.
35. In a quadrilateral, one of whose angles is a right angle, the perimeter is 80. The lengths of the sides are represented by $4x$, $5x - 5$, $3x + 5$, and $6x - 10$. (*a*) Find the length of each side of the quadrilateral. (*b*) Prove that the quadrilateral is a regular polygon.
36. In an equilateral pentagon, the measures of the angles are represented by $3x - 12$, $x + 68$, $4x - 52$, $2x + 28$, and $5x - 92$. (*a*) Find the measure of each angle of the pentagon. (*b*) Prove that the polygon is a regular polygon.
37. If the length of a side of a regular pentagon is represented by $2s$, the

length of the apothem by r, and the length of the radius of the circumscribed circle by R, prove:

a. $r = R \cos 36°$ b. $s = r \tan 36°$ c. $s = R \sin 36°$

38. If the length of a side of a regular decagon is represented by s, the length of the apothem by r, and the length of the radius of the circumscribed circle by R, prove:

a. $r = R \cos 18°$ b. $s = 2r \tan 18°$ c. $s = 2R \sin 18°$

39. R represents the length of the radius of a circle circumscribed about a regular decagon. Prove that the perimeter of the decagon is represented by $20R \sin 18°$.

40. In the figure, $ABCDE$ is a regular pentagon inscribed in the circle. Diagonals $\overline{AC}$, $\overline{AD}$, $\overline{BD}$, $\overline{BE}$, and $\overline{CE}$ are drawn, determining points V, W, X, Y, and Z. Prove that polygon $VWXYZ$ is a regular pentagon.

Ex. 40

2. The Area of a Regular Polygon

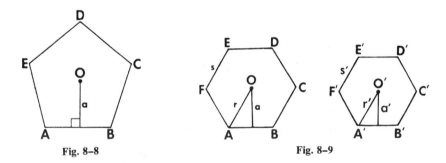

Fig. 8–8   Fig. 8–9

Theorem 120. **The area of a regular polygon is equal to one-half the product of its perimeter and the length of its apothem.**

[The proof for this theorem appears on pages 615–616.]

In Fig. 8–8, if $ABCDE$ is a regular polygon the length of whose apothem is represented by a, whose perimeter is represented by p, and whose area is represented by A, then the area of polygon $ABCDE$ is given by the formula $A = \frac{1}{2}ap$.

NOTE. In the statement of theorem 120, we might have used the word *apothem* to refer to the "length of its apothem," which is a number. In the future, we may use this abbreviated language in situations where there can be no confusion.

Theorem 121. The ratio of the areas of regular polygons of the same number of sides is equal to the ratio of the squares of the lengths of their sides, or the squares of the lengths of their radii, or the squares of the lengths of their apothems.

In Fig. 8–9, if regular polygons $ABCDEF$ and $A'B'C'D'E'F'$ have the same number of sides and their areas are represented by A and A', then

$$\frac{A}{A'} = \frac{(s)^2}{(s')^2} \quad \text{and} \quad \frac{A}{A'} = \frac{(r)^2}{(r')^2} \quad \text{and} \quad \frac{A}{A'} = \frac{(a)^2}{(a')^2}$$

MODEL PROBLEMS

1. If the length of a side of a regular polygon of 12 sides is represented by s and the length of its apothem is represented by a, represent the area of the polygon, A, in terms of a and s.

Solution:

1. Since the regular polygon has 12 sides, the perimeter, $p = 12s$.

2. $A = \frac{1}{2}ap = \frac{1}{2}(a)(12s) = 6as$.

Answer: Area $= 6as$.

2. A side of a regular hexagon is 8 inches in length.
   a. Find the length of the apothem of the hexagon.
   b. Find the area of the hexagon. [Answers may be left in radical form.]

Solution:

a. 1. Triangle AOB is an equilateral triangle.

2. The apothem whose length is represented by a is an altitude in the equilateral triangle.

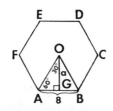

3. $a = \dfrac{\text{length of side}}{2}\sqrt{3} = \dfrac{8}{2}\sqrt{3} = 4\sqrt{3}$.

Answer: Apothem $= 4\sqrt{3}$ in.

b. 1. Perimeter of the hexagon, $p = 6 \times 8 = 48$.

2. Area of the hexagon, $A = \frac{1}{2}ap$

3. $\qquad A = \frac{1}{2}(4\sqrt{3})(48)$

4. $\qquad A = (4\sqrt{3})(24)$

5. $\qquad A = 96\sqrt{3}$

Answer: Area $= 96\sqrt{3}$ sq. in.

3. A side of a regular pentagon is 20 inches in length.

a. Find to the *nearest tenth of an inch* the length of the apothem of the pentagon.

b. Using the result obtained in answer to *a*, find to the *nearest ten square inches* the area of the pentagon.

Solution:

a. 1. The measure of central angle $AOB = \dfrac{360}{n}$ $n = 5$.

2. $m\angle AOB = \dfrac{360}{5} = 72$

3. $m\angle AOF = \frac{1}{2}(m\angle AOB) = \frac{1}{2}(72) = 36.$

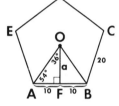

4. $m\angle OAF = 90 - m\angle AOF = 90 - 36 = 54.$

5. $\tan \angle OAF = \dfrac{\text{length of leg opposite } \angle OAF}{\text{length of leg adjacent to } \angle OAF}$

6. $\tan 54° = \dfrac{a}{10}$

7. $1.3764 = \dfrac{a}{10}$

8. $a = 10(1.3764)$

9. $a = 13.764$

10. $a = 13.8$, to the nearest tenth.

Answer: Apothem = 13.8 in.

b. 1. $p = 5(20) = 100$

2. $A = \frac{1}{2}ap$

3. $A = \frac{1}{2}(13.8)(100)$

4. $A = 690$, to the nearest ten.

Answer: Area = 690 sq. in.

NOTE. It is also possible to find the area of $\triangle AOB$ and multiply the result by 5 in order to find the area of the pentagon.

EXERCISES

1. The area K of a regular polygon the length of whose apothem is represented by a and the length of whose perimeter is represented by p is given by the formula $K = $ _____ .

2. A regular polygon has a side whose length is represented by s and an apothem whose length is represented by a. Represent its area in terms of s and a if the polygon is a:
   a. square   *b.* hexagon   *c.* decagon   *d.* pentagon

3. The perimeter of a regular polygon is 24. If its apothem is 3, then its area is _____.

4. The area of a regular polygon is 144 and its perimeter is 48. Find its apothem.

5. Find the apothem and the area of a square the length of whose side is:
   a. 4   *b.* 6   *c.* 8   *d.* 5   *e.* 9   *f.* $4\sqrt{2}$

6. Find, in radical form, the length of the apothem and the area of a regular hexagon the length of whose side is:
   a. 2   *b.* 4   *c.* 6   *d.* 10   *e.* 5   *f.* 1

7. Find, in radical form, the apothem and the area of an equilateral triangle whose side is 12.

8. The length of a side of a regular polygon of 10 sides is 6 inches.   (*a*) Find to the *nearest tenth of an inch* the length of an apothem of the polygon.   (*b*) Using the result obtained in answer to *a*, find the area of the polygon to the *nearest ten square inches.*

9. The length of a side of a regular pentagon is 8. Find its area to the *nearest integer.*

10. The perimeter of a regular pentagon is 50 inches. Find its area to the *nearest ten square inches.*

11. The length of a diameter of a circle is 20 inches.   (*a*) Find the length of the apothem and the area of a regular inscribed hexagon.   (*b*) Find the length of a side and the area of an inscribed equilateral triangle. [Both answers may be left in radical form.]

12. Find the apothem and the area of an equilateral triangle which is circumscribed about a circle whose radius is 10. [Answer may be left in radical form.]

13. Find the apothem and the area of a regular hexagon which is circumscribed about a circle whose radius is 6. [Answer may be left in radical form.]

14. A regular pentagon is circumscribed about a circle whose radius is 10.   (*a*) Find a side of the pentagon to the *nearest tenth.*   (*b*) Using the result obtained in answer to *a*, find the area of the pentagon to the *nearest integer.*

15. A regular decagon (10 sides) whose side is 18 inches in length is inscribed in a circle.   (*a*) Find to the *nearest tenth of an inch* the apothem of the decagon.   (*b*) Using the result obtained in answer to *a*, find to the *nearest square inch* the area of the decagon.

16. (*a*) If r represents the length of the radius of a circle circumscribed about

a regular pentagon, show that the length of an apothem of the pentagon is equal to $r \cos 36°$ and its perimeter is equal to $10r \sin 36°$. (*b*) Find to the *nearest integer* the length of the apothem and the perimeter of the pentagon when $r = 4$. (*c*) Using the results found in answer to *b*, find the area of the pentagon.

17. The area of a regular hexagon is $54\sqrt{3}$. Find the length of an altitude of an equilateral triangle that has its perimeter equal to that of the hexagon.

18. An equilateral triangle is inscribed in a circle the length of whose radius is represented by r. (*a*) Show that the length of an apothem of the equilateral triangle is represented by $\frac{1}{2}r$. (*b*) Show that the area of the equilateral triangle is represented by $\frac{3}{4}r^2\sqrt{3}$.

19. A square is inscribed in a circle of radius r. (*a*) Show that the apothem of the square is represented by $\frac{1}{2}r\sqrt{2}$. (*b*) Show that the area of the square is represented by $2r^2$.

20. Find the length of a side of a regular hexagon whose area is:
a. $6\sqrt{3}$ *b.* $54\sqrt{3}$ *c.* $150\sqrt{3}$ *d.* $216\sqrt{3}$ *e.* $\frac{27}{2}\sqrt{3}$

21. *Prove:* The area of the square circumscribed about a circle equals twice the area of the square inscribed in the circle.

22. *Prove:* The area of a regular hexagon inscribed in a circle is twice the area of an equilateral triangle inscribed in the same circle.

23. The radii of two regular hexagons are 8 and 2. Find the ratio of the areas of the two polygons.

24. The areas of two regular polygons which have the same number of sides are 900 sq. in. and 100 sq. in. Find the ratio of their apothems.

25. The area of the larger of two regular polygons which have the same number of sides is 16 times the area of the smaller polygon. Find the ratio of the lengths of the radii of the two polygons.

3. The Circumference of a Circle

Observe in Fig. 8–10 that as the number of sides of a regular polygon inscribed in a circle is increased from 3 to 6 to 12 to 24, the polygon resembles the circle more and more. Yet, no matter how large the number of sides of the polygon may become, the polygon never really becomes a circle.

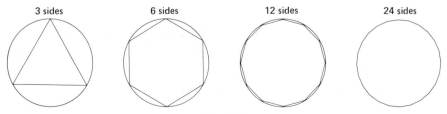

Fig. 8–10

As the number of sides of the regular polygon is increased, the perimeter of the polygon approaches the perimeter of the circle, which is called the *circumference* of the circle.

Definition. The *circumference* of a circle is the length of the circle expressed in linear units (inches or feet).

If the perimeter of each circle in Fig. 8–10 is 3 inches, we say that the circumference of each circle is 3 inches.

In light of the previous discussion, it appears reasonable to accept the following postulate:

Postulate 45. When the number of sides of a regular polygon which is inscribed in a circle increases without bound, the perimeter of the polygon approaches the circumference of the circle and may be used as an approximation of the circumference of the circle.

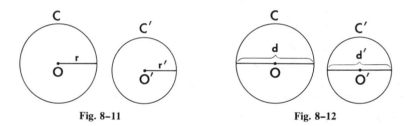

Fig. 8–11   Fig. 8–12

Theorem 122. The ratio of the circumferences of two circles is equal to the ratio of the lengths of their radii.

In circles O and O' (Fig. 8–11), whose circumferences are represented by C and C' and the lengths of whose radii are represented by r and r', $\dfrac{C}{C'} = \dfrac{r}{r'}$.

Corollary T122–1. The ratio of the circumferences of two circles is equal to the ratio of the lengths of their diameters.

In circles O and O' (Fig. 8–12), whose circumferences are represented by C and C' and the lengths of whose diameters are represented by d and d', $\dfrac{C}{C'} = \dfrac{d}{d'}$.

Corollary T122–2. The ratio of the circumference of any circle to the length of its diameter is equal to the ratio of the circumference of any other circle to the length of its diameter.

In the two circles pictured in Fig. 8–12, $\dfrac{C}{d} = \dfrac{C'}{d'}$.

Since the ratio of the circumference of a circle to the length of its diameter is always the same no matter what the size of the circle may be, we say that this ratio is a *constant*. This constant is represented by the Greek letter π, read "pi." Therefore, we have:

$$\frac{C}{d} = \pi$$

The number π is an irrational number which cannot be expressed exactly as an integer, a terminating decimal, or a repeating decimal. The approximate value of π can be expressed to any desired degree of accuracy. The most frequently used approximate values of π are: 3.1, 3.14, 3.1416, $3\frac{1}{7}$, and $\frac{22}{7}$.

Corollary T122–3. **The circumference, C, of a circle the length of whose diameter is represented by d and the length of whose radius is represented by r is given by the formula:**

$$C = \pi d \quad \text{or} \quad C = 2\pi r$$

MODEL PROBLEMS

1. Find the circumference of a circle whose radius is 21 in. [Use $\pi = \frac{22}{7}$.]

Solution:

1. $C = 2\pi r \qquad r = 21, \pi = \frac{22}{7}$.

2. $C = 2(\frac{22}{7})(21)$

3. $C = 132$

Answer: Circumference = 132 in.

2. Find the diameter of a circle whose circumference is 628 ft. [Use $\pi = 3.14$.]

Solution:

1. $\qquad C = \pi d \qquad C = 628, \pi = 3.14$.

2. $\qquad 628 = 3.14\,d$

3. $62,800 = 314\,d \qquad \mathbf{M}_{100}$

4. $\qquad 200 = d$

Answer: Diameter = 200 ft.

EXERCISES

1. In any circle, what is the ratio of the circumference to the diameter exactly equal to?

2. The formula for the circumference C of a circle in terms of its radius r is $C = $ _____ .

3. Represent, in terms of x, the circumference of a circle whose radius is represented by:
   a. x *b.* $2x$ *c.* $3x$ *d.* $4x$ *e.* $2x + 1$

4. Represent, in terms of x, the circumference of a circle whose diameter is represented by:
   a. $2x$ *b.* $4x$ *c.* x *d.* $3x$ *e.* $x + 3$

5. Use $\pi = \frac{22}{7}$ or 3.14 to find the circumference of a circle in which:
   a. $r = 14$ *b.* $r = 20$ *c.* $r = 3.5$ *d.* $d = 28$ *e.* $d = 60$

6. Find the number of inches in the circumference of a circle in which the longest chord that can be drawn measures 16 inches.

7. Find the number of miles in the length of the equator if the radius of the earth is taken as 4000 miles. $[\pi = 3.14]$

8. A wagon wheel has a radius of 2.8 feet. How many feet will it travel if it makes 50 revolutions?

9. A circle is inscribed in a square whose side is 8. Find the circumference of the circle in terms of π.

10. If the circumference of a circle is 10π, find its radius.

11. Find the diameter of a circle whose circumference is 8π.

12. Find, in terms of π, the circumference of a circle which is circumscribed about a square whose side is:
    a. 4 in.   *b.* 5 in.   *c.* 12 in.

13. Find the radius and diameter of a circle whose circumference is:
    a. 40π *b.* 3.5π *c.* 44   *d.* 15.7   *e.* 25

14. The circumference of a circle is increased from 30π inches to 50π inches. By how many inches is the length of the radius *increased?*

15. If the radius of a circle is increased by x, the circumference of the circle is increased by   *(a)* x *(b)* $2x$ *(c)* $2\pi x$.

16. If the circumference of a circle is 88 inches, the radius of the circle is _____ inches. $[\pi = \frac{22}{7}]$

17. Find the radius of a pipe if the circumference of the pipe is 12.56 ft.

18. Represent, in terms of x, the diameter of a circle whose circumference is represented by:
    a. $2x\pi$ *b.* $4x\pi$ *c.* $10\pi x$ *d.* $3x\pi$ *e.* $5\pi x$

19. Represent, in terms of x, the radius of a circle whose circumference is represented by:
    a. $2\pi x$ *b.* $6x\pi$ *c.* $8\pi x$ *d.* $3x\pi$ *e.* $7\pi x$

20. Find the number of inches in the diagonal of a square inscribed in a circle whose circumference is:
    a. 12π in.   *b.* 9π in.   *c.* 44 ft.

21. The circumference of a circle is 18π. Find the perimeter of a regular hexagon inscribed in this circle.

22. Points *L*, *M*, and *N* lie on a circle with *M* the midpoint of the major arc $\overset{\frown}{LN}$. The diameter through *M* intersects chord $\overline{LN}$ at *R* and minor arc $\overset{\frown}{LN}$ at *P*. The length of chord $\overline{LN}$ is 4 inches and $\overline{MR}$ is 3 inches longer than $\overline{RP}$.   (*a*) If the length of $\overline{RP}$ is represented by *x*, represent the length of $\overline{MR}$ in terms of *x*.   (*b*) Find the length of $\overline{RP}$.   (*c*) Find the circumference of the circle in terms of π.

23. Quadrilateral *QRST* is inscribed in a circle and the degree measures of arcs $\overset{\frown}{RS}$, $\overset{\frown}{ST}$, $\overset{\frown}{TQ}$, and $\overset{\frown}{QR}$ are represented by $x + 30$, $2x$, $x + 10$, and $4x - 80$ respectively.   (*a*) Find the number of degrees contained in each of the four arcs.   (*b*) If $\overline{RT}$ is drawn, find the number of degrees contained in angle *QRT*.   (*c*) If the length of chord $\overline{QT}$ is 14, find the circumference of the circle. $[\pi = \frac{22}{7}]$

24. Points *A*, *B*, and *C* lie on a circle with *B* the midpoint of the major arc $\overset{\frown}{AC}$. The diameter through *B* intersects chord $\overline{AC}$ at *D* and minor arc $\overset{\frown}{AC}$ at *E*. $\overline{AC}$ is 8 inches in length, and $\overline{BD}$ is 6 inches longer than $\overline{DE}$.
    a. If the length of $\overline{DE}$ is represented by *x*, express the length of $\overline{BD}$ in terms of *x*.
    b. Which of the following equations can be used to find the length of $\overline{DE}$?
       (1) $2x + 6 = 8$ (2) $x^2 + 6x = 16$ (3) $x^2 + 6x = 8$
    c. Find the length of $\overline{DE}$.
    d. Find the circumference of the circle. [Answer may be left in terms of π.]

25. The circumference of a circle is equal to the perimeter of a square the length of whose side is represented by *s*. Show that the length of the radius of this circle is equal to $\dfrac{2s}{\pi}$.

4. Finding the Length of an Arc

The *length of an arc* (Fig. 8–13), which is the number of linear units it contains, is frequently confused with the number of arc degrees it contains. To say that an arc $\overset{\frown}{AB}$ contains 90 arc degrees indicates that the circle has been divided into 360 congruent parts

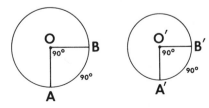

Fig. 8–13

each of which is called an *arc degree* and that arc $\overset{\frown}{AB}$ contains 90 of these arc degrees. Such an arc would be $\frac{90}{360}$ or one-fourth of the circle. In a large circle, an arc of 90° would have a greater length than an arc of 90° in a smaller circle. In circles O and O', $\overset{\frown}{AB}$ and $\overset{\frown}{A'B'}$ each contain 90°, yet $\overset{\frown}{AB}$ has a greater length than $\overset{\frown}{A'B'}$.

Theorem 123. In a circle whose circumference is represented by C, the length of an arc which contains $n°$, or whose central angle contains $n°$, is given by the formula:

$$\frac{\textbf{length of an arc}}{\textbf{circumference of the circle}} = \frac{\boldsymbol{n}}{\textbf{360}} \quad \text{or} \quad \textbf{length of an arc} = \frac{\boldsymbol{n}}{\textbf{360}} \times \boldsymbol{C}$$

Corollary T123–1. In a circle the length of whose radius is represented by r, the length of an arc which contains $n°$, or whose central angle contains $n°$, is given by the formula:

$$\frac{\textbf{length of an arc}}{\textbf{2}\boldsymbol{\pi r}} = \frac{\boldsymbol{n}}{\textbf{360}} \quad \text{or} \quad \textbf{length of an arc} = \frac{\boldsymbol{n}}{\textbf{360}} \times \textbf{2}\boldsymbol{\pi r}$$

MODEL PROBLEMS ╌╌╌╌╌╌╌╌╌╌╌╌╌╌╌╌╌╌

1. Find to the *nearest tenth of an inch* the length of an arc of 60° in a circle whose radius is 12 in.

Solution:

Let l = length of the arc.

Method 1	Method 2
1. $\dfrac{\text{length of arc}}{\text{circumference of circle}} = \dfrac{n}{360}$	1. $l = \dfrac{n}{360} \times 2\pi r$
2. $\dfrac{l}{2\pi r} = \dfrac{60}{360} \quad n = 60.$ $r = 12.$	2. $l = \dfrac{60}{360} \times 2\pi(12)$
3. $\dfrac{l}{24\pi} = \dfrac{1}{6}$	
4. $6l = 24\pi$	
5. $l = 4\pi \qquad$ Use $\pi = 3.14.$	3. $l = \frac{1}{6} \times 24\pi$
6. $l = 4(3.14) = 12.56$	4. $l = 4\pi$
7. $l = 12.6$ to the nearest tenth	5. $l = 4(3.14) = 12.56$
	6. $l = 12.6$ to the nearest tenth

Answer: Length of arc = 12.6 in. to the nearest tenth of an inch.

2. In a circle whose radius is 8 inches, find the number of degrees contained in the central angle of an arc whose length is 2π inches.

Solution:

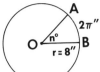

1. $\dfrac{\text{length of arc}}{\text{circumference of circle}} = \dfrac{n}{360}$.

2. Since $r = 8$, circumference of circle $= 2(\pi)(8) = 16\pi$.

3. $\dfrac{2\pi}{16\pi} = \dfrac{n}{360}$

4. $\dfrac{1}{8} = \dfrac{n}{360}$

5. $8n = 360$

6. $n = 45$

Answer: Central angle contains $45°$.

EXERCISES

1. In a circle whose circumference is 36 inches, find the length of an arc which contains:
   a. $30°$ *b.* $60°$ *c.* $90°$ *d.* $240°$ *e.* $45°$

2. Find the circumference of a circle if the length of an arc of the circle which contains $90°$ is 5 inches.

3. An arc of a circle contains $72°$ and is 10 inches long. Find the circumference of the circle.

4. In a circle whose radius is 12, find the length of an arc whose central angle contains:
   a. $60°$ *b.* $90°$ *c.* $150°$ *d.* $240°$ *e.* $50°$

5. In a circle whose radius is 18, a central angle measures $80°$. Find the length of the arc which the central angle intercepts.

6. In a circle whose circumference is 24 in., find the measure of the central angle of an arc whose length is 8 in.

7. In a circle whose radius is 16, find the measure of the central angle of an arc whose length is
   a. 4π *b.* 8π *c.* 12π *d.* 16π *e.* 20π

8. Find the radius of a circle in which an arc which contains $120°$ has a length of 6π in.

9. Find the radius of a circle in which an arc which contains $60°$ has the length of:
   a. 3π *b.* 5π *c.* 6π *d.* 8π *e.* 12π

10. Find the length of an arc intercepted by a side of a regular hexagon inscribed in a circle whose radius is 18.

11. In a circle whose radius is 4, a chord is drawn perpendicular to one radius and bisecting that radius. (*a*) How many degrees are contained in the minor arc of this chord? (*b*) Find the length of this arc to the *nearest integer*. [$\pi = 3.14$] (*c*) Find the length of the chord to the *nearest integer*.

12. Tangents $\overline{PA}$ and $\overline{PB}$ are drawn to a circle from an external point P. $m\angle BPA = 80$ and $PA = 21$. (*a*) Find the number of degrees contained in minor arc $\widehat{AB}$. (*b*) Find to the *nearest tenth* the radius of the circle. (*c*) Find to the *nearest integer* the length of minor arc $\widehat{AB}$. [$\pi = 3.14$]

13. A belt moves over two wheels which have the same size and crosses itself at right angles as shown in the figure. A, B, C, and D are points of tangency; E is the intersection of the tangents; and O is the center of one of the circles. The radius of each wheel is 7 inches.

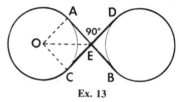

Ex. 13

 a. Show that $m\angle AOE = 45$.
 b. Find:
   (1) the length of $\overline{AE}$.
   (2) the length of major arc $\widehat{AC}$. [$\pi = \frac{22}{7}$]
   (3) the length of the entire belt.

14. In a circle whose radius is 4 inches, find to the *nearest inch* the length of the minor arc intercepted by a chord 6 inches in length.

15. In a circle whose radius is 20 inches, find to the *nearest inch* the length of the minor arc intercepted by a chord 24 inches in length.

16. In circle O, $\overline{AB}$ is a diameter. Radius $\overline{OC}$ is extended to meet the tangent $\overleftrightarrow{BD}$ at D. The measures of arc $\widehat{AC}$ and arc $\widehat{CB}$ are in the ratio 2:1, and $AB = 32$.

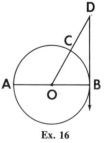

 a. Find the number of degrees contained in arc $\widehat{CB}$.
 b. Find to the *nearest integer* the perimeter of the figure bounded by $\overline{BD}$, $\overline{DC}$, and arc $\widehat{CB}$. [$\pi = 3.14$]

Ex. 16

5. Finding the Area of a Circle

Definition. A *circular region* is the union of a circle and its interior.

A circular region is pictured in Fig. 8–14. For convenience when we are discussing the area of a circular region, we will refer to it as the *area of a circle*.

Fig. 8–14

Observe in Fig. 8–15 that as the number of sides of a regular polygon inscribed in a circle O is increased from 3 to 6 to 12, etc., the length of the apothem, a, approaches r, the length of the radius of the polygon, which is also the radius of the circle. Also, the area of the polygon approaches the area of the circle.

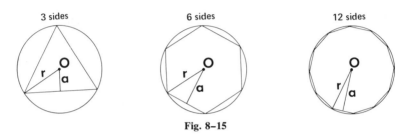

Fig. 8–15

Hence, it appears reasonable to accept the following postulate:

Postulate 46. **When the number of sides of a regular polygon inscribed in a circle increases without bound, (a) the length of the apothem of the polygon approaches the length of the radius of the circle and may be used as an approximation of the length of the radius of the circle, and (b) the area of the regular polygon approaches the area of the circle and may be used as an approximation of the area of the circle.**

Theorem 124. **The area of a circle is equal to one-half the product of its radius and circumference.**

If the length of the radius of a circle is represented by r and the circumference of the circle is represented by C, the area of the circle, A, is given by the formula $A = \frac{1}{2} rC$.

Corollary T124–1. **The area of a circle is equal to π times the square of the length of the radius.**

If the length of the radius of a circle is represented by r, the area of the circle, A, is given by the formula $A = \pi r^2$.

Corollary T124–2. **The area of a circle is equal to $\frac{1}{4}\pi$ times the square of the length of the diameter.**

If the length of the diameter of a circle is represented by d, the area of the circle, A, is given by the formula $A = \frac{1}{4}\pi d^2$.

MODEL PROBLEMS

1. Find the area of a circle whose radius is 7 in. [Use $\pi = \frac{22}{7}$.]

Solution:

1. $A = \pi r^2$ $r = 7, \pi = \frac{22}{7}$.

2. $A = \pi(7)^2$

3. $A = 49\pi$

4. $A = 49 \times \frac{22}{7} = 154$

Answer: Area $= 154$ sq. in.

2. If the circumference of a circle is 24π ft., find the area of the circle. [Leave answer in the form of π.]

Solution:

1. $C = 2\pi r$ $C = 24\pi$.

2. $24\pi = 2\pi r$

3. $r = \dfrac{24\pi}{2\pi} = 12$

4. $A = \pi r^2$

5. $A = \pi(12)^2 = 144\pi$

Answer: Area $= 144\pi$ sq. ft.

EXERCISES

1. The formula for the area A of a circle, in terms of its diameter d, is
(a) πd^2 (b) $\frac{1}{4}\pi d^2$ (c) $\frac{1}{2}\pi d^2$.

2. Represent, in terms of x, the area of a circle whose radius is represented by:
a. $2x$ *b.* $3x$ *c.* $4x$ *d.* $8x$ *e.* $x + 1$

3. Represent, in terms of x, the area of a circle whose diameter is represented by:
a. $2x$ *b.* $4x$ *c.* $10x$ *d.* $3x$ *e.* $5x$

4. Find, in terms of π, the area of a circle in which:
a. $r = 4$ *b.* $r = 8$ *c.* $r = 2\frac{1}{2}$ *d.* $d = 12$ *e.* $d = 5$

5. Find the area of a circle inscribed in a square whose side is 8. [Answer may be left in terms of π.]

6. The area of a square is 16 sq. in. Find the area of the inscribed circle. [Answer may be left in terms of π.]

7. Find the area of a circle circumscribed about a square whose apothem has a length of 1 inch.
8. Find the radius of a circle whose area is:
   $a.$ 4π $b.$ 49π $c.$ $.64\pi$ $d.$ $\frac{9}{25}\pi$ $e.$ $6\frac{1}{4}\pi$ $f.$ 8
9. Represent, in terms of x, the radius of a circle whose area is represented by:
   $a.$ $4x^2\pi$ $b.$ $25x^2\pi$ $c.$ $\frac{64}{9}x^2\pi$ $d.$ $100\pi x^2$ $e.$ $\frac{1}{9}\pi x^2$
10. Find the area of a circle circumscribed about a regular hexagon whose side is:
    $a.$ 4 $b.$ 12 $c.$ 20 $d.$ 1 $e.$ 5
11. Find the area of a circle whose circumference is:
    $a.$ 16π $b.$ 10π $c.$ 5π $d.$ $\frac{49\pi}{4}$ $e.$ 10
12. Represent, in terms of x, the area of a circle whose circumference is represented by:
    $a.$ $4x\pi$ $b.$ $6x\pi$ $c.$ $12\pi x$ $d.$ $3x\pi$ $e.$ $9\pi x$
13. Find the circumference of a circle whose area is:
    $a.$ 25π $b.$ 36π $c.$ 100π $d.$ $\frac{49}{4}\pi$ $e.$ π
14. Represent, in terms of x, the circumference of a circle whose area is represented by:
    $a.$ $4x^2\pi$ $b.$ $25\pi x^2$ $c.$ $16\pi x^2$ $d.$ $\frac{49}{4}\pi x^2$
15. The area of a circle is 81π; find the length of a side of the inscribed regular hexagon.
16. Diagonals $\overline{AC}$ and $\overline{BD}$ of rhombus $ABCD$ intersect at O, $\overline{BD}$ being the shorter diagonal. A line is drawn from O perpendicular to $\overline{AB}$, meeting it at X. $AB = BD = 12$. (a) Find OB, BX, and OX. (b) Find, in terms of π, the area of the circle that can be inscribed in the rhombus.
17. The lengths of the diagonals of a rhombus are 60 and 80. Find the (a) area of the rhombus (b) length of one side (c) length of the altitude of the rhombus (d) area of the inscribed circle. [Answer may be left in terms of π.]
18. Given a square the length of whose side is represented by s. (a) Express the area of the inscribed circle in terms of π and s. (b) Express the area of the circumscribed circle in terms of π and s. (c) Find, in simplest form, the ratio of the area of the inscribed circle to the area of the circumscribed circle.
19. Find the radius of a circle whose area is equal to the sum of the areas of two circles whose radii are 12 in. and 16 in.
20. Find the area of a circle circumscribed about a square whose side is 2.
21. Quadrilateral $ABCD$ is inscribed in circle O; and the measures of arcs $\overset{\frown}{AB}$, $\overset{\frown}{BC}$, $\overset{\frown}{CD}$, and $\overset{\frown}{DA}$ are in the ratio 3:4:5:6 respectively. (a) Find the number of degrees contained in each arc. (b) Find the number of degrees contained in angle BAD. (c) If the length of side $\overline{AB}$ of the

quadrilateral equals 10, find the area of the circle. [*Hint:* Draw $\overline{BD}$.]
[Use $\pi = 3.14$.]

22. In the figure, $\overline{AB}$ and $\overline{CD}$ are parallel chords on opposite sides of the center of circle O. $CD = 12$, $AB =$
   16, and RS, the distance between the chords, is 14.
   a. If the length of $\overline{OR}$ is represented by x, express
      the length of $\overline{OS}$ in terms of x.
   b. What is the length of $\overline{RB}$? of $\overline{SD}$?
   c. In terms of x, write *two* expressions for the square
      of the length of the radius of the circle. [*Hint:*
      Draw $\overline{OB}$ and $\overline{OD}$.]
   d. Using the results obtained in answer to c, find the length of $\overline{OR}$.
   e. Find the area of the circle. [Answer may be left in terms of π.]

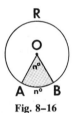

Ex. 22

6. Finding the Area of a Sector of a Circle

In Fig. 8–16, the part of the circular region which is
shaped like a "slice of pie" is called a *sector of a circle.*

**Definition. A *sector of a circle* is the union of an arc of the
circle, the two radii which are drawn from the center of the
circle to the endpoints of the arc, and the interior of the region
bounded by these two radii and the arc.**

Fig. 8–16

In circle O (Fig. 8–16), shaded sector AOB is a *minor
sector*. Sector $OARB$ is a *major sector.* In minor sector AOB,
angle AOB is referred to as the "central angle of the sector," or the angle of
the sector. In this case, we would say that the degree measure of the angle
of sector AOB is n.

Theorem 125. **In a circle whose area is represented by A, the area of a sector whose central angle or intercepted arc contains $n°$ is given by the formula:**

$$\frac{\text{area of a sector}}{\text{area of the circle}} = \frac{n}{360} \quad \text{or} \quad \text{area of a sector} = \frac{n}{360} \times A$$

Corollary T125–1. **In a circle the length of whose radius is represented by r,
the area of a sector whose central angle or intercepted arc contains $n°$ is given
by the formula:**

$$\frac{\text{area of a sector}}{\pi r^2} = \frac{n}{360} \quad \text{or} \quad \text{area of a sector} = \frac{n}{360} \times \pi r^2$$

MODEL PROBLEMS

1. The area of circle O is 36 sq. in. If there are 40° contained in central angle COD, find the number of square inches in the area of sector COD.

Solution:

1. Area of sector $= \dfrac{n}{360} \times A$ $n = 40$.

2. Area of sector $= \frac{40}{360} \times 36$ A, the area of circle $O = 36$.

3. Area of sector $= \frac{1}{9} \times 36 = 4$

Answer: Area of sector $= 4$ sq. in.

2. In circle O, a sector whose angle contains 120° has an area of 3π sq. in. Find the radius of the circle.

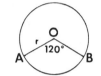

Solution:

Method 1	*Method* 2
1. $\dfrac{\text{area of sector}}{\text{area of circle}} = \dfrac{n}{360}$	1. Since the central angle of the sector, $\angle AOB$, contains 120°, the area of the sector is $\frac{120}{360}$, or $\frac{1}{3}$ of the area of the circle.
area of sector $= 3\pi$.	
$n = 120$.	
2. $\dfrac{3\pi}{\pi r^2} = \dfrac{120}{360}$	2. Since the area of the sector is 3π, the area of the circle is $3(3\pi) = 9\pi$.
3. $\dfrac{3\pi}{\pi r^2} = \dfrac{1}{3}$	3. $\pi r^2 = 9\pi$
4. $\pi r^2 = 9\pi$	4. $r^2 = 9$
5. $r^2 = 9$	5. $r = 3$
6. $r = 3$	

Answer: Radius of the circle is 3 in.

EXERCISES

1. Find what fractional part of the area of a circle the area of a sector is if its central angle contains: *a.* 90°   *b.* 30°   *c.* 135°   *d.* 240°   *e.* 40°

2. If the central angle of a sector of a circle contains 40°, the area of the circle is _____ times the area of the sector.

3. If the area of a sector of a circle is to the area of the circle as 1:8, then the number of degrees contained in the angle of the sector is _____.

4. The area of a circle is 80 square inches. Find the area of a sector whose central angle contains 45°.

5. The area of a circle is 60 sq. ft. Find the area of a sector whose central angle measures 120.

6. The angle of a sector of a circle measures 90 and the area of the circle is 64π. Find, in terms of π, the area of the sector.

7. The angle of a sector of a circle measures 60 and the area of the circle is 144π sq. in. Find the area of the sector to the *nearest square inch*.

8. In a circle whose radius is 12, find the area of a sector whose central angle contains: *a.* 90°   *b.* 45°   *c.* 60°   *d.* 120°   *e.* 80°

9. The radius of a circle is 9 and the angle of a sector of this circle measures 40. The area of this sector, in terms of π, is _____.

10. Find the radius of a circle in which a sector whose central angle measures 90 has an area of: *a.* 4π *b.* 25π *c.* 36π *d.* 9π *e.* π

11. The angle of a sector of a circle measures 120 and the area of the sector is 27π. Find the radius of the circle.

12. The area of the sector of a circle whose angle measures 40 is 4π. Find the radius of the circle.

13. In a circle whose radius is 12, find the measure of the central angle of a sector whose area is: *a.* 36π *b.* 12π *c.* 72π *d.* 16π *e.* 60π

14. Find the number of degrees contained in the angle of a sector if its area is 5π and the radius of the circle is 6.

15. $\overline{BA}$ and $\overline{BC}$ are tangents to circle O at A and C respectively, and form an angle of 50°. Line segments $\overline{OA}, \overline{OB},$ and $\overline{OC}$ are drawn. The length of $\overline{OB}$ is 14.2 inches.   (*a*) Find to the *nearest inch* the length of the radius of the circle.   (*b*) Using the value of the radius obtained in answer to *a* and using $\pi = \frac{22}{7}$, find to the *nearest square inch* the area of minor sector AOC.

16. $\overline{AB}$ is the diameter of the large semicircle and $\overline{AC}$ and $\overline{CB}$ are the diameters of the small semicircles. Prove that the area of the shaded region is equal to the sum of the areas of the two small semicircles.

Ex. 16

17. $\overline{AB}$ is the diameter of the large circle. $\overline{AC}$ and $\overline{CB}$ are the diameters of the small semicircles. Prove that the area of the shaded part of the large circle is equal to the area of the unshaded part of the large circle.

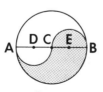

Ex. 17

7. Finding the Area of a Segment of a Circle

Definition. A *segment of a circle* is the union of an arc of the circle, its chord, and the interior of the region bounded by the arc and the chord.

In circle O (Fig. 8–17), the shaded segment ASB is a *minor segment.* Segment ARB, the segment that is not shaded, is a *major segment.*

To find the area of a minor segment of a circle (for example, minor segment ASB in Fig. 8–18), we can use the following relationship:

Area of segment ASB = area of minor sector $OASB$ − area of triangle OAB.

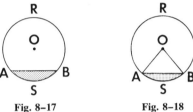

Fig. 8–17   Fig. 8–18

To find the area of a major segment of a circle, we subtract the area of the minor segment from the area of the circle. In Fig. 8–18:

Area of major segment ARB = area of circle O − area of minor segment ASB.

MODEL PROBLEMS

1. In a circle whose radius is 12, find the area of a minor segment whose arc has a central angle which contains 60°. [Answer may be left in radical form and in terms of π.]

Solution:

1. Area of sector $OASB = \dfrac{n}{360} \times \pi r^2$ $n = 60$, $r = 12$.

2. Area of sector $OASB = \frac{60}{360} \times (12)^2 \pi = \frac{1}{6}(144\pi) = 24\pi$

3. Area of equilateral triangle $OAB = \dfrac{s^2}{4}\sqrt{3} = \dfrac{(12)^2}{4}\sqrt{3}$

4. Area of equilateral triangle $OAB = \frac{144}{4}\sqrt{3} = 36\sqrt{3}$

5. Area of segment ASB = area of sector $OASB$ − area of triangle OAB

6. Area of segment $ASB = 24\pi - 36\sqrt{3}$

Answer: Area of segment $= 24\pi - 36\sqrt{3}$.

2. In a circle whose radius is 6 in., find to the *nearest square inch* the area of a segment whose chord has an arc which contains 80°. [Use $\pi = 3.14$.]

Solution:

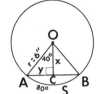

1. Since $m\overset{\frown}{AB} = 80$, $m\angle AOB = 80$.

2. Area of sector $OASB = \dfrac{n}{360} \times \pi r^2$ $n = 80$.
     $r = 6$.

3. Area of sector $OASB = \frac{80}{360} \times (6)^2\pi = \frac{2}{9} \times 36\pi$

4. Area of sector $OASB = 8\pi = 8(3.14) = 25.12$, or 25.1

NOTE. Since the answer is to be correct to the nearest whole number, we will round off to tenths all numbers that lead to the answer.

5. To find the area of $\triangle AOB$, we will use $A = \frac{1}{2}$ base $\times$ altitude.

6. Draw $\overline{OC} \perp \overline{AB}$.

7. In isosceles triangle AOB, $\overline{OC}$ bisects $\angle AOB$, making $m\angle AOC = 40$.

8. In rt. $\triangle AOC$,

$$\cos 40° = \frac{\text{length of adj. leg}}{\text{length of hypotenuse}}$$

$$\cos 40° = \frac{x}{6}$$

$$.7660 = \frac{x}{6}$$

$$x = 6(.7660)$$

$$x = 4.5960, \text{ or}$$

$$x = 4.6$$

In rt. $\triangle AOC$,

$$\sin 40° = \frac{\text{length of opp. leg}}{\text{length of hypotenuse}}$$

$$\sin 40° = \frac{y}{6}$$

$$.6428 = \frac{y}{6}$$

$$y = 6(.6428)$$

$$y = 3.8568, \text{ or}$$

$$y = 3.9$$

9. In isosceles triangle AOB, $\overline{OC}$ bisects base $\overline{AB}$. Therefore, AC, or $y = \frac{1}{2}AB$.

10. Area of $\triangle AOB = \frac{1}{2}$ base $\times$ altitude $= (y)(x) = (3.9)(4.6) = 17.94$, or 17.9.

NOTE. The area of $\triangle AOB$ can also be found by using the formula: area of $\triangle AOB = \frac{1}{2}AO \times OB \times \sin \angle AOB$, or $\frac{1}{2} \times 6 \times 6 \times \sin 80°$, etc.

11. Area of segment $ASB =$ area of sector $OASB -$ area of $\triangle AOB$.

12. Area of segment $ASB = 25.1 - 17.9 = 7.2$, or 7.

Answer: Area of segment $ASB = 7$ sq. in.

EXERCISES

In 1 and 2, the answers may be left in radical form and in terms of π.

1. In a circle whose radius is 6, find the area of a minor segment whose arc has a central angle which contains:
   a. 90°   *b*. 60°   *c*. 30°   *d*. 120°   *e*. 140°

2. In a circle, a chord is drawn whose length is equal to the length of a radius. Find the area of the minor segment formed by the chord and its arc if the length of a radius of the circle is:
   a. 6   *b*. 18   *c*. 4   *d*. 10   *e*. 5

3. [In this exercise, use $\pi = 3.14$, $\sqrt{3} = 1.73$, and express each result to the *nearest tenth*.] In circle O, chord $\overline{AB}$ and a radius are each 6 inches in length. If radii $\overline{OA}$ and $\overline{OB}$ are drawn, find: (*a*) the length of minor arc $\overset{\frown}{AB}$.   (*b*) the area of triangle AOB.   (*c*) the area of sector AOB.   (*d*) the area of the minor segment of the circle.

4. A chord $\overline{AB}$ of circle O is 10 inches long and is 5 inches from the center of the circle. Radii $\overline{OA}$ and $\overline{OB}$ are drawn. Find: (*a*) the number of degrees contained in angle AOB.   (*b*) the length of a radius of the circle. [Answer may be left in radical form.]   (*c*) the area of triangle AOB. (*d*) the area of the minor sector of the circle. [Answer may be left in terms of π.]   (*e*) the area of the minor segment of the circle. [Answer may be left in terms of π.]   (*f*) the area of the major segment of the circle. [Answer may be left in radical form.]

5. The length of a radius of a circle is 12 and a minor segment of this circle has a chord whose length is equal to the length of the radius.   (*a*) Find the perimeter of the minor segment.   (*b*) Find the area of the minor segment.   (*c*) Find the area of the major segment of the circle. [Answers may be left in radical form and in terms of π.]

6. A man has a flower garden in the shape of a minor segment of a circle. The arc of the segment contains 90° and the radius of the circle is 28 feet long. [Use $\pi = \frac{22}{7}$.]   (*a*) Find to the *nearest foot* the number of feet of fencing required to enclose the garden.   (*b*) Find the area of the garden.

7. In circle O, central angle AOB contains 90°, the length of $\overset{\frown}{AB} = 6\pi$, and chord $\overline{AB}$ is drawn.   (*a*) Find the length of radius $\overline{OA}$.   (*b*) Find the area of triangle AOB.   (*c*) Find the area of sector AOB. [Answer may be left in terms of π.]   (*d*) Find the area of minor segment AB. [Answer may be left in terms of π.]

8. Find the sum of the areas of the three segments formed by inscribing an equilateral triangle in a circle whose radius is 24. [Answer may be left in terms of radicals and π.]

9. Find the sum of the areas of the four segments formed by inscribing a square in a circle whose radius is 8.

8. The Equilateral Triangle and Its Circles

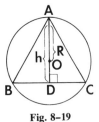

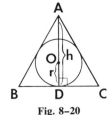

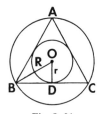

Fig. 8–19   Fig. 8–20   Fig. 8–21

Theorem 126. **The length of the radius of a circle circumscribed about an equilateral triangle is equal to two-thirds of the length of the altitude of the triangle.**

In Fig. 8–19, if circle O is circumscribed about equilateral triangle ABC, the length of the radius of the circle, OA, represented by R, is equal to $\frac{2}{3}$ of the length of the altitude of the triangle, AD, represented by h, or $R = \frac{2}{3}h$.

Theorem 127. **The length of the radius of a circle inscribed in an equilateral triangle is equal to one-third of the length of the altitude of the triangle.**

In Fig. 8–20, if circle O is inscribed in equilateral triangle ABC, the length of the radius of the circle, OD, represented by r, is equal to $\frac{1}{3}$ of the length of the altitude of the triangle, AD, represented by h, or $r = \frac{1}{3}h$.

Corollary T126, 127–1. **The length of the radius of a circle circumscribed about an equilateral triangle is twice the length of the radius of the circle inscribed in the equilateral triangle.**

In Fig. 8–21, if the length of the radius of the circle circumscribed about equilateral triangle ABC is represented by R and the length of the radius of the circle inscribed in equilateral triangle ABC is represented by r, then $R = 2r$.

MODEL PROBLEM

Find, in radical form, the length of the radius of a circle circumscribed about an equilateral triangle the length of whose side is 24.

Solution:

1. In equilateral triangle ABC, draw $\overline{AD}$, the altitude to side $\overline{BC}$. Represent the length of $\overline{AD}$ by h.

2. $h = \frac{s}{2}\sqrt{3} = \frac{24}{2}\sqrt{3} = 12\sqrt{3}.$ $s = 24.$

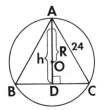

3. $R = \frac{2}{3}h = \frac{2}{3}(12\sqrt{3}) = 8\sqrt{3}.$

Answer: Length of the radius is $8\sqrt{3}$.

EXERCISES

1. Find the length of the radius of the circle inscribed in an equilateral triangle the length of whose altitude is:
   a. 12   *b.* 6   *c.* 15   *d.* 24   *e.* 7

2. Find the length of the radius of the circle circumscribed about an equilateral triangle the length of whose altitude is:
   a. 6   *b.* 12   *c.* 18   *d.* 36   *e.* 5

3. Find the length of the radius of the circle inscribed in an equilateral triangle the length of whose side is:
   a. 6   *b.* 12   *c.* 18   *d.* 9   *e.* 4

4. Find the length of the radius of the circle circumscribed about an equilateral triangle the length of whose side is:
   a. 6   *b.* 12   *c.* 18   *d.* 9   *e.* 8

5. The length of the radius of a circle inscribed in an equilateral triangle is 5. Find the length of the radius of the circumscribed circle.

6. The length of the radius of a circle inscribed in an equilateral triangle is 6. Find the length of the altitude of the triangle.

7. The length of the radius of a circle circumscribed about an equilateral triangle is 12. Find the length of the altitude of the triangle.

8. The altitudes of an equilateral triangle ABC are concurrent in point O. If O is 4 inches from side $\overline{AB}$, how many inches is O from vertex A?

9. If the area of an equilateral triangle is $36\sqrt{3}$, find: (*a*) the length of a side of the triangle.   (*b*) the length of an altitude of the triangle.   (*c*) the circumference of the inscribed circle in terms of π.   (*d*) the circumference of the circumscribed circle in terms of π.   (*e*) the ratio of the circumferences of the two circles.   (*f*) the area of the inscribed circle in terms of π.   (*g*) the area of the circumscribed circle in terms of π.   (*h*) the ratio of the areas of the two circles.

10. The area of a circle inscribed in an equilateral triangle is 16π.   (*a*) Find the circumference of the circumscribed circle in terms of π.   (*b*) Find the area of the circumscribed circle in terms of π.   (*c*) The area of the circumscribed circle is how many times as large as the area of the inscribed circle?

9. Solving More Difficult Area Problems

Sometimes the region whose area we are required to find is one for which there is no convenient area formula. In such a case, we try to combine regions for which there are convenient area formulas so that the result will be the area we are required to find. See how this is done in the following problems:

MODEL PROBLEMS

1. Find, in terms of π, the area of the shaded region.

   Solution:

   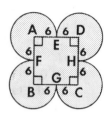

   1. The shaded region consists of square $ABCD$, whose side is 12, and four major sectors whose areas are equal. In each sector, the central angle contains $(360° - 90°)$, or $270°$, and the length of the radius is 6.

   2. Area of the square $= (AB)^2 = (12)^2 = 144$.

   3. Area of each sector $= \dfrac{n}{360} \times \pi r^2 = \dfrac{270}{360} \times (6)^2\pi$
      $$= \tfrac{3}{4}(36\pi) = 27\pi$$

   4. Area of shaded region = area of square + area of 4 sectors

   5. Area of shaded region $= 144 + 4(27\pi)$

   6. Area of shaded region $= 144 + 108\pi$

   Answer: Area of shaded region $= 144 + 108\pi$.

2. A circle is inscribed in an equilateral triangle whose side is 12. Find to the *nearest integer* the difference between the area of the triangle and the area of the circle $[\pi = 3.14$ and $\sqrt{3} = 1.73]$

   Solution:

   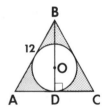

   1. Area of equilateral $\triangle ABC = \dfrac{s^2}{4}\sqrt{3} = \dfrac{(12)^2}{4}\sqrt{3}$
      $$= \tfrac{144}{4}\sqrt{3} = 36\sqrt{3}$$
      $$= 36(1.73) = 62.28,$$
      $$\text{or } 62.3$$

   2. In equilateral $\triangle ABC$, $BD = h = \dfrac{s}{2}\sqrt{3} = \dfrac{12}{2}\sqrt{3} = 6\sqrt{3}$.

   3. Length of radius $\overline{OD} = r = \tfrac{1}{3}h = \tfrac{1}{3}(6\sqrt{3}) = 2\sqrt{3}$.

   4. Area of circle $O = \pi r^2 = \pi(2\sqrt{3})^2 = 12\pi = 12(3.14) = 37.68$, or 37.7.

   5. Required area = area of triangle ABC − area of circle O

   6. Required area $= 62.3 - 37.7 = 24.6$

   7. Required area $= 25$ to the nearest integer

   Answer: 25.

EXERCISES

In 1–8, find the area of the shaded region. [Answers may be left in terms of radicals and π.]

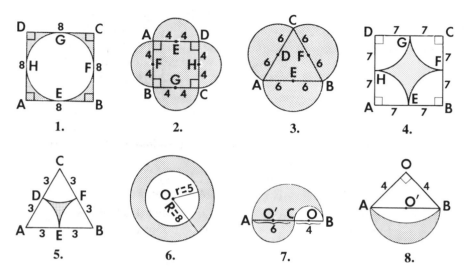

1.   2.   3.   4.

5.   6.   7.   8.

9. From a square piece of tin, each of whose sides is 14 inches, is cut a circle whose diameter is 14 inches. Find to the *nearest square inch* the amount of tin that is wasted.

10. Nine circular discs, each 3 inches in diameter, were cut from a square of aluminum alloy 9 inches on a side. How much of the metal was wasted? Give your answer to the *nearest square inch*. $[\pi = \frac{22}{7}]$

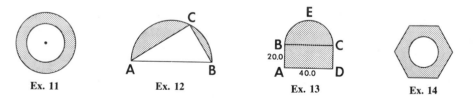

Ex. 11   Ex. 12   Ex. 13   Ex. 14

11. Find, in terms of π, the area of the circular ring (annulus) formed by two concentric circles, one with a radius of 7 and the other with a radius of 10.

12. In the semicircle, the length of chord $\overline{AC}$ is 16, and the length of chord $\overline{BC}$ is 12. Find the area of the shaded region to the *nearest integer*. $[\pi = 3.14]$

13. $ABECD$ represents the cross section of an underground tunnel. $ABCD$ is a rectangle 40.0 feet by 20.0 feet, surmounted by the semicircle BEC. Find to the *nearest square foot* the area of the cross section. $[\pi = 3.14]$

14. The figure represents the cross section of a hexagonal nut. Assuming that the diameter of the circle and the side of the regular hexagon are each 2 inches in length, find to the *nearest square inch* the area of the cross section (the shaded region).

15. A circle whose radius is 4 is inscribed in an equilateral triangle. (*a*) Find the length of the altitude of the triangle. (*b*) Find the length of the side of the triangle. [Answer may be left in radical form.] (*c*) Show that the difference between the area of the triangle and the area of the circle is approximately 33. [$\pi = 3.14$ and $\sqrt{3} = 1.73$]

16. A circle and an equilateral triangle each have a perimeter of 132 feet. (*a*) Find the length of a side of the triangle. (*b*) Find the length of the radius of the circle. (*c*) Show that the difference between the area of the circle and the area of the triangle is approximately 549 square feet. [$\pi = \frac{22}{7}$ and $\sqrt{3} = 1.73$]

17. The area of a regular hexagon is $96\sqrt{3}$. Find the area of an equilateral triangle whose perimeter is equal to the perimeter of the hexagon.

18. The radius of a circular flower bed is 30 feet and this bed is surrounded by a circular path 3 feet wide. Find the cost of paving the path at $1.25 per square foot. [$\pi = \frac{22}{7}$]

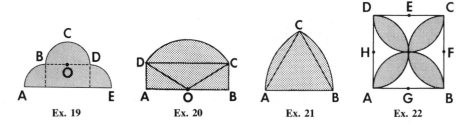

Ex. 19   Ex. 20   Ex. 21   Ex. 22

19. BCD is a semicircle and $\overset{\frown}{AB}$ and $\overset{\frown}{ED}$ are quadrants of congruent circles. (A quadrant is a quarter of a circle.) $\overline{AE}$ measures 56 inches and the diameter of the semicircle is 28 inches. Find the area of the entire region. [Use $\pi = \frac{22}{7}$.]

20. $ABCD$ is a rectangle. O is the midpoint of the longer side $\overline{AB}$. Arc $\overset{\frown}{DC}$ is an arc of the circle whose center is O. If $\overline{AD}$ measures 6 feet and angle DOC contains 120°, find the area of the entire region to the *nearest square foot.* [Use $\pi = 3.14$ and $\sqrt{3} = 1.73$.]

21. Arc $\overset{\frown}{CB}$ is the arc of a circle with A as the center, arc $\overset{\frown}{AC}$ is the arc of a circle with B as the center, and $AB = 24$.
   a. Find the area of sector BAC. [Answer may be left in terms of π.]
   b. Find the area of the segment bounded by chord $\overline{BC}$ and arc $\overset{\frown}{BC}$. [Answer may be left in radical form and in terms of π.]

c. Find the area of the entire region. [Answer may be left in radical form and in terms of π.]

22. *ABCD* is a square each of whose sides is 6 inches in length. *E, F, G,* and *H* are the centers of semicircles which are constructed on the sides of the square, each side of the square being a diameter. Find to the *nearest square inch* the area of the shaded region.

10. Ratios of Circumferences of Circles

We have previously learned the following relationships:

The ratio of the circumferences of two circles is equal to the ratio of the lengths of their radii or the ratio of the lengths of their diameters:

$$\frac{C}{C'} = \frac{r}{r'} \quad \text{and} \quad \frac{C}{C'} = \frac{d}{d'}$$

Another way of stating these relationships is as follows:

The circumference of a circle varies directly as its radius or as its diameter.

This means that when the length of the radius or the diameter of a circle is multiplied by (or divided by) a positive number, the circumference is multiplied by (or divided by) the *same* number. If the length of the radius of a circle is multiplied by 5, the circumference of the circle is also multiplied by 5; if the length of the radius of a circle is divided by 2, the circumference of the circle is also divided by 2.

MODEL PROBLEMS ⸜⸝⸜⸝⸜⸝⸜⸝⸜⸝

1. The lengths of the radii of two circles are 15 in. and 5 in. Find the ratio of the circumferences of the two circles.

Solution:

1. $\dfrac{C}{C'} = \dfrac{r}{r'}$ $r = 15$ in., $r' = 5$ in.

2. $\dfrac{C}{C'} = \dfrac{15}{5} = \dfrac{3}{1}$

Answer: Ratio of the circumferences is 3:1.

2. The ratio of the circumferences of two circles is 3:2 and the smaller circle has a radius of 8. Find the length of a radius of the larger circle.

Solution:

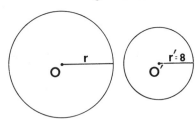

1. $\dfrac{C}{C'} = \dfrac{r}{r'}$ $\dfrac{C}{C'} = \dfrac{3}{2}$, $r' = 8$.

2. $\dfrac{3}{2} = \dfrac{r}{8}$

3. $2r = 24$

4. $r = 12$

Answer: Length of a radius of the larger circle is 12.

EXERCISES

1. Find the ratio of the circumferences of two circles if the ratio of the lengths of their radii is:
   a. 3:1   *b.* 1:2   *c.* 5:4   *d.* r:s

2. Find the ratio of the circumferences of two circles if the ratio of the lengths of their diameters is:
   a. 2:1   *b.* 1:4   *c.* 4:7   *d.* m:n

3. The diameters of two circles are 6 feet and 4 feet in length. Find the ratio of the circumferences of the circles.

4. The radii of two circles are 6 inches and 2 feet in length. Find the ratio of the circumferences of the circles.

5. The circumferences of two circles are in the ratio of 2:5. Find the ratio of the lengths of the radii of the circles.

6. State by what number the circumference of a circle is multiplied when the length of its radius is multiplied by:
   a. 2   *b.* 5   *c.* 10   *d.* x

7. By what number must the circumference of a circle be multiplied in order to multiply the length of the diameter by 3?

8. The ratio of the circumferences of two circles is 5:4 and the larger circle has a radius whose length is 25. Find the length of the radius of the smaller circle.

9. The lengths of the radii of two circles are in the ratio of 4:1. If the circumference of the larger circle is 24π, find the circumference of the smaller circle.

10. The lengths of the diameters of two circles are in the ratio of 3:5. If the circumference of the smaller circle is 15π, find the circumference of the larger circle.

11. The ratio of the circumferences of two circles is 5:1. If the length of the radius of the larger circle exceeds the length of the radius of the smaller circle by 8, find the length of the radius of the smaller circle.

12. The lengths of the radii of two circles are in the ratio 2:1. If the circumference of the larger circle is 16π more than the circumference of the smaller circle, find the circumference of the larger circle.

13. What is the ratio of the circumference of the circle inscribed in an equilateral triangle to the circumference of the circle circumscribed about the equilateral triangle?

14. What is the ratio of the circumference of the circle circumscribed about a square to the circumference of the circle inscribed in the square?

11. Ratios of Areas of Circles

Theorem 128. **The ratio of the areas of two circles is equal to the ratio of the squares of the lengths of their radii, the squares of the lengths of their diameters, or the squares of their circumferences.**

In circles O and O' (Fig. 8–22), whose areas are represented by A and A', the lengths of whose radii are represented by r and r', the lengths of whose diameters are represented by d and d', and whose circumferences are represented by C and C':

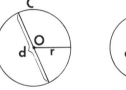

Fig. 8–22

$$\frac{A}{A'} = \frac{(r)^2}{(r')^2} \qquad \frac{A}{A'} = \frac{(d)^2}{(d')^2} \qquad \frac{A}{A'} = \frac{(C)^2}{(C')^2}$$

Another way of stating these relationships is as follows:

The area of a circle varies directly as the square of the radius, as the square of the diameter, or as the square of the circumference.

This means that when the length of the radius, the length of the diameter, or the circumference of a circle is multiplied by (or divided by) a positive number, the area is multiplied by (or divided by) the square of that number. If the length of the radius of a circle is multiplied by 3, the area of the circle is multiplied by the square of 3, that is, by 3^2, or 9; if the length of the diameter of a circle is divided by 4, the area of the circle is divided by the square of 4, that is, 4^2, or 16.

MODEL PROBLEMS

1. The lengths of the radii of two circles are in the ratio of 1:4. Find the ratio of the areas of the circles.

Solution:

1. $\dfrac{A}{A'} = \dfrac{(r)^2}{(r')^2} = \left(\dfrac{r}{r'}\right)^2 \qquad \dfrac{r}{r'} = \dfrac{1}{4}.$

2. $\dfrac{A}{A'} = \left(\dfrac{1}{4}\right)^2 = \dfrac{1}{16}$

Answer: 1:16.

2. The ratio of the areas of two circles is 9:4. The length of the radius of the larger circle is how many times the length of the radius of the smaller circle?

Solution:

1. $\dfrac{A}{A'} = \dfrac{(r)^2}{(r')^2} \qquad \dfrac{A}{A'} = \dfrac{9}{4}.$

2. $\dfrac{9}{4} = \dfrac{(r)^2}{(r')^2}$

3. $\dfrac{3}{2} = \dfrac{r}{r'}$ \qquad Positive square roots of equal quantities are equal.

4. Since the ratio of the length of the radius of the larger circle to the length of the radius of the smaller circle is $\frac{3}{2}$, the radius of the larger circle is $1\frac{1}{2}$ times as long as the radius of the smaller circle.

Answer: $1\frac{1}{2}$ times.

3. The ratio of the areas of two circles is 16:1. If the diameter of the smaller circle is 3, find the diameter of the larger circle.

Solution:

1. $\dfrac{A}{A'} = \dfrac{(d)^2}{(d')^2} \qquad \dfrac{A}{A'} = \dfrac{16}{1},\ d' = 3.$

2. $\dfrac{16}{1} = \dfrac{d^2}{(3)^2}$

3. $\dfrac{16}{1} = \dfrac{d^2}{9}$

4. $d^2 = 144$

5. $d = 12$

Answer: Diameter of the larger circle is 12.

EXERCISES

1. Find the ratio of the areas of two circles if the ratio of the lengths of their radii is:

   a. 1:2   *b.* 4:1   *c.* 3:2   *d.* 4:25   *e.* 9:4   *f.* $a:b$

2. Find the ratio of the areas of two circles if the ratio of the lengths of their diameters is:

   a. 1:5   *b.* 1:4   *c.* 1:9   *d.* 9:4   *e.* 9:16   *f.* $x:y$

3. The radii of two circles are 4 inches and 8 inches in length. Find the ratio of the areas of the circles.

4. The diameters of two circles are 8 inches and 1 foot in length. Find the ratio of the areas of the circles.

5. Find the ratio of the lengths of the radii of two circles if the ratio of their areas is:

   a. 4:1   *b.* 1:9   *c.* 9:4   *d.* 9:16   *e.* 49:81   *f.* $a^2:b^2$

6. State by what number the area of a circle is multiplied when the length of its radius is multiplied by:

   a. 2   *b.* 3   *c.* 4   *d.* 9   *e.* 10   *f.* m *g.* $2a$

7. State by what number the length of the radius of a circle must be multiplied in order to multiply the area by:

   a. 4   *b.* 9   *c.* 1.44   *d.* $2\frac{1}{4}$ *e.* 2   *f.* x^2 *g.* x

8. If the length of the radius of a circle is increased by 100%, by how many per cent is the area increased?

9. If the length of the diameter of a large circular pipe is 3 times the length of the diameter of a small circular pipe, find the ratio of the area of the cross section of the small pipe to the area of the cross section of the large pipe.

10. The areas of two circles are in the ratio of 9:16. If the length of a radius of the large circle is 8, find the length of a radius of the small circle.

11. The lengths of the radii of two circles are in the ratio of 3:1. If the area of the smaller circle is 16π, find the area of the larger circle.

12. The area of a circle is 9 times the area of a smaller circle. If the length of a diameter of the larger circle exceeds the length of a diameter of the smaller circle by 8, find the length of a diameter of the smaller circle.

13. The lengths of the radii of two circles are in the ratio 2:1. If the area of the larger circle exceeds the area of the smaller circle by 75π, find the area of the smaller circle.

14. *a.* If the length of the radius of a circle is 16, find the length of an arc of this circle which contains 45°.

    b. In another circle, an arc which contains 60° has the same length as the arc of 45° found in part *a*. Find the length of the radius of this other circle.

c. Find the ratio of the area of the smaller circle to the area of the larger circle.

15. In the figure, circles O and O', which are not congruent, intersect at P. Chord $\overline{PR}$ is tangent to circle O' and chord $\overline{PQ}$ is tangent to circle O. Radii $\overline{OP}$, $\overline{OR}$, $\overline{O'P}$, and $\overline{O'Q}$ are drawn.
a. Prove that:
(1) $\angle OPR \cong \angle O'PQ$.
(2) $\triangle OPR \sim \triangle O'PQ$.
b. If the ratio of PR to PQ is $a{:}b$, find the ratio of the area of circle O to the area of circle O'.

Ex. 15

16. Find the ratio of the area of a circle circumscribed about an equilateral triangle to the area of the circle inscribed in the equilateral triangle.
17. Find the ratio of the area of a circle circumscribed about a square to the area of the circle inscribed in the square.

12. Completion Exercises

Write a word or expression that, when inserted in the blank, will make the resulting statement true.

1. If a polygon is both equiangular and equilateral, it is a(an) _____ polygon.
2. A radius of a regular polygon is a radius of the _____ circle.
3. An apothem of a regular polygon is a radius of the _____ circle.
4. A circle may be circumscribed about any _____ polygon.
5. The apothem of a regular polygon is _____ to the side to which it is drawn.
6. A regular polygon of four sides is called a(an) _____ .
7. Regular polygons of the same number of sides are _____ .
8. The area of a regular octagon the length of whose side is represented by s and the length of whose apothem is represented by a is represented by _____ .
9. If an exterior angle of a regular polygon has the same measure as an interior angle, the polygon is a(an) _____ .
10. The number π is a constant which represents the ratio of the circumference of a circle to the _____ of the circle.
11. A side of a regular hexagon inscribed in a circle is congruent to a(an) _____ of the circle.
12. The circumference of a circle is equal to π times the _____ of the circle.

13. The area of a circle is equal to π times the _____ of the length of the radius of the circle.

14. A region bounded by an arc of a circle and its chord is the interior region of a(an) _____ of the circle.

15. A region bounded by two radii of a circle and the arc which they intercept on the circle is the interior region of a(an) _____ of the circle.

16. The length of a radius of a circle inscribed in an equilateral triangle is equal to _____ of the length of an altitude of the triangle.

17. The length of a radius of a circle circumscribed about an equilateral triangle is _____ times the length of a radius of the inscribed circle.

18. The ratio of the _____ of two circles is the same as the ratio of the lengths of their radii.

19. The ratio of the areas of two circles is the same as the ratio of the _____ of their radii.

20. The regular polygon the length of whose apothem is one-half the length of its side is a(an) _____.

21. If the length of a radius of a circle is multiplied by 2, the circumference of the circle is multiplied by _____.

22. If the length of a radius of a circle is multiplied by 2, the area of the circle is multiplied by _____.

23. In order to multiply the circumference of a circle by 9, the length of the radius of the circle must be multiplied by _____.

24. In order to multiply the area of a circle by 9, the length of a radius of the circle must be multiplied by _____.

25. In order to multiply the area of a circle by 3, the length of a diameter of the circle must be multiplied by _____.

13. True-False Exercises

If the statement is always true, write *true;* if the statement is not always true, write *false.*

1. Polygons that are equiangular must be equilateral.

2. Regular polygons of the same number of sides are similar.

3. Sectors of circles that are not congruent may be congruent.

4. The length of a radius of a circle inscribed in a triangle is one-third the length of an altitude.

5. An apothem of a regular polygon is a radius of the circumscribed circle.

6. The diagonals of a regular polygon must be congruent.

7. The area of a regular polygon is equal to one-half the product of its perimeter and the length of its apothem.

8. A radius of a regular polygon bisects the angle to whose vertex it is drawn.

9. The length of an apothem of a square equals one-half the length of a side of the square.

10. If the radius of a circle is 2 inches, the number of square inches in the area of the circle is the same as the number of inches in its circumference.

11. If the length of a radius of a circle is multiplied by a positive number s, the circumference of the circle is multiplied by s.

12. If the length of a radius of a circle is multiplied by d, a positive number other than 1, the area of the circle is multiplied by d.

13. The ratio of the circumference of a circle to the length of its diameter is a constant.

14. A rhombus is a regular polygon.

15. The ratio of the length of a radius of the circle circumscribed about an equilateral triangle to the length of a radius of the inscribed circle is 2:1.

16. As the number of sides of a regular polygon inscribed in a circle increases, the length of the apothem of the polygon decreases.

17. If an equilateral polygon is inscribed in a circle, the segments drawn from the center of the circle perpendicular to the sides are congruent.

18. A central angle of a regular polygon is supplementary to an interior angle of the polygon.

19. As the number of sides of a regular polygon increases, the number of degrees contained in a central angle of the polygon increases.

20. It is possible for an exterior angle of a regular polygon to contain 70°.

14. "Always, Sometimes, Never" Exercises

If the blank space in each of the following exercises is replaced by the word *always, sometimes,* or *never,* the resulting statement will be true. Select the word which will correctly complete each statement.

1. An equilateral polygon is _____ a regular polygon.

2. A regular polygon is _____ equiangular.

3. An equilateral polygon inscribed in a circle is _____ regular.

4. Two polygons are _____ congruent if their corresponding sides are congruent.

5. If the length of a radius of a circle is multiplied by a positive number k, the circumference is _____ multiplied by k.

6. The ratio of the areas of two regular polygons is _____ equal to the ratio of the squares of the lengths of their sides.

7. A circle can _____ be circumscribed about any regular polygon.

8. If a polygon is equilateral, it is _____ equiangular.

9. Sectors whose central angles contain the same number of degrees and which are drawn in circles that are not congruent are _____ congruent.

10. As the number of sides of a regular polygon inscribed in a circle increases, the length of its apothem _____ increases.

11. The diagonals of a regular polygon are _____ congruent.

12. The length of an apothem of a regular polygon is _____ one-half the length of a side of the polygon.

13. The length of a radius of a regular polygon is _____ twice the length of an apothem of the polygon.

14. An equiangular polygon inscribed in a circle is _____ a regular polygon.

15. An interior angle of a regular polygon is _____ supplementary to a central angle of the polygon.

16. Regular polygons of the same number of sides are _____ similar.

17. A radius of a regular polygon _____ bisects the angle to whose vertex it is drawn.

18. The ratio of the areas of two circles that are not congruent is _____ the same as the ratio of the lengths of the radii of the two circles.

19. If the line segments which are drawn from the center of a circle perpendicular to and ending in the sides of an inscribed polygon are congruent, the polygon is _____ equilateral.

20. A regular polygon of n sides is inscribed in a circle. In the same circle a regular polygon of $2n$ sides is inscribed. The length of a side of the new polygon is _____ one-half the length of a side of the original polygon.

21. The area of an equilateral triangle inscribed in a circle _____ exceeds the area of a square inscribed in that circle.

22. The area of a regular polygon inscribed in a circle _____ exceeds the area of the circle.

23. If a circle is divided into three or more congruent arcs, the chords of these arcs _____ form a regular polygon.

24. A central angle of a regular polygon is _____ congruent to an exterior angle of the polygon.

25. The length of a side of a regular hexagon inscribed in a circle is _____ equal to the length of a radius of the circle.

15. Multiple-Choice Exercises

Write the letter preceding the word or expression that best completes the statement.

1. A circle can always be circumscribed about (*a*) an equiangular polygon (*b*) an equilateral polygon (*c*) a regular polygon.

2. The regular quadrilateral is a (*a*) rectangle (*b*) square (*c*) rhombus.

3. A regular decagon has a side whose length is represented by s and an apothem whose length is represented by a. The area of the decagon is represented by   (a) $20as$ (b) $10as$ (c) $5as$.

4. Regular polygons of the same number of sides are always   (a) equal in area   (b) congruent   (c) similar.

5. As the length of a radius of a circle increases, the ratio of the circumference to the length of a diameter of the circle   (a) is constant   (b) increases   (c) decreases.

6. If the circumference of a circle is represented by C, the length of a radius of the circle is represented by   (a) $\dfrac{C}{\pi}$ (b) $\dfrac{C}{2\pi}$ (c) $\sqrt{\dfrac{C}{\pi}}$.

7. If the length of a radius of a circle is increased by x, the circumference of the circle is increased by   (a) x (b) $2x$ (c) $2\pi x$.

8. A regular polygon is defined as a polygon whose   (a) angles are congruent   (b) sides are congruent   (c) sides are congruent and whose angles are congruent.

9. The ratio of the areas of any two regular polygons which have equal perimeters is equal to the ratio of   (a) the lengths of their apothems   (b) the squares of the lengths of their apothems   (c) their perimeters.

10. The ratio of the areas of two circles is equal to the ratio of   (a) the lengths of their radii   (b) the square roots of the lengths of their radii   (c) the squares of the lengths of their radii.

11. In a circle of radius r, the area of a sector whose central angle contains $n°$ is represented by   (a) $\dfrac{n}{360} \times \pi r^2$ (b) $\dfrac{n}{180} \times \pi r^2$ (c) $\dfrac{n}{360} \times \pi d^2$.

12. The degree measure of a central angle of a regular polygon of n sides is represented by   (a) $\dfrac{360}{n}$ (b) $\dfrac{180}{n}$ (c) $\dfrac{n}{360}$.

13. If the length of a radius of a circle is multiplied by 4, the area of the circle is multiplied by   (a) 16   (b) 4   (c) 2.

14. If the circumference of a circle is multiplied by 9, the length of a radius of the circle is multiplied by   (a) 3   (b) 9   (c) 81.

15. Which conclusion makes the following statement false? If the number of sides of a regular polygon inscribed in a circle is increased   (a) the length of an apothem decreases   (b) the measure of each interior angle increases   (c) the perimeter increases.

16. As the number of sides of a regular polygon inscribed in a given circle increases   (a) the measure of the central angle increases   (b) the length of an apothem increases   (c) the measure of each exterior angle increases.

17. A central angle of a regular polygon and an interior angle of the polygon are always   (a) supplementary   (b) complementary   (c) congruent.

18. If a regular polygon has diagonals which are not congruent, it may be (*a*) a square (*b*) a hexagon (*c*) a pentagon.

19. The area of a circle the length of whose diameter is represented by *d* is represented by (*a*) $\frac{1}{4}\pi d^2$ (*b*) $\frac{1}{2}\pi d^2$ (*c*) πd^2.

20. A central angle of a regular polygon and an exterior angle drawn at one of the vertices of the polygon are always (*a*) complementary (*b*) supplementary (*c*) congruent.

16. Construction Exercises

1. Inscribe a square in a given circle.
2. Inscribe a regular octagon in a given circle.
3. Inscribe a regular hexagon in a given circle.
4. Inscribe an equilateral triangle in a given circle.
5. Circumscribe a square about a given circle.
6. Circumscribe an equilateral triangle about a given circle.
7. Using a given line segment as a side, construct a regular hexagon.
8. Construct a circle whose circumference is equal to the sum of the circumferences of two given circles whose radii are *R* and *r*.
9. Construct a circle whose circumference is equal to the difference of the circumferences of two given circles whose radii are *R* and *r*.
10. Construct a circle whose circumference is twice the circumference of a given circle whose radius is *R*.
11. Construct a circle whose area is equal to the sum of the areas of two given circles whose radii are *R* and *r*.
12. Construct a circle whose area is equal to the difference of the areas of two given circles whose radii are *R* and *r*.
13. Construct a circle whose area is twice the area of a given circle whose radius is *R*.
14. Construct a circle whose area is 4 times the area of a given circle whose radius is *R*.
15. Construct a circle whose area is one-quarter the area of a given circle whose radius is *R*.
16. The diagram shows the construction for inscribing a square in a given circle. Which statement, *a* or *b*, is used to prove the construction correct?
    a. An equiangular polygon inscribed in a circle is a regular polygon.
    b. If a circle is divided into any number of congruent arcs, the chords of these arcs form a regular inscribed polygon.

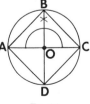

Ex. 16

CHAPTER IX
Inequalities

1. Symbols of Inequality

Up to this point, we have devoted a great deal of our attention to proving line segments congruent, angles congruent, measures of lines equal, and measures of angles equal. Sometimes we have talked about line segments or angles whose measures are unequal. Now we will study (1) methods of proving that the measure of one line segment is greater than the measure of another line segment, and (2) methods of proving that the measure of one angle is greater than the measure of another angle; that is, we will concern ourselves with the comparison of sizes of line segments and sizes of angles.

Let us recall the meanings of some of the symbols that you probably used in the study of algebra to indicate the inequality of two real numbers.

$4 \neq 3$ means 4 is not equal to 3 $a \neq b$ means a is not equal to b

$8 > 6$ means 8 is greater than 6 $a > b$ means a is greater than b

$5 < 7$ means 5 is less than 7 $a < b$ means a is less than b

A statement of inequality may be a true statement or it may be a false statement. For example, $5 \neq 4$, $8 > 7$, and $6 < 9$ are inequalities which are true, whereas $7 \neq 7$, $5 > 9$, and $7 < 4$ are inequalities which are false.

Consider the inequalities $8 > 5$ and $9 > 2$. Since the same inequality symbol of order is used in the two inequalities, we say they are *inequalities of the same order*. Also, $a < b$ and $c < d$ are inequalities of the same order.

Consider the inequalities $10 > 9$ and $6 < 8$. Since different inequality symbols of order are used in the two inequalities, we say they are *inequalities of the opposite order*. Also, $a > b$ and $c < d$ are inequalities of the opposite order.

Recall that the measure of a line segment is a real number. Hence, the inequality $AB > CD$ indicates that the number of a certain linear unit contained in line segment $\overline{AB}$ is greater than the number of the same linear unit contained in line segment $\overline{CD}$. Also, recall that the degree measure of an angle is a real number. Hence, the inequality $m\angle A > m\angle B$ indicates that the number of degrees contained in angle A is greater than the number of degrees contained in angle B.

In the discussion of inequalities involving geometric situations, we will simplify the language used in statements in the following manner:

Instead of saying that the measure of one line segment is greater than the measure of a second line segment, we will say that the first line segment is greater than the second line segment. We will follow a similar practice in dealing with lengths of arcs.

Instead of saying that the measure of one angle is greater than the measure of a second angle, we will say that the first angle is greater than the second angle.

EXERCISES

In 1–8, state whether the inequality is true or false.

1. $8 + 7 \neq 12$ **2.** $8 - 3 \neq 5$ **3.** $8 \times 0 \neq 7 \times 0$

4. $5 + 6 \neq 6 + 5$ **5.** $6 \times 1 \neq 6 \div 1$ **6.** $\frac{1}{4} + \frac{1}{4} \neq \frac{1}{4} \times \frac{1}{4}$

7. The product of 6 and 4 is not equal to the sum of 6 and 4.

8. The sum of 10 and 30 is not equal to 60 decreased by 20.

In 9–14, write the symbol $>$ or the symbol $<$ between each pair of numbers so that the resulting statement will be true.

9. 5   7   **10.** 12   8   **11.** 1   4   **12.** 15   20   **13.** 9   15   **14.** 25   17

In 15–20, express the inequality in words.

15. $25 > 17$ **16.** $16 < 22$ **17.** $9 + 4 > 8 + 2$

18. $7 - 3 < 13 - 4$ **19.** $3 \times 0 < 3 + 0$ **20.** $9 + 1 > 9 \times 1$

In 21–23, state whether the inequality is true or false.

21. $3 \times 5 < 4 + 6$ **22.** $6 \times 0 > 3 + 1$ **23.** $10 \times 1 > 20 \times 1$

In 24–27, state whether the two inequalities are of the same order or of opposite order.

24. $a > b, c > d$ **25.** $x < y, r > s$

26. $AB < DE, BC < EF$ **27.** $m\angle A > m\angle B, m\angle C < m\angle D$

2. Using Inequality Postulates in Proving Conclusions

We will now study postulates which involve unequal quantities, and we will learn how to use these postulates in proving conclusions.

Uniqueness of Order Postulate (The Trichotomy Postulate)

Postulate 47. **Given any two quantities, exactly one of the following relations is true:**

1. **The first quantity is less than the second.**
2. **The first quantity is equal to the second.**
3. **The first quantity is greater than the second.**

Thus, if a and b are real numbers, then exactly one of the following relations is true: $a < b$, $a = b$, $a > b$.

Transitivity Property of Inequality

Postulate 48. **If the first of three quantities is greater than the second and the second is greater than the third, then the first is greater than the third.**

Thus, if a, b, and c are real numbers such that $a > b$ and $b > c$, then $a > c$.

EXAMPLE 1.   If $10 > 8$
            and $8 > 5$,
            then $10 > 5$.

EXAMPLE 2.   If $BA > BD$
(Fig. 9–1)   and $BD > BC$,
            then $BA > BC$.

Fig. 9–1

MODEL PROBLEM

Given: $m\angle DBC > m\angle ABC$.
          $m\angle ABC > m\angle ACB$.

To prove: $m\angle DBC > m\angle ACB$.

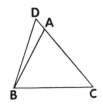

Proof: *Statements*	*Reasons*
1. $m\angle DBC > m\angle ABC$.	1. Given.
2. $m\angle ABC > m\angle ACB$.	2. Given.
3. $m\angle DBC > m\angle ACB$.	3. The transitive property of inequality: If the first of three quantities is greater than the second and the second is greater than the third, then the first is greater than the third.

EXERCISES

In 1–3, state whether the conclusion is correct. Justify your answer with a property of inequality.

1. If Harry is older than Sam and Sam is older than Bill, then Harry is older than Bill.
2. If Sue weighs more than Marian and Marian weighs more than Roberta, then Sue weighs more than Roberta.
3. If a plane is traveling faster than a car and the car is traveling faster than a ship, then the plane is traveling faster than the ship.

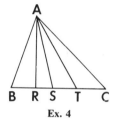

Ex. 4   Ex. 5   Ex. 6

4. *Given: $AT > AS$, $AS > AR$.*
   Prove: $AT > AR$.
5. *Given: $m\angle 1 > m\angle 2$, $m\angle 2 > m\angle 3$.*
   Prove: $m\angle 1 > m\angle 3$.
6. *Given: In $\square ABCD$, $AC > AB$, $AB > BC$.*
   Prove: $AC > BC$.

Substitution Postulate for Inequalities

Postulate 49. **A quantity may be substituted for its equal in any inequality.**

Thus, if a, b, and c are real numbers such that $a > b$ and $c = b$, then $a > c$.

EXAMPLE 1.   If $x > 7$
             and $y = x$,
             then $y > 7$.

EXAMPLE 2. (Fig. 9–2)   If $m\angle 3 > m\angle 1$
             and $m\angle 2 = m\angle 1$,
             then $m\angle 3 > m\angle 2$.

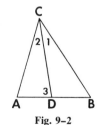

Fig. 9–2

MODEL PROBLEM

Given: $CB < CA.$
         $CD = CB.$

To prove: $CD < CA.$

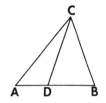

Proof: *Statements*	*Reasons*
1. $CB < CA.$	1. Given.
2. $CD = CB.$	2. Given.
3. $CD < CA.$	3. Substitution postulate for inequalities: A quantity may be substituted for its equal in any inequality.

EXERCISES

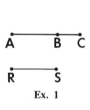
   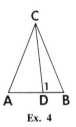
   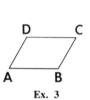

Ex. 1   Ex. 2   Ex. 3   Ex. 4

1. *Prove:* If $AC > AB$ and $RS = AB$, then $AC > RS$.
2. *Prove:* If $m\angle ABC < m\angle CBD$ and also if $m\angle ABC = m\angle DBE$, then $m\angle DBE < m\angle CBD$.
3. *Prove:* If $ABCD$ is a parallelogram and $AB > BC$, then $DC > BC$.
4. *Prove:* If $\triangle ABC$ is an isosceles triangle in which $\overline{AC} \cong \overline{CB}$ and $m\angle 1 > m\angle A$, then $m\angle 1 > m\angle B$.

Postulate Relating a Whole Quantity and Its Parts

Postulate 50. **A whole quantity is greater than any of its parts.**

Thus, if a, b, and c are positive numbers such that $a = b + c$, then $a > b$ and $a > c$.

EXAMPLE 1. (Fig. 9–3) The measure of the whole line segment $\overline{AB}$ is greater than the measure of its part $\overline{AC}$ and is also greater than the measure of its part $\overline{CB}$, or $AB > AC$ and $AB > CB$. Segments $\overline{AC}$ and $\overline{CB}$ are referred to as parts of segment $\overline{AB}$.

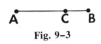

Fig. 9–3

EXAMPLE 2. (Fig. 9–4) The measure of the whole $\angle ABC$ is greater than the measure of its part $\angle ABD$ and is also greater than the measure of its part $\angle CBD$, or $m\angle ABC > m\angle ABD$ and $m\angle ABC > m\angle CBD$. $\angle ABD$ and $\angle CBD$ are referred to as parts of $\angle ABC$.

Fig. 9–4

EXERCISES

In 1–4, which refer to the figure, state whether the inequality is a true statement or a false statement. Justify your answer with an inequality postulate.

1. $m\angle ACB > m\angle ACD$.
2. $AB > BD$.
3. $m\angle ACB > m\angle BCD$.
4. $AB > AD$.

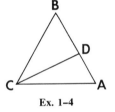

Ex. 1–4

Postulate Involving Addition of Equal Quantities and Unequal Quantities

Postulate 51. **If equal quantities are added to unequal quantities, the sums are unequal in the same order.**

Thus, if a, b, c, and d are real numbers such that $a > b$, and $c = d$, then $a + c > b + d$.

EXAMPLE 1.   If $5 < 8$
and $4 = 4$
then $5 + 4 < 8 + 4$,
or $9 < 12$.

EXAMPLE 2. (Fig. 9–5)   If $AB > CD$
and $BE = DF$,
then $AB + BE > CD + DF$,
or $AE > CF$.

MODEL PROBLEM

Given: $m\angle ABG < m\angle DEH.$
             $m\angle GBC = m\angle HEF.$

To prove: $m\angle ABC < m\angle DEF.$

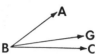

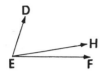

Proof: *Statements*	*Reasons*
1. $m\angle ABG < m\angle DEH.$	1. Given.
2. $m\angle GBC = m\angle HEF.$	2. Given.
3. $m\angle ABG + m\angle GBC < m\angle DEH + m\angle HEF,$	3. If equal quantities are added to un-
or $m\angle ABC < m\angle DEF.$	equal quantities, the sums are unequal in the same order.

EXERCISES

1. *Prove:* If $10 > 7$, then $18 > 15$.
2. *Prove:* If $4 < 14$, then $15 < 25$.
3. *Prove:* If $x - 3 > 12$, then $x > 15$.
4. *Prove:* If $y - 9 < 5$, then $y < 14$.

Ex. 5

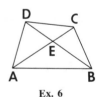

Ex. 6

5. *Prove:* If $AB = AD$ and $BC < DE$, then $AC < AE.$

6. *Prove:* If $m\angle DAC > m\angle DBC$ and $\overline{AE} \cong \overline{EB}$, then $m\angle DAB > m\angle CBA.$

Postulate Involving Addition of Unequal Quantities of the Same Order

Postulate 52. If unequal quantities are added to unequal quantities of the same order, the sums are unequal in the same order.

Thus, if a, b, c, and d are real numbers such that $a > b$ and $c > d$, then $a + c > b + d.$

EXAMPLE 1.　　　If $6 > 4$
and $8 > 5$,
then $6 + 8 > 4 + 5$,
or $14 > 9$.

EXAMPLE 2. (Fig. 9–6) If $CD < AB$
and $DF < BE$,
then $CD + DF < AB + BE$,
or $CF < AE$.

Fig. 9–6

MODEL PROBLEM

Given:　　$m\angle BCE > m\angle DBC.$
　　　　　$m\angle ACE > m\angle ABD.$

To prove: $m\angle ACB > m\angle ABC.$

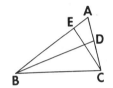

Proof:　　*Statements*	*Reasons*
1. $m\angle BCE > m\angle DBC.$	1. Given.
2. $m\angle ACE > m\angle ABD.$	2. Given.
3. $m\angle BCE + m\angle ACE >$ $m\angle DBC + m\angle ABD,$ or $m\angle ACB > m\angle ABC.$	3. If unequal quantities are added to unequal quantities of the same order, the sums are unequal in the same order.

EXERCISES

In 1 and 2 state whether the conclusion is correct. Justify your answer with an inequality postulate.

1. If Sidney weighs more than Ruth, and Jack weighs more than Martha, then Sidney and Jack together weigh more than Ruth and Martha together.

2. If Hilda has less money than Craig, and Rose has less money than Norman, then Hilda and Rose together have less money than Craig and Norman together.

3. *Prove:* If $8 > 6$, then $12 > 9$.
4. *Prove:* If $15 < 21$, then $18 < 27$.

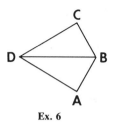

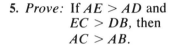
Ex. 5

Ex. 6

5. *Prove:* If $AE > AD$ and $EC > DB$, then $AC > AB$.

6. *Prove:* If $m\angle CDB < m\angle CBD$ and $m\angle ADB < m\angle ABD$, then $m\angle CDA < m\angle CBA$.

Postulate Involving Subtraction of Equal Quantities From Unequal Quantities

Postulate 53. **If equal quantities are subtracted from unequal quantities, the differences are unequal in the same order.**

Thus, if a, b, c, and d are real numbers such that $a > b$ and $c = d$, then $a - c > b - d$.

EXAMPLE 1.   If $15 > 12$
and $5 = 5$,
then $15 - 5 > 12 - 5$,
or $10 > 7$.

EXAMPLE 2. (Fig. 9–7) If $AC < AB$
and $EC = DB$,
then $AC - EC < AB - DB$,
or $AE < AD$.

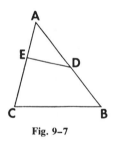
Fig. 9–7

MODEL PROBLEM

Given: $m\angle ABC > m\angle DEF$.
$m\angle ABG = m\angle DEH$.

To prove: $m\angle GBC > m\angle HEF$.

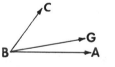

Proof: *Statements*	*Reasons*
1. $m\angle ABC > m\angle DEF$.	1. Given.
2. $m\angle ABG = m\angle DEH$.	2. Given.
3. $m\angle ABC - m\angle ABG >$ $m\angle DEF - m\angle DEH$, or $m\angle GBC > m\angle HEF$.	3. If equal quantities are subtracted from unequal quantities, the differences are unequal in the same order.

EXERCISES

1. *Prove:* If $18 > 12$, then $15 > 9$.
2. *Prove:* If $9 < 13$, then $7 < 11$.
3. *Prove:* If $x + 5 > 13$, then $x > 8$.
4. *Prove:* If $y + 3 < 9$, then $y < 6$.

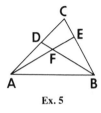

Ex. 5

Ex. 6

5. *Prove:* If $AE > BD$ and
$AF = BF$, then
$FE > FD$.

6. *Prove:* If $m\angle DCB < m\angle DAB$ and
$\overline{AD} \cong \overline{DC}$, then
$m\angle ACB < m\angle CAB$.

Postulate Involving Subtraction of Unequal Quantities From Equal Quantities

Postulate 54. If unequal quantities are subtracted from equal quantities, the differences are unequal in the opposite order.

Thus, if a, b, c, and d are real numbers such that $a = b$ and $c < d$, then $a - c > b - d$.

Example 1.   If $10 = 10$
and $8 > 4$,
then $10 - 8 < 10 - 4$,
or $2 < 6$.

Example 2. (Fig. 9–8) If $CD = AB$
and $CF < AE$,
then $CD - CF > AB - AE$,
or $FD > EB$.

Fig. 9–8

MODEL PROBLEM

Given: $m\angle DEF = m\angle ABC$.
$m\angle DEH > m\angle ABG$.

To prove: $m\angle HEF < m\angle GBC$.

[The proof is given on the next page.]

Proof: *Statements*	*Reasons*
1. $m\angle DEF = m\angle ABC.$	1. Given.
2. $m\angle DEH > m\angle ABG.$	2. Given.
3. $m\angle DEF - m\angle DEH < m\angle ABC$ $- m\angle ABG,$ or $m\angle HEF < m\angle GBC.$	3. If unequal quantities are sub- tracted from equal quantities, the differences are unequal in the opposite order.

EXERCISES

1. *Prove:* If $90 = 90$ and $x > y$, then $(90 - x) < (90 - y)$.
2. *Prove:* If $x < y$, then $(180 - x) > (180 - y)$.

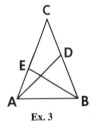

Ex. 3

Ex. 4

3. *Prove:* If $m\angle CAB = m\angle CBA$ and $m\angle BAD > m\angle ABE$, then $m\angle CAD < m\angle CBE$.

4. *Prove:* If $ABCD$ is a parallelo-gram and $ED < BF$, then $AE > FC$.

Postulate Involving Multiplication of Unequal Quantities by Equal Positive Quantities

Postulate 55. **If unequal quantities are multiplied by equal positive quanti-ties, the products are unequal in the same order. [A special case of this postu-late is: Doubles of unequal quantities are unequal in the same order.]**

Thus, if a, b, c, and d are positive numbers such that $a > b$ and $c = d$, then $ac > bd$.

EXAMPLE 1.   If $9 > 7$
and $4 = 4,$
then $4 \times 9 > 4 \times 7,$
or $36 > 28.$

EXAMPLE 2. (Fig. 9–9)   If $AB > DE$
                               and $AC = 2AB$,
                                     $DF = 2DE$
                               then $AC > DF$ because
doubles of unequal quantities are
unequal in the same order.

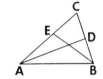

Fig. 9–9

MODEL PROBLEM

Given: $m\angle DAB < m\angle EBA$.
            $\overline{AD}$ bisects $\angle CAB$, $\overline{BE}$ bisects $\angle CBA$.

To prove: $m\angle CAB < m\angle CBA$.

Proof: *Statements*	*Reasons*
1. $m\angle DAB < m\angle EBA$.	1. Given.
2. $2m\angle DAB < 2m\angle EBA$.	2. Doubles of unequal quantities are unequal in the same order.
3. $\overline{AD}$ bisects $\angle CAB$, $\overline{BE}$ bisects $\angle CBA$.	3. Given.
4. $m\angle CAB = 2m\angle DAB$, $m\angle CBA = 2m\angle EBA$.	4. A bisector of an angle divides the angle into two congruent angles.
5. $m\angle CAB < m\angle CBA$.	5. A quantity may be substituted for its equal in any inequality.

EXERCISES

1. *Prove:* If $\dfrac{x}{2} > 6$, then $x > 12$.

2. *Prove:* If $\dfrac{y}{5} < 4$, then $y < 20$.

3. If $a > b$ and c is a positive number, which of the following relationships is *not* true?
(1) $ac > bc$ (2) $c - a > c - b$ (3) $a + c > b + c$ (4) $a - c > b - c$

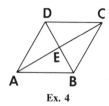

Ex. 4   Ex. 5

4. *Prove:* If $m\angle DBA > m\angle CAB$, $m\angle CBA = 2m\angle DBA$, and $m\angle DAB = 2m\angle CAB$, then $m\angle CBA > m\angle DAB$.

5. *Prove:* If $BD < BE$, D is the midpoint of $\overline{AB}$, and E is the midpoint of $\overline{BC}$, then $BA < BC$.

Postulate Involving Division of Unequal Quantities by Equal Positive Quantities

Postulate 56. **If unequal quantities are divided by equal positive quantities, the quotients are unequal in the same order. [A special case of this postulate is: Halves of unequal quantities are unequal in the same order.]**

Thus, if a, b, c, and d are positive numbers such that $a > b$ and $c = d$, then $\dfrac{a}{c} > \dfrac{b}{d}$.

EXAMPLE 1.　　If $12 > 8$
and $4 = 4$,
then $\frac{12}{4} > \frac{8}{4}$,
or $3 > 2$.

EXAMPLE 2. (Fig. 9–10)　　　　If $AC < AB$
and $AE = \frac{1}{2}AC$,
$AD = \frac{1}{2}AB$,
then $AE < AD$, be-
cause halves of unequal quantities are unequal in the same
order.

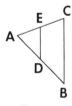

Fig. 9–10

MODEL PROBLEM

Given:　　$m\angle ABC > m\angle DEF$.
　　　　$\overrightarrow{BG}$ bisects $\angle ABC$.
　　　　$\overrightarrow{EH}$ bisects $\angle DEF$.
To prove: $m\angle ABG > m\angle DEH$.

Proof: *Statements*	*Reasons*

Statements	Reasons
1. $m\angle ABC > m\angle DEF$.	1. Given.
2. $\dfrac{m\angle ABC}{2} > \dfrac{m\angle DEF}{2}$, or $\frac{1}{2}m\angle ABC > \frac{1}{2}m\angle DEF$.	2. Halves of unequal quantities are unequal in the same order.
3. $\overrightarrow{BG}$ bisects $\angle ABC$, $\overrightarrow{EH}$ bisects $\angle DEF$.	3. Given.
4. $m\angle ABG = \frac{1}{2}m\angle ABC$, $m\angle DEH = \frac{1}{2}m\angle DEF$.	4. A bisector of an angle divides the angle into two congruent angles.
5. $m\angle ABG > m\angle DEH$.	5. A quantity may be substituted for its equal in any inequality.

EXERCISES

1. *Prove:* If $2x > 14$, then $x > 7$.
2. *Prove:* If $5y < 40$, then $y < 8$.

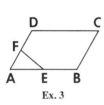

Ex. 3

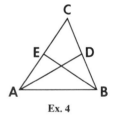

Ex. 4

3. *Prove:* If $AB > AD$, $AE = \frac{1}{2}AB$, and $AF = \frac{1}{2}AD$, then $AE > AF$.

4. *Prove:* If $m\angle CAB < m\angle CBA$, $\overline{AD}$ bisects $\angle CAB$, and $\overline{BE}$ bisects $\angle CBA$, then $m\angle DAB < m\angle EBA$.

Postulate Involving Positive Powers and Positive Roots of Unequal Positive Quantities

Postulate 57. Like positive integral powers and like positive integral roots of unequal positive quantities are unequal in the same order.

Thus, if a, b, and n are positive integers such that $a > b$, then $a^n > b^n$, and $\sqrt[n]{a} > \sqrt[n]{b}$.

EXAMPLE 1. If $y > 7$, then $y^2 > 49$.

EXAMPLE 2. If $x^2 < 25$, then $x < 5$, when x is a positive number.

3. Additional Exercises Using Inequality Postulates in Proving Conclusions

Now let us see how the inequality postulates we have just studied can be combined with other postulates, theorems, and corollaries in proving conclusions.

MODEL PROBLEMS

1. *Given:*   Isosceles triangle ABC with $\overline{AB} \cong \overline{BC}$.
$m\angle BAD > m\angle BCD$.

   To prove: $m\angle CAD > m\angle ACD$.

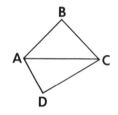

Proof:	*Statements*	*Reasons*
1.	$m\angle BAD > m\angle BCD$.	1. Given.
2.	$\overline{AB} \cong \overline{BC}$.	2. Given.
3.	$m\angle BAC = m\angle BCA$.	3. If two sides of a triangle are congruent, the angles opposite these sides are congruent.
4.	$m\angle BAD - m\angle BAC > m\angle BCD - m\angle BCA$, or $m\angle CAD > m\angle ACD$.	4. If equal quantities are subtracted from unequal quantities, the differences are unequal in the same order.

2. Prove that the supplement of an obtuse angle is an acute angle.

   Given: $\angle DEF$ is an obtuse angle.
$\angle ABC$ is supplementary to $\angle DEF$.

   To prove: $\angle ABC$ is an acute angle.

   Plan: To prove that $\angle ABC$ is an acute angle, prove that $m\angle ABC < 90$.

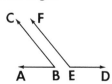

Proof: Statements	Reasons
1. $\angle DEF$ is an obtuse angle, $\angle ABC$ is supplementary to $\angle DEF$.	1. Given.
2. $m\angle ABC + m\angle DEF = 180$.	2. The sum of the measures of two angles which are supplementary is 180.
3. $m\angle DEF > 90$.	3. The measure of an obtuse angle is greater than 90 and less than 180.
4. $m\angle ABC < 90$.	4. If unequal quantities are subtracted from equal quantities, the differences are unequal in the opposite order.
5. $\angle ABC$ is an acute angle.	5. An angle whose measure is less than 90 and greater than 0 is an acute angle.

EXERCISES

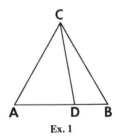

Ex. 1

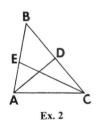

Ex. 2

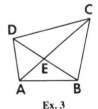

Ex. 3

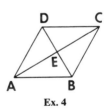

Ex. 4

1. *Given:* Isosceles triangle ABC with $\overline{AC} \cong \overline{CB}$, $m\angle CDB > m\angle CAD$.
   Prove: $m\angle CDB > m\angle CBA$.
2. *Given:* $m\angle BAC > m\angle BCA$, $\overline{AD}$ bisects $\angle BAC$, $\overline{CE}$ bisects $\angle BCA$.
   Prove: $m\angle DAC > m\angle ECA$.
3. *Given:* Quadrilateral $ABCD$, diagonals $\overline{AC}$ and $\overline{BD}$, $AE + EB > AB$, $CE + ED > DC$.
   Prove: $AC + BD > AB + DC$.
4. *Given:* In parallelogram $ABCD$, $AE > BE$.
   Prove: $AC > BD$.

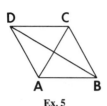
Ex. 5

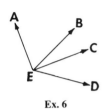
Ex. 6

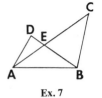
Ex. 7

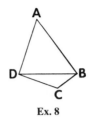
Ex. 8

5. *Given:* $ABCD$ is a rhombus, $m\angle CBA < m\angle DAB$.
   Prove: $m\angle DBA < m\angle CAB$.
6. *Given:* $m\angle AEB > m\angle CED$.
   Prove: $m\angle AEC > m\angle DEB$.
7. *Given:* $m\angle CBA > m\angle DAB$, $\overline{AE} \cong \overline{EB}$.
   Prove: $m\angle CBD > m\angle DAE$.
8. *Given:* $\overline{AB} \perp \overline{BC}$, $\overline{AD} \perp \overline{DC}$, $m\angle ADB > m\angle ABD$.
   Prove: $m\angle BDC < m\angle DBC$.

9. *Given:* $\overleftrightarrow{ABC}$ and $\overleftrightarrow{EFG}$.
   $m\angle HFG < m\angle DBC$.
   Prove: $m\angle HFE > m\angle DBA$.
10. *Prove:* The supplement of an acute angle is an obtuse angle.

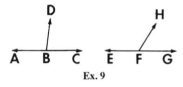
Ex. 9

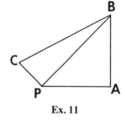
Ex. 11

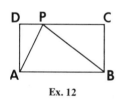
Ex. 12

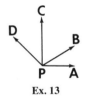
Ex. 13

Ex. 14

11. *Given:* $m\angle CPB > m\angle CBP$, $\overline{AP} \cong \overline{AB}$.
    Prove: $m\angle CPA > m\angle CBA$.
12. *Given:* $ABCD$ is a rectangle, $m\angle PAB > m\angle PBA$.
    Prove: $m\angle PAD < m\angle PBC$.
13. *Given:* $m\angle CPB > m\angle BPA$.
    Prove: (a) $m\angle DPB > m\angle CPB$.
    (b) $m\angle DPB > m\angle BPA$.
14. *Given:* $m\angle DAB > m\angle DBA$.
    Prove: $m\angle CAB > m\angle DBA$.

15. *Given:* $m\angle ABC > m\angle ADB$.
    Prove: $m\angle ABD > m\angle ADB$.

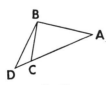
Ex. 15

16. In $\triangle DEF$ and $\triangle D'E'F'$, $m\angle D = m\angle D'$, $m\angle E > m\angle E'$.
    Prove: $m\angle F < m\angle F'$.

17. *Prove:* If $m\angle A$ is greater than $m\angle B$, then the measure of the complement of $\angle A$ is less than the measure of the complement of $\angle B$.

18. *Prove:* If $m\angle R$ is less than $m\angle S$, then the measure of the supplement of $\angle R$ is greater than the measure of the supplement of $\angle S$.

4. Inequalities in a Triangle

We have already studied the postulate "The shortest path between two points is the line segment joining the two points." Using this postulate, we can readily show:

Theorem 129. **The sum of the lengths of two sides of a triangle is greater than the length of the third side.**

In $\triangle ABC$ (Fig. 9–11), the sum of the lengths of two sides is greater than the length of the third side, or $AC + CB > BA$, $CB + BA > AC$, and also $BA + AC > CB$.

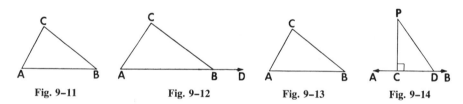

Fig. 9–11   Fig. 9–12   Fig. 9–13   Fig. 9–14

Theorem 130. **The measure of an exterior angle of a triangle is greater than the measure of either nonadjacent interior angle.**

In Fig. 9–12, if $\angle CBD$ is an exterior angle of triangle ABC, then $m\angle CBD > m\angle A$ and $m\angle CBD > m\angle C$.

Theorem 131. **If two sides of a triangle are unequal, the angles opposite these sides are unequal and the greater angle lies opposite the greater side.**

In $\triangle ABC$ (Fig. 9–13), if CB is greater than CA, then the measure of the angle opposite $\overline{CB}$ is greater than the measure of the angle opposite $\overline{CA}$, or $m\angle A > m\angle B$.

Theorem 132. **If two angles of a triangle are unequal, the sides opposite these angles are unequal and the greater side lies opposite the greater angle.**

In $\triangle ABC$ (Fig. 9–13), if $m\angle A$ is greater than $m\angle B$, then the measure of the side opposite $\angle A$ is greater than the measure of the side opposite $\angle B$, or $CB > CA$.

Corollary T132-1. **The shortest line segment that can be drawn joining a point not on a given line to the given line is the line segment drawn perpendicular to the given line from the given point.**

In Fig. 9–14, if $\overleftrightarrow{PC}$ is perpendicular to $\overleftrightarrow{AB}$, then segment $\overline{PC}$ is shorter than any other segment that can be drawn joining P and a point in $\overline{AB}$, such as $\overline{PD}$.

Methods of Proof:

1. To prove that the length of one line segment is greater than the length of a second line segment, show that the two segments are two sides in a triangle and that the measure of the angle opposite the first segment is greater than the measure of the angle opposite the second segment.
2. To prove that the measure of one angle is greater than the measure of a second angle:
   a. show that they are angles of a triangle and that the length of the side opposite the first angle is greater than the length of the side opposite the second angle.

OR

   b. show that the first angle is an exterior angle of a triangle in which the second angle is a nonadjacent interior angle.

MODEL PROBLEMS

1. If the lengths of two sides of a triangle are 10 and 14, the length of the third side may be   (*a*) 2   (*b*) 4   (*c*) 22   (*d*) 24.

   Solution: In a triangle, the sum of the lengths of any two sides must be greater than the length of the third side. We can therefore discover if three lengths can be the sides of a triangle by determining whether or not the sum of the two shorter lengths is greater than the third length.

   a. 2 cannot be the third side because $2 + 10$ is not > 14.

   b. 4 cannot be the third side because $4 + 10$ is not > 14.

   c. 22 can be the third side because $10 + 14 > 22$.

   d. 24 cannot be the third side because $10 + 14$ is not > 24.

   Answer: The third side may be 22.

2. In $\triangle ABC$, $m\angle C = 125$, $m\angle B = 35$. Which is the shortest side of the triangle?

   Solution:

   1. Since $m\angle B = 35$ and $m\angle C = 125$,
      $m\angle A = 180 - (125 + 35) = 180 - 160 = 20.$

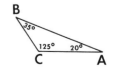

2. Since the shortest side of a triangle is opposite the smallest angle, the shortest side of $\triangle ABC$ is $\overline{BC}$, which is opposite the smallest angle, $\angle A$.

Answer: $\overline{BC}$ is the shortest side of $\triangle ABC$.

3. In isosceles $\triangle ABC$, with $\overline{AC} \cong \overline{CB}$, base $\overline{AB}$ is extended to D and $\overline{CD}$ is drawn. *Prove: $CD > CA$.*

Given: $\overline{AC} \cong \overline{CB}$.
            $\overline{AB}$ is extended to D.
            $\overline{CD}$ is drawn.

To prove: $CD > CA$.

Plan: To prove that $CD > CA$, show that $\overline{CD}$ and $\overline{CA}$ are in $\triangle ACD$ with $m\angle 3$, which is opposite $\overline{CD}$, greater than $m\angle 1$, which is opposite $\overline{CA}$.

Proof: *Statements*	*Reasons*
1. In $\triangle CBD$, $m\angle 2 > m\angle 1$.	1. The measure of an exterior angle of a triangle is greater than the measure of either nonadjacent interior angle.
2. $\overline{AC} \cong \overline{CB}$.	2. Given.
3. $\angle 3 \cong \angle 2$, or $m\angle 3 = m\angle 2$.	3. Base angles of an isosceles triangle are congruent.
4. $m\angle 3 > m\angle 1$.	4. A quantity may be substituted for its equal in any inequality.
5. $CD > CA$.	5. If two angles of a triangle are unequal, the sides opposite these angles are unequal, and the greater side lies opposite the greater angle.

4. *Given:*   In $\triangle ABC$, $BC > BA$.
           $\overline{CD}$ bisects $\angle BCA$.
           $\overline{AE}$ bisects $\angle BAC$.

To prove: $m\angle EAC > m\angle DCA$.

Plan: To prove $m\angle EAC > m\angle DCA$, show that in $\triangle ABC$, $m\angle BAC > m\angle BCA$ because $BC > BA$; and then show that $m\angle EAC$, which is $\frac{1}{2}m\angle BAC$, is greater than $m\angle DCA$, which is $\frac{1}{2}m\angle BCA$.

[The proof is given on the next page.]

Proof: Statements	*Reasons*
1. In $\triangle ABC$, $BC > BA$.	1. Given.
2. $m\angle BAC > m\angle BCA$.	2. If two sides of a triangle are un-equal, the angles opposite these sides are unequal, and the greater angle lies opposite the greater side.
3. $\overline{AE}$ bisects $\angle BAC$, $\overline{CD}$ bisects $\angle BCA$.	3. Given.
4. $m\angle EAC = \frac{1}{2}m\angle BAC$, $m\angle DCA = \frac{1}{2}m\angle BCA$.	4. A bisector of an angle divides the angle into two congruent angles.
5. $m\angle EAC > m\angle DCA$.	5. Halves of unequal quantities are unequal in the same order.

EXERCISES

1. Tell whether the given lengths may be the measures of the sides of a triangle:
   a. 6 in., 4 in., 10 in.   *b.* 6 in., 4 in., 12 in.   *c.* 6 in., 4 in., 8 in.
2. Tell which of the following number triples may be used as the lengths of the sides of a triangle:
   a. $(7, 8, 9)$ *b.* $(3, 5, 8)$ *c.* $(8, 5, 2)$ *d.* $(3, 10, 6)$ *e.* $(6, 9, 10)$
3. The lengths of two sides of a triangle are 3 in. and 6 in. The length of the third side may be:
   a. 3 in.   *b.* 6 in.   *c.* 9 in.   *d.* 12 in.
4. Which one of the following number triples can *not* represent the length units of the sides of a triangle?
   a. $(2, 3, 4)$ *b.* $(3, 1, 1)$ *c.* $(3, 4, 5)$ *d.* $(3, 4, 4)$
5. In triangle ABC, $AB = 8$, $BC = 10$, and $CA = 14$. Name the largest angle of triangle ABC.
6. In triangle ABC, angle C contains $60°$ and AB is greater than AC. Angle B contains   (*a*) $60°$ (*b*) less than $60°$ (*c*) more than $60°$.
7. In triangle ABC, $CA > CB$ and $m\angle B = 35$. Angle C is   (*a*) an acute angle   (*b*) a right angle   (*c*) an obtuse angle.
8. In $\triangle ABC$, $m\angle c = 90$ and $m\angle B = 35$. Name the shortest side of this triangle.

9. In $\triangle ABC$, $m\angle A = 74$ and $m\angle B = 58$. Which is the longest side of the triangle?

10. If in $\triangle RST$, $m\angle R = 71$ and $m\angle S = 37$, then (a) $ST > RS$ (b) $RS > RT$ (c) $RS = ST$ (d) $RT > ST$.

11. In $\triangle RST$, an exterior angle at R contains $120°$. If $m\angle S > m\angle T$, the longest side of the triangle is (a) $\overline{RS}$ (b) $\overline{ST}$ (c) $\overline{TR}$.

12. In $\triangle RST$, $m\angle T = 60$ and an exterior angle at R contains $130°$. Which is the longest side of the triangle?

13. In $\triangle RST$, $\angle R$ is obtuse and $m\angle S = 50$. Name the shortest side of the triangle.

14. In $\triangle RST$, $m\angle R > m\angle S$ and the bisectors of $\angle R$ and $\angle S$ meet in P. PS is (a) equal to PR (b) less than PR (c) greater than PR.

15. In $\triangle ABC$, if an exterior angle at C contains $110°$, then (a) $m\angle A < 110$ (b) $m\angle A = 110$ (c) $m\angle A > 110$.

16. In $\triangle DEF$, if an exterior angle at D contains $90°$, then $\angle E$ is (a) an acute angle (b) a right angle (c) an obtuse angle.

17. Given $\triangle RST$ with side $\overline{RT}$ extended through T to W. Then for any $\triangle RST$ (a) $m\angle WTS < m\angle STR$ (b) $m\angle WTS > m\angle STR$ (c) $m\angle WTS > m\angle R$ (d) $m\angle WTS < m\angle R$.

18. In isosceles triangle ABC, $\overline{AC} \cong \overline{CB}$. If D is a point on the base $\overline{AB}$ lying between A and B, and $\overline{CD}$ is drawn, then (a) $AC > CD$ (b) $CD > AC$ (c) $m\angle A > m\angle ADC$ (d) $m\angle B > m\angle BDC$.

19. In isosceles triangle RQS, $\overline{QR} \cong \overline{QS}$. If $\overline{RS}$ is extended to point P and $\overline{QP}$ is drawn, it is always true that (a) $m\angle QRS > m\angle RQS$ (b) $m\angle QRS > m\angle RPQ$ (c) $m\angle SQP > m\angle RPQ$ (d) $m\angle SPQ > m\angle RQS$.

20. $\triangle DEF$ is an acute triangle. The shortest line segment drawn from D to $\overline{EF}$ is (a) the bisector of angle D (b) the altitude to $\overline{EF}$ (c) the median to $\overline{EF}$.

In 21–27, if the blank space is replaced by the word *always*, *sometimes*, or *never*, the resulting statement will be true. Select the word which will correctly complete each statement.

21. In triangle ABC, angle A contains more than $60°$. Side $\overline{BC}$ is _____ the longest side of the triangle.

22. If one angle of a scalene triangle contains 60 degrees, the side opposite this angle is _____ the longest side of the triangle.

23. If one of the congruent sides of an isosceles triangle is longer than the base, then the measure of the angle opposite the base is _____ greater than 60.

24. In triangle ABC, if AB is greater than AC, then $m\angle C$ is _____ greater than $m\angle B$.

25. The angles whose vertices are the endpoints of the longest side of a triangle are _____ acute angles.

26. If the three sides of a triangle are unequal in length, the altitude upon any side is _____ equal to the median to that side.

27. An altitude and a median are drawn from the same vertex of a triangle to the opposite side. The altitude is _____ greater than the median.

28. *Given: $m\angle DEB = m\angle DAB$. Points B, E, and C are collinear.*
   Prove: $m\angle BAC > m\angle BCD$.

Ex. 28

29. *Given: $m\angle RST > m\angle RTS$.*
   Prove: $m\angle RST > m\angle RWS$.

30. In circle O, radii $\overline{OC}$ and $\overline{OD}$ and chord $\overline{CD}$ are drawn. Point T is taken on radius $\overline{OC}$ between O and C, and $\overline{TD}$ is drawn. Prove that $TD > TC$.

31. In circle O if $\overline{OBA}$ and $\overline{OC}$ are radii and $\overline{BC}$ is drawn, prove:
   a. $OB + BC > OA$.
   b. $BC > BA$.

Ex. 29

32. In isosceles $\triangle ABC$, $\overline{CA} \cong \overline{CB}$. If D is a point on $\overline{AC}$ between A and C, prove that $DB > DA$.

33. Given $\triangle ABC$ with $\overline{AB} \cong \overline{AC}$; D is any point between B and C on $\overline{BC}$; line segment $\overline{AD}$ is drawn. Prove that $AB > AD$.

34. In $\triangle ABC$, $\overline{AB} \cong \overline{AC}$. Prove that an exterior angle at B is an obtuse angle.

35. In $\triangle ABC$, the bisector of $\angle C$ meets $\overline{AB}$ in D. Prove that $CB > BD$.

36. In $\triangle ABC$, $AC > AB$. The bisector of $\angle B$ and the bisector of $\angle C$ intersect in D. Prove that $DC > DB$.

37. In $\triangle ABC$, $\overline{AB} \cong \overline{AC}$. If $\overline{AD}$ is the median to $\overline{BC}$, prove that $AB > AD$.

38. In $\triangle RST$, $\overline{SR} \cong \overline{ST}$. The bisector of $\angle R$ and the bisector of $\angle T$ intersect in P. Prove that $RT > PT$.

39. In parallelogram $ABCD$, $\overline{AD}$ is longer than $\overline{DC}$ and diagonal $\overline{AC}$ is drawn. Prove that $\overline{CA}$ does not bisect angle C.

40. $ABCD$ is a quadrilateral in which $AD > DC$ and $AB > BC$. Prove that $m\angle BCD > m\angle DAB$. [*Hint:* Draw $\overline{AC}$.]

41. In parallelogram $PQRS$, $PQ > QR$ and diagonal $\overline{PR}$ is drawn. Prove that $m\angle SPR > m\angle RPQ$.

42. In quadrilateral $PRST$, $\overline{PR} \cong \overline{RS}$ and $PT > ST$. Prove that $m\angle RST > m\angle RPT$.

43. In acute $\triangle ABC$, the altitude from B meets $\overline{AC}$ at D. If $m\angle ABD > m\angle CBD$, prove that $AB > BC$.

44. If median $\overline{AD}$ of $\triangle ABC$ is longer than $\overline{BD}$, prove that $m\angle BAC$ is less than the sum of $m\angle B$ and $m\angle C$.

45. Prove that the sum of the lengths of the diagonals of a quadrilateral is greater than the sum of the lengths of a pair of opposite sides.

46. In parallelogram $ABCD$, $\overline{AC}$ is the longer diagonal. Point P is taken on $\overline{AC}$ so that $AP = AB$. Prove that $BC > PC$.

47. In $\triangle ABC$, $AC > AB$. $\overline{CA}$ is extended through A to a point D and $\overline{BD}$ is drawn. Prove that $DC > DB$.

48. In the figure, $\overline{BC} \cong \overline{BD}$ and $\overline{BE}$ is the bisector of angle DBC. (*a*) Prove that $\overline{ED} \cong \overline{EC}$. (*b*) Using the fact that $\overline{ED} \cong \overline{EC}$, prove $AC > AD$.

49. In $\triangle ABC$, $\overline{AB} \cong \overline{AC}$. A line through B intersects $\overline{AC}$ at D. $\overline{BD}$ is extended through D to point E and $\overline{CE}$ is drawn. Prove that $BE > CE$.

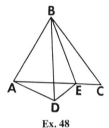

Ex. 48

50. *Prove:* The difference between the lengths of two sides of a triangle is less than the length of the third side.

51. *Prove:* The sum of the lengths of the three altitudes of a triangle is less than the perimeter of the triangle.

52. *Given:* Point P is in the interior of $\triangle RST$.
  a. *Prove:* $RT + TS > RP + PS$. [*Hint:* Extend $\overline{SP}$ until it intersects $\overline{RT}$ at Q.]
  b. *Prove:* $m\angle RPS > m\angle RTS$.

53. Point P is in the interior of $\triangle RST$. Prove that the sum of the distances from P to the vertices of $\triangle RST$ is (*a*) less than the perimeter of $\triangle RST$ (*b*) greater than half the perimeter of $\triangle RST$. [*Hint:* In proving part *a*, use the fact proved in exercise 52*a*.]

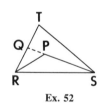

Ex. 52

54. *Prove:* The perimeter of a quadrilateral is greater than the sum of the lengths of its diagonals.

55. *Prove:* The length of a median drawn to a side of a triangle is less than one-half the sum of the lengths of the other two sides. [*Hint:* In $\triangle ABC$, extend median $\overline{AM}$ to point D so that $AM = MD$. Show that $\overline{CD} \cong \overline{AB}$. Use the fact that in $\triangle ACD$, $AC + CD > AD$.]

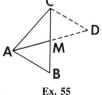

Ex. 55

56. *Prove:* The sum of the lengths of the medians of a triangle is less than the perimeter of the triangle.

5. Inequalities in Two Triangles

Theorem 133. **If two triangles have two sides of one congruent respectively to two sides of the other and the included angles are unequal, then the triangle which has the greater included angle has the greater third side.**

In $\triangle ABC$ and $A'B'C'$ (Fig. 9–15), if $\overline{AB} \cong \overline{A'B'}$, $\overline{BC} \cong \overline{B'C'}$, and $m\angle B > m\angle B'$, then $AC > A'C'$.

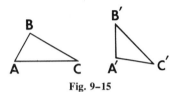

Fig. 9–15

Theorem 134. **If two triangles have two sides of one congruent respectively to two sides of the other and the third sides are unequal, then the triangle which has the greater third side has the greater angle opposite this side.**

In $\triangle ABC$ and $A'B'C'$ (Fig. 9–15), if $\overline{AB} \cong \overline{A'B'}$, $\overline{BC} \cong \overline{B'C'}$, and $AC > A'C'$, then $m\angle B > m\angle B'$.

Methods of Proof:

1. To prove that the lengths of two line segments which are not in the same triangle are unequal, show that the segments are sides in two triangles which have two sides of one congruent to two sides of the other and that the angles included between these sides are unequal.

2. To prove that the measures of two angles which are not in the same triangle are unequal, show that the angles are opposite unequal sides in two triangles which have two sides of one congruent to two sides of the other.

MODEL PROBLEM ⁓⁓⁓⁓⁓⁓⁓⁓⁓⁓⁓⁓⁓⁓⁓

Given: $ABCD$ is a parallelogram with diagonals $\overline{AC}$ and $\overline{BD}$. $\angle ABC$ is an obtuse angle.

To prove: $AC > BD$.

Plan: Since $\overline{AC}$ and $\overline{BD}$ are in different triangles ($\triangle ABC$ and $\triangle BAD$), show that two sides in $\triangle ABC$ ($\overline{BC}$ and $\overline{AB}$) are congruent to two sides in $\triangle BAD$ ($\overline{AD}$ and $\overline{AB}$), and that the measure of the included angle ABC is greater than the measure of the included angle BAD.

Proof: Statements	*Reasons*
1. $ABCD$ is a parallelogram.	1. Given.
2. $\overline{AD} \cong \overline{BC}$.	2. Both pairs of opposite sides of a parallelogram are congruent.
3. $\angle BAD$ is supplementary to $\angle ABC$.	3. The consecutive angles of a parallelogram are supplementary.
4. $\angle ABC$ is an obtuse angle.	4. Given.
5. $\angle BAD$ is an acute angle.	5. The supplement of an obtuse angle is an acute angle.
6. $m\angle ABC > m\angle BAD$.	6. The measure of an obtuse angle is greater than the measure of an acute angle.
7. $\overline{AB} \cong \overline{AB}$.	7. Reflexive property of congruence.
8. $AC > BD$.	8. If two triangles have two sides of one congruent respectively to two sides of the other and the included angles are unequal, then the triangle which has the greater included angle has the greater third side.

EXERCISES

1. In triangle ABC, $AB = 5$ in., $BC = 10$ in., and $m\angle B = 40$. In triangle $A'B'C'$, $A'B' = 5$ in., $B'C' = 10$ in., and $m\angle B' = 90$. Prove that $A'C' > AC$.

2. $\overline{AC}$ and $\overline{BD}$ are diagonals of parallelogram $ABCD$. If $m\angle DAB = 50$, then   (a) $AC = BD$ (b) $AC < BD$ (c) $AC > BD$.

3. If, in rhombus $ABCD$, $m\angle A = 110$, then   (a) $AC = BD$ (b) $AC > BD$ (c) $AC < BD$.

4. In triangle DEF, $DE = 6$ in., $EF = 8$ in., and $FD = 10$ in. In triangle $D'E'F'$, $D'E' = 6$ in., $E'F' = 8$ in., and $D'F' = 12$ in.
   a. Prove that $m\angle E' > m\angle E$.
   b. Prove that $\angle E'$ is an obtuse angle.

5. In parallelogram $ABCD$, with diagonals $\overline{AC}$ and $\overline{BD}$, $AC < BD$.
   a. Prove that $m\angle CDA < m\angle DAB$.
   b. Prove that $\angle CDA$ is an acute angle.

6. In triangle ABC, $\overline{CD}$ is a median to $\overline{AB}$. If $m\angle CDB > m\angle CDA$, prove that $CB > CA$.

7. In isosceles triangle RST, $\overline{RT} \cong \overline{TS}$. If Q is a point on $\overline{RS}$ such that $RQ > QS$, prove that $m\angle RTQ > m\angle QTS$.

8. If $\overline{AC} \cong \overline{AD}$, prove that $CB > DB$.

9. In triangle RST, $RS > ST$. P is a point on $\overline{RS}$ and Q is a point on $\overline{ST}$ such that $\overline{RP} \cong \overline{TQ}$. Prove that $RQ > TP$.

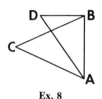

Ex. 8

6. Inequalities in Circles

Previously we have studied theorems about congruent (equal in measure) central angles, arcs, and chords in a circle or in equal circles. Now we will study theorems dealing with central angles, arcs, and chords which are of unequal measure when they are in the same circle or in equal circles.

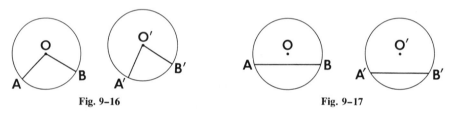

Fig. 9–16   Fig. 9–17

Theorem 135. **In a circle or in equal circles, if two central angles are unequal, then their arcs are unequal, and the greater angle has the greater arc.**

In Fig. 9–16, if circle O = circle O' and the measure of central $\angle AOB >$ the measure of central $\angle A'O'B'$, then $\overset{\frown}{AB} > \overset{\frown}{A'B'}$.

Theorem 136. **In a circle or in equal circles, if two arcs are unequal, then their central angles are unequal, and the greater arc has the greater central angle.**

In Fig. 9–16, if circle O = circle O' and $\overset{\frown}{AB} > \overset{\frown}{A'B'}$, then the measure of central $\angle AOB >$ the measure of central $\angle A'O'B'$.

Theorem 137. **In a circle or in equal circles, if two chords are unequal, then their minor arcs are unequal, and the greater chord has the greater minor arc.**

In Fig. 9–17, if circle O = circle O' and the length of chord $\overline{AB} >$ the length of chord $\overline{A'B'}$, then $\overset{\frown}{AB} > \overset{\frown}{A'B'}$.

Theorem 138. **In a circle or in equal circles, if two minor arcs are unequal, then their chords are unequal, and the greater minor arc has the greater chord.**

In Fig. 9–17, if circle O = circle O' and $\overset{\frown}{AB} > \overset{\frown}{A'B'}$, then the length of chord $\overline{AB} >$ the length of chord $\overline{A'B'}$.

Theorem 139. **In a circle or in equal circles, if two chords are unequal, then they are at unequal distances from the center, and the greater chord is the smaller distance from the center.**

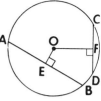

In circle O (Fig. 9–18), if $AB > CD$, $\overline{OE} \perp \overline{AB}$, and $\overline{OF} \perp \overline{CD}$, then $OE < OF$.

Fig. 9–18

Theorem 140. **In a circle or in equal circles, if two chords are not equally distant from the center, then they are unequal, and the chord that is the smaller distance from the center is the greater chord.**

In circle O (Fig. 9–18), if $\overline{OE} \perp \overline{AB}$, $\overline{OF} \perp \overline{CD}$, and $OE < OF$, then $AB > CD$.

Methods of Proof:

1. To prove that two arcs are unequal, show that they are in a circle or in equal circles and that:
   a. their central angles are unequal.   OR
   b. their chords are unequal.
2. To prove that two chords are unequal, show that they are in a circle or in equal circles and that:
   a. their arcs are unequal.   OR
   b. they are not equally distant from the center.

MODEL PROBLEM

Triangle ABC is inscribed in a circle. If $m\angle A = 70$, $m\angle B = 60$, and $m\angle C = 50$, which side of triangle ABC is nearest the center of the circle?

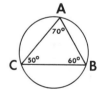

Solution:

1. $\angle A$, $\angle B$, and $\angle C$ are inscribed angles.

2. Since $m\angle A = 70$, $m\widehat{CB} = 140$.

3. Since $m\angle B = 60$, $m\widehat{AC} = 120$.

4. Since $m\angle C = 50$, $m\widehat{AB} = 100$.

5. Since $m\widehat{CB} > m\widehat{AC} > m\widehat{AB}$, then $\widehat{CB} > \widehat{AC} > \widehat{AB}$.

6. Since $\widehat{CB} > \widehat{AC} > \widehat{AB}$, then $CB > AC > AB$ because in a circle the greatest of several unequal arcs has the greatest chord.

7. Since chord $\overline{CB}$ is the greatest of the unequal chords, it is nearest the center of the circle because in a circle the greatest of several chords is nearest the center.

Answer: Side $\overline{CB}$.

EXERCISES

1. Triangle ABC is inscribed in a circle. If $m\angle A = 100$, $m\angle B = 50$, and $m\angle C = 30$ (*a*) name the largest intercepted arc (*b*) name the side of the triangle that is nearest the center of the circle.

2. Triangle RST is inscribed in a circle. If $m\angle R = 85$ and $m\angle S = 45$ (*a*) name the smallest intercepted arc (*b*) name the side of the triangle which is farthest from the center of the circle.

3. If acute triangle ABC is inscribed in a circle and $m\angle B > m\angle A$, then $\widehat{BC}$ is (*a*) greater than $\widehat{AC}$ (*b*) equal to $\widehat{AC}$ (*c*) less than $\widehat{AC}$.

4. Triangle ABC is inscribed in a circle. $m\angle A = 80$, $m\angle B = 70$, and $m\angle C = 30$. Which side of triangle ABC is nearest the center of the circle?

5. Triangle DEF is inscribed in a circle. If $m\angle E > m\angle D$, prove that $\widehat{DF} > \widehat{EF}$.

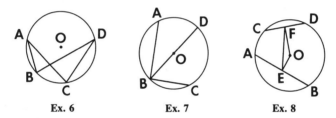

Ex. 6   Ex. 7   Ex. 8

6. In circle O, $BD > AC$. Prove that $CD > AB$.

7. In circle O, $\overline{BD}$ is a diameter, $\overline{AB}$ and $\overline{BC}$ are chords, and $AB > BC$. Prove that $m\angle ABD < m\angle CBD$.

8. In circle O, $\overline{OE} \perp \overline{AB}$, $\overline{OF} \perp \overline{CD}$, and $m\angle OEF > m\angle OFE$. Prove that $AB > CD$.

9. An equilateral triangle and a regular hexagon are inscribed in the same circle. Prove that the length of an apothem of the hexagon is greater than the length of an apothem of the equilateral triangle.

10. Triangle ABC is inscribed in circle O and $m\angle A > m\angle B$. Prove that $\overline{BC}$ is nearer the center of the circle than $\overline{AC}$ is.

11. $\overline{AB}$ is a chord of a circle and C is the midpoint of minor arc $\widehat{AB}$. Chord $\overline{CD}$ is drawn intersecting $\overline{AB}$ at E. Chords $\overline{BD}$ and $\overline{BC}$ are drawn. Prove that if BE is greater than EC, then BD is greater than BC.

12. *Prove:* The shortest chord that can be drawn through a point inside a circle is the chord which is perpendicular to the radius drawn through this point.

CHAPTER X

Locus

1. The Meaning of Locus

If a point is moving so that it is always satisfying a given condition, its path is called a *locus*. "Locus" is the Latin word for place. The plural of *locus* is *loci*.

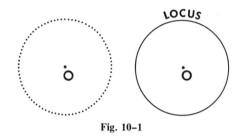

Fig. 10–1

For example, in Fig. 10–1, if a point is moving in a plane so that it is always one-half inch from a given point in the plane, *O*, its path, or locus, is a circle whose center is *O* and whose radius is one-half inch in length. This circle is the set of all points which satisfy the condition that they are one-half inch from *O*. There is an infinite number of these points.

It is also possible to think of a locus as the place where all points, and only those points, that fulfill or satisfy a given condition are found.

Definition. **A *locus* is the set of all points, and only those points, that satisfy a given condition or set of conditions.**

2. Discovering a Probable Locus

To discover a probable locus, it is helpful to use the following procedure:

1. Make a diagram which contains the fixed lines or points that are given.
2. Decide what condition must be satisfied.
3. Locate a point which satisfies the given condition. Then, locate several other points which satisfy the given condition. These should be sufficiently close together to develop the shape or the nature of the locus.
4. Through these points, draw a smooth line, straight or curved, which appears to be the locus.
5. Describe in words the geometric figure that appears to be the locus.

NOTE. In this chapter, we will assume that all given points, segments, rays, lines, and circles lie in the same plane and that the desired locus lies in that plane also.

MODEL PROBLEMS

1. What is the probable locus of points equidistant from the endpoints of a given line segment $\overline{AB}$?

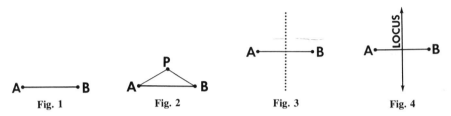

Fig. 1   Fig. 2   Fig. 3   Fig. 4

Solution:

1. $\overline{AB}$ is the given line segment (Fig. 1).

2. The condition to be satisfied is that P is to be equidistant from A and B, or $PA = PB$ (Fig. 2).

3. Locate several points which are equidistant from A and B (Fig. 3).

4. Through these points, draw a straight line which appears to be the locus (Fig. 4).

5. The probable locus is a straight line which is the perpendicular bisector of the given line segment $\overline{AB}$.

2. What is the probable locus of points in the interior of an angle equidistant from the sides of the given angle?

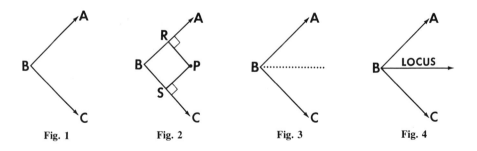

Fig. 1   Fig. 2   Fig. 3   Fig. 4

Solution:

1. $\angle ABC$ is the given angle (Fig. 1).

2. The condition to be satisfied is that P is to be equidistant from $\overrightarrow{BA}$ and $\overrightarrow{BC}$, the sides of $\angle ABC$, or $PR = PS$ when $\overline{PR} \perp \overrightarrow{BA}$ and $\overline{PS} \perp \overrightarrow{BC}$ (Fig. 2).

3. Locate several points equidistant from $\overrightarrow{BA}$ and $\overrightarrow{BC}$ (Fig. 3).

4. Through these points, draw a ray which appears to be the locus (Fig. 4).

5. The probable locus is a ray which is the bisector of $\angle ABC$.

3. What is the probable locus of the midpoints of the radii of a given circle?

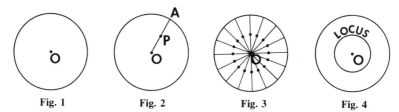

| Fig. 1 | Fig. 2 | Fig. 3 | Fig. 4 |

Solution:

1. O is the center of the given circle (Fig. 1).

2. The condition to be satisfied is that P is to be the midpoint of radius $\overline{OA}$, or $OP = PA$ (Fig. 2).

3. Locate several points which are the midpoints of radii in circle O (Fig. 3).

4. Through these points, draw a smooth curve which appears to be the locus (Fig. 4).

5. The probable locus is a circle which has the same center as the given circle and the length of whose radius is one-half the length of the radius of the given circle.

EXERCISES

In each of the following, use the procedure illustrated in the preceding model problems to discover the probable locus:

1. What is the locus of the outer end of the hour hand of a clock during a 12-hour period?

2. What is the locus of the center of a train wheel which is moving along a straight, level track?

3. What is the locus of a car which is being driven down a street equidistant from the two opposite parallel curbs?

4. A dog is tied to a stake by a rope 15 ft. long. Discover the boundary of the surface over which he may roam.

5. A girl walks through an open field which is bounded on two sides by straight intersecting roads. She walks so that she is always equidistant from the two intersecting roads. Determine her path.

6. There are two floats on a lake. A boy swims so that he is always equidistant from both floats. Determine his path.

7. A dime is rolled along a horizontal line so that the dime always touches the line. What is the locus of the center of the dime?

8. What is the locus of a point on a spoke of a wagon wheel which makes a complete revolution when the center of the wheel remains in a fixed position?

9. What is the locus of all points which are 10 ft. from a given point?

10. What is the locus of all points equidistant from the sides of an angle of 120°?

11. What is the locus of all points equidistant from two points A and B which are 8 inches apart?

12. What is the locus of all points equidistant from two parallel lines 10 inches apart?

13. What is the locus of all points 4 inches away from a given line $\overleftrightarrow{AB}$?

14. What is the locus of all points 3 in. from each of two parallel lines which are 6 in. apart?

15. If point P is on line $\overleftrightarrow{AB}$, what is the locus of the centers of all circles tangent to line $\overleftrightarrow{AB}$ at point P?

16. What is the locus of the centers of circles tangent to each of two parallel lines which are 12 inches apart?

17. What is the locus of the center of a penny which is rolling around a quarter if the edges of the two coins are always touching each other?

18. What is the locus of points in the interior of a circle of radius 3 inches and 2 inches from the circle?

19. What is the locus of points in the exterior of a circle of radius 3 inches and 2 inches from the circle?

20. What is the locus of points 2 inches from a circle whose radius is 3 inches?

21. What is the locus of points in the exterior of circle O and at a distance m from the circle?

22. What is the locus of points m inches from a circle whose radius is r inches, r being greater than m?

23. What is the locus of points equidistant from two concentric circles whose radii are 10 inches and 18 inches?

24. What is the locus of the centers of circles each of which is tangent to the sides of an angle which contains 80°?

25. What is the locus of the centers of circles of radius 6 inches which pass through a given point *P?*

26. What is the locus of the vertices of all isosceles triangles which have a given line segment $\overline{AB}$ 4 inches in length as their bases?

27. What is the locus of the vertices of all triangles which have a given line segment $\overline{AB}$ as their bases and whose altitudes are 3 inches in length?

3. Proving That a Locus Is Correct

In Model Problem 1 on page 486, we saw that the locus of points equidistant from the ends of a given line segment appears to be the perpendicular bisector of the line segment. In order to prove that this locus is correct, we must prove two things: (1) if a point is on the perpendicular bisector of the line segment, it is equidistant from the ends of the line segment and (2) if a point is equidistant from the ends of the line segment, it is on the perpendicular bisector of the line segment.

In general, to prove that a locus is correct, or to prove a locus theorem, we prove both of the following statements:

1. If a point is on the locus, the point satisfies the given condition(s).
2. If a point satisfies the given condition(s), it is on the locus.

Note that statement 2 is the converse of statement 1.

There is another method that may be used to prove that the locus of points equidistant from the ends of a given line segment is the perpendicular bisector of the line segment. We can show that (1) if a point is on the perpendicular bisector of the line segment, it is equidistant from the ends of the line segment and (2) if a point is *not* on the perpendicular bisector of the line segment, the point is *not* equidistant from the ends of the line segment.

In general, another method that may be used to prove that a locus is correct, or to prove a locus theorem, is to prove both of the following statements:

1. If a point is on the locus, the point satisfies the given condition(s).
2. If a point is not on the locus, the point does not satisfy the given condition(s).

Statement 2 is called the *inverse* of statement 1.

Forming the Inverse of a Statement

To contradict or negate the statement "Tom is an athlete," we can say, "It is not true that Tom is an athlete," or "Tom is not an athlete."

In general, the negation of the statement p is the statement "It is not true that p" (denoted by $\sim p$).

To contradict "The lengths of two sides of a triangle are equal," we can write, "The lengths of two sides of a triangle are unequal."

To contradict "The measures of two angles of a triangle are unequal," we can write, "The measures of two angles of a triangle are equal."

Consider the statement "If a point is on the perpendicular bisector of a line segment, it is equidistant from the ends of the line segment." We can contradict the hypothesis, "A point is on the perpendicular bisector of a line segment," by inserting the word *not* as follows: "A point is *not* on the perpendicular bisector of a line segment." To contradict or negate the conclusion, "It is equidistant from the ends of the line segment," we write, "It is not equidistant from the ends of the line segment."

When we contradict or negate both the hypothesis and conclusion of a conditional statement whose hypothesis has one condition and whose conclusion has one condition, the newly formed statement is called the *inverse* of the given statement. For example:

1. *Given Statement:*   If a point is on the perpendicular bisector of a line segment, it is equidistant from the ends of the line segment.

   Inverse of Statement: If a point is not on the perpendicular bisector of a line segment, it is not equidistant from the ends of the line segment.

2. *Given Statement:*   If two angles are right angles, they are congruent.

   Inverse of Statement: If two angles are not right angles, they are not congruent.

In general, for a given conditional statement we have the following:

Given Statement: If p, then q.
Inverse Statement: If not p, then not q, symbolized as
                    If $\sim p$, then $\sim q$.

Observe that in example 1 the original statement is true and the inverse of the original statement is also true. However, in example 2, the original statement is true but the inverse of the original statement is false. Hence, we see that the inverse of a true statement is not necessarily a true statement. Therefore, we cannot assume that the inverse of a true statement is also a true statement.

We will discuss the topic of inverses in greater detail in the chapter dealing with the "Improvement of Reasoning."

KEEP IN MIND

To prove that a locus is correct, or to prove a locus theorem, prove *both* of the following:

1. Prove that if a point is on the locus, the point satisfies the given condition(s).
2. Prove either (*a*) the converse of statement 1 or (*b*) the inverse of statement 1.

MODEL PROBLEM

Prove that the locus of points equidistant from the ends of a given line segment is the perpendicular bisector of the line segment.

Plan· (*a*) We will prove the statement "If a point is on the perpendicular bisector of a line segment, it is equidistant from the ends of the line segment." (*b*) We will also prove the converse of this statement; namely, "If a point is equidistant from the ends of a line segment, it is on the perpendicular bisector of the line segment."

a. Prove the statement: "If a point is on the perpendicular bisector of a line segment, it is equidistant from the ends of the line segment."

Given: $\overleftrightarrow{CD}$ is the ⊥ bisector of $\overline{AB}$.
             P is any point on $\overleftrightarrow{CD}$.

To prove: $PA = PB$.

Plan: Show that $\overline{PA}$ and $\overline{PB}$ are corresponding sides of congruent △APE and BPE, proved congruent by s.a.s. ≅ s.a.s.

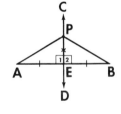

Proof: *Statements*	*Reasons*
1. $\overleftrightarrow{CD}$ is the ⊥ bisector of $\overline{AB}$ and P is a point on $\overleftrightarrow{CD}$.	1. Given.
2. $\overline{AE} \cong \overline{EB}$. (s. ≅ s.)	2. A bisector divides a line segment into two congruent parts.
3. ∠1 and ∠2 are right angles.	3. Perpendicular lines are lines that intersect and form right angles.
4. ∠1 ≅ ∠2. (a. ≅ a.)	4. All right angles are congruent.
5. $\overline{PE} \cong \overline{PE}$. (s. ≅ s.)	5. Reflexive property of congruence.

[The proof is continued on the next page.]

Proof: *Statements*	*Reasons*
6. $\triangle APE \cong \triangle BPE$.	6. s.a.s. $\cong$ s.a.s.
7. $\overline{PA} \cong \overline{PB}$.	7. Corresponding sides of congruent triangles are congruent.
8. $PA = PB$.	8. Congruent segments are equal in length.

b. Prove the converse: "If a point is equidistant from the ends of a line segment, it is on the perpendicular bisector of the line segment."

Given: Line segment $\overline{AB}$.
            P is any point such that $\overline{PA} \cong \overline{PB}$.

To prove: P is on the perpendicular bisector of $\overline{AB}$.

Plan: Join P to E, the midpoint of $\overline{AB}$. Now prove that $\overleftrightarrow{PE}$, the bisector of $\overline{AB}$, is also perpendicular to $\overline{AB}$. We can do this by showing that $\angle PEA \cong \angle PEB$.

Proof: *Statements*	*Reasons*
1. Let E be the midpoint of $\overline{AB}$.	1. Every line segment has one and only one midpoint.
2. Draw $\overleftrightarrow{PE}$.	2. One and only one straight line can be drawn between two points.
3. $\overline{AE} \cong \overline{EB}$. (s. $\cong$ s.)	3. A midpoint divides a line segment into two congruent parts.
4. $\overline{PA} \cong \overline{PB}$. (s. $\cong$ s.)	4. Given.
5. $\overline{PE} \cong \overline{PE}$. (s. $\cong$ s.)	5. Reflexive property of congruence.
6. $\triangle APE \cong \triangle BPE$.	6. s.s.s. $\cong$ s.s.s.
7. $\angle PEA \cong \angle PEB$.	7. Corresponding angles of congruent triangles are congruent.
8. $\overleftrightarrow{PE} \perp \overleftrightarrow{AB}$.	8. If two lines intersect forming congruent adjacent angles, the lines are perpendicular.
9. $\overleftrightarrow{PE}$ is the $\perp$ bisector of $\overline{AB}$.	9. If a line is perpendicular to a line segment and bisects the line segment, the line is the perpendicular bisector of the line segment.

EXERCISES

In 1–4, write the inverse of the given statement.

1. If a boy has rich parents, he will be a good student.

2. A dishonest person is a bad credit risk.

3. If two sides of a triangle are congruent, the angles opposite these sides are congruent.

4. If two triangles are congruent, they are equal in area.

5. Given statement *A:* "The points in a plane at a given distance from a given point lie on a circle whose center is the given point and the length of whose radius is the given distance." In order to prove that statement *A* satisfies the requirements of a locus theorem, we must prove (1) statement *A* and its converse (2) the converse and inverse of statement *A* (3) only the converse of statement *A* (4) only statement *A*.

6. Given statement *A:* "The set of points in a plane equidistant from two intersecting lines is the pair of lines which bisect the angles formed by the two intersecting lines." In order to prove that statement *A* satisfies the requirements of a locus theorem, we must prove (1) only statement *A* (2) only the converse of statement *A* (3) statement *A* and its inverse (4) both the converse and the inverse of statement *A*.

7. *Prove:* The locus of points in the interior of an angle equidistant from the sides of the angle is the bisector of the angle.

4. Fundamental Locus Theorems

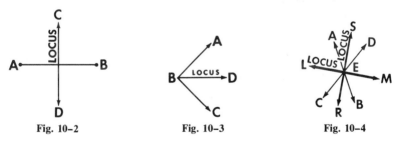

Fig. 10–2   Fig. 10–3   Fig. 10–4

Theorem 141. **The locus of points equidistant from the ends of a line segment is the perpendicular bisector of the line segment.**

In Fig. 10–2, if $\overline{AB}$ is the line segment, then $\overleftrightarrow{CD}$, the perpendicular bisector of $\overline{AB}$, is the locus of points equidistant from *A* and *B*.

Theorem 142. **The locus of points in the interior of an angle or on the angle equidistant from the sides of the angle is the ray that bisects the angle.**

In Fig. 10–3, if $\angle ABC$ is the angle, then ray $\overrightarrow{BD}$, which is the bisector of $\angle ABC$, is the locus of points in the interior of $\angle ABC$ or on $\angle ABC$ which are equidistant from $\overrightarrow{BA}$ and $\overrightarrow{BC}$, the sides of $\angle ABC$.

Theorem 143. **The locus of points equidistant from two intersecting lines is the pair of lines which bisect the angles formed by the two intersecting lines.**

In Fig. 10-4, if $\overleftrightarrow{AB}$ and $\overleftrightarrow{CD}$ are the intersecting lines, then $\overleftrightarrow{RS}$ and $\overleftrightarrow{LM}$, the bisectors of the angles formed by lines $\overleftrightarrow{AB}$ and $\overleftrightarrow{CD}$, are the locus of points equidistant from $\overleftrightarrow{AB}$ and $\overleftrightarrow{CD}$.

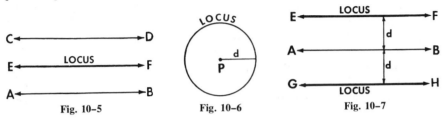

Fig. 10-5   Fig. 10-6   Fig. 10-7

Theorem 144. **The locus of points equidistant from two parallel lines is a third line parallel to the two lines and midway between them.**

In Fig. 10-5, if $\overleftrightarrow{CD}$ and $\overleftrightarrow{AB}$ are parallel lines, then $\overleftrightarrow{EF}$, a line parallel to $\overleftrightarrow{AB}$ and to $\overleftrightarrow{CD}$ and midway between them, is the locus of points equidistant from $\overleftrightarrow{AB}$ and $\overleftrightarrow{CD}$.

Theorem 145. **The locus of points at a given distance from a given point is a circle whose center is the given point and the length of whose radius is the given distance.**

In Fig. 10-6, if P is the given point and d is the given distance, circle P is the locus of points whose distance from P is d.

Theorem 146. **The locus of points at a given distance from a given line is a pair of lines each of which is parallel to the given line and at the given distance from it.**

In Fig. 10-7, if $\overleftrightarrow{AB}$ is the given line and d is the given distance, then the pair of lines $\overleftrightarrow{EF}$ and $\overleftrightarrow{GH}$, each parallel to $\overleftrightarrow{AB}$ and each at distance d from $\overleftrightarrow{AB}$, is the locus of points whose distance from $\overleftrightarrow{AB}$ is d.

EXERCISES

In each exercise, determine the required locus.

1. The locus of points in the interior of an angle which are equidistant from the sides of the angle is the _____ of that angle.

2. The locus of points at a given distance from a given straight line is (*a*) a circle (*b*) one straight line (*c*) two parallel lines.

3. The locus of points equidistant from two fixed points is (*a*) one circle (*b*) one straight line (*c*) two circles (*d*) two straight lines.

4. The locus of the midpoints of all radii of a given circle is a(an) _____ .

5. The locus of points equidistant from the four vertices of a given rectangle is   (*a*) a pair of lines   (*b*) one line   (*c*) a point.

6. A non-empty set of line segments parallel to the base of a triangle end in the other two sides. The locus of the midpoints of these segments is a(an) _____ of the triangle.

7. *a.* What is the locus of the midpoints of all chords of a given length in a given circle?
   b. What is the locus of the midpoints of all chords that are parallel to a given chord in a circle?

8. What is the locus of points in the interior of the square *ABCD* and equidistant from its sides $\overline{AB}$ and $\overline{BC}$?

9. The locus of the midpoints of all chords drawn from a given point on a circle is   (*a*) a diameter of the circle   (*b*) a circle concentric with the given circle   (*c*) a circle whose diameter is the radius of the given circle.

10. The locus of the centers of all circles having a given line segment as a chord is   (*a*) a line parallel to the chord   (*b*) the midpoint of the chord   (*c*) the perpendicular bisector of the chord   (*d*) a circle with the chord as diameter.

11. The locus of the centers of circles which are tangent to a given line segment $\overline{XY}$ at the point *P* which is on $\overline{XY}$ is   (*a*) a line parallel to $\overline{XY}$ (*b*) a circle drawn on $\overline{XY}$ as a diameter   (*c*) the line perpendicular to $\overline{XY}$ at the point *P*, not including point *P*.

12. The locus of the centers of congruent circles passing through a given point is   (*a*) a point   (*b*) a straight line   (*c*) a circle.

13. What is the locus of points outside circle *O* and at a distance *d* from it?

14. The locus of the centers of all circles of given radius and tangent externally to a given circle is _____ a circle. [Answer *always, sometimes,* or *never.*]

15. Given a quadrilateral *ABCD*. The locus of points equidistant from $\overleftrightarrow{AB}$ and $\overleftrightarrow{AD}$ must include point *C* if *ABCD* is a   (*a*) trapezoid   (*b*) rectangle   (*c*) parallelogram   (*d*) rhombus.

16. The locus of the centers of all circles tangent to each of two parallel lines is   (*a*) one straight line   (*b*) two straight lines   (*c*) a point.

17. The locus of the centers of all circles which pass through two given points is   (*a*) a circle   (*b*) a straight line   (*c*) a point.

18. The vertices of the right angles of all right triangles having a common hypotenuse lie on   (*a*) a line parallel to the hypotenuse   (*b*) a circle whose diameter is the hypotenuse   (*c*) a semicircle whose diameter is the hypotenuse.

19. The locus of the vertices of all triangles which have the same base and whose medians to that base are all equal in length is   (*a*) a straight line   (*b*) a pair of straight lines   (*c*) a circle not including the two points of the circle that are collinear with the base.

20. In triangle *DEF*, points *D* and *F* are fixed with *DF* = 20 inches. Describe fully the locus of points *E* if (*a*) the area of triangle *DEF* is 60 sq. in. (*b*) angle *DEF* is a right angle (*c*) triangle *DEF* is an isosceles triangle with $\overline{DE} \cong \overline{EF}$.

21. What is the locus of the midpoint of a line segment which has a fixed length and which moves so that its endpoints always lie on two lines which are perpendicular to each other?

22. The distance between two given points *O* and *P* is *r*. What is the locus of all points of contact of the tangents that can be drawn from *P* to all circles whose centers are *O* and whose radii are less than *r* in length?

23. The locus of the midpoints of all line segments whose endpoints are a given point not on a given line and a point on the given line is (*a*) one circle (*b*) one line (*c*) two circles (*d*) two lines.

5. Intersections of Loci

If a set of points is to satisfy more than one condition, each of these points, and only these points, must be common to the loci for the separate conditions. Points that are to satisfy each of two conditions can be located in the following manner:

1. Construct the locus of points which satisfy the first condition.
2. Construct the locus of points which satisfy the second condition.
3. Determine the points of intersection of these loci.

These points of intersection must be the required points because they satisfy both conditions. Sometimes there may be only one point of intersection. At other times there may be two or more points of intersection. In cases where the loci do not intersect, there is no point that satisfies both of the given conditions.

MODEL PROBLEMS

1. Given line *t*. Find the number of points at a given distance *d* from *t* and also equidistant from two points *X* and *Y* on *t*.

Solution:

1. The locus of points that are at a given distance *d* from line *t* is a pair of lines parallel to *t*, each line being at a distance *d* from *t*.

2. The locus of points equidistant from points *X* and *Y* is the perpendicular bisector of line segment $\overline{XY}$.

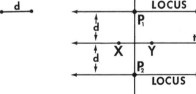

3. The points of intersection of the two loci, P_1 and P_2, satisfy both conditions because they lie on both loci.

Answer: 2 points.

2. Locate the points that are a given distance d from a given point S and are equidistant from the ends of line segment $\overline{AB}$.

   Solution:

   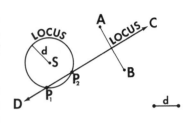

   1. The locus of points that are a distance d from point S is the circle whose center is S and the length of whose radius is d.

   2. The locus of points equidistant from the ends of line segment $\overline{AB}$ is the perpendicular bisector of $\overline{AB}$, line $\overleftrightarrow{CD}$.

   3. The points of intersection of the two loci, P_1 and P_2, are the required points because they lie on both loci and thus satisfy both conditions.

   Answer: Points P_1 and P_2.

   NOTE.

   1. If d is equal to the distance from S to $\overleftrightarrow{DC}$, the perpendicular bisector of line segment $\overline{AB}$, then $\overleftrightarrow{DC}$ will be tangent to the circle whose center is S and the length of whose radius is d. In this case, there will be one point that satisfies both conditions.

   2. If d is less than the distance from S to $\overleftrightarrow{DC}$, the perpendicular bisector of line segment $\overline{AB}$, then $\overleftrightarrow{DC}$ will not intersect the circle whose center is S and the length of whose radius is d. In this case, there will be no point that satisfies both conditions.

3. *Given:* Two concentric circles have radii whose lengths are 2 in. and 6 in. Line m is tangent to the smaller circle.

   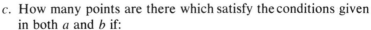
   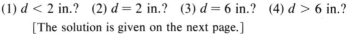

   a. Describe fully the locus of points equidistant from the two circles.

   b. Describe fully the locus of points at a given distance d from line m.

   c. How many points are there which satisfy the conditions given in both a and b if:
      (1) $d < 2$ in.?   (2) $d = 2$ in.?   (3) $d = 6$ in.?   (4) $d > 6$ in.?

   [The solution is given on the next page.]

Solution:

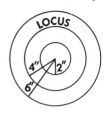

a. The locus of points equidistant from the two concentric circles is a third concentric circle the length of whose radius is 4 in.

b. The locus of points at a given distance *d* from the given line *m* is a pair of lines parallel to *m* and at the given distance *d* from *m*.

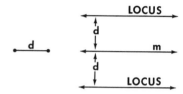

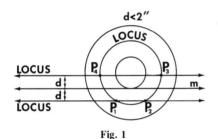

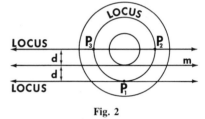

Fig. 1   Fig. 2

c. (1) $d < 2$ in.

   In Fig. 1, the four points P_1, P_2, P_3, P_4, where the loci intersect, satisfy both conditions.

Answer: 4 points.

   (2) $d = 2$ in.

   In Fig. 2, the three points P_1, P_2, P_3, where the loci intersect, satisfy both conditions.

Answer: 3 points.

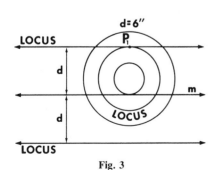

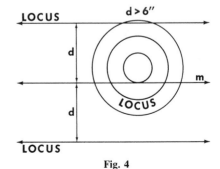

Fig. 3   Fig. 4

(3) $d = 6$ in.

In Fig. 3, the one point P_1, where the loci intersect, satisfies both conditions.

Answer: 1 point.

(4) $d > 6$ in.

In Fig. 4, there is no point where the loci intersect. Thus, no point satisfies both conditions.

Answer: No point.

EXERCISES

1. How many points are there which are 2 inches from a given line and 3 inches from a given point in that line?

2. The number of points which are equidistant from two given parallel lines and at the same time are equidistant from two given points on one of these lines is   (a) one   (b) two   (c) three.

3. The number of points which are at a given distance from a given line and also equidistant from two given points on the line is   (a) one   (b) two (c) four.

4. Two points A and B are 6 inches apart. How many points are there that are equidistant from both A and B and also 5 inches from $A?$

5. How many points are there that are equidistant from two given points A and B and also 2 inches from the straight line passing through A and $B?$

6. $\overleftrightarrow{LM}$ and $\overleftrightarrow{RS}$ are two parallel lines 10 inches apart and A is a point on $\overleftrightarrow{LM}$. How many points are there which are equidistant from $\overleftrightarrow{LM}$ and $\overleftrightarrow{RS}$ and 7 inches from $A?$

7. Two straight lines $\overleftrightarrow{AB}$ and $\overleftrightarrow{CD}$ intersect at E. Locate the points which are 2 units from E and equidistant from $\overleftrightarrow{AB}$ and $\overleftrightarrow{CD}$.

8. A point P is 1 unit from line $\overleftrightarrow{AB}$. Locate the points which are 2 units from line $\overleftrightarrow{AB}$ and 4 units from P.

9. Locate the point which is equidistant from two given points on a side of a given acute angle and equidistant from the sides of the angle.

10. Point C is 3 inches from given line $\overleftrightarrow{AB}$. The number of points in $\overleftrightarrow{AB}$ that are 5 inches from C is   (a) 0   (b) 1   (c) 2.

11. Line segment $\overline{AB}$ is 1 inch long. The number of points 2 inches from both A and B is   (a) 0   (b) 1   (c) 2.

12. The number of points equidistant from two intersecting lines and at a distance d from their point of intersection is   (a) 1   (b) 2   (c) 8 (d) 4.

13. A given point is 9 inches from a given straight line. The number of points which are 4 inches from this line and also 6 inches from this point is (*a*) 0 (*b*) 2 (*c*) 3 (*d*) 4.

14. Parallel lines $\overleftrightarrow{AB}$ and $\overleftrightarrow{CD}$ are 6 inches apart and point *P* is on $\overleftrightarrow{AB}$. The number of points equidistant from these two lines and also 5 inches from point *P* is (*a*) 1 (*b*) 2 (*c*) 0 (*d*) 4.

15. Two points *A* and *B* are 7 inches apart. How many points are there which are 12 inches from *A* and also 4 inches from *B?*

16. In any triangle, the point which is equidistant from the three vertices is the intersection of (*a*) the angle bisectors (*b*) the perpendicular bisectors of the sides (*c*) the medians.

17. If a point is equidistant from the sides of a triangle, it must be the intersection of the three (*a*) altitudes (*b*) medians (*c*) angle bisectors.

18. The center of a circle inscribed in a triangle is the point of intersection of (*a*) the bisectors of its angles (*b*) its altitudes (*c*) the perpendicular bisectors of its sides.

19. The center of the circle circumscribed about a triangle is always the intersection of (*a*) the bisectors of two angles (*b*) two altitudes (*c*) the perpendicular bisectors of two sides.

20. A parallelogram *ABCD* has two adjacent sides, $\overline{AB}$ and $\overline{AD}$ with $AB = 3$ units and $AD = 2$ units, and angle *A* contains 60°. (*a*) Draw the locus of points equidistant from $\overline{AB}$ and $\overline{AD}$. (*b*) Draw the locus of points $1\frac{1}{2}$ units from vertex *D*. (*c*) How many points in the interior of the parallelogram satisfy both conditions stated in part *a* and part *b?*

21. *Given:* Two lines *m* and *n* intersect each other at right angles, and point *P* is on one of these lines. (*a*) Describe completely the locus of points which are at a given distance *s* from *P*. (*b*) Describe completely the locus of points equidistant from *m* and *n*. (*c*) How many points are there which will satisfy both conditions given in *a* and *b* if *P* is 4 inches from the intersection of *m* and *n* and: (1) *s* is 5 inches long? (2) *s* is $2\sqrt{2}$ inches long? (3) *s* is 1 inch long?

22. Given two concentric circles whose center is *O* and the lengths of whose radii are 6 and 10, and given straight line $\overleftrightarrow{AB}$ through *O*. (*a*) Describe fully the locus of points equidistant from the two concentric circles. (*b*) Describe fully the locus of points at a given distance *d* from $\overleftrightarrow{AB}$. (*c*) Find the number of points that satisfy the conditions in both part *a* and part *b* if: (1) $d = 6$. (2) $d = 8$. (3) $d = 10$.

23. Draw two lines $\overleftrightarrow{AB}$ and $\overleftrightarrow{CD}$ which intersect at *E*. Take *P*, a point on $\overrightarrow{EB}$.
    a. Construct the locus of points equidistant from $\overleftrightarrow{AB}$ and $\overleftrightarrow{CD}$.
    b. Construct the locus of points at a fixed distance *k* from *P*, where $k > EP$.

    c. Indicate by *Q*, *R*, etc., all the points that satisfy both conditions given in *a* and *b*.

    d. If *k* is equal to *EP*, the number of different points which are at a distance *k* from *P* and also equidistant from $\overleftrightarrow{AB}$ and $\overleftrightarrow{CD}$ is (1) 1 (2) 0 (3) 3.

24. $\overleftrightarrow{AB}$ and $\overleftrightarrow{CD}$ are straight lines that intersect at *Q*. *P* is a point on $\overleftrightarrow{AB}$.

    a. Construct the locus of points equidistant from $\overleftrightarrow{AB}$ and $\overleftrightarrow{CD}$.

    b. Construct the locus of points at a distance *PQ* from *P*.

    c. How many points are there equidistant from $\overleftrightarrow{AB}$ and $\overleftrightarrow{CD}$ and also at a distance from *P* equal to *PQ?*

    d. How many points are there equidistant from $\overleftrightarrow{AB}$ and $\overleftrightarrow{CD}$ and also at a distance from *P* greater than *PQ?*

25. Perpendicular lines *r* and *s* intersect at *O*, and *P* is a point on *r*.

    a. State in full the locus of points which are:

        (1) at a given distance *k* from *P*.

        (2) equidistant from *r* and *s*.

    b. Find the number of points satisfying both conditions given in *a* if:

        (1) *OP* = 6 and *k* = 8.

        (2) *OP* = 6 and *k* = $3\sqrt{2}$.

        (3) *OP* = 6 and *k* = 3.

6. Construction Exercises Involving Locus

1. Construct the locus of points equidistant from two given intersecting lines.

2. Construct the locus of points equidistant from two given points.

3. Find by construction the locus of points in the interior of a given acute angle *ABC* and equidistant from the sides of the angle.

4. Draw an obtuse angle on your paper and construct the locus of points in the interior of the angle and equidistant from its sides.

5. Construct the locus of points equidistant from two given parallel lines *r* and *s*.

6. Construct the locus of points outside a given circle *O* and at the given distance *d* from the circle.

7. Construct the locus of the centers of all circles which pass through two given points *A* and *B*.

8. Construct the locus of the centers of circles each of which is tangent to the sides of a given acute angle *ABC*.

9. Construct a circle of given radius *r* which shall pass through the two given points *A* and *B*.

10. Find the point in the interior of angle CBA that is equidistant from sides $\vec{BC}$ and $\vec{BA}$ and at the given distance d from vertex B.

11. Given a line segment whose length is represented by a and fixed point P. Construct the locus of points whose distance from P is $\frac{1}{2}a$.

12. Given P on line m. Construct the locus of the centers of circles tangent to line m at point P.

Ex. 12

13. Construct a circle of radius r that will be tangent to line m at point P.

Ex. 13

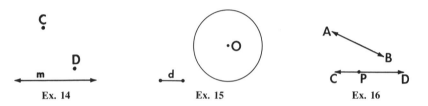

Ex. 14   Ex. 15   Ex. 16

14. On line m, find the point which is equidistant from points C and D.

15. Construct the locus of all points in the interior of circle O and at the given distance d from the circle, d being less than the length of the radius of circle O.

16. Construct a circle which is tangent to line $\overleftrightarrow{CD}$ at point P and whose center is on line $\overleftrightarrow{AB}$.

17. Given line m, P a point on m, and S a point not on m.
    a. Construct and label:
       (1) the locus of the centers of circles passing through S and P.
       (2) the locus of the centers of circles tangent to line m at P.
    b. How many circles can be drawn tangent to line m at P and passing through S?

18. Given parallel lines r and s are d distance apart, and point P is any point between the two lines.   (a) What is the length of the radius of a circle that is tangent to both r and s?   (b) What is the locus of the centers of the circles that are tangent to both r and s?   (c) What is the locus of the center of a circle the length of whose radius is represented by $\dfrac{d}{2}$ and which passes through P?   (d) Construct a circle tangent to the two parallel lines and passing through the given point P.   (e) How many different circles are there that satisfy the requirements specified in part d?

CHAPTER XI

Coordinate Geometry

In *coordinate geometry,* or *analytic geometry,* algebraic principles and methods are used in studying geometric figures. This algebraic approach to geometry was first developed and systematized by the French mathematician René Descartes in the seventeenth century.

1. Plotting Points

Early in this book, we studied the real number line. We assumed that there exists a one-to-one correspondence between the set of points on a line and the set of real numbers; that is, each point on a line corresponds to a unique real number, and each real number corresponds to a unique point on a line.

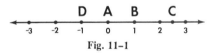
Fig. 11–1

In Fig. 11–1, point A, which is called the *origin,* is identified with the number 0; point B is identified with the number 1; point C corresponds to the number $2\frac{1}{2}$; point D corresponds to the number -1. The number that corresponds to a point on a line is called the *coordinate* of the point; the point to which a number corresponds is called the *graph* of the number. For example, the number 1 is the coordinate of point B, and point B is the graph of the number 1.

In view of the fact that in our study of geometry we deal not only with figures that are on a line, but also with figures that are in a plane, we will now devise a coordinate system in which every point in a plane is associated with a pair of numbers.

We will start with two number lines, called *coordinate axes,* which are perpendicular to each other. One line is horizontal and the other is vertical. The horizontal line is called the *x-axis;* the vertical line is called the *y-axis.* The point O at which the two axes intersect is called the *origin.* The axes divide the points of the plane which are not on the axes into four regions called *quadrants.* They are numbered in a counterclockwise direction as shown in Fig. 11-2.

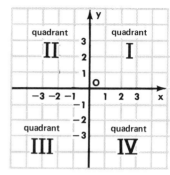

Fig. 11-2

The scales on the axes are marked so that the coordinates of points along the x-axis to the right of O are positive, and coordinates of points along the x-axis to the left of O are negative. Coordinates of points along the y-axis above O are positive, and coordinates of points along the y-axis below O are negative.

Let us use the two number lines to determine a pair of numbers that is associated with a point P in a plane. (See Fig. 11-3.) We draw, through P, a line that is perpendicular to the x-axis. This line intersects the x-axis at 2. The number 2 is called the *x-coordinate,* or *abscissa,* of point P. We also draw, through P, a line that is perpendicular to the y-axis. This line intersects the y-axis at 4. This number 4 is called the *y-coordinate,* or *ordinate,* of point P. The x-coordinate, 2, and the y-coordinate, 4, are called the *coordinates* of point P.

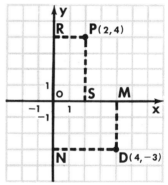

Fig. 11-3

To designate the coordinates of a point, the abscissa and ordinate are written in parentheses with a comma between them. Note that the abscissa is always written first. The pair of numbers (2, 4) is called the coordinates of point P. Since the abscissa was written first, the pair of numbers (2, 4) is called an *ordered pair of numbers.* The pair of numbers (2, 4) is not the same as the pair of numbers (4, 2) because (4, 2) locates a point whose abscissa is 4 and whose ordinate is 2.

Similarly, in the plane pictured in Fig. 11-3, the ordered pair of numbers $(4, -3)$ is associated with point D, whose abscissa is 4 and whose ordinate is -3. Point D is the graph of the ordered pair of numbers $(4, -3)$. When we graph the point described by an ordered pair of numbers, we are *plotting the point.*

In Fig. 11–4, since all points in quadrant I must be to the right of the y-axis and above the x-axis, every point in quadrant I represents an ordered pair of numbers whose abscissa and ordinate are both positive.

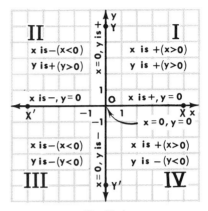

Fig. 11–4

Since all points in quadrant II must be to the left of the y-axis and above the x-axis, every point in quadrant II represents an ordered pair of numbers whose abscissa is negative and whose ordinate is positive.

Since all points in quadrant III must be to the left of the y-axis and below the x-axis, every point in quadrant III represents an ordered pair of numbers whose abscissa and ordinate are both negative.

Since all points in quadrant IV must be to the right of the y-axis and below the x-axis, every point in quadrant IV represents an ordered pair of numbers whose abscissa is positive and whose ordinate is negative.

Every point on $\overrightarrow{OX}$, the positive part of the x-axis (except point O), represents an ordered pair of numbers whose abscissa is positive and whose ordinate is 0. Every point on $\overrightarrow{OX'}$, the negative part of the x-axis (except point O), represents an ordered pair of numbers whose abscissa is negative and whose ordinate is 0. Every point on $\overrightarrow{OY}$, the positive part of the y-axis (except point O), represents an ordered pair of numbers whose abscissa is 0 and whose ordinate is positive. Every point on $\overrightarrow{OY'}$, the negative part of the y-axis (except point O), represents an ordered pair of numbers whose abscissa is 0 and whose ordinate is negative.

The origin, point O, represents the ordered pair of numbers (0, 0); that is, the x-coordinate of the origin is 0, and the y-coordinate of the origin is 0.

Note that the graph of every ordered pair of numbers (x, y) is a unique point in the plane. Also, every point in the plane represents a unique ordered pair of numbers (x, y). We say that there is a one-to-one correspondence between the sets of points in the plane and the set of ordered pairs of real numbers. This correspondence is called a *coordinate system*.

Since the axes in the coordinate system that we are using are perpendicular to each other, this system is called a *rectangular coordinate system*. It is also called the *Cartesian coordinate system*, named after René Descartes, its originator.

MODEL PROBLEM

Describe the location of the point $(-1, -2)$, and then plot the point on coordinate graph paper. [The solution is given on the next page.]

Solution: The ordered number pair describes a point in quadrant III which is 1 unit to the left of the *y*-axis and 2 units below the *x*-axis.

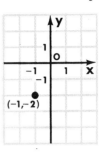

EXERCISES

For each point named in 1–10, refer to the graph below and tell:

a. the abscissa of the point.
b. the ordinate of the point.
c. the coordinates of the point given as an ordered pair.

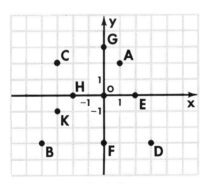

Ex. 1–10

1. point *A*	**2.** point *B*	**3.** point *C*	**4.** point *D*	**5.** point *E*
6. point *F*	**7.** point *G*	**8.** point *H*	**9.** point *K*	**10.** point *O*

In 11–26, describe the location of the point, and then plot the point on coordinate graph paper.

11. (4, 5)	**12.** (−2, 5)	**13.** (3, −4)	**14.** (−5, −4)
15. (2, 7)	**16.** (−6, 3)	**17.** $(5, -2\frac{1}{2})$	**18.** $(-\frac{3}{4}, -7)$
19. (4, 0)	**20.** (−5, 0)	**21.** (3, 0)	**22.** (−8, 0)
23. (0, 6)	**24.** (0, −8)	**25.** (0, 1)	**26.** (0, −9)

27. If a point is on the *x*-axis, what is the value of its ordinate?

28. What is the value of the abscissa of every point which is on the *y*-axis?

29. What are the coordinates of the origin?

30. Tell the type of number that the abscissa of a point and the ordinate of that point must be if the point lies in quadrant (*a*) I   (*b*) II   (*c*) III (*d*) IV.

31. If *x* is a positive number and *y* is a negative number, name the quadrant in which each of the following points lies:
    a. (*x, y*)   *b*. (*x, −y*)   *c*. (−*x, y*)   *d*. (−*x, −y*)

32. If *x* is a negative number and *y* is a negative number, name the quadrant in which each of the following points lies:
    a. (*x, y*)   *b*. (*x, −y*)   *c*. (−*x, y*)   *d*. (−*x, −y*)

2. Informal Proofs in Coordinate Geometry

We will now make use of several properties of graphs. We will illustrate and discuss these properties, but we will not prove them formally.

Notice the following properties in the graph in Fig. 11–5:

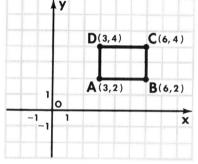

Fig. 11–5

1. Points *A* and *D* have the same abscissa, 3. Thus, $\overleftrightarrow{AD}$ is parallel to the *y*-axis. Similarly, $\overleftrightarrow{BC}$ is parallel to the *y*-axis.

2. Points *A* and *B* have the same ordinate, 2. Thus, $\overleftrightarrow{AB}$ is parallel to the *x*-axis. Similarly, $\overleftrightarrow{DC}$ is parallel to the *x*-axis.

3. $\overleftrightarrow{DC}$ and $\overleftrightarrow{AB}$ are parallel to each other because they are each parallel to the *x*-axis.

4. $\overleftrightarrow{AD}$ and $\overleftrightarrow{BC}$ are parallel to each other because they are each parallel to the *y*-axis.

5. $\overleftrightarrow{AD} \perp \overleftrightarrow{AB}$, $\overleftrightarrow{BC} \perp \overleftrightarrow{AB}$, $\overleftrightarrow{BC} \perp \overleftrightarrow{DC}$, and $\overleftrightarrow{AD} \perp \overleftrightarrow{DC}$ because on rectangular coordinate graph paper every horizontal line is perpendicular to every vertical line. Then ∠*DAB*, ∠*ABC*, ∠*BCD*, and ∠*CDA* are right angles.

6. The length of $\overline{AB}$ is 3 units. We can find this length either by counting the number of units contained in line segment $\overline{AB}$ or by subtracting 3 from 6. Similarly, the length of $\overline{DC}$ is 3 units. Therefore, $\overline{AB} \cong \overline{DC}$.

7. The length of $\overline{AD}$ is 2 units. We can find this length either by counting the number of units contained in line segment $\overline{AD}$ or by subtracting 2 from 4. Similarly, the length of $\overline{BC}$ is 2 units. Therefore, $\overline{AD} \cong \overline{BC}$.

We will use the preceding properties of graphs in developing informal proofs for exercises in coordinate geometry. These proofs may be written in paragraph form or they may be arranged step by step. A reason should be given only when the reason is not one of the properties of graphs discussed in this unit.

MODEL PROBLEM

Given: The vertices of $\triangle ABC$ are $A(-3, 0)$, $B(3, 0)$, and $C(0, 2)$.

To show: $\triangle ABC$ is an isosceles triangle.

Plan: Use congruent triangles to prove $\overline{CA} \cong \overline{CB}$.

Solution 1 (step by step):

1. Since the y-axis $\perp$ the x-axis, rt. $\angle COA \cong$ rt. $\angle COB$.

2. $OA = 3$ units and $OB = 3$ units. Therefore, $\overline{OA} \cong \overline{OB}$.

3. $\overline{OC} \cong \overline{OC}$ by the reflexive property of congruence.

4. $\triangle COA \cong \triangle COB$ by s.a.s. $\cong$ s.a.s.

5. Therefore, $\overline{CA} \cong \overline{CB}$, and $\triangle ABC$ is an isosceles triangle.

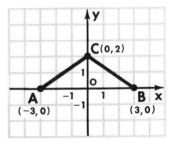

Solution 2 (paragraph form):

$\overleftrightarrow{OC} \perp \overleftrightarrow{AB}$, making $\angle COA$ and $\angle COB$ congruent right angles. Since O is $(0, 0)$ and lies halfway between $(-3, 0)$ and $(3, 0)$, it is the midpoint of $\overline{AB}$, and $\overline{OA} \cong \overline{OB}$. $\overline{OC} \cong \overline{OC}$ by the reflexive property of equality. $\triangle COA \cong \triangle COB$ by s.a.s. $\cong$ s.a.s. Therefore, $\overline{CA} \cong \overline{CB}$, and $\triangle ABC$ is isosceles because it is a triangle which has two congruent sides.

EXERCISES

1. Plot the following points: $A(0, 0)$, $B(0, 3)$, $C(4, 0)$. Connect these points in the order given. What kind of triangle is triangle ABC? Show why your conclusion is correct.

2. Show that the triangle whose vertices are the points $(-1, 1)$, $(-3, 2)$, and $(-1, 2)$ is a right triangle.

3. Plot the following points: $A(-2, 0)$, $B(0, -3)$, $C(2, 0)$. Connect the points in the order given. What kind of triangle is triangle ABC? Give an informal proof of your conclusion.

4. Show that the triangle whose vertices are the points (1, 1), (9, 4), (1, 7) is an isosceles triangle.

5. Plot the following points: $A(5, 3)$, $B(-5, 3)$, $C(-5, -3)$, $D(5, -3)$. Connect these points in the order given. What kind of quadrilateral is $ABCD$? Prove your conclusion informally.

6. Draw the quadrilateral which has the following points as its vertices. What type of quadrilateral is formed? Prove your conclusion informally.

   a. (1, 1), (4, 1), (4, −2), (1, −2)   b. (2, 2), (3, 4), (5, 2), (6, 4)
   c. (−1, −1), (−1, −3), (3, −1), (3, −3)   d. (6, 0), (9, 4), (6, 8), (3, 4)

7. Draw the quadrilateral which has the following points as its vertices. What type of quadrilateral appears to be formed?

   a. (2, 2), (3, 4), (5, 4), (9, 2)   b. (0, 0), (−6, 0), (−4, 2), (−2, 2)
   c. (1, 2), (3, 5), (5, 2), (3, −1)   d. (−3, 1), (−1, 3), (1, 3), (3, 1)

8. Plot the following points: $A(0, 0)$, $B(4, -2)$, $C(8, 0)$, $D(4, 2)$. (a) Connect these points in the given order. (b) Show that $\overleftrightarrow{BD}$ is the perpendicular bisector of $\overline{AC}$. (c) What type of quadrilateral is $ABCD$?

9. Show that the quadrilateral whose vertices are the points (−1, 1), (1, −2), (3, 1), and (1, 4) is a rhombus.

10. Triangle ABC has as its vertices the points $A(1, 1)$, $B(4, 1)$, and $C(4, 5)$. Triangle DEF has as its vertices the points $D(1, -1)$, $E(4, -1)$, and $F(4, -5)$. Show that triangle ABC is congruent to triangle DEF.

3. The Distance Between Two Points

Finding the Distance Between Two Points Having the Same Ordinate

Since the points $A(2, 1)$ and $B(6, 1)$ in Fig. 11–6 have the same ordinate, 1, they lie on a line which is parallel to the x-axis. We can discover that the distance between point A and point B is 4, either by counting the number of units contained in $\overline{AB}$, or by finding the difference between the abscissa of B, 6, and the abscissa of A, 2, obtaining $6 - 2 = 4$.

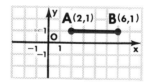

Fig. 11–6

Suppose we had subtracted the abscissa of B, 6, from the abscissa of A, 2. We would then have obtained the result $2 - 6$, or -4, which is different from the previous result, 4. We can resolve this inconsistency by agreeing that the distance between A and B is equal to the absolute value of the difference of their abscissas. Then, the order in which we subtract the abscissas would not matter because

$$|6 - 2| = |4| = 4 \qquad \text{also} \qquad |2 - 6| = |-4| = 4$$

Postulate 58. **The distance between two points having the same ordinate is the absolute value of the difference of their abscissas.**

In Fig. 11-7, the distance, d, between two points $A(x_1, y_1)$ and $B(x_2, y_1)$ having the same ordinate, y_1, is the absolute value of the result obtained when x_1, the abscissa of point A, is subtracted from x_2, the abscissa of point B, or

$$d = |x_2 - x_1|$$

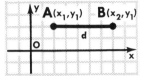

Fig. 11-7

Finding the Distance Between Two Points Having the Same Abscissa

Since the points $E(3, 2)$ and $F(3, 5)$ in Fig. 11-8 have the same abscissa, 3, they lie on a line which is parallel to the y-axis. We can discover that the distance between point E and point F is 3, either by counting the number of units contained in $\overline{EF}$, or by finding the difference between the ordinate of F, 5, and the ordinate of E, 2, or $5 - 2 = 3$.

Suppose we had subtracted the ordinate of F, 5, from the ordinate of E, 2. We would then have obtained the result $2 - 5$, or -3, which is different from the previous result, 3. We can resolve this inconsistency by agreeing that the distance between E and F is equal to the absolute value of the difference of their ordinates. Then, the order in which we subtract the ordinates would not matter because

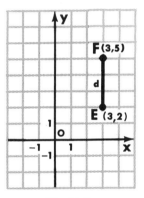

Fig. 11-8

$$|5 - 2| = |3| = 3 \quad \text{also} \quad |2 - 5| = |-3| = 3$$

Postulate 59. **The distance between two points having the same abscissa is the absolute value of the difference of their ordinates.**

In Fig. 11-9, the distance, d, between two points $E(x_1, y_1)$ and $F(x_1, y_2)$ having the same abscissa, x_1, is the absolute value of the result obtained when y_1, the ordinate of point E, is subtracted from y_2, the ordinate of point F, or

$$d = |y_2 - y_1|$$

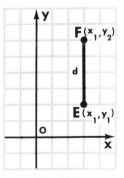

Fig. 11-9

Finding the Distance Between Any Two Points

The methods previously discussed cannot be used to find the distance between the point $A(2, 3)$ and the point $B(5, 7)$ because these two points have different abscissas and different ordinates. However, if we form a right triangle as shown in Fig. 11–10, we can use the Pythagorean Theorem to find d, the length of $\overline{AB}$.

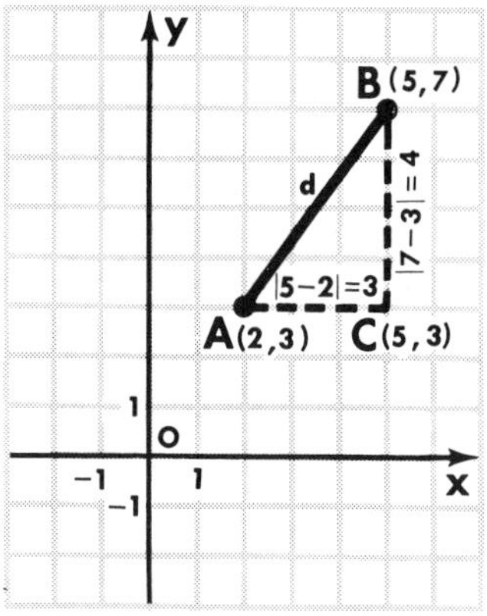

The coordinates of C, the vertex of right angle ACB, are $(5, 3)$.

The length of $\overline{AC} = |5 - 2| = |3| = 3$, and the length of $\overline{BC} = |7 - 3| = |4| = 4$. Therefore,

$$d^2 = 3^2 + 4^2$$
$$d^2 = 9 + 16$$
$$d^2 = 25$$
$$d = 5$$

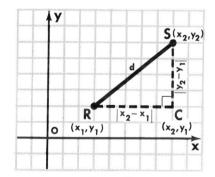

Fig. 11–10

Let us now derive a formula for the distance, d, between any two points $R(x_1, y_1)$ and $S(x_2, y_2)$ in Fig. 11–11.

1. Form right triangle RCS by drawing through S a line parallel to the y-axis and by drawing through R a line parallel to the x-axis, with the two lines intersecting at C.

2. Since the coordinates of point C are (x_2, y_1), then $RC = |x_2 - x_1|$ and $CS = |y_2 - y_1|$.

3. In right triangle RCS, let $RS = d$.

4. $(RS)^2 = (RC)^2 + (CS)^2$, or
$d^2 = |x_2 - x_1|^2 + |y_2 - y_1|^2$, or
$d^2 = (x_2 - x_1)^2 + (y_2 - y_1)^2$
$d = \sqrt{(x_2 - x_1)^2 + (y_2 - y_1)^2}$

Fig. 11–11

Theorem 147. **The distance, d, between two points (x_1, y_1) and (x_2, y_2) is given by the formula**

$$d = \sqrt{(x_2 - x_1)^2 + (y_2 - y_1)^2}$$

MODEL PROBLEMS

1. Find the distance between the point $A(1, 3)$ and the point $B(5, 3)$.

Solution:

1. Let the coordinates of point A be (x_1, y_1). Then $x_1 = 1, y_1 = 3$.

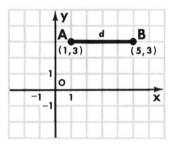

2. Let the coordinates of point B be (x_2, y_2). Then $x_2 = 5, y_2 = 3$.

3. Since points A and B have the same ordinate, 3, the distance, d, between point A and point B is given by the formula

$$d = |x_2 - x_1| = |5 - 1| = |4| = 4$$

Answer: 4.

NOTE. It is also possible to use the general formula for the distance between two points.

1. $d = \sqrt{(x_2 - x_1)^2 + (y_2 - y_1)^2}$

2. $d = \sqrt{(5 - 1)^2 + (3 - 3)^2} = \sqrt{(4)^2 + (0)^2} = \sqrt{16 + 0} = \sqrt{16} = 4$

2. Find the distance between the point $C(-3, -2)$ and the point $D(-3, 4)$.

Solution:

1. Let the coordinates of point C be (x_1, y_1). Then $x_1 = -3, y_1 = -2$.

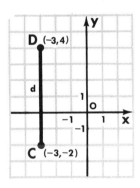

2. Let the coordinates of point D be (x_2, y_2). Then $x_2 = -3, y_2 = 4$.

3. Since points C and D have the same abscissa, -3, the distance, d, between point C and point D is given by the formula

$$d = |y_2 - y_1|$$
$$d = |4 - (-2)| = |4 + 2| = |6| = 6$$

Answer: 6.

NOTE. It is also possible to use the general formula for the distance between two points.

1. $d = \sqrt{(x_2 - x_1)^2 + (y_2 - y_1)^2}$

2. $d = \sqrt{[-3 - (-3)]^2 + [4 - (-2)]^2} = \sqrt{(-3 + 3)^2 + (4 + 2)^2}$

3. $d = \sqrt{(0)^2 + (6)^2} = \sqrt{0 + 36} = \sqrt{36} = 6$

3. A circle whose center is at $C(-4, 2)$ passes through the point $D(-3, 5)$. Find R, the length of radius $\overline{CD}$, in radical form.

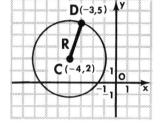

Solution:

1. Let the coordinates of point C be (x_1, y_1). Then $x_1 = -4$, $y_1 = 2$.

2. Let the coordinates of point D be (x_2, y_2). Then $x_2 = -3$, $y_2 = 5$.

3. $d = \sqrt{(x_2 - x_1)^2 + (y_2 - y_1)^2}$

4. $R = \sqrt{[-3 - (-4)]^2 + [5 - 2]^2} = \sqrt{(-3 + 4)^2 + (5 - 2)^2}$

5. $R = \sqrt{(1)^2 + (3)^2} = \sqrt{1 + 9} = \sqrt{10}$

Answer: $R = \sqrt{10}$.

NOTE. When we use the formula $d = \sqrt{(x_2 - x_1)^2 + (y_2 - y_1)^2}$ to find the distance between two points, either of the points may be named (x_1, y_1) provided that the other point is named (x_2, y_2). This is true because $(x_2 - x_1)^2 = (x_1 - x_2)^2$ and $(y_2 - y_1)^2 = (y_1 - y_2)^2$.

4. *Given:*   The quadrilateral with vertices $A(2, 2)$, $B(5, -2)$, $C(9, 1)$, and $D(6, 5)$.

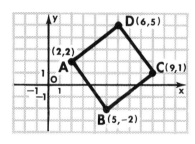

To show: $ABCD$ is a rhombus.

Plan: To show that $ABCD$ is a rhombus, show that it is a quadrilateral with four sides of equal lengths.

Solution:

1. $d = \sqrt{(x_2 - x_1)^2 + (y_2 - y_1)^2}$

2. $AB = \sqrt{(5 - 2)^2 + (-2 - 2)^2} = \sqrt{(3)^2 + (-4)^2}$

3. $AB = \sqrt{9 + 16} = \sqrt{25} = 5$

4. $BC = \sqrt{[9 - 5]^2 + [1 - (-2)]^2} = \sqrt{(4)^2 + (1 + 2)^2}$

5. $BC = \sqrt{(4)^2 + (3)^2} = \sqrt{16 + 9} = \sqrt{25} = 5$

6. $CD = \sqrt{(9 - 6)^2 + (1 - 5)^2} = \sqrt{(3)^2 + (-4)^2}$

7. $CD = \sqrt{9 + 16} = \sqrt{25} = 5$

8. $DA = \sqrt{(6 - 2)^2 + (5 - 2)^2} = \sqrt{(4)^2 + (3)^2} = \sqrt{16 + 9} = \sqrt{25} = 5$

9. $AB = BC = CD = DA$.

10. Since $ABCD$ is an equilateral quadrilateral, it is a rhombus.

5. *Given:*   The triangle whose vertices are $A(4, -1)$, $B(5, 6)$,
and $C(1, 3)$.

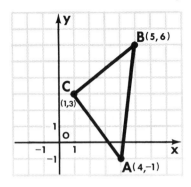

To show: $\triangle ABC$ is an isosceles right
triangle.

Plan: To show that $\triangle ABC$ is an
isosceles right triangle,
show that two sides are
equal in length and that
the square of the length of
the longest side is equal to
the sum of the squares of the lengths of the other two sides.

Solution:

1. $d = \sqrt{(x_2 - x_1)^2 + (y_2 - y_1)^2}$

2. $AB = \sqrt{[5 - 4]^2 + [6 - (-1)]^2} = \sqrt{(5 - 4)^2 + (6 + 1)^2}$

3. $AB = \sqrt{(1)^2 + (7)^2} = \sqrt{1 + 49} = \sqrt{50}$

4. $BC = \sqrt{(5 - 1)^2 + (6 - 3)^2} = \sqrt{(4)^2 + (3)^2} = \sqrt{16 + 9} = \sqrt{25} = 5$

5. $CA = \sqrt{(4 - 1)^2 + (-1 - 3)^2} = \sqrt{(3)^2 + (-4)^2}$

6. $CA = \sqrt{9 + 16} = \sqrt{25} = 5$

7. $BC = CA$. Therefore, triangle ABC is an isosceles triangle.

8. $(AB)^2 = (\sqrt{50})^2 = 50$, $(BC)^2 = (5)^2 = 25$, $(CA)^2 = (5)^2 = 25$.

9. Since $50 = 25 + 25$, $(AB)^2 = (BC)^2 + (CA)^2$, and triangle ABC is a
right triangle.

10. Therefore, triangle ABC is an isosceles right triangle.

EXERCISES

1. Find the distance between each of the following pairs of points: [An-
swers may be left in radical form.]

   a. $(2, 7)$ and $(12, 7)$ *b.* $(-3, 4)$ and $(5, 4)$ *c.* $(-1, -2)$ and $(-1, 4)$
   d. $(0, 0)$ and $(4, 3)$ *e.* $(0, 0)$ and $(-3, 4)$ *f.* $(-6, -8)$ and $(0, 0)$
   g. $(1, 4)$ and $(4, 8)$ *h.* $(4, 2)$ and $(-2, 10)$ *i.* $(-10, -12)$ and $(5, 8)$

    j. (6, 4) and (3, 6)   *k.* (−5, 0) and (−9, 6)   *l.* (0, 0) and (−2, 5)
    m. (0, *c*) and (*b*, 0)   *n.* (0, 0) and (*a*, *b*)

2. Find the length of the line segment joining the points whose coordinates are: [Answers may be left in radical form.]

    a. (5, 2) and (8, 6)   *b.* (−5, 1) and (7, 6)
    c. (0, 5) and (−3, 3)   *d.* (−4, −5) and (1, −2)

3. Find the lengths of the sides of a triangle whose vertices are: [Answers may be left in radical form.]

    a. (0, 0), (8, 0), (4, 3)   *b.* (1, 5), (5, 5), (5, 1)
    c. (3, 6), (−1, 3), (5, −5)   *d.* (6, −3), (0, 4), (8, −1)
    e. (−1, 7), (0, 0), (8, 4)   *f.* (−4, 2), (−1, 6), (5, 4)

4. Find the length of the shortest side of the triangle whose vertices are $R(-2, -1)$, $S(1, 3)$, $T(1, 10)$.

5. Show that points A, B, and C are collinear; that is, they lie on the same straight line. [*Hint:* Show that $AB + BC = AC$.]

    a. $A(0, 0)$, $B(5, 12)$, $C(10, 24)$ *b.* $A(-1, -2)$, $B(2, 2)$, $C(8, 10)$
    c. $A(-2, -2)$, $B(0, 2)$, $C(1, 4)$ *d.* $A(-1, 2)$, $B(2, -1)$, $C(4, -3)$

6. Show that the triangles which have the following vertices are isosceles triangles:

    a. (2, 3), (5, 7), (1, 4)   *b.* (1, 0), (5, 0), (3, 4)
    c. (7, −1), (2, −2), (3, 3)   *d.* (4, −7), (−3, −4), (7, 0)

7. Show that the triangles which have the following vertices are right triangles:

    a. (1, 1), (4, 5), (4, 1)   *b.* (5, 6), (8, 5), (2, −3)
    c. (−1, 0), (6, 1), (2, 4)   *d.* (−4, −1), (0, −5), (1, 4)

8. The vertices of triangle ABC are $A(2, 4)$, $B(5, 8)$, and $C(9, 5)$. (*a*) Show that triangle ABC is an isosceles triangle. (*b*) Show that triangle ABC is a right triangle.

9. Show that the line segments joining the points (−1, 3), (9, 3), and (4, 8) form an isosceles right triangle.

10. The points (1, 1), (7, 1), (7, 4), and (1, 4) are the vertices of a rectangle. Show that the diagonals are equal in length.

11. Show that the quadrilaterals which have the following vertices are parallelograms.

    a. (1, 2), (2, 5), (5, 7), (4, 4)   *b.* (−1, 1), (−3, 4), (1, 5), (3, 2)

12. Show that the quadrilaterals which have the following vertices are rhombuses:

    a. (1, 1), (5, 3), (7, 7), (3, 5)   *b.* (−3, 2), (−2, 6), (2, 7), (1, 3)

13. *a.* Show that the quadrilateral whose vertices are (1, 4), (4, 9), (−1, 12), (−4, 7) is equilateral.

   b. Show that the diagonals of this quadrilateral are equal in length.

   c. What type of quadrilateral have you shown this to be?

14. The vertices of trapezoid $ABCD$ are $A(1, -4)$, $B(10, -4)$, $C(9, 2)$, and $D(2, 2)$. (*a*) Show that $ABCD$ is an isosceles trapezoid. (*b*) Show that the length of diagonal $\overline{AC}$ equals the length of diagonal $\overline{BD}$.

15. Find the length of a radius of a circle whose center is at (0, 0) and which passes through the point (12, 5).

16. The point (2, 4) is on the circle whose center is (6, 1). Find the length of a radius of the circle.

17. Find the length of a radius of a circle whose center is at the origin and which passes through the point (−3, 4).

18. A circle whose center is at the point (5, 6) passes through the origin. Without constructing the circle, show that the point (11, 11) lies on the circle and that the point (9, 12) does not lie on the circle.

19. Show that a circle whose center is (2, 3) and which passes through the point (8, 11) also passes through the points (10, 9), (−4, −5), (8, −5).

20. A circle whose center is the point (2, 3) is tangent to the *x*-axis. Find the coordinates of the point of tangency.

21. A circle whose center is at the point (−6, 3) is tangent to the *y*-axis. Find the coordinates of the point of tangency.

22. (*a*) A circle whose center is at (6, 8) passes through the point (12, 16). Find the length of a radius of the circle. (*b*) On the circle given in *a*, there is another point whose abscissa is 12. Find its ordinate. (*c*) Find the distance of the center from the origin.

23. Point $A(-6, 2)$ is the center of a circle, and point $C(-3, 8)$ lies on the circle. A line segment joins point $B(9, 2)$ to point C. Using coordinate geometry, show that $\overleftrightarrow{BC}$ is tangent to the circle at point C.

4. The Midpoint of a Line Segment

Theorem 148. **Each coordinate of the midpoint of a line segment is equal to one-half the sum of the corresponding coordinates of the endpoints of the line segment.**

The coordinates of the midpoint $M(x_m, y_m)$ of line segment $\overline{AB}$ which joins any point $A(x_1, y_1)$ and any other point $B(x_2, y_2)$ are given by the formulas

$$x_m = \frac{1}{2}(x_1 + x_2) \qquad y_m = \frac{1}{2}(y_1 + y_2)$$

INFORMAL PROOF FOR
$x_m = \frac{1}{2}(x_1 + x_2)$:

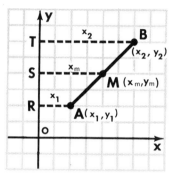

Fig. 11–12

INFORMAL PROOF FOR
$y_m = \frac{1}{2}(y_1 + y_2)$:

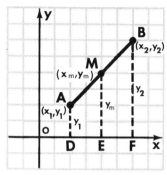

Fig. 11–13

In Fig. 11–12, draw $\overleftrightarrow{AR} \perp y$-axis, $\overleftrightarrow{MS} \perp y$-axis, and $\overleftrightarrow{BT} \perp y$-axis. Then $\overleftrightarrow{RA} \parallel \overleftrightarrow{SM} \parallel \overleftrightarrow{TB}$. Since M is the midpoint of $\overline{AB}$, $AM = MB$. Therefore, $RS = ST$ because three parallel lines which cut off segments whose lengths are equal on one transversal cut off segments whose lengths are equal on any transversal. $\overline{SM}$ is a median in trapezoid $RABT$ and its length is equal to one-half the sum of the lengths of the bases $\overline{RA}$ and $\overline{TB}$. Therefore, $SM = \frac{1}{2}(RA + TB)$, or $x_m = \frac{1}{2}(x_1 + x_2)$.

In Fig. 11–13, draw $\overleftrightarrow{AD} \perp x$-axis, $\overleftrightarrow{ME} \perp x$-axis, and $\overleftrightarrow{BF} \perp x$-axis. Then $\overleftrightarrow{DA} \parallel \overleftrightarrow{EM} \parallel \overleftrightarrow{FB}$. Since M is the midpoint of $\overline{AB}$, $AM = MB$. Therefore, $DE = EF$ because three parallel lines which cut off segments whose lengths are equal on one transversal cut off segments whose lengths are equal on any transversal. $\overline{EM}$ is a median in trapezoid $BFDA$ and its length is equal to one-half the sum of the lengths of the bases $\overline{DA}$ and $\overline{FB}$. Therefore, $EM = \frac{1}{2}(DA + FB)$, or $y_m = \frac{1}{2}(y_1 + y_2)$.

MODEL PROBLEMS

1. Find the coordinates of the midpoint of the line segment which joins the point $R(4, 6)$ and the point $S(8, -2)$.

Solution:

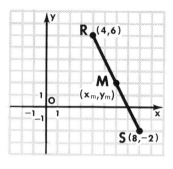

1. Let the point $R(4, 6)$ be (x_1, y_1).

2. Let the point $S(8, -2)$ be (x_2, y_2).

3. Therefore, $x_1 = 4$, $y_1 = 6$, $x_2 = 8$, $y_2 = -2$.

4. Let the midpoint of $\overline{RS}$, point M, be (x_m, y_m).

5. At the midpoint of $\overline{RS}$, $x_m = \frac{1}{2}(x_1 + x_2)$.

6. $x_m = \frac{1}{2}(4 + 8) = \frac{1}{2}(12) = 6$.

7. At the midpoint of $\overline{RS}$, $y_m = \frac{1}{2}(y_1 + y_2)$.

8. $y_m = \frac{1}{2}[6 + (-2)] = \frac{1}{2}[4] = 2$.

Answer: The coordinates of the midpoint of line segment $\overline{RS}$ are $x = 6$, $y = 2$, or $(6, 2)$.

2. $\overline{CD}$ is a diameter of the circle whose center is the point $P(2, 1)$. If the coordinates of C are $(0, -2)$, find the coordinates of D.

Solution:

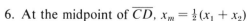

1. Since P is the center of a circle whose diameter is $\overline{CD}$, P is the midpoint of $\overline{CD}$.

2. Let the point $C(0, -2)$ be (x_1, y_1).

3. Let the point $D(a, b)$ be (x_2, y_2).

4. Therefore, $x_1 = 0$, $y_1 = -2$, $x_2 = a$, $y_2 = b$.

5. Since $P(2, 1)$ is the midpoint of $\overline{CD}$, x_m at the midpoint is 2 and y_m at the midpoint is 1.

6. At the midpoint of $\overline{CD}$, $x_m = \frac{1}{2}(x_1 + x_2)$

7. $\qquad\qquad\qquad 2 = \frac{1}{2}(0 + a)$

8. $\qquad\qquad\qquad 4 = 0 + a$

9. $\qquad\qquad\qquad 4 = a$

10. At the midpoint of $\overline{CD}$, $y_m = \frac{1}{2}(y_1 + y_2)$

11. $\qquad\qquad\qquad 1 = \frac{1}{2}(-2 + b)$

12. $\qquad\qquad\qquad 2 = -2 + b$

13. $\qquad\qquad\qquad 4 = b$

Answer: The coordinates of D are $a = 4$, $b = 4$, or $(4, 4)$.

3. Given the quadrilateral whose vertices are $A(-2, 2)$, $B(1, 4)$, $C(2, 8)$, and $D(-1, 6)$.

   a. Find the coordinates of the midpoint of diagonal $\overline{AC}$.

   b. Find the coordinates of the midpoint of diagonal $\overline{BD}$.

   c. Show that $ABCD$ is a parallelogram.

   Plan: To show that $ABCD$ is a parallelogram, prove that its diagonals bisect each other. They bisect each other when both diagonals have the same midpoint.

   Solution:

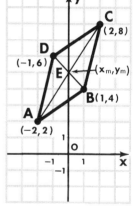

   a. 1. Let $A(-2, 2)$ be (x_1, y_1) and $C(2, 8)$ be (x_2, y_2). Therefore, $x_1 = -2$, $y_1 = 2$, $x_2 = 2$, $y_2 = 8$. Let the midpoint of $\overline{AC}$ be (x_m, y_m).

      2. At the midpoint of $\overline{AC}$, $x_m = \frac{1}{2}(x_1 + x_2)$ and $y_m = \frac{1}{2}(y_1 + y_2)$.

      3. $x_m = \frac{1}{2}(-2 + 2) = \frac{1}{2}(0) = 0$ and $y_m = \frac{1}{2}(2 + 8) = \frac{1}{2}(10) = 5$.

   Answer: The midpoint of diagonal $\overline{AC}$ is the point $(0, 5)$.

   b. 1. Let $D(-1, 6)$ be (x_1, y_1) and $B(1, 4)$ be (x_2, y_2). Therefore, $x_1 = -1$, $y_1 = 6$, $x_2 = 1$, $y_2 = 4$. Let the midpoint of $\overline{BD}$ be (x_m, y_m).

      2. At the midpoint of $\overline{BD}$, $x_m = \frac{1}{2}(x_1 + x_2)$ and $y_m = \frac{1}{2}(y_1 + y_2)$.

      3. $x_m = \frac{1}{2}(-1 + 1) = \frac{1}{2}(0) = 0$ and $y_m = \frac{1}{2}(6 + 4) = \frac{1}{2}(10) = 5$.

   Answer: The midpoint of diagonal $\overline{BD}$ is the point $(0, 5)$.

   c. 1. Since the point $E(0, 5)$ is the midpoint of each diagonal, the diagonals bisect each other at point E.

      2. Since $ABCD$ is a quadrilateral whose diagonals bisect each other, it is a parallelogram.

EXERCISES

1. Find the coordinates of the midpoint of the line segment which joins each of the following pairs of points:

    a. (6, 8), (4, 10)   b. (2, 6), (8, 4)   c. (2, 11), (7, 6)
    d. (5, −6), (−1, 9)   e. (−4, −8), (−6, −5)   f. (12, 11), (−1, −2)
    g. (2, 0), (5, 9)   h. (−2, 7), (0, −5)   i. (0, 0), (8, 10)
    j. (2, −7), (−2, 7)   k. (5c, 2c), (c, 8c)   l. (m, 0), (0, n)

2. Find the abscissa of the midpoint of the line segment whose endpoints are:

    a. (4, 8), (10, 12)   b. (8, 7), (6, 3)   c. (6, −6), (12, −4)
    d. (−7, −3), (−5, −7)   e. (0, 0), (6, 10)   f. (0, −5), (−7, 0)
    g. (2a, 3b), (4a, 6b)   h. (−4c, 2d), (8c, 6d)   i. (a, 0), (0, b)

3. Find the ordinate of the midpoint of the line segment whose endpoints are:

    a. (6, 10), (8, 6)   b. (10, 5), (8, 1)   c. (8, −8), (14, −4)
    d. (−5, −9), (−3, −5)   e. (6, −4), (−9, 1)   f. (−7, 6), (0, 0)
    g. (a, 2b), (3a, 4b)   h. (2c, −4d), (6c, 8d)   i. (c, 0), (0, d)

4. In a circle whose center is P, A and B are the endpoints of a diameter. Find the coordinates of point P when the coordinates of A and B are respectively:

    a. (4, 6), (6, 8)   b. (5, 7), (7, 8)   c. (−4, −1), (−8, −4)
    d. (−5, −2), (3, 7)   e. (0, 0), (10, 4)   f. (8, 0), (−4, 0)
    g. (2a, b), (4a, 3b)   h. (−2c, −4d), (2c, 4d)   i. (a, 0), (0, b)

5. Find the midpoints of the sides of a triangle whose vertices are:

    a. $A(2, 8)$, $B(4, 12)$, $C(6, 4)$ b. $A(−5, 2)$, $B(7, 4)$, $C(3, −6)$
    c. $D(8, 0)$, $E(0, 5)$, $F(4, 6)$ d. $D(−2, 0)$, $E(0, −8)$, $F(0, 0)$

6. Find the midpoints of the sides of a quadrilateral whose vertices are the points:

    a. $A(0, 0)$, $B(10, 0)$, $C(7, 5)$, $D(3, 5)$
    b. $P(−3, 3)$, $Q(11, 3)$, $R(7, 7)$, $S(1, 7)$

7. M is the midpoint of line segment $\overline{CD}$. The coordinates of point C are (8, 4) and of point $M(8, 10)$. Find the coordinates of point D.

8. In triangle ABC, M is the midpoint of side $\overline{AB}$. The coordinates of A are (6, 10) and of point $M(7, −2)$. Find the coordinates of point B.

9. $\overline{CD}$ is a diameter of a circle whose center is P. If the coordinates of point C are (2, 3) and those of point P are (4, 7), find the coordinates of point D.

10. $\overline{CD}$ is a diameter in a circle whose center is P. If the abscissa of point C is $−8a$ and the abscissa of point P is $2a$, find the abscissa of point D.

11. Given the points $A(−4, 6)$, $B(2, 7)$, and $C(r, s)$. If B is the midpoint of line segment $\overline{AC}$, find the value of r and the value of s.

12. The x-axis is the perpendicular bisector of line segment $\overline{AB}$. Find the

coordinates of point B if the coordinates of point A are:
a. (3, 6)   *b.* (5, −3)   *c.* (−3, 5)   *d.* (−2, −6)   *e.* (0, 4)   *f.* (0, −2)

13. The y-axis is the perpendicular bisector of line segment $\overline{CD}$. Find the coordinates of point D if the coordinates of point C are:
a. (2, 4)   *b.* (3, −2)   *c.* (−1, 5)   *d.* (−3, −6)   *e.* (4, 0)   *f.* (−5, 0)

14. The origin is the midpoint of line segment $\overline{EF}$. Find the coordinates of point F if the coordinates of point E are:
a. (4, 3)   *b.* (2, −1)   *c.* (−5, 2)   *d.* (−6, −3)   *e.* (6, 0)   *f.* (0, −4)

15. In parallelogram $ABCD$ the coordinates of A are (6, 7), and the coordinates of C are (12, 3). What are the coordinates of the point of intersection of the diagonals?

16. The points $A(2, 3)$, $B(7, 5)$, $C(8, 8)$, and $D(3, 6)$ are the vertices of a quadrilateral. (*a*) Show that the diagonals of quadrilateral $ABCD$ bisect each other. (*b*) Show that $ABCD$ is a parallelogram.

17. Show that the points $A(1, -3)$, $B(5, -2)$, $C(8, 2)$, and $D(4, 1)$ are the vertices of a parallelogram.

18. Show that the diagonals of the quadrilateral whose vertices are $A(3, 5)$, $B(6, 4)$, $C(7, 8)$, and $D(4, 12)$ do *not* bisect each other.

19. The points $A(4, 0)$, $B(14, 0)$, and $C(8, 6)$ are the vertices of triangle ABC. Show that the length of the line segment which joins the midpoints of $\overline{CA}$ and $\overline{CB}$ is equal to one-half of AB.

20. The points $A(2, 2)$, $B(6, -6)$, $C(8, 2)$, and $D(4, 4)$ are the vertices of polygon $ABCD$. (*a*) Show that $\overline{LM}$, the line segment which joins the midpoints of $\overline{AD}$ and $\overline{DC}$, is congruent and parallel to $\overline{PN}$, the line segment which joins the midpoints of $\overline{BA}$ and $\overline{BC}$. (*b*) If $\overline{MN}$ and $\overline{LP}$ are also drawn, what type of quadrilateral is $LMNP$?

21. Given quadrilateral $ABCD$ whose vertices are $A(0, 0)$, $B(6, 8)$, $C(16, 8)$, and $D(10, 0)$.
a. Using graph paper, construct quadrilateral $ABCD$.
b. If R is the midpoint of $\overline{AB}$, S the midpoint of $\overline{BC}$, and T the midpoint of $\overline{AD}$:
  (1) find the length of $\overline{RS}$.
  (2) find the length of $\overline{ST}$.
  (3) find the length of $\overline{RT}$.
c. Show that RST is a right triangle.

22. The vertices of quadrilateral $ABCD$ are the points $A(4, 0)$, $B(13, 3)$, $C(12, 6)$, and $D(3, 3)$. (*a*) Find the coordinates of the midpoint of $\overline{AC}$. (*b*) Find the coordinates of the midpoint of $\overline{BD}$. (*c*) Show that $ABCD$ is a parallelogram. (*d*) Find the length of diagonal $\overline{AC}$ and the length of diagonal $\overline{BD}$. (*e*) Show that quadrilateral $ABCD$ is a rectangle.

23. The vertices of a triangle are $R(7, 1)$, $S(2, 1)$, $T(4, 7)$. Find the length of the median from R to $\overline{ST}$.

24. Find the length of each median of a triangle whose vertices are $A(4, 8)$, $B(-2, 6)$, $C(0, -4)$.

25. The vertices of triangle ABC are $A(0, 1)$, $B(6, 1)$, and $C(3, 5)$. (a) Show that triangle ABC is isosceles. (b) Find the length of the altitude from C to $\overline{AB}$.

26. The vertices of triangle ABC are $A(11, -1)$, $B(13, 10)$, and $C(3, 5)$. (a) Show that triangle ABC is isosceles. (b) Find the length of the altitude from B to $\overline{AC}$.

27. Given triangle RST with vertices $(-3, -4)$, $(3, 4)$, and $(-5, 0)$ respectively.
    a. Show by means of coordinate geometry that triangle RST is a right triangle.
    b. Show by methods of coordinate geometry that the length of the median to the hypotenuse of triangle RST is equal to one-half the length of the hypotenuse.

28. Point $P(2, 3)$ is the center of a circle.
    a. A and B are the endpoints of a diameter of this circle. If the coordinates of A are $(7, 3)$, find the coordinates of B.
    b. Using coordinate geometry, show that point $C(-1, 7)$ is a point on the circle.
    c. Using coordinate geometry, show that triangle ABC is a right triangle.

29. The vertices of triangle ABC are $A(3, 1)$, $B(9, 9)$, and $C(9, 1)$. (a) Show that M, the midpoint of $\overline{AB}$, is equidistant from A, B, and C. (b) Show that M is the center of the circle which circumscribes triangle ABC. (c) Show that triangle ABC is a right triangle.

30. a. Given the vertices $R(9, 10)$, $S(13, 2)$, $T(-3, -6)$, draw triangle RST.
    b. Show that $\triangle RST$ is a right triangle.
    c. Find the coordinates of the center of the circle which circumscribes $\triangle RST$.

5. The Slope of a Line Segment and the Slope of a Line

The Slope of a Line Segment

In Fig. 11–14, we can see that line segment $\overline{DE}$ "rises more steeply" than line segment $\overline{AB}$ because $\overline{DE}$ "rises" 20 ft. vertically over a horizontal distance of 60 ft., whereas $\overline{AB}$ "rises" only 10 ft. vertically over the same horizontal

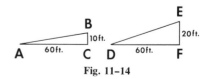

Fig. 11–14

distance of 60 ft. We would say that the *slope* of $\overline{DE}$ is steeper than the slope of $\overline{AB}$. The slope of a line segment involves a comparison of the vertical change with the horizontal change. In mathematics, we define the slope of a line segment in such a way that the general ideas that we have mentioned are expressed more precisely.

Definition. The *slope, m, of a line segment* whose endpoints are $P_1(x_1, y_1)$ and $P_2(x_2, y_2)$, where $x_1 \neq x_2$, is the ratio of the difference of the y-values, $y_2 - y_1$, to the difference of the corresponding x-values, $x_2 - x_1$.

Hence, in Fig. 11–15, the slope of the line segment whose endpoints are $P_1(x_1, y_1)$ and $P_2(x_2, y_2)$ is given by the formula

$$m = \frac{y_2 - y_1}{x_2 - x_1} \qquad (x_1 \neq x_2)$$

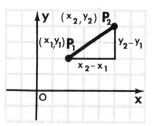

Fig. 11–15

The expression "difference in x-values, $x_2 - x_1$" may be represented by the symbol Δx, read "delta x." Likewise, "the difference in y-values, $y_2 - y_1$" may be represented by Δy, read "delta y." Therefore, we may write the formula for the slope of the line segment whose endpoints are $P_1(x_1, y_1)$ and $P_2(x_2, y_2)$ more simply as

$$m = \frac{\Delta y}{\Delta x}$$

Note that in finding the slope of a line segment whose endpoints are two given points, it does not matter which point is represented by (x_1, y_1) and which by (x_2, y_2) since $\frac{y_2 - y_1}{x_2 - x_1} = \frac{y_1 - y_2}{x_1 - x_2}$.

We will now see that the slope of a non-vertical line segment may be a positive number or a negative number or zero.

Positive Slope

In Fig. 11–16, reading from left to right, if the segment $\overline{P_1P_2}$ slants upward, then $y_2 - y_1$, or Δy, is a positive number $(+3)$; and $x_2 - x_1$, or Δx, is also a positive number $(+2)$. Since both Δy and Δx are positive numbers, the slope of $\overline{P_1P_2}$, $\frac{\Delta y}{\Delta x}$, must be a positive number.

In this case,

$$\text{slope of } \overline{P_1P_2} = m = \frac{\Delta y}{\Delta x} = \frac{+3}{+2} = +\frac{3}{2}$$

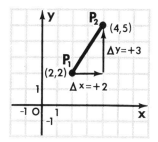

Fig. 11–16

Thus, we have illustrated the truth of the following statement:

The slope of a non-vertical line segment that slants upward from left to right is a positive number.

Negative Slope

In Fig. 11–17, reading from left to right, if the segment $\overline{P_1P_2}$ slants downward, then $y_2 - y_1$, or Δy, is a negative number (-3); and $x_2 - x_1$, or Δx, is a positive number ($+2$). Since Δy is a negative number and Δx is a positive number, the slope of $\overline{P_1P_2}$, $\dfrac{\Delta y}{\Delta x}$, must be a negative number.

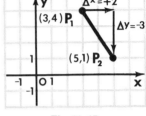

Fig. 11–17

In this case,

$$\text{slope of } \overline{P_1P_2} = m = \frac{\Delta y}{\Delta x} = \frac{-3}{+2} = -\frac{3}{2}$$

Thus, we have illustrated the truth of the following statement:

The slope of a non-vertical line segment that slants downward from left to right is a negative number.

Zero Slope

In Fig. 11–18, $\overline{AB} \parallel x$-axis. Hence, the ordinates of points A and B must be equal. Therefore, we can represent the coordinates of point A by (x_1, y_1) and the coordinates of point B by (x_2, y_1), where $x_1 \neq x_2$.

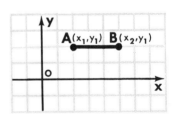

Fig. 11–18

The slope of $\overline{AB} = \dfrac{\Delta y}{\Delta x} = \dfrac{y_1 - y_1}{x_2 - x_1} = \dfrac{0}{x_2 - x_1} = 0.$

Hence, we have proved:

Theorem 149. **The slope of a line segment parallel to the *x*-axis (a horizontal line segment) is zero.**

[NOTE. Later, we will see that the slope of the *x*-axis itself is also zero.]

No Slope

In Fig. 11–19, $\overline{CD} \parallel y$-axis. Hence, the abscissas of points C and D must be equal. Therefore, the coordinates of C may be represented by (x_1, y_1) and the coordinates of D may be represented by (x_1, y_2) where $y_1 \neq y_2$.

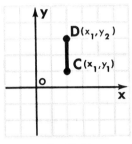

The slope of $\overline{CD} = \dfrac{\Delta y}{\Delta x} = \dfrac{y_2 - y_1}{x_1 - x_1} = \dfrac{y_2 - y_1}{0}$.

The expression $\dfrac{y_2 - y_1}{0}$ is undefined or meaningless since division by zero is undefined or meaningless.

Fig. 11–19

Hence, we have proved:

Theorem 150. A line segment parallel to the y-axis (a vertical line segment) has no defined slope.

[NOTE. Later, we shall see that the y-axis itself has no defined slope.]

The Slope of a Line

Suppose P_1, P_2, and P_3 are points on non-vertical line $\overset{\leftrightarrow}{LM}$, as in Fig. 11–20.

The slope of $\overline{P_1P_2} = \dfrac{P_2R}{P_1R}$.

The slope of $\overline{P_2P_3} = \dfrac{P_3S}{P_2S}$.

Since $\triangle P_1RP_2 \sim \triangle P_2SP_3$, then $\dfrac{P_2R}{P_1R} = \dfrac{P_3S}{P_2S}$.

Therefore, the slope of $\overline{P_1P_2} =$ the slope of $\overline{P_2P_3}$.
Hence, we have outlined the proof of:

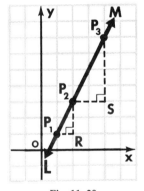

Fig. 11–20

Theorem 151. The slopes of all segments that lie on a non-vertical straight line are equal.

Definition. The *slope of a non-vertical line* is equal to the slope of any segment on the line.

We also say that a vertical line (a line parallel to the y-axis, or the y-axis itself) has no defined slope.

We see, therefore, that although the slope of a non-vertical line segment is a number which is associated with the line segment, it is also the slope of the line which contains the line segment.

It can be shown that two distinct lines that pass through the same point must have unequal slopes.

Recall that collinear points are points that lie on the same straight line. In Fig. 11–21, since points P_1, P_2, and P_3 all lie on $\overleftrightarrow{LM}$, they are collinear points.

Theorem 152. **Three points are collinear if the slope of the line segment which joins the first point and the second point is equal to**

(*a*) **the slope of the line segment which joins the first point and the third point, or**

(*b*) **the slope of the line segment which joins the second point and the third point.**

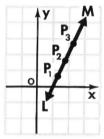

Fig. 11–21

In Fig. 11–21, P_1, P_2, and P_3 are collinear if the slope of $\overline{P_1P_2}$ is equal to the slope of $\overline{P_1P_3}$, or if the slope of $\overline{P_1P_2}$ is equal to the slope of $\overline{P_2P_3}$.

MODEL PROBLEMS

1. Find the slope of the line which passes through the points $C(-3, 1)$ and $D(-1, 4)$.

Solution:

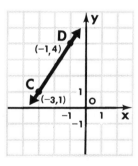

1. Let the coordinates of C be (x_1, y_1). Then $x_1 = -3$ and $y_1 = 1$.

2. Let the coordinates of D be (x_2, y_2). Then $x_2 = -1$ and $y_2 = 4$.

3. Slope of $\overleftrightarrow{CD} = \dfrac{y_2 - y_1}{x_2 - x_1} = \dfrac{4 - 1}{-1 - (-3)}$.

4. Slope of $\overleftrightarrow{CD} = \dfrac{4 - 1}{-1 + 3} = \dfrac{3}{2}$.

Answer: Slope of $\overleftrightarrow{CD}$ is $\dfrac{3}{2}$.

2. Show that the points $A(2, 3)$, $B(4, 4)$, and $C(8, 6)$ are collinear.

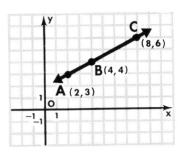

Plan: To show that points A, B, and C are collinear, show that the slope of line segment $\overline{AB}$ is equal to the slope of line segment $\overline{AC}$.

Solution:

1. Let the coordinates of A be (x_1, y_1). Then $x_1 = 2$ and $y_1 = 3$.

2. Let the coordinates of B be (x_2, y_2). Then $x_2 = 4$ and $y_2 = 4$.

3. Slope of line segment $\overline{AB} = \dfrac{y_2 - y_1}{x_2 - x_1} = \dfrac{4 - 3}{4 - 2} = \dfrac{1}{2}$.

4. Let the coordinates of A be (x_1, y_1). Then $x_1 = 2$ and $y_1 = 3$.

5. Let the coordinates of C be (x_2, y_2). Then $x_2 = 8$ and $y_2 = 6$.

6. Slope of line segment $\overline{AC} = \dfrac{y_2 - y_1}{x_2 - x_1} = \dfrac{6 - 3}{8 - 2} = \dfrac{3}{6} = \dfrac{1}{2}$.

7. Since A is a point on line segment $\overline{AB}$ as well as on line segment $\overline{AC}$, and the slope of $\overline{AB}$ is equal to the slope of $\overline{AC}$, points A, B, and C all lie on the same straight line, $\overleftrightarrow{AC}$, and are therefore collinear.

EXERCISES

1. In each part, tell whether the line has a positive slope, a negative slope, a slope of zero, or no slope.

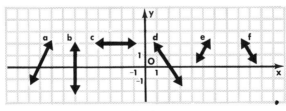

Ex. 1

2. In each part, find the slope of the line; if the line has no slope, indicate that fact.

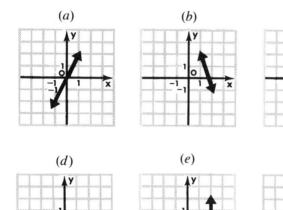

Ex. 2

3. In each part, plot both points on coordinate graph paper, draw the line segment which joins them, and find the slope of this line segment.

a. (0, 0) and (9, 3)   *b.* (0, 0) and (−2, 4)   *c.* (−2, −6) and (0, 0)
d. (0, 4) and (2, 8)   *e.* (−5, 6) and (−1, 0)   *f.* (0, −3) and (−6, 0)
g. (1, 5) and (3, 9)   *h.* (2, 3) and (4, 15)   *i.* (5, 8) and (4, 3)
j. (2, 7) and (6, 9)   *k.* (4, 6) and (−5, 9)   *l.* (5, −2) and (7, −8)

4. Find the slope of the line which passes through the points (3, 5) and (8, 5).

5. Choose the correct answer: The straight line which passes through the points (6, 3) and (2, 3) has (*a*) a slope of 4 (*b*) a slope of zero (*c*) no slope.

6. Find the value of x so that the slope of the line passing through the points (5, 3) and (x, 6) will be 1.

7. Find the value of y so that the slope of the line passing through the points (2, y) and (6, 10) will be $\frac{1}{2}$.

8. Find the value of y so that the slope of the line passing through the points (−8, −2) and (4, y) will be 0.

9. Find the value of x so that the line passing through the points (−4, 8) and (x, −2) will have no slope.

10. In each of the following, determine whether the points are collinear:

a. (1, 2), (4, 5), (6, 7)   *b.* (−1, −4), (2, −2), (8, 2)
c. (1, 1̄), (3, 4), (6, 5)   *d.* (−2, 6), (0, 2), (1, 0)
e. (0, 0), (−8, −2), (4, 1)   *f.* (−3, 4), (−1, 1), (1, −3)

11. Line $\overleftrightarrow{CD}$ passes through the points $(-4, -2)$ and $(8, 7)$. (*a*) Find the slope of line $\overleftrightarrow{CD}$. (*b*) Tell whether each of the following is *true* or *false:* (1) Line $\overleftrightarrow{CD}$ passes through the point $(0, 1)$. (2) The tangent of the acute angle which line $\overleftrightarrow{CD}$ makes with the *x*-axis is $\frac{3}{4}$.

6. Parallel Lines and Perpendicular Lines

The number which represents the slope of a line makes it possible for us to state numerical conditions for the parallelism or perpendicularity of two non-vertical lines. We already know that (1) two vertical lines (lines that have no defined slopes) are parallel (2) two horizontal lines (lines that have a slope of 0) are parallel (3) a vertical line (a line with no defined slope) and a horizontal line (a line whose slope is 0) are perpendicular to each other.

Parallel Lines

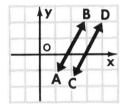
Fig. 11–22

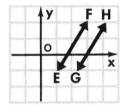
Fig. 11–23

Theorem 153. **If two non-vertical lines are parallel, then their slopes are equal.**

In Fig. 11–22, if $\overleftrightarrow{AB}$ is parallel to $\overleftrightarrow{CD}$, the slope of $\overleftrightarrow{AB} = m_1$, and the slope of $\overleftrightarrow{CD} = m_2$, then $m_1 = m_2$.

Theorem 154. **If two non-vertical lines have equal slopes, then the lines are parallel.**

In Fig. 11–23, if the slope of line $\overleftrightarrow{EF}$ is equal to the slope of line $\overleftrightarrow{GH}$, then $\overleftrightarrow{EF}$ is parallel to $\overleftrightarrow{GH}$.

Perpendicular Lines

Definition. **One number is the *reciprocal* of a second number if the product of the two numbers is 1.**

Thus, $\dfrac{4}{5}$ is the reciprocal of $\dfrac{5}{4}$ since $\left(\dfrac{5}{4}\right)\left(\dfrac{4}{5}\right) = 1$.

Also, $\dfrac{b}{a}$ is the reciprocal of $\dfrac{a}{b}$ since $\left(\dfrac{a}{b}\right)\left(\dfrac{b}{a}\right) = 1$.

Thus, to find the reciprocal of a fraction, we simply invert the fraction.

Definition. **One number is the *negative reciprocal* of a second number if the product of the two numbers is −1.**

Thus, $-\dfrac{1}{3}$ is the negative reciprocal of 3 since $(3)\left(-\dfrac{1}{3}\right) = -1$.

Also, $-\dfrac{b}{a}$ is the negative reciprocal of $\dfrac{a}{b}$ since $\left(\dfrac{a}{b}\right)\left(-\dfrac{b}{a}\right) = -1$.

Thus, to find the negative reciprocal of a fraction, we simply invert the fraction and change its sign.

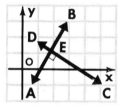

Fig. 11–24

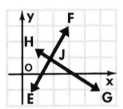

Fig. 11–25

Theorem 155. **If two non-vertical lines are perpendicular, then the slope of one line is the negative reciprocal of the slope of the other line.**

In Fig. 11–24, if line $\overleftrightarrow{AB}$ whose slope is m_1 is perpendicular to line $\overleftrightarrow{CD}$ whose slope is m_2, then $m_1 m_2 = -1$, or $m_1 = -\dfrac{1}{m_2}$.

Theorem 156. **If the slope of one line is the negative reciprocal of the slope of a second line, then the lines are perpendicular.**

In Fig. 11–25, if the slope of line $\overleftrightarrow{EF}$ is m_1, the slope of line $\overleftrightarrow{GH}$ is m_2, and $m_1 m_2 = -1$, then $\overleftrightarrow{EF}$ is perpendicular to $\overleftrightarrow{GH}$.

KEEP IN MIND

1. To show that two non-vertical lines are parallel, show that the slopes of the lines are equal.
2. To show that two non-vertical lines are perpendicular, show that the slope of one line is the negative reciprocal of the slope of the other line.

MODEL PROBLEMS

1. Show, by means of slopes, that the quadrilateral whose vertices are the points $A(1, 1)$, $B(3, -2)$, $C(4, 1)$, and $D(2, 4)$ is a parallelogram.

    Plan: To show that $ABCD$ is a parallelogram, show that its opposite sides are parallel. To show that two sides are parallel, show that their slopes are equal.

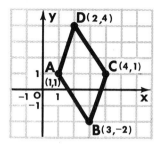

Solution:

1. Let the coordinates of A be (x_1, y_1). Then $x_1 = 1$ and $y_1 = 1$.

2. Let the coordinates of B be (x_2, y_2). Then $x_2 = 3$ and $y_2 = -2$.

3. Slope of $\overline{AB} = \dfrac{y_2 - y_1}{x_2 - x_1} = \dfrac{-2 - 1}{3 - 1} = \dfrac{-3}{2} = -\dfrac{3}{2}$.

4. Let the coordinates of D be (x_1, y_1). Then $x_1 = 2$ and $y_1 = 4$.

5. Let the coordinates of C be (x_2, y_2). Then $x_2 = 4$ and $y_2 = 1$.

6. Slope of $\overline{DC} = \dfrac{y_2 - y_1}{x_2 - x_1} = \dfrac{1 - 4}{4 - 2} = \dfrac{-3}{2} = -\dfrac{3}{2}$.

7. Since slope of $\overline{AB}$ = slope of $\overline{DC}$, $\overline{AB}$ is parallel to $\overline{DC}$.

8. Let the coordinates of B be (x_1, y_1). Then $x_1 = 3$ and $y_1 = -2$.

9. Let the coordinates of C be (x_2, y_2). Then $x_2 = 4$ and $y_2 = 1$.

10. Slope of $\overline{BC} = \dfrac{y_2 - y_1}{x_2 - x_1} = \dfrac{1 - (-2)}{4 - 3} = \dfrac{1 + 2}{4 - 3} = \dfrac{3}{1} = 3$.

11. Let the coordinates of A be (x_1, y_1). Then $x_1 = 1$ and $y_1 = 1$.

12. Let the coordinates of D be (x_2, y_2). Then $x_2 = 2$ and $y_2 = 4$.

13. Slope of $\overline{AD} = \dfrac{y_2 - y_1}{x_2 - x_1} = \dfrac{4 - 1}{2 - 1} = \dfrac{3}{1} = 3$.

14. Since slope of $\overline{BC}$ = slope of $\overline{AD}$, $\overline{BC}$ is parallel to $\overline{AD}$.

15. Since the opposite sides of quadrilateral $ABCD$ are parallel, quadrilateral $ABCD$ is a parallelogram.

2. Show, by means of slopes, that the triangle whose vertices are $A(0, 2)$, $B(2, 3)$, and $C(1, 5)$ is a right triangle.

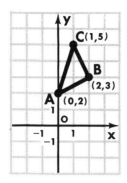

Plan: To show that triangle ABC is a right triangle, show that two of its sides are perpendicular by showing that the slope of one side is the negative reciprocal of the slope of the other side.

Solution:

1. Let the coordinates of A be (x_1, y_1). Then $x_1 = 0$ and $y_1 = 2$.

2. Let the coordinates of B be (x_2, y_2). Then $x_2 = 2$ and $y_2 = 3$.

3. Slope of $\overline{AB} = \dfrac{y_2 - y_1}{x_2 - x_1} = \dfrac{3 - 2}{2 - 0} = \dfrac{1}{2}$.

4. Let the coordinates of B be (x_1, y_1). Then $x_1 = 2$ and $y_1 = 3$.

5. Let the coordinates of C be (x_2, y_2). Then $x_2 = 1$ and $y_2 = 5$.

6. Slope of $\overline{BC} = \dfrac{y_2 - y_1}{x_2 - x_1} = \dfrac{5 - 3}{1 - 2} = \dfrac{2}{-1} = -2$.

7. The slope of $\overline{AB}$ is the negative reciprocal of the slope of $\overline{BC}$ because $(\frac{1}{2})(-2) = -1$.

8. Therefore, $\overline{AB}$ is perpendicular to $\overline{BC}$.

9. Triangle ABC is a right triangle because it contains right angle ABC.

EXERCISES

1. Show that the line which joins the points $(1, 3)$ and $(5, 6)$ is parallel to the line which joins the points $(5, 1)$ and $(9, 4)$.

2. The vertices of quadrilateral $ABCD$ are $A(2, 3)$, $B(8, 5)$, $C(9, 9)$, and $D(3, 7)$. (*a*) Using graph paper, plot these vertices and draw the quadrilateral. (*b*) Find the slope of each side of the quadrilateral. (*c*) Show that $ABCD$ is a parallelogram.

3. Using the formula for the slope of a line, show that the points $(-2, 3)$, $(2, 7)$, $(8, 5)$, and $(4, 1)$ are the vertices of a parallelogram.

4. (*a*) Show by using the formula for the slope of a line that the points

(3, 1), (6, 3), (10, 0), and (7, −2) are the vertices of a parallelogram. (b) Show the same conclusion by showing that the diagonals of the quadrilateral bisect each other.

5. (a) Show by using the formula for the slope of a line that the points (−4, 0), (−1, 3), (3, 1), and (0, −2) are the vertices of a parallelogram. (b) Show the same conclusion by showing that both pairs of opposite sides of the quadrilateral are equal in length.

6. $A(1, 3)$, $B(7, 5)$, $C(9, −3)$ are the vertices of triangle ABC. E is the midpoint of $\overline{AB}$ and F is the midpoint of $\overline{BC}$. Show that $\overline{EF}$ is parallel to $\overline{AC}$ and $EF = \frac{1}{2}AC$.

7. The vertices of quadrilateral $ABCD$ are the points $A(−2, −2)$, $B(4, 0)$, $C(2, 4)$, and $D(−6, 6)$. E is the midpoint of $\overline{AB}$, F is the midpoint of $\overline{BC}$, G is the midpoint of $\overline{CD}$, and H is the midpoint of $\overline{AD}$. (a) Find the coordinates of E, F, G, and H. (b) Show that $\overline{EF}$ is parallel to $\overline{GH}$. (c) Show that $EF = GH$. (d) Show that $EFGH$ is a parallelogram.

8. The coordinates of the vertices of quadrilateral $ABCD$ are $A(0, 5)$, $B(3, 4)$, $C(0, −5)$, and $D(−3, −4)$.
   a. Using graph paper, draw quadrilateral $ABCD$.
   b. Show that $ABCD$ is a parallelogram.
   c. Show that $ABCD$ is a rectangle.

9. Find the slope of a line which is perpendicular to a line whose slope is:
   a. $\frac{3}{4}$ b. $\frac{5}{9}$ c. $−\frac{2}{3}$ d. 4   e. −3   f. $1\frac{1}{4}$ g. .1

10. Find the slope of a line which is perpendicular to the line which passes through the points:
    a. (5, 6) and (8, 11)   b. (1, 4) and (3, −7)   c. (−2, −3) and (0, 3)

11. Show that the line which passes through the points (2, 3) and (5, 1) is perpendicular to the line which passes through the points (5, 4) and (1, −2).

In 12 and 13, the given points A, B, and C are the vertices of a triangle. (a) Find the slope of each side of the triangle. (b) Find the slope of each altitude of the triangle.

12. $A(1, 1)$, $B(5, 2)$, $C(3, 4)$ 13. $A(−3, −2)$, $B(3, −1)$, $C(5, 4)$

14. Determine by means of slopes which of the following groups of points are the vertices of a right triangle. Check your answer by using the distance formula.
    a. (2, 2), (4, 1), (4, 6)   b. (2, 5), (−4, 3), (−3, 0)
    c. (1, 1), (4, 4), (7, 2)   d. (1, 1), (3, 0), (0, −4)

15. The vertices of a quadrilateral are (3, 1), (5, 6), (7, 6), and (10, 2). Show that the diagonals of the quadrilateral are perpendicular to each other.

16. *Given:* $A(0, 4)$, $B(-5, 0)$, and $C(3, 0)$
    a. Find the length of $\overline{AC}$.
    b. Find the coordinates of point D so that $ABCD$ is a parallelogram.
    c. Find the coordinates of point E so that $ABEC$ is a parallelogram.
    d. What is the greatest number of parallelograms possible with the points A, B, and C as three of the vertices?

17. The points $A(2, 1)$, $B(9, 4)$, $C(5, 8)$ are the vertices of triangle ABC. Show that the median from A is perpendicular to $\overline{BC}$.

18. $\overleftrightarrow{AB} \parallel \overleftrightarrow{CD}$. The slope of $\overleftrightarrow{AB}$ is $\dfrac{3}{4}$. The slope of $\overleftrightarrow{CD}$ is $\dfrac{9}{x}$. Find x.

19. $\overleftrightarrow{EF} \parallel \overleftrightarrow{GH}$. The slope of $\overleftrightarrow{EF}$ is $-\dfrac{2}{3}$. The slope of $\overleftrightarrow{GH}$ is $\dfrac{8}{x-6}$. Find x.

20. $\overleftrightarrow{AB} \parallel \overleftrightarrow{CD}$. The slope of $\overleftrightarrow{AB}$ is $\dfrac{3}{5}$. The slope of $\overleftrightarrow{CD}$ is $\dfrac{10}{x}$. Find x.

21. $\overleftrightarrow{PQ} \perp \overleftrightarrow{RS}$. The slope of $\overleftrightarrow{PQ}$ is $\dfrac{x-1}{4}$. The slope of $\overleftrightarrow{RS}$ is $\dfrac{8}{3}$. Find x.

22. The vertices of parallelogram $ABCD$ have the following coordinates: $A(-2, 4)$, $B(2, 6)$, $C(7, 2)$, $D(x, 0)$. (*a*) Find the slope of $\overline{AB}$. (*b*) Express the slope of $\overline{DC}$ in terms of x. (*c*) Using the results found in answer to *a* and *b*, find the value of x.

23. (*a*) Find the slope of line $\overleftrightarrow{CD}$ which passes through the points $(2, 3)$ and $(10, 9)$. (*b*) Without using graph paper, show that the point $(-2, 0)$ lies on line $\overleftrightarrow{CD}$. (*c*) If the point $P(14, y)$ lies on $\overleftrightarrow{CD}$, find the value of y.

24. The points $A(-1, 4)$, $B(-2, 1)$, $C(4, 3)$, and $D(t, 5)$ are the vertices of trapezoid $ABCD$ whose bases are $\overline{BC}$ and $\overline{AD}$. (*a*) Find the slope of $\overline{BC}$. (*b*) Express, in terms of t, the slope of $\overline{AD}$. (*c*) Using the results found in answer to *a* and *b*, find the value of t. (*d*) Show that $ABCD$ is not an isosceles trapezoid.

7. Proving Theorems by Using Coordinate Geometry

We can use coordinate geometry to prove some of the theorems that we have already proved in our study of plane geometry. When we prepare the figure for the discussion of the proof of a theorem, it is best to place it in a position which will simplify the details of the proof. In the case of a polygon, it is usually helpful to place one vertex at the origin and one side along the positive half-line of the x-axis. In the case of a circle, the center is usually placed at the origin.

KEEP IN MIND

1. To prove that line segments are congruent or equal in length, show that the length of each segment is represented by the same number symbol.
2. To prove that lines are parallel, show that the slopes of the lines are represented by the same number symbol.
3. To prove that lines are perpendicular, show that the product of the number symbols which represent their slopes is -1.
4. To prove that line segments bisect each other show that the same ordered pair of number symbols represents the midpoint of each line segment.

MODEL PROBLEMS

1. Prove that the diagonals of a rectangle are congruent.

Place the rectangle so that one vertex, O, is at the origin, side $\overline{OA}$ is on the x-axis, and vertex B is in quadrant I. The coordinates of the vertices can be represented by $O(0, 0)$, $A(b, 0)$, $B(b, a)$, $C(0, a)$.

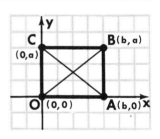

Given: Rectangle $OABC$.

To prove: $\overline{OB} \cong \overline{AC}$.

Plan: Use the distance formula to find the lengths of $\overline{OB}$ and $\overline{AC}$. Show that these lengths are equal.

Proof:

1. Let the coordinates of O be (x_1, y_1). Then $x_1 = 0$ and $y_1 = 0$.

2. Let the coordinates of B be (x_2, y_2). Then $x_2 = b$ and $y_2 = a$.

3. $OB = \sqrt{(x_2 - x_1)^2 + (y_2 - y_1)^2} = \sqrt{(b - 0)^2 + (a - 0)^2} = \sqrt{b^2 + a^2}$.

4. Let the coordinates of C be (x_1, y_1). Then $x_1 = 0$ and $y_1 = a$.

5. Let the coordinates of A be (x_2, y_2). Then $x_2 = b$ and $y_2 = 0$.

6. $AC = \sqrt{(x_2 - x_1)^2 + (y_2 - y_1)^2} = \sqrt{(b - 0)^2 + (0 - a)^2} = \sqrt{b^2 + a^2}$.

7. Since $OB = \sqrt{b^2 + a^2}$ and $AC = \sqrt{b^2 + a^2}$, $OB = AC$, and $\overline{OB} \cong \overline{AC}$.

2. Prove that the line segment joining the midpoints of two sides of a triangle is parallel to
the third side.

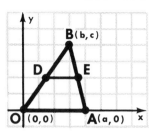

   Place the triangle so that one vertex, O,
is at the origin, side $\overline{OA}$ is on the x-axis, and
vertex B is in quadrant I. The coordinates of
the vertices can be represented by $O(0, 0)$,
$A(a, 0)$, $B(b, c)$.

Given: In triangle ABO, D is the mid-
         point of $\overline{OB}$ and E is the midpoint of $\overline{AB}$.

To prove: $\overline{DE} \parallel \overline{OA}$.

Plan: To prove that $\overline{DE}$ and $\overline{OA}$ are parallel, show that the slopes of
         these line segments are equal.

1. Since D is the midpoint of $\overline{OB}$, x at $D = \frac{1}{2}(0 + b) = \frac{1}{2}b$, and y at $D = \frac{1}{2}(0 + c) = \frac{1}{2}c$. Therefore, the coordinates of D are $(\frac{1}{2}b, \frac{1}{2}c)$.

2. Since E is the midpoint of $\overline{AB}$, x at $E = \frac{1}{2}(b + a)$, and y at $E = \frac{1}{2}(c + 0) = \frac{1}{2}c$. Therefore, the coordinates of E are $[\frac{1}{2}(b + a), \frac{1}{2}c]$.

3. Slope of $DE = \dfrac{y_2 - y_1}{x_2 - x_1} = \dfrac{\frac{1}{2}c - \frac{1}{2}c}{\frac{1}{2}(b + a) - \frac{1}{2}b} = \dfrac{0}{\frac{1}{2}a} = 0.$ $(a \neq 0)$

4. Slope of $\overline{OA} = \dfrac{y_2 - y_1}{x_2 - x_1} = \dfrac{0 - 0}{a - 0} = \dfrac{0}{a} = 0.$ $(a \neq 0)$

5. Since the slope of $\overline{DE}$ is equal to the slope of $\overline{OA}$, $\overline{DE}$ is parallel to $\overline{OA}$.

EXERCISES

In 1–6, prove the theorems using coordinate geometry.

1. The diagonals of a square are congruent.
2. The length of the line segment that joins the midpoints of two sides of a
   triangle is equal to one-half the length of the third side.
3. The midpoint of the hypotenuse of a right triangle is equidistant from
   the vertices of the triangle. [*Hint:* Represent the vertices of the triangle
   by $(0, 0)$, $(0, 2a)$, and $(2b, 0)$.]
4. The line segments joining the midpoints of the sides of a square, taken
   in order, form an equilateral quadrilateral.
5. The median to the base of an isosceles triangle is perpendicular to the
   base of the triangle.

6. The length of the median of a trapezoid is equal to one-half the sum of the lengths of its bases.

7. The vertices of quadrilateral $RSTV$ are $R(0, 0)$, $S(a, 0)$, $T(a + b, c)$, and $V(b, c)$. (a) Find the slope of $\overline{RV}$ and the slope of $\overline{ST}$. (b) Show that $RSTV$ is a parallelogram.

8. The vertices of quadrilateral $ABCD$ are $A(0, 0)$, $B(r, s)$, $C(r, s + t)$, and $D(0, t)$. (a) Represent the slope of $\overline{AB}$ and the slope of $\overline{CD}$. (b) Represent the length of $\overline{AB}$ and the length of $\overline{CD}$. (c) Show that $ABCD$ is a parallelogram.

9. The vertices of triangle RST are $R(0, 0)$, $S(a, b)$, and $T(c, d)$. (a) Find the coordinates of E, the midpoint of $\overline{TR}$. (b) Find the coordinates of F, the midpoint of $\overline{TS}$. (c) Find the slope of $\overline{EF}$ and the slope of $\overline{RS}$. (d) Show that $\overline{EF}$ is parallel to $\overline{RS}$.

10. The vertices of triangle ABC are $A(0, 0)$, $B(4a, 0)$, and $C(2a, 2b)$. (a) Find the coordinates of D, the midpoint of $\overline{AC}$. (b) Find the coordinates of E, the midpoint of $\overline{BC}$. (c) Show that $AB = 2DE$.

11. The vertices of quadrilateral $ABCD$ are $A(0, 0)$, $B(a, 0)$, $C(a, b)$, and $D(0, b)$. (a) Show that $ABCD$ is a parallelogram. (b) Show that diagonal $\overline{AC}$ is congruent to diagonal $\overline{BD}$. (c) Show that quadrilateral $ABCD$ is a rectangle.

12. The vertices of $\triangle RST$ are $R(0, 0)$, $S(2a, 2b)$, and $T(4a, 0)$. The midpoints of $\overline{RS}$, $\overline{ST}$, and $\overline{TR}$ are L, M, and N respectively.
    a. Express the coordinates of L, M, and N in terms of a and b.
    b. Express the lengths of the medians from R, S, and T in terms of a and b.
    c. $\triangle RST$ must be (1) equilateral (2) right (3) isosceles (4) scalene.

8. Graphing a Linear Equation

In your algebra course, you learned that an ordered pair of numbers which satisfies an equation is a *solution* of the equation. For example, (3, 1) is a solution of the equation $x + 3y = 6$ because when x is replaced by 3 and y is replaced by 1 we obtain $3 + 3(1) = 6$, which is a true statement. The set of all ordered pairs of numbers which are the solutions of the equation $x + 3y = 6$ is called the *solution set* of $x + 3y = 6$. The equation $x + 3y = 6$ is an example of a first-degree equation in two variables. The general form of such an equation is $ax + by = c$, where a and b are not both 0.

You have also learned that:

Definition. The *graph of an equation* is the graph of the solution set of that equation.

From this definition, we can state that:

1. Any ordered pair of numbers that is a member of the solution set of an equation (that is, the ordered pair satisfies the equation) represents the coordinates of a point of the graph of that equation.
2. Any point on the graph of an equation has as its coordinates an ordered pair of numbers which is a member of the solution set of that equation (that is, the ordered pair satisfies that equation).

In this book, we will assume the truth of the following two statements:

Postulate 60. **The graph of every first-degree equation in two variables of the form** $ax + by = c$, **where** a **and** b **are not both 0, is a straight line.**

We will soon see that the graph of $x + 3y = 6$ is a straight line.

Postulate 61. **Every graph which is a straight line is the graph of a first-degree equation of the form** $ax + by = c$, **where** a **and** b **are not both 0.**

Therefore, a first-degree equation in two variables is called a *linear equation.* For example, $x + y = 8$ and $y = 2x - 1$ are linear equations.

The following model problems will help you recall some methods that are used to graph linear equations.

MODEL PROBLEMS

1. Draw the graph of $x + 3y = 6$.

Solution:

1. Make a table of values by assuming three convenient values for x, such as 0, 3, and 6. Substitute these values in the equation $x + 3y = 6$ to find the corresponding y-values.

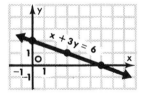

If $x = 0$, then $0 + 3y = 6$; $y = 2$
If $x = 3$, then $3 + 3y = 6$; $y = 1$
If $x = 6$, then $6 + 3y = 6$; $y = 0$

x	y
0	2
3	1
6	0

2. Plot the points represented by the number pairs $(0, 2)$, $(3, 1)$, and $(6, 0)$.

3. Draw a straight line through the three points.

In the previous graph of the equation $x + 3y = 6$, the value of y at the point where the graph intersects the y-axis is 2. We therefore say that the y-*intercept* is 2. Notice that the value of x at this point is 0. Also, the value of x at the point where the graph intersects the x-axis is 6. We therefore say that the *x-intercept* is 6. Notice that the value of y at this point is 0.

Procedure. To find the x-intercept and y-intercept of the graph of an equation:

1. Substitute 0 for y in the given equation to find the x-intercept.
2. Substitute 0 for x in the given equation to find the y-intercept.

2. Find (*a*) the x-intercept and (*b*) the y-intercept of the graph of the equation $3x - 2y = 12$.

Solution: (*a*) To find the x-intercept, let $y = 0$ in the equation $3x - 2y = 12$

$$3x - 2(0) = 12, \ 3x - 0 = 12, \ x = 4$$

(*b*) To find the y-intercept, let $x = 0$ in the equation $3x - 2y = 12$

$$3(0) - 2y = 12, \ 0 - 2y = 12, \ y = -6$$

Answer: x-intercept $= 4$, y-intercept $= -6$.

EXERCISES

1. Draw the graphs of the following equations:

a. $y = 2x$	*b.* $y = 5x$	*c.* $y = -3x$	*d.* $y = -x$
e. $x = 2y$	*f.* $x = 3y$	*g.* $x = -y$	*h.* $x = \frac{1}{2}y$
i. $y = x + 3$	*j.* $y = 2x - 1$	*k.* $y = 3x + 1$	*l.* $y = -2x + 4$
m. $x + y = 8$	*n.* $y + x = 4$	*o.* $x - y = 5$	*p.* $y - x = 6$
q. $2x + y = 10$	*r.* $x + 3y = 12$	*s.* $x - 2y = 6$	*t.* $y - 3x = -5$
u. $2x + 3y = 6$	*v.* $3x + 4y = 12$	*w.* $3x - 2y = -6$	*x.* $4x - 3y = -12$

2. Which of the following ordered pairs of numbers are members of the solution set of the equation (satisfy) $2x - y = 6$? (*a*) $(4, -2)$ (*b*) $(2, 2)$ (*c*) $(4, 2)$ (*d*) $(0, 6)$ (*e*) $(3, 0)$

3. What are the coordinates of the point at which the graph of $2x - 3y = 8$ intersects the x-axis?

4. Find the x-intercept and y-intercept of each equation in exercise 1.

In 5–10, state whether the given line passes through the given point.

5. $x + y = 7$, $(4, 3)$ **6.** $x - y = 5$, $(9, 4)$

7. $2y + x = 7$, $(1, 3)$ **8.** $3x - 2y = 8$, $(2, -1)$

9. $4x + y = 10$, $(2, -2)$ **10.** $2y = 3x - 5$, $(-1, -4)$

In 11–13, a point is to lie on the given line. Find its abscissa if its ordinate is the number indicated.

11. $x + y = 12$, (5)   **12.** $2x - y = 8$, (−2)   **13.** $3x + 2y = 24$, (3)

In 14–16, a point is to lie on the given line. Find its ordinate if its abscissa is the number indicated.

14. $x + 2y = 9$, (3)   **15.** $4x - y = 7$, (−1)   **16.** $2x + 3y = 5$, (−2)

In 17–20, find the value of k so that the given line will pass through the given point.

17. $x + y = k$, (2, 5)   **18.** $x - y = k$, (5, −3)
19. $4x + y = k$, (−1, −3)   **20.** $5y - 2x = k$, (−2, 1)

9. Writing an Equation of a Straight Line

The Point Slope Form

Now we will learn how to write an equation of the line which passes through a given fixed point $P_1(x_1, y_1)$ and which has a given slope, m (Fig. 11–26).

Let us represent any other point on the line as $P(x, y)$. ($x \neq x_1$)

The slope of the line, $m = \dfrac{y - y_1}{x - x_1}$, or

$$y - y_1 = m(x - x_1)$$

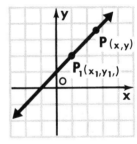

Fig. 11–26

Theorem 157. **An equation of the line passing through the point (x_1, y_1) and having the slope m is $y - y_1 = m(x - x_1)$.**

The equation $y - y_1 = m(x - x_1)$ is called the *point slope form* of an equation of a line.

MODEL PROBLEMS

1. Write an equation of the straight line whose slope is 2 and which passes through the point (2, 3).

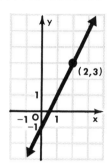

   Solution:

   1. Since the coordinates of the given point are (2, 3), $x_1 = 2$ and $y_1 = 3$.

   2. Since the given slope is 2, $m = 2$.

   3. The point slope form of an equation of the line is

$$y - y_1 = m(x - x_1)$$
$$y - 3 = 2(x - 2)$$
$$y - 3 = 2x - 4$$
$$y = 2x - 1$$

   Answer: $y = 2x - 1$.

2. Write an equation of the line which passes through the points $P_1(-1, -2)$ and $P_2(5, 1)$.

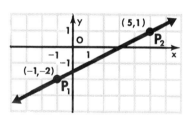

   Solution:

   1. Since we know two points on the line, we can find the slope of a segment of the line which is the same as the slope of the line. Then we can use the point slope form of an equation of a line

      [The solution continues on the next page.]

2. Slope of the line, $m = \dfrac{y_2 - y_1}{x_2 - x_1}$ $x_1 = -1$, $y_1 = -2$.
$x_2 = 5$, $y_2 = 1$.

$$m = \frac{1 - (-2)}{5 - (-1)} = \frac{1 + 2}{5 + 1} = \frac{3}{6} = \frac{1}{2}$$

3. Now we will write an equation of the line which passes through the point (5, 1) and has a slope of $\frac{1}{2}$.

4. $y - y_1 = m(x - x_1)$ $m = \frac{1}{2}$, $x_1 = 5$, $y_1 = 1$.
$y - 1 = \frac{1}{2}(x - 5)$
$y - 1 = \frac{1}{2}x - \frac{5}{2}$
$y = \frac{1}{2}x - \frac{3}{2}$

Answer: $y = \frac{1}{2}x - \frac{3}{2}$, or $2y = x - 3$.

The Slope Intercept Form

Let us write an equation of a line whose y-intercept is b and whose slope is m (Fig. 11–27).

If the y-intercept is b, the line passes through the point (0, b).

If we use the point slope form of an equation of a straight line, we have:

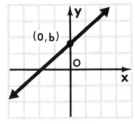

Fig. 11–27

$y - y_1 = m(x - x_1)$ slope $= m$, $x_1 = 0$, $y_1 = b$.
$y - b = m(x - 0)$
$y - b = mx$
$y = mx + b$

Theorem 158. **An equation of a line whose slope is m and whose y-intercept is b is $y = mx + b$.**

The equation $y = mx + b$ is called the *slope intercept form* of an equation of a line.

Hence, when an equation of a line is expressed in the form $y = mx + b$, then m, the coefficient of x, represents the slope of the line and b represents the y-intercept of the line.

For example, in the equation $y = 3x + 4$, the slope of the line is 3 and the y-intercept is 4.

MODEL PROBLEMS

1. Write an equation of the line whose slope is $\frac{1}{3}$ and y-intercept is -2.

Solution:

1. Use the slope intercept form of an equation of a line.

2. $y = mx + b$ $\qquad\qquad\qquad m = \frac{1}{3}, b = -2.$

3. $y = \frac{1}{3}x - 2$, or $3y = x - 6$

Answer: $3y = x - 6$.

2. Find the slope and y-intercept of the line whose equation is $4x + 2y = 5$.

Solution:

1. Transform the equation $4x + 2y = 5$ to the form $y = mx + b$.

2. $4x + 2y = 5$

3. $\qquad 2y = -4x + 5$

4. $\qquad y = -2x + \frac{5}{2}$ $\qquad$ Hence, the slope $= -2$, the y-intercept $= \frac{5}{2}$.

Answer: Slope $= -2$; y-intercept $= \frac{5}{2}$.

3. Write an equation of the line which is parallel to the line $6x + 3y = 4$ and whose y-intercept is -6.

Solution:

1. Transform the equation $6x + 3y = 4$ to the slope intercept form in order to find its slope.

2. $6x + 3y = 4$

3. $\qquad 3y = -6x + 4$

4. $\qquad y = -2x + \frac{4}{3}$ $\qquad$ [The slope of this line is -2.]

5. The slope of the line $6x + 3y = 4$ is -2.

6. Hence, the slope of a line parallel to the line $6x + 3y = 4$ is also -2.

7. The y-intercept of the required line is -6.

8. Use the slope intercept form of an equation of a line.

9. $y = mx + b$ $\qquad m = -2, b = -6.$

10. $y = -2x - 6$

Answer: $y = -2x - 6$.

4. Draw the graph of $3y - 2x = -6$ using its slope and y-intercept.

Solution:

1. Transform the equation to the slope intercept form.

2. $3y - 2x = -6$

3. $\qquad 3y = 2x - 6$

4. $\qquad y = \tfrac{2}{3}x - 2$

5. Slope $= \tfrac{2}{3}$; y-intercept $= -2$.

6. Since the y-intercept of the line is -2, the point $(0, -2)$ is on its graph.

7. Plot the point $(0, -2)$ on the graph.

8. Since slope $= \dfrac{\Delta y}{\Delta x} \xrightarrow{} \dfrac{2}{3}$, when x increases 3 units, y increases 2 units.

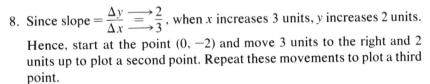

Hence, start at the point $(0, -2)$ and move 3 units to the right and 2 units up to plot a second point. Repeat these movements to plot a third point.

9. Draw the straight line which passes through the three points plotted.

EXERCISES

1. Write an equation of the straight line which has the given slope, m, and which passes through the given point.
   a. $m = 3, (1, 5)$ *b.* $m = 2, (-3, 5)$ *c.* $m = \tfrac{1}{2}, (-2, -3)$
   d. $m = \tfrac{2}{3}, (-1, 4)$ *e.* $m = -\tfrac{2}{5}, (0, 0)$ *f.* $m = -\tfrac{4}{3}, (-2, 0)$

2. Through the given point, draw the graph of a line with the given slope m.
   a. $(0, 0), m = 2$ *b.* $(1, 3), m = 3$ *c.* $(2, -5), m = 4$
   d. $(4, 6), m = \tfrac{2}{3}$ *e.* $(-4, 5), m = \tfrac{1}{2}$ *f.* $(-3, -4), m = -2$

   g. $(1, -5), m = -1$ *h.* $(2, 4), m = -\tfrac{3}{2}$ *i.* $(-2, 3), m = -\tfrac{1}{2}$

3. Write an equation of the line which passes through the given points.
   a. $(1, 5)$ and $(5, 13)$ *b.* $(0, 3)$ and $(2, 9)$
   c. $(-1, 3)$ and $(1, -1)$ *d.* $(0, 0)$ and $(-2, -4)$
   e. $(-4, -1)$ and $(-1, 11)$ *f.* $(12, -5)$ and $(-4, -1)$

4. Write an equation of the straight line whose slope and y-intercept are respectively:

  a. 4 and 5   *b.* 2 and -5 *c.* -3 and 2

  d. $\frac{3}{4}$ and 4   *e.* $-\frac{2}{3}$ and -1 *f.* $-\frac{5}{3}$ and 4

5. For each of the following lines, find the slope and the y-intercept:

  a. $y = 3x + 1$ *b.* $y = x - 4$ *c.* $y = -x$

  d. $y = \frac{1}{4}x + 5$ *e.* $2x + y = 9$ *f.* $4y - 2x = 16$

6. Determine the coordinates of the point at which each of the following lines intersects the y-axis:

  a. $y = x + 1$ *b.* $y = x - 4$ *c.* $y = 2x + 5$

  d. $x + y = 6$ *e.* $x - y = 3$ *f.* $3x - 2y = 12$

7. Draw the graph of each of the following lines using its slope and y-intercept:

  a. $y = 2x + 5$ *b.* $y = 3x - 1$ *c.* $y = 4x$

  d. $y = \frac{2}{3}x + 1$ *e.* $y = -\frac{1}{3}x + 2$ *f.* $3x + y = 4$

  g. $y - 2x = 8$ *h.* $3x + y = 4$ *i.* $3x + 4y = 12$

8. In each part, state whether or not the two lines are parallel.

  a. $y = 3x + 2$, $y = 3x + 5$ *b.* $y = -2x - 6$, $y = -3x - 6$

  c. $y - 2x = 8$, $2x - y = 4$ *d.* $2x + 3y = 12$, $3x + 2y = 8$

9. Write an equation of the line whose slope is 4 and which passes through a point on the y-axis 2 units above the origin.

10. Write an equation of the line whose slope is 3 and which passes through a point on the y-axis 5 units below the origin.

11. Write an equation of the line which is:

  a. parallel to the line $y = 3x - 5$ and whose y-intercept is 7.

  b. parallel to the line $y - 2x = 4$ and whose y-intercept is -1.

  c. parallel to the line $2x + 3y = 6$ and which passes through the origin.

12. Write an equation of the line which passes through the point $(3, 2)$ and is parallel to the line $y = 5x + 1$.

13. Write an equation of the line which passes through the point $(1, 6)$ and is parallel to the line $y - 3x = 5$.

14. Write an equation of the line which passes through the point $(-2, 1)$ and is parallel to the line $2y - 4x = 9$.

15. Write an equation of the line which is parallel to the line $y = 3x + 5$ and which has the same y-intercept as the line $y = 4x - 3$.

16. Write an equation of the line which is perpendicular to the line $y = \frac{2}{3}x$ and which passes through the origin.

17. Write an equation of the line which is perpendicular to the line $2x + y = 3$ and whose y-intercept is 4.

18. Write an equation of the line which passes through the point $(2, 4)$ and which is perpendicular to the line $y = -\frac{2}{3}x + 2$.

19. Tell whether each of the following statements is true or false: The straight line whose equation is $y = 2x$ (*a*) does not pass through the

origin. (*b*) has each abscissa twice its ordinate. (*c*) is parallel to the line which passes through the points (1, −3) and (3, 1).

20. (*a*) Using graph paper, on the same set of coordinate axes draw the graph of each of the following equations: (1) $y = 6$ (2) $y = 3x$ (3) $y = \frac{3}{2}x + 6$. (*b*) Find the coordinates of the vertices of the triangle whose sides are the line segments joining the points of intersection of the graphs made in answer to *a*.

21. Given points (−1, −2) and (3, 4).
    a. Find the distance between the two points.
    b. Find the slope of the line containing these points.
    c. Find the coordinates of the midpoint of the segment determined by these points.
    d. Write an equation of the line containing the two given points.
    e. If the point (2, *k*) lies on the line determined in part *d*, find the value of *k*.

22. Given points $A(3, 1)$, $B(0, −1)$, and $C(−3, −3)$.
    a. Write an equation of the line which passes through point *A* and is parallel to the *y*-axis.
    b. Write an equation of the line which passes through point *B* and has a slope of 1.
    c. Show that *A*, *B*, and *C* lie on the same straight line.
    d. Write an equation of the line which is parallel to $\overset{\leftrightarrow}{AB}$ and passes through the origin.

23. In isosceles triangle ABC with vertices $A(3, −1)$, $B(7, 3)$, and $C(−1, 7)$, $\overline{CD}$ is the altitude to $\overline{AB}$.
    a. If the slope of $\overline{CD}$ is −1, write an equation of the line passing through *C* and *D*.
    b. Write an equation of the line passing through *A* and *B*.
    c. Using coordinate geometry, show that the altitude of isosceles $\triangle ABC$ intersects the base $\overline{AB}$ at its midpoint.

24. The vertices of parallelogram $ABCD$ are $A(−2, 4)$, $B(2, 6)$, $C(7, 2)$, and $D(k, 0)$.
    a. Find the slope of line $\overset{\leftrightarrow}{AB}$.
    b. Express the slope of line $\overset{\leftrightarrow}{CD}$ in terms of *k*.
    c. Using the results found in answer to *a* and *b*, find the value of *k*.
    d. Write an equation of line $\overset{\leftrightarrow}{BD}$.

25. In triangle ABC, side $\overline{AB}$ lies on the line whose equation is $y = x + 3$ and side $\overline{AC}$ lies on the *y*-axis. The coordinates of *M* and *N*, the midpoints of sides $\overline{AC}$ and $\overline{BC}$, are (0, −3) and (2, *k*) respectively.
    a. Find the coordinates of *A* and of *C*.

    b. Find the slope of $\overline{AB}$.

    c. Express the slope of $\overline{MN}$ in terms of k.

    d. Find the value of k.

    e. Write an equation of the line through M and N.

26. Given the points $A(x, 4)$, $B(5, 6)$, $C(7, 5)$, and $D(11, 6)$.

    a. Find the slope of the line through the points C and D.

    b. Write an expression which represents the slope of the line through the points A and B.

    c. Find the value of x that will make the line through A and B parallel to the line through C and D.

    d. Write an equation of the line passing through the point B and perpendicular to the y-axis.

    e. Write an equation of the line passing through the origin and point D.

27. The points $A(-2, 0)$, $B(10, 3)$, $C(5, 7)$, and $D(2, k)$ are the vertices of a trapezoid whose bases are $\overline{AB}$ and $\overline{DC}$.

    a. Find the slope of $\overleftrightarrow{AB}$.

    b. Express the slope of $\overleftrightarrow{DC}$ in terms of k.

    c. Using the results found in answer to parts a and b, find the value of k.

    d. Show by means of slopes that $\overleftrightarrow{AB}$ does not pass through the origin.

    e. Write an equation of $\overleftrightarrow{AB}$.

28. The vertices of quadrilateral $ABCD$ are $A(-6, -6)$, $B(14, 4)$, $C(3, 5)$, and $D(-5, 1)$.

    a. Show by means of slopes that $\overline{DC}$ is parallel to $\overline{AB}$.

    b. Write an equation of line $\overleftrightarrow{BC}$.

29. *a.* On a set of coordinate axes, plot the points $A(1, 1)$, $B(10, 4)$, $C(7, 7)$, $D(7, 3)$, and $E(5, 5)$.

    b. Using the formula for the slope of a line, show that A, E, and C lie on the same straight line.

    c. Point D lies on $\overline{AB}$. Show that triangle ADE is similar to triangle ABC.

30. Given the points $A(2, 4)$, $B(6, 13)$, and $C(x, y)$.

    a. Write an equation of the line through A and C if its slope is -1.

    b. Write an equation of the line through B and C if its slope is $\frac{1}{2}$.

    c. Find the coordinates of point C.

31. The vertices of parallelogram $ABCD$ are $A(1, 1)$, $B(4, 6)$, $C(x, y)$, and $D(2, 10)$.

    a. Express in terms of x and y the slopes of lines $\overleftrightarrow{BC}$ and $\overleftrightarrow{DC}$.

    b. Using the results obtained in part a, write two equations that can be used to find x and y.

    c. Find the coordinates of C.

32. The vertices of an isosceles triangle ABC are $A(0, 0)$, $B(2r, 2s)$, and $C(2s, 2r)$, where r and s are positive and unequal.
   a. Find in terms of r and s the coordinates of D, the midpoint of base $\overline{BC}$.
   b. Find the numerical value of the slope of $\overline{AD}$.
   c. Find the numerical value of the slope of $\overline{BC}$.
   d. Write an equation of the line which contains points A and D.
   e. Point P is a point on the median $\overline{AD}$. If its abscissa is k, find its ordinate.

33. In the figure, $\overline{AM}$ and $\overline{BN}$ are medians of $\triangle ABC$.
   a. The coordinates of A, B, and C are $(0, 0)$, $(6k, 4k)$, and $(8k, 0)$ respectively.
      (1) Find the coordinates of point M in terms of k.
      (2) Find the numerical value of the slope of $\overset{\leftrightarrow}{AM}$.
      (3) Write an equation of $\overset{\leftrightarrow}{AM}$.
   b. If $k = 3$, write an equation of $\overset{\leftrightarrow}{BN}$.

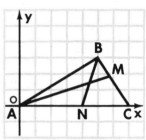

Ex. 33

10. Locus in Coordinate Geometry

We have learned that a locus may be a point, a straight line, a collection of several lines, or a curved line that is the set of all points, and only those points, that satisfy a given set of conditions. When the coordinates of all points on a locus determined by a given set of conditions satisfy an equation, and when all points not on the locus do not satisfy the equation, such an equation is called the **equation of the locus**. The equation of a locus gives the relationship which exists between the coordinates x and y of all points on the locus.

In Fig. 11–28, we see a set of points lying on a straight line, the abscissa of each point being the number 3. If we take any point P, for example $(-2, 3)$, which is not on this line, its coordinates do not satisfy the equation of the line ($x = 3$). We see, therefore, that the locus of points whose abscissas are the constant 3 is a line parallel to the y-axis and 3 units to the right of it. The equation of this line is $x = 3$.

Theorem 159. The locus of points whose abscissas are the constant a is a line which is parallel to the y-axis and whose equation is $x = a$.

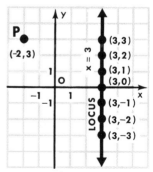

Fig. 11–28

In Fig. 11–29, we see a set of points lying on a straight line, the ordinate of each point being the number −2. If we take any point P, for example (2, 1), which is not on this line, its coordinates do not satisfy the equation of the line ($y = -2$). We see, therefore, that the locus of points whose ordinates are the constant −2 is a line parallel to the x-axis and 2 units below it. The equation of this line is $y = -2$.

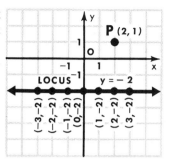

Fig. 11–29

Theorem 160. **The locus of points whose ordinates are the constant b is a line which is parallel to the x-axis and whose equation is $y = b$.**

In Fig. 11–30, we see a set of points lying on a straight line, the ordinate of each point being 2 times the abscissa of that point. If we take any point P, for example (2, −3), which is not on this line, its coordinates do not satisfy the equation of the line ($y = 2x$). We see, therefore, that the locus of points in which the ordinate of each point is twice the abscissa of that point is a line which passes through the origin and whose slope is 2. The equation of this line is $y = 2x$.

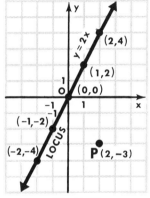

Fig. 11–30

Theorem 161. **The locus of points in which the ordinate of each point is m times the abscissa of that point is a line which passes through the origin and whose equation is $y = mx$.**

In Fig. 11–31, we see a set of points lying on a straight line, the ordinate of each point being the sum of 3 times the abscissa of that point and (−2). If we take any point P, for example (1, −4), which is not on this line, its coordinates do not satisfy the equation of the line, which is $y = 3x + (-2)$. We see, therefore, that the locus of points in which the ordinate of each point is the sum of 3 times the abscissa of that point and (−2) is a line whose slope is 3 and which intersects the y-axis 2 units below the origin. The equation of this line can be written $y = 3x + (-2)$, or, more simply, $y = 3x - 2$.

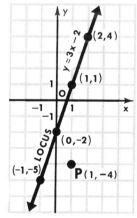

Fig. 11–31

Theorem 162. **The locus of points in which the ordinate of each point is the sum of *m* times the abscissa of that point and the number *b* is a line whose slope is *m*, whose *y*-intercept is *b*, and whose equation is $y = mx + b$.**

In Fig. 11–32, we see a set of points lying on a circle, each point being 3 units from a fixed point, the origin. If we take any point *T*, for example $(3, -4)$, which is not on this circle, point *T* is not 3 units from the origin, and its coordinates do not satisfy the equation of the circle $(x^2 + y^2 = 9)$. We see, therefore, that the locus of points 3 units from the origin is a circle whose center is at the origin and whose radius is 3. If $P(x, y)$ is any point on this circle, by using either the distance formula or the Pythagorean Theorem, we find that the equation of the circle can be written $x^2 + y^2 = (3)^2$, or $x^2 + y^2 = 9$.

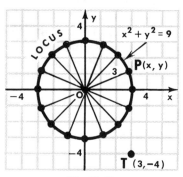

Fig. 11–32

Theorem 163. **The locus of points whose distance from the origin is *r* is a circle whose center is the origin, the length of whose radius is *r*, and whose equation is $x^2 + y^2 = r^2$.**

MODEL PROBLEMS ‿‿‿‿‿‿‿‿‿‿‿‿‿‿‿‿‿‿‿‿

1. Write an equation of the locus of points in which the ordinate of each point is 3 more than 4 times the abscissa of that point.

   Solution:

   1. Let $P(x, y)$ represent the points on the locus that satisfy the given condition: The ordinate of each point is 3 more than 4 times the abscissa of that point.

   2. If we replace "ordinate" by "*y*" and "abscissa" by "*x*," we obtain the equation $y = 4x + 3$.

   Answer: $y = 4x + 3$.

2. Write an equation of the locus of points equidistant from the points $(2, 2)$, and $(6, 2)$.

Solution:

1. The locus of points equidistant from the given points $P_1(2, 2)$ and $P_2(6, 2)$ is $\overleftrightarrow{CD}$, the perpendicular bisector of the line segment $\overline{P_1P_2}$.

2. $\overleftrightarrow{CD}$ is parallel to the y-axis and 4 units to the right of the y-axis.

3. Therefore, the equation of $\overleftrightarrow{CD}$ is $x = 4$.

Answer: $x = 4$.

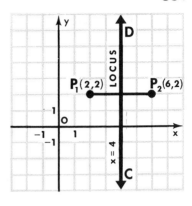

---

3. *a.* Write an equation of the locus of points whose distance from the origin is 5.

b. Determine whether the point $(-3, 4)$ is on the locus.

Solution:

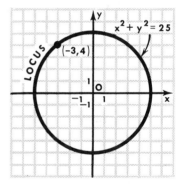

(*a*) 1. The locus of points whose distance from the origin is 5 is a circle whose center is O and whose radius is 5.

2. The equation of this circle is $x^2 + y^2 = (5)^2$, or $x^2 + y^2 = 25$.

Answer: $x^2 + y^2 = 25$.

(*b*) 1. If the point $(-3, 4)$ is to be on the locus, $x = -3$, $y = 4$ must satisfy the equation $x^2 + y^2 = 25$.

2. $(-3)^2 + (4)^2 \stackrel{?}{=} 25$

3. $9 + 16 \stackrel{?}{=} 25$

4. $25 = 25$

Answer: The point $(-3, 4)$ is on the locus.

EXERCISES

1. Write an equation and plot the graph of the equation of the line which is the locus of all points:
   a. whose ordinate is 5.
   b. whose ordinate is 8.
   c. whose abscissa is 4.
   d. whose abscissa is 0.
   e. whose ordinate is -1.
   f. whose abscissa is -6.
   g. whose ordinate is 4 times its abscissa.
   h. whose ordinate is equal to its abscissa.
   i. whose ordinate is $\frac{3}{4}$ of its abscissa.
   j. whose ordinate is 5 more than its abscissa.
   k. whose ordinate is 4 less than its abscissa.
   l. whose ordinate exceeds its abscissa by 3.
   m. whose ordinate is 2 greater than 3 times its abscissa.
   n. whose ordinate is 1 less than 4 times its abscissa.
   o. whose abscissa is 2 more than its ordinate.
   p. whose abscissa is 3 less than twice its ordinate.
   q. the sum of whose abscissa and ordinate is 10.
   r. the sum of whose coordinates is 6.
   s. the sum of whose ordinate and abscissa is 8.
   t. whose ordinate decreased by its abscissa is 5.
   u. whose abscissa decreased by its ordinate is 4.
   v. whose ordinate is 3 more than one-half its abscissa.
   w. whose abscissa is 4 less than one-third its ordinate.

2. Write an equation of the locus of all points equidistant from the points:
   a. $(0, 2)$ and $(0, 10)$ *b.* $(3, 0)$ and $(9, 0)$
   c. $(2, 6)$ and $(2, 12)$ *d.* $(9, 3)$ and $(15, 3)$
   e. $(0, -4)$ and $(0, 8)$ *f.* $(-3, 0)$ and $(5, 0)$
   g. $(-1, 4)$ and $(-1, 12)$ *h.* $(1, -5)$ and $(7, -5)$

3. Choose the correct answer: The equation $x = 3$ represents the locus of points equidistant from the two points   (*a*) $(2, 0)$ and $(1, 0)$ (*b*) $(0, 3)$ and $(3, 0)$ (*c*) $(10, 0)$ and $(-4, 0)$.

4. Write an equation of the locus of points:
   a. whose abscissa is 6.   *b.* whose abscissa is 9.
   c. whose abscissa is -2.   *d.* whose abscissa is -4.
   e. whose ordinate is 1.   *f.* whose ordinate is 4.
   g. whose ordinate is -5.   *h.* whose ordinate is -8.

5. Write an equation of the locus of all points:
   a. 2 units from the *x*-axis and above it.
   b. 5 units from the *y*-axis and to the right of it.
   c. 4 units from the *y*-axis and to the left of it.

    d. 3 units from the *x*-axis and below it.

    e. equidistant from the *x*-axis and *y*-axis and whose coordinates have the same sign.

    f. equidistant from the *x*-axis and *y*-axis and whose coordinates have opposite signs.

6. Write an equation of the locus of points which are 6 units above the *x*-axis.

7. Write an equation of the locus of points which are 5 units to the right of the *y*-axis.

8. Write an equation of the locus of points which are 12 units below the *x*-axis.

9. Write an equation of the straight line passing through the point (3, 4) and perpendicular to the *x*-axis.

10. Write an equation of the straight line passing through the point $(-1, 3)$ and parallel to the *y*-axis.

11. Write an equation of the straight line passing through the point (5, 2) and perpendicular to the *y*-axis.

12. Write an equation of the line passing through the point $(-2, -4)$ and parallel to the *x*-axis.

13. Write an equation of the locus of points which are 3 units from the line whose equation is $y = 7$.

14. Choose the correct answer: The locus of points in the coordinate plane at a distance of 8 units from the *x*-axis consists of the graph(s) of the equation(s) $(a)\ y = 8$ $(b)\ x = 8$ $(c)\ y = 8, y = -8$ $(d)\ x = 8, x = -8$.

15. Write an equation of the locus of points which are 5 units from the line whose equation is $y = -2$.

16. Write an equation of the locus of points 2 units from the line whose equation is $x = 6$.

17. Write an equation of the locus of points which are 3 units from the line whose equation is $x = -1$.

18. Give the coordinates of a point on the *x*-axis which is equidistant from the points (8, 5) and (12, 5).

19. Give the coordinates of a point on the *y*-axis which is equidistant from the points (4, 3) and $(4, -9)$.

20. Write an equation of the locus of the centers of circles which are tangent to both lines:

    a. $y = 10$ and $y = 4$ *b.* $x = 2$ and $x = 12$

    c. $y = -4$ and $y = -6$ *d.* $x = -8$ and $x = -2$

    e. $y = 6$ and $y = -14$ *f.* $x = -5$ and $x = 9$

21. Write an equation of the locus of all points whose distance from the origin is:

    a. 4 units   *b.* 9 units   *c.* 12 units   *d.* 6 units   *e.* $2\frac{1}{2}$ units

22. Describe the locus whose algebraic representation is:

    a. $x^2 + y^2 = 36$ b. $x^2 + y^2 = 64$ c. $x^2 + y^2 = \frac{81}{4}$ d. $x^2 + y^2 = 3$

23. Determine whether the given point is on the locus whose equation is given.

    a. $x + y = 10$, $(8, 2)$ b. $x - y = 4$, $(8, -4)$

    c. $2y + x = 7$, $(1, 3)$ d. $4x - 2y = 10$, $(3, -1)$

    e. $y = 3$, $(2, 3)$ f. $x = -8$, $(3, -8)$

24. Find the value of k so that the graph of the given equation will pass through the given point.

    a. $x + y = k$, $(2, 3)$ b. $2x - 3y = k$, $(1, -4)$

25. A point is on the locus whose equation is given. Find its ordinate if its abscissa is the number indicated.

    a. $x + 3y = 5$, (2) b. $2x - y = 6$, (-1) c. $3x + 2y = 8$, (6)

26. A point is on the locus whose equation is given. Find its abscissa if its ordinate is the number indicated.

    a. $x - y = 3$, (6) b. $3x - y = 10$, (-2) c. $3x + 2y = 5$, (-5)

27. (a) Write an equation of the locus of points whose distance from the origin is 13. (b) Determine whether the point $(-12, 5)$ is on the locus. (c) Determine whether the point $(8, -9)$ is on the locus.

28. (a) Write an equation of the locus of points whose distance from the origin is 5. (b) Without constructing the circle, determine the coordinates of every point on the locus whose abscissa is 3.

29. Line $\overleftrightarrow{CD}$ passes through the points $(2, 0)$ and $(8, 0)$. Point $P(4, 0)$ is on line $\overleftrightarrow{CD}$. Write an equation of the locus of the centers of circles which are tangent to line $\overleftrightarrow{CD}$ at point P.

30. Write an equation of the locus of the centers of circles which will pass through the two given points $A(0, 1)$ and $B(0, 5)$.

31. The vertices of triangle ABC are $A(5, 2)$, $B(10, 2)$, and $C(7, 8)$. Write equations for the locus of points which are vertices of triangles equal in area to triangle ABC and which have $\overline{AB}$ as their base.

32. The endpoints of line segment $\overline{AB}$ are $(-4, 0)$ and $(4, 0)$. Write an equation of the locus of points which are the vertices C of all right triangles $A'BC$ having $\overline{AB}$ as their hypotenuse.

33. Write an equation of the locus of points equidistant from the circles whose equations are $x^2 + y^2 = 4$ and $x^2 + y^2 = 64$.

11. Intersection of Loci in Coordinate Geometry

If points are to satisfy each of two conditions, these points must be members of the intersection set of the set of points that satisfy the first condition and the set of points that satisfy the second condition. In coordinate geometry, these points can be located graphically or geometrically by using the following procedure:

1. Draw the graph of the locus of points that satisfy the first condition.
2. Draw the graph of the locus of points that satisfy the second condition.
3. Locate the points of intersection of these loci. These points must be the required points because they satisfy both conditions.

MODEL PROBLEMS

1. *a.* Describe the locus of points 2 units from the *y*-axis and write an equation of this locus.
   b. Describe the locus of points equidistant from the points $P_1(-4, 2)$ and $P_2(-4, 6)$ and write an equation of this locus.
   c. Find the number of points which satisfy both conditions stated in part *a* and part *b* and give the coordinates of each point.

Solution:

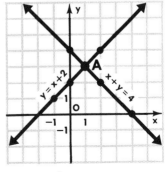

a. The locus is the union of a pair of lines, $\overleftrightarrow{AB}$ and $\overleftrightarrow{CD}$, parallel to the *y*-axis, each line being 2 units from the *y*-axis. An equation of $\overleftrightarrow{CD}$ is $x = 2$. An equation of $\overleftrightarrow{AB}$ is $x = -2$.

b. The locus is $\overleftrightarrow{EF}$, the perpendicular bisector of the line segment $\overline{P_1P_2}$. An equation of $\overleftrightarrow{EF}$ is $y = 4$.

c. There are two points, *R* and *S*, which are the points of intersection of the loci and which therefore satisfy both stated conditions. The coordinates of *R* are $(2, 4)$. The coordinates of *S* are $(-2, 4)$.

2. Find graphically the common solution for the system of equations
$$\begin{cases} x + y = 4 \\ y = x + 2 \end{cases}$$

Solution:

1. The locus of points whose coordinates satisfy the equation $x + y = 4$ is a straight line. Graph this line.

If $x = \ldots,$	0	2	4
then $y = \ldots.$	4	2	0

[The solution continues on the next page.]

2. The locus of points whose coordinates satisfy the equation $y = x + 2$ is a straight line. Graph this line.

If $x = $ . . . ,	-1	0	2
then $y = $	1	2	4

3. Point $A(1, 3)$ is the point of intersection of the two graphs that were drawn. Hence, $\{(1, 3)\}$ is the intersection of the solution sets of the given equations. Therefore, $x = 1$, $y = 3$ is the common solution for the given system of equations.

Answer: $x = 1$, $y = 3$, or $(1, 3)$.

Note. Recall that when you studied algebra, you learned algebraic methods of discovering that the common solution for the given system of equations is the ordered pair of numbers $(1, 3)$.

EXERCISES

1. (*a*) Represent graphically the locus of points   (1) 3 units from the line $x = 1$.   (2) 4 units from the line $y = -2$.   (*b*) Write the equations for the loci represented in part *a*.   (*c*) Find the coordinates of the points of intersection of the loci represented in answer to part *a*.

2. *a.* Draw the locus of points equidistant from the points $(4, 1)$ and $(4, 5)$ and write an equation for this locus.

   b. Draw the locus of points equidistant from the points $(3, 2)$ and $(9, 2)$ and write an equation for this locus.

   c. Find the number of points that satisfy both conditions stated in part *a* and part *b*. Give the coordinates of each point found.

3. The total number of points equidistant from both the x-axis and the y-axis and 3 inches distant from the origin is   (*a*) 1   (*b*) 2   (*c*) 3   (*d*) 4.

4. (*a*) On a sheet of graph paper, draw two perpendicular axes and on this set of axes represent graphically the locus of points: (1) 8 units from the y-axis   (2) 10 units from the origin.   (*b*) Write equations for the loci represented in part *a*.   (*c*) Find the coordinates of the points of intersection of the loci represented in answer to part *a*.

5. (*a*) On a sheet of graph paper, draw the graph of $y = 6$ and $y = 2$.   (1) Draw the graph of the locus of the centers of circles which are tangent to both lines whose equations are $y = 6$ and $y = 2$.   (2) Write an equation of this locus.   (*b*) Using the same set of axes, draw the graph of the lines whose equations are $x = 4$ and $x = 8$.   (1) Draw the graph of the

locus of the centers of circles which are tangent to both lines whose equations are $x = 4$ and $x = 8$. (2) Write an equation of this locus. (c) What are the coordinates of the center of a circle which will be tangent to the lines whose equations are $y = 2$, $y = 6$, $x = 4$, and $x = 8$? (d) What is the length of a radius of this circle?

6. The vertices of triangle RST are $R(2, 3)$, $S(6, 3)$, and $T(3, 10)$. (a) Draw the graph and write an equation of the locus of points equidistant from R and S. (b) Draw line $\overleftrightarrow{TW}$ which passes through T and is parallel to $\overleftrightarrow{RS}$ and write an equation of $\overleftrightarrow{TW}$. (c) Write the coordinates of the points of intersection of the lines drawn in parts a and b. (d) What are the coordinates of a point on line $\overleftrightarrow{TW}$ which can be used as the center of a circle which passes through points R and S?

7. Draw the graphs of the lines whose equations are given and use the graphs to find the coordinates of the point of intersection of:
   a. $y = 3x - 1$ and $y = x + 9$ b. $y = 5x + 2$ and $y = -2x + 16$

8. Solve the following systems of equations graphically:

   a. $x + y = 8$ b. $x - y = 2$ c. $y = 2x + 1$
       $x - y = 4$ $y = 2x$ $x + y = 10$
   d. $2x + y = 8$ e. $y - x = -2$ f. $x - 3y = 9$
       $y - x = 2$ $x - 2y = 4$ $2x - y = 8$

9. a. Draw the locus of points equidistant from the circles whose equations are $x^2 + y^2 = 4$ and $x^2 + y^2 = 36$. Write an equation of the locus.
   b. Draw the locus of points 4 units from the x-axis. Write an equation of the locus.
   c. Find the number of points that satisfy both conditions stated in part a and part b. Write the coordinates of each of the points found.

10. a. Using graph paper, draw the triangle whose vertices are $A(1, 2)$, $B(7, 2)$, and $C(5, 6)$.
    b. Draw the locus of points equidistant from A and B.
    c. Write an equation of the line drawn in answer to part b.
    d. Write an equation of the line through A and C.
    e. Point P in line $\overleftrightarrow{AC}$ is equidistant from points A and B. Find the coordinates of point P.

11. The vertices of a triangle are $A(2, 3)$, $B(8, 3)$, and $C(4, 7)$.
    a. Find the equations of the three medians of triangle ABC.
    b. Show that the three medians pass through the same point; that is, they are *concurrent*.

12. The vertices of triangle ABC are $A(1, 1)$, $B(7, 11)$, and $C(7, 5)$. Prove that the medians of triangle ABC are concurrent.

13. The vertices of triangle ABC are $A(0, 0)$, $B(6, 0)$, and $C(0, 8)$. Prove that the perpendicular bisectors of the sides of triangle ABC are concurrent.

12. Areas in Coordinate Geometry

To find areas of polygons in coordinate geometry, we use the area formulas previously developed. When a figure has one or more sides parallel to either of the axes, the process of finding its area usually becomes simplified.

MODEL PROBLEMS

1. Find the area of a triangle whose vertices are $A(3, 2)$, $B(7, 2)$, and $C(6, 5)$.

Solution:

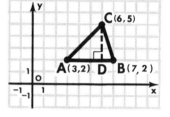

1. Since points A and B have the same ordinate, $\overline{AB}$ is parallel to the x-axis.

2. In $\triangle ABC$, $\overline{AB}$ is the base and $AB = 4$.

3. Draw altitude $\overline{CD}$. $CD = 3$.

4. Area of $\triangle ABC = \frac{1}{2}AB \times CD$.

5. Area of $\triangle ABC = \frac{1}{2} \times 4 \times 3 = 6$.

Answer: Area $= 6$.

2. Points $A(-4, -2)$, $B(2, -2)$, $C(4, 3)$, and $D(-2, 3)$ are the vertices of quadrilateral $ABCD$.

   a. Plot these points on graph paper and draw the quadrilateral.

   b. What kind of quadrilateral is $ABCD$?

   c. Find the area of quadrilateral $ABCD$.

Solution:

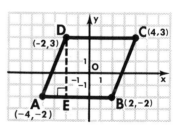

   a. See graph.

   b. 1. $\overline{AB}$ is parallel to $\overline{CD}$.

      2. $AB = |2 - (-4)| = |2 + 4| = |6| = 6$
      and $CD = |4 - (-2)| = |4 + 2| = |6| = 6$. Hence, $AB = CD$, or $\overline{AB} \cong \overline{CD}$.

      3. $ABCD$ is a parallelogram since it is a quadrilateral with one pair of opposite sides both parallel and congruent.

 c. 1. Draw altitude $\overline{DE}$ to side $\overline{AB}$.
      $DE = 5$.

   2. Area of $\square ABCD = AB \times DE$.

   3. Area of $\square ABCD = 6 \times 5 = 30$.

Answer: Area $= 30$.

Often the polygon whose area we are trying to find does not have sides parallel to either of the axes. We then draw lines parallel to the axes through the vertices, forming rectangles and trapezoids whose areas can be used to find the area of the given polygon, as shown in Model Problems 3 and 4 below.

3. Plot the points $A(-2, 3)$, $B(1, 5)$, $C(4, 2)$ and find the area of $\triangle ABC$.

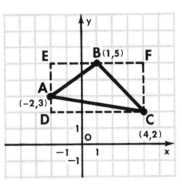

Method 1

Plan: Through points B and C, draw lines parallel to the x-axis. Through points A and C, draw lines parallel to the y-axis, forming rectangle $CDEF$. The area of $\triangle ABC$ is equal to the area of rectangle $CDEF$ minus the sum of the areas of rt. $\triangle CDA$, BEA, and BFC.

Solution:

1. Area of $\triangle ABC$ = area of rectangle $CDEF$ − (area of rt. $\triangle CDA$ + area of rt. $\triangle BEA$ + area of rt. $\triangle BFC$).

2. Area of rectangle $CDEF = DC \times DE = 6 \times 3 = 18$.

3. Area of rt. $\triangle CDA = \frac{1}{2}DC \times DA = \frac{1}{2}(6)(1) = 3$.

4. Area of rt. $\triangle BEA = \frac{1}{2}BE \times EA = \frac{1}{2}(3)(2) = 3$.

5. Area of rt. $\triangle BFC = \frac{1}{2}BF \times FC = \frac{1}{2}(3)(3) = 4.5$.

6. Area of $\triangle ABC = 18 - (3 + 3 + 4.5) = 18 - 10.5$.

7. Area of $\triangle ABC = 7.5$.

Answer: Area of $\triangle ABC = 7.5$.

Method 2

Plan: Draw $\overleftrightarrow{AD}$ ‖ the *y*-axis, $\overleftrightarrow{BE}$ ‖ the *y*-axis, $\overleftrightarrow{CF}$ ‖ the *y*-axis, forming trapezoids *DEBA*, *EFCB*, and *DFCA*. The area of $\triangle ABC$ can be found by adding the areas of trapezoids *DEBA* and *EFCB* and then subtracting the area of trapezoid *DFCA* from the sum.

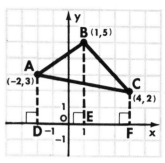

Solution:

1. Area of $\triangle ABC$ = (area of trapezoid *DEBA* + area of trapezoid *EFCB*) − area of trapezoid *DFCA*.

2. Area of trapezoid $DEBA = \frac{1}{2}(DE)(DA + EB) = \frac{1}{2}(3)(3 + 5) = \frac{1}{2}(3)(8) = 12$.

3. Area of trapezoid $EFCB = \frac{1}{2}(EF)(EB + FC) = \frac{1}{2}(3)(5 + 2) = \frac{1}{2}(3)(7) = 10.5$.

4. Area of trapezoid $DFCA = \frac{1}{2}(DF)(DA + FC) = \frac{1}{2}(6)(3 + 2) = \frac{1}{2}(6)(5) = 15$.

5. Area of $\triangle ABC = (12 + 10.5) - 15 = 22.5 - 15$.

6. Area of $\triangle ABC = 7.5$.

Answer: Area of $\triangle ABC = 7.5$.

4. Find the area of the polygon whose vertices are $A(2, 2)$, $B(9, 3)$, $C(7, 6)$, and $D(4, 5)$.

Plan: Draw $\overleftrightarrow{AL}$ ‖ the *y*-axis, $\overleftrightarrow{DM}$ ‖ the *y*-axis, $\overleftrightarrow{CR}$ ‖ the *y*-axis, $\overleftrightarrow{BS}$ ‖ the *y*-axis, forming trapezoids *LMDA*, *MRCD*, *RSBC*, and *LSBA*. The area of polygon *ABCD* can be found by adding the areas of trapezoids *LMDA*, *MRCD*, *RSBC* and subtracting the area of trapezoid *LSBA* from the sum.

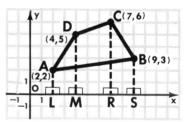

Solution:

1. Area of *ABCD* = (area of trapezoid *LMDA* + area of trapezoid *MRCD* + area of trapezoid *RSBC*) − area of trapezoid *LSBA*.

2. Area of trapezoid $LMDA = \frac{1}{2}(LM)(AL + DM) = \frac{1}{2}(2)(2 + 5) = \frac{1}{2}(2)(7) = 7$.

3. Area of trapezoid $MRCD = \frac{1}{2}(MR)(DM + CR) = \frac{1}{2}(3)(5 + 6) = \frac{1}{2}(3)(11) = 16.5$.

4. Area of trapezoid $RSBC = \frac{1}{2}(RS)(CR + BS) = \frac{1}{2}(2)(6 + 3) = \frac{1}{2}(2)(9) = 9$.

5. Area of trapezoid $LSBA = \frac{1}{2}(LS)(AL + BS) = \frac{1}{2}(7)(2 + 3) = \frac{1}{2}(7)(5) = 17.5$.

6. Area of $ABCD = (7 + 16.5 + 9) - 17.5 = 32.5 - 17.5$.

7. Area of $ABCD = 15$.

Answer: Area of $ABCD = 15$.

5. *a.* Using graph paper, on the same set of axes draw the graph of each of the following equations: (1) $x = 6$ (2) $y = x$ (3) $y = 2x$.

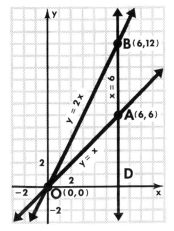

b. Find the coordinates of the vertices of the triangle whose sides are the line segments joining the points of intersection of the graphs made in answer to part *a*.

c. Find the area of the triangle described in part *b*.

Solution:

a. See graph.

b. 1. Line $y = x$ intersects line $y = 2x$ at $O(0, 0)$.

  2. Line $y = x$ intersects line $x = 6$ at $A(6, 6)$.

  3. Line $y = 2x$ intersects line $x = 6$ at $B(6, 12)$.

Answer: $O(0, 0)$, $A(6, 6)$, and $B(6, 12)$.

c. 1. Area of $\triangle AOB = \frac{1}{2}$ the length of side $\overline{BA} \times$ the length of altitude $\overline{OD}$ drawn to side $\overline{BA}$ extended.

  2. Area of $\triangle AOB = \frac{1}{2}BA \times OD = \frac{1}{2}(6)(6)$.

  3. Area of $\triangle AOB = 18$.

Answer: 18.

EXERCISES

1. Find the area of a rectangle whose vertices are:
    a. (0, 0), (8, 0), (0, 5), (8, 5)   *b.* (−2, 3), (4, 3), (−2, 8), (4, 8)
2. Find the area of a parallelogram whose vertices are:
    a. (0, 0), (4, 0), (2, 3), (6, 3)   *b.* (−2, 8), (−3, 4), (5, 8), (4, 4)
3. Find the area of a triangle whose vertices are:
    a. (0, 0), (12, 0), (2, 8)   *b.* (0, 8), (0, −3), (4, 5)
    c. (2, −2), (8, −2), (4, −6)
4. Find the area of a right triangle whose vertices are $A(0, 0)$, $B(6, 0)$, and $C(0, 3)$.
5. Find the area of a trapezoid whose vertices are:
    a. (0, 0), (12, 0), (2, 6), (7, 6)   *b.* (0, 4), (0, −8), (3, 1), (3, −4)
6. Points $Q(8, 2)$, $R(14, 6)$, $S(4, 6)$, $T(−2, 2)$ are the vertices of quadri-lateral $QRST$. (*a*) Plot these points on graph paper and draw the quad-rilateral. (*b*) What kind of quadrilateral is $QRST$? (*c*) Find the area of quadrilateral $QRST$.
7. Points $C(1, −4)$, $D(9, −4)$, $E(9, 2)$, $F(1, 3)$ are the vertices of quadri-lateral $CDEF$. (*a*) Plot these points on graph paper and draw the quad-rilateral. (*b*) Find the lengths of $\overline{CD}$, $\overline{DE}$, and diagonal $\overline{CE}$. (*c*) What kind of quadrilateral is $CDEF$? (*d*) Find the area of the quadrilateral.
8. Plot the points $A(2, 4)$, $B(10, 6)$, $C(8, 12)$. Through A, draw lines paral-lel to both axes. Through B, draw a line parallel to the *y*-axis. Through C, draw a line parallel to the *x*-axis. (*a*) Find the area of the rectangle thus formed. (*b*) Draw $\overline{AB}$, $\overline{BC}$, and $\overline{CA}$. Find the area of triangle ABC.
9. Plot the points $R(5, −4)$, $S(2, 7)$, $T(−2, 2)$. Through R, draw lines paral-lel to both axes. Through S, draw a line parallel to the *x*-axis. Through T, draw a line parallel to the *y*-axis. (*a*) Find the area of the rectangle thus formed. (*b*) Draw $\overline{RS}$, $\overline{ST}$, and $\overline{TR}$. Find the area of triangle RST.
10. Find the area of a triangle whose vertices are the points:
    a. (2, 4), (8, 8), (16, 6)   *b.* (6, −2), (8, −10), (12, −6)
    c. (6, 4), (9, 2), (13, 6)   *d.* (−5, 4), (2, 1), (6, 5)
11. Plot the points $A(2, 5)$, $B(11, 2)$, $C(9, 8)$, and $D(4, 8)$. Draw $\overline{AB}$, $\overline{BC}$, $\overline{CD}$, and $\overline{DA}$. Find the area of $ABCD$.
12. Find the area of a quadrilateral whose vertices are the points:
    a. (−2, 3), (3, 7), (8, 6), (12, 4)   *b.* (2, 2), (4, 6), (10, 12), (8, 4)
13. The coordinates of the vertices of triangle RST are $R(4, 5)$, $S(12, 5)$, and $T(8, 11)$. (*a*) Find the length of the altitude of triangle RST drawn to side $\overline{RS}$. (*b*) Find the area of triangle RST.
14. The coordinates of the vertices of triangle ABC are $A(−2, −5)$, $B(7, −2)$,

and $C(-2, 1)$. (*a*) Find the length of the altitude of triangle ABC drawn to side $\overline{AC}$. (*b*) Find the area of triangle ABC.

15. Using graph paper, draw triangle RST whose vertices are $R(4, 4)$, $S(12, 10)$, and $T(6, 13)$. (*a*) Find the area of triangle RST. (*b*) Find the length of side $\overline{RS}$. (*c*) Find the length of the altitude drawn to $\overline{RS}$ from T.

16. The vertices of triangle ABC are the points $A(2, 5)$, $B(13, 3)$, and $C(10, 11)$. (*a*) Find the area of triangle ABC. (*b*) Find the length of side $\overline{AC}$. (*c*) Using the results found in answer to parts *a* and *b*, find the length of the altitude drawn from point B to side $\overline{AC}$.

17. The vertices of a triangle are $A(0, 4)$, $B(4, 7)$, and $C(6, 2)$. (*a*) Find the area of triangle ABC. (*b*) Find the length of $\overline{AB}$. (*c*) Find the length of the altitude drawn from C to $\overline{AB}$.

18. The coordinates of the vertices of triangle ABC are $A(4, 4)$, $B(15, 2)$, and $C(12, 8)$. (*a*) Draw triangle ABC on graph paper. (*b*) Show that triangle ABC is a right triangle. (*c*) Find the area of triangle ABC.

19. The vertices of a triangle are $A(0, 6)$, $B(6, 2)$, and $C(12, 10)$. (*a*) Find the area of triangle ABC. (*b*) Find the length of $\overline{BC}$. (*c*) Find the length of the altitude drawn from A to $\overline{BC}$. (*d*) Write an equation of the line determined by point A and the midpoint of $\overline{BC}$.

20. The vertices of a triangle are $A(2, 1)$, $B(5, 8)$, and $C(7, -1)$. (*a*) Using graph paper, draw triangle ABC. (*b*) Find the area of triangle ABC. (*c*) If the median $\overline{AD}$ is drawn to side $\overline{BC}$, find the coordinates of D.

21. In triangle ABC, the coordinates of B are $(-3, -2)$ and those of C are $(5, 4)$. The midpoint of $\overline{AB}$ is M, whose coordinates are $(-3, 2)$. Find the:
a. coordinates of vertex A.
b. coordinates of N, the midpoint of $\overline{BC}$.
c. length of $\overline{MN}$.
d. area of $\triangle MNC$.

22. A triangle whose vertices are $A(2, 3)$, $B(8, 11)$, and $C(0, 7)$ is inscribed in a circle. (*a*) Using the lengths of the sides, show that triangle ABC is a right triangle. (*b*) Find the coordinates of the center of the circumscribed circle. (*c*) Find the area of the circle. [Answer may be expressed in terms of π.]

23. (*a*) Show that the quadrilateral whose vertices are $A(2, 1)$, $B(6, -2)$, $C(10, 1)$, and $D(6, 4)$ is a rhombus. (*b*) Find the area of the rhombus. (*c*) Find a side of the rhombus. (*d*) Find the altitude of the rhombus.

24. (*a*) Show that the quadrilateral whose vertices are the points $A(-7, 3)$, $B(-1, -5)$, $C(5, 3)$, and $D(-1, 11)$ is a rhombus. (*b*) Find the area of the rhombus. (*c*) Find a side of the rhombus. (*d*) Find the altitude of the rhombus.

25. The lines $y = 6$, $y = -2$, $x = 4$, and $x = 10$ intersect. The line segments which join the four points of intersection form a quadrilateral. (*a*) Using graph paper, draw the graphs of these four lines. (*b*) Find the area of the quadrilateral.

26. The lines $x = 8$, $y = 4$, $x = -3$, and $y = -5$ intersect. The line segments which join the four points of intersection form a quadrilateral. (*a*) Using graph paper, draw the graphs of these lines. (*b*) Find the area of the quadrilateral.

27. The lines $x = 0$, $x = 3$, $y = x$, and $y = x + 4$ intersect. The line segments which join the four points of intersection form a quadrilateral. (*a*) Using graph paper, draw the graphs of these lines. (*b*) Find the area of the quadrilateral.

28. The lines $y = x$, $y = x - 5$, $y = 0$, and $y = -3$ intersect. The line segments which join the four points of intersection form a quadrilateral. (*a*) Using graph paper, draw the graphs of these lines. (*b*) Find the area of the quadrilateral.

29. (*a*) Using graph paper, on the same set of axes draw the graph of each of the equations, $y = x$, $y = 3x$, and $y = 9$. (*b*) Find the coordinates of the vertices of the triangle whose sides are the line segments joining the points of intersection of the graphs made in answer to part *a*. (*c*) Find the area of the triangle described in part *b*.

30. (*a*) Using graph paper, on the same set of axes draw the graph of each of the equations, $y = x$, $y = 4x$, and $x = 3$. (*b*) Find the coordinates of the vertices of the triangle whose sides are the line segments joining the points of intersection of the graphs made in answer to part *a*. (*c*) Find the area of the triangle described in part *b*.

CHAPTER XII

Improvement of Reasoning

The study of geometry contributes to the development of critical thinking and sound reasoning. The methods of sound reasoning that are developed in the study of geometry are frequently used in life situations.

1. Definitions

In Chapter I, on pages 1 and 2, we learned that it is important to define clearly the terms used in any discussion. We realized, however, that in a postulational system it is impossible to define all terms; a few basic terms must be left undefined. We also learned that a good definition must have six properties with which you should be familiar. See pages 3 and 4.

Defining Terms in Proper Sequence

When we define a group of related terms, the most inclusive term is defined first. For example, the group of terms *polygon, rhombus, parallelogram,* and *quadrilateral* must be defined in the following order:

First, we define the *polygon* because it is the most inclusive set of objects among the four sets mentioned. It contains among its members the remaining three—the rhombus, the quadrilateral, and the parallelogram.

The polygon may be called the **universal set** of this group of terms. The set of rhombuses, the set of quadrilaterals, and the set of parallelograms are called **subsets** of the universal set, which is the set of polygons.

Second, we define the *quadrilateral* because it is the most inclusive set of objects among the remaining three sets. It contains among its members the other two—the rhombus and the parallelogram. The set of rhombuses and the set of parallelograms are subsets of the set of quadrilaterals.

Third, we define the *parallelogram* because it is the more inclusive set of objects of the remaining two sets. It contains among its members the rhombus. The set of rhombuses is a subset of the set of parallelograms.

Fourth, we define the *rhombus.*

To help us understand the proper sequence in definitions, we may picture the relationships among the sets just discussed in the following manner (see Fig. 12–1):

1. Since the set of polygons is the most inclusive set, represent this universal set by a rectangle and its interior.

2. Within this rectangle, draw a circle to represent the set of all quadrilaterals because all quadrilaterals are polygons. The circle does not cover the whole interior of the rectangle because there are polygons that are not quadrilaterals.

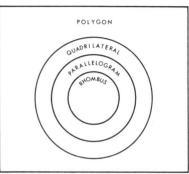

Venn Diagram

Fig. 12–1

3. Within the first circle, draw a smaller circle to represent the set of all parallelograms because all parallelograms are quadrilaterals but not all quadrilaterals are parallelograms.

4. Within the second circle, draw a still smaller circle to represent the set of all rhombuses because all rhombuses are parallelograms but not all parallelograms are rhombuses.

A picture such as the one we have just drawn is called a *Venn diagram.*

Circular Definitions

Suppose we give the following two definitions:

1. "A right angle is an angle which contains 90 degrees."
2. "An angle of one degree is $\frac{1}{90}$ of a right angle."

We have given *circular definitions* because we have defined a right angle in terms of degrees, and a degree in terms of a right angle. Since circular definitions result from a failure to observe a proper sequence in definition, they are an example of faulty definitions.

EXERCISES

1. In order to answer each of the following questions, it is essential to define a key word or phrase. Select the word or phrase.
   a. Was Abraham Lincoln an educated man?
   b. Is Soviet Russia a democracy?
   c. If Mr. Walker spent $100 for a suit, did he buy an expensive suit?

    d. Charles came to school wearing dungarees. Should he be sent home because he is improperly dressed?

    e. A sign says that children will be admitted for $.50, adults for $1.00. John is 16 years old. How much should he pay to be admitted?

    f. A subway sign reads, "Smoking Prohibited." Mr. Price is standing in a subway station and is holding a lighted cigar in his hand. Is he guilty of smoking in the subway?

2. Arrange the following terms in the order in which their definitions should be given:

    a. triangle, polygon, isosceles triangle

    b. triangle, hypotenuse, polygon, right triangle

    c. polygon, rectangle, parallelogram, quadrilateral

    d. isosceles trapezoid, quadrilateral, polygon, trapezoid

3. (*a*) Arrange the following geometric sets in an order such that each set after the first is a subset of the preceding set. (*b*) Draw a Venn diagram using the answer you gave for part *a*.

    (1) the set of triangles, the set of polygons, the set of equilateral triangles

    (2) the set of quadrilaterals, the set of squares, the set of parallelograms, the set of rectangles

    (3) the set of trapezoids, the set of quadrilaterals, the set of polygons, the set of isosceles trapezoids

4. Using the fact that good definitions are reversible, define each of the following terms in two forms:

    a. perpendicular lines   *b.* parallel lines

    c. a right triangle   *d.* a parallelogram

5. The following statements do not constitute good definitions. Tell why they are poor. Then rewrite them in acceptable form.

    a. An obtuse angle is an angle whose measure is greater than 90.

    b. A median is a line segment drawn from the vertex of a triangle to the opposite side.

    c. An isosceles triangle is one in which two sides are congruent and the angles opposite these sides are also congruent.

    d. Parallel lines are two straight lines that do not intersect.

    e. A parallelogram is a quadrilateral whose opposite sides are congruent and parallel.

    f. A rhombus is a quadrilateral with two consecutive sides congruent.

    g. A trapezoid is a polygon two and only two of whose sides are parallel.

6. Sam defined an equilateral triangle as a polygon in which all sides are congruent. Bill objected to this definition, claiming that the definition should also contain the fact that all the angles are congruent. Tom objected to this definition and said that neither was correct. Who was right?

7. Which statement is the best illustration of a good definition? (*a*) An obtuse angle is an angle that contains less than 180°. (*b*) Right angles are congruent angles. (*c*) An equilateral triangle is a triangle that has three congruent sides and three congruent angles. (*d*) Two angles are complementary if the sum of their measures is 90 degrees.

8. Give the reason why each of the following sets of definitions is an example of a poor pair of definitions:

    a. (1) A husband is a person who has a wife.

       (2) A wife is a person who has a husband.

    b. (1) A straight angle is an angle whose measure is 180 degrees.

       (2) An angle which contains 1 degree is an angle that is $\frac{1}{180}$ of a straight angle.

2. Postulates

In geometry, some basic assumptions must be accepted without proof before reasoning or deduction can take place. These basic assumptions, called *postulates,* are the unproved statements which serve as part of the foundation upon which the whole structure of demonstrative geometry rests. In the study of geometry, we discover the necessary consequences of those postulates.

In daily living, too, discussions which require reasoning are based upon basic assumptions which must be agreed upon and accepted so that proper conclusions can be made. These assumptions are often cleverly concealed, and their truth may be questionable. Therefore, to evaluate a statement, it is essential to discover the hidden assumptions upon which it rests and then determine whether to accept or reject these assumptions.

Many advertisers use slogans whose appeal would be destroyed if their "hidden" assumptions were not carefully concealed. For example, one automobile manufacturer used the slogan "Buy Superba; it costs less." The hidden assumption is that the cheaper car is the better car to buy.

EXERCISES

1. In each of the following, mention some of the assumptions on which the statement is based:

    a. Harold Bright will make a good salesman because he is a handsome man.

    b. Richard Walker cannot be an intelligent man. He didn't even graduate from high school.

    c. Tom Richstone was voted the boy in the senior class most likely to succeed because his father was the richest man in town.

    d. Because she was the prettiest girl among all the applicants, Ruth Weber was given the job as receptionist.

2. Mention the hidden assumptions in each of the following statements:

    a. Buy "White" soap. It floats.

    b. This must be good music. It's grand opera.

    c. "The People" must be an excellent play. It is being produced on Broadway.

    d. Use "Relaxo" for tired nerves. It contains vitamin P.

3. State whether you agree or disagree with the following statements. Mention the basic assumptions you used in arriving at your decision.

    a. He who takes a life should pay with his life.

    b. Since all people are created equal, they should have equal rights in a democracy.

    c. The United States should not tax its citizens in order to provide funds for giving economic aid to foreign countries.

4. Give an example showing how a certain theory, belief, or doctrine is based on one or more unproved propositions or assumptions.

3. Logical Sequence

We have learned that deductive reasoning is based upon using undefined terms, defined terms, and postulates as the instruments with which to deduce or prove statements called theorems. Once a theorem, *A*, has been proved, it may be used to prove a second theorem, *B*. After theorem *B* has been proved, it in turn may be used to prove a third theorem, *C,* etc. In this way, the subject of demonstrative geometry expands, and the set of theorems develops in proper, logical sequence.

In proving a theorem, we may not use another theorem which comes later in the logical sequence, that is, a theorem whose own proof depends upon the theorem we are now trying to prove. To do this would be a violation of logical sequence. This faulty method of reasoning is sometimes called *circular reasoning,* and is discussed in Unit 10 of this chapter.

The following statements are arranged in an order such that they form a logical sequence:

1. Parallel lines are two coplanar lines that do not intersect.
2. Through a given outside point, there is one and only one line parallel to a given line.
3. If two parallel lines are cut by a transversal, then the alternate interior angles are congruent.
4. The sum of the measures of the angles of a triangle is 180.
5. If two angles of one triangle are congruent to two angles of another triangle, the third angles are congruent.

EXERCISES

1. Indicate the order in which the following statements should be arranged
   so that they form a logical sequence:
   a. If two sides of a triangle are congruent, the angles opposite these
   sides are congruent.
   b. Two triangles are congruent if two sides and the included angle of one
   triangle are congruent respectively to two sides and the included angle
   of the other triangle.
   c. If a triangle is equilateral, it is equiangular.

2. Indicate the order in which the following statements should be arranged
   in order to form a logical sequence:
   a. A diameter perpendicular to a chord of a circle bisects the chord.
   b. Two triangles are congruent if two angles and a side opposite one of
   them are congruent to the corresponding parts of the other.
   c. Two right triangles are congruent if the hypotenuse and a leg of one
   are congruent to the corresponding parts of the other.
   d. The sum of the measures of the angles of a triangle is 180.

3. Indicate the order in which the following statements should be arranged
   so that they form a logical sequence:
   a. The measure of an angle inscribed in a circle is one-half the measure
   of its intercepted arc.
   b. The measure of a central angle is the measure of its intercepted arc.
   c. The measure of an angle formed by two chords intersecting within a
   circle is equal to one-half the sum of the measures of the intercepted
   arcs.
   d. A circle is a set of points in a plane that are a fixed distance from a
   fixed point within, called the center.

4. Which one of the following theorems has no place in the sequence which
   the others form? Arrange the remaining three in their proper sequence.
   a. Two right triangles are congruent if the hypotenuse and a leg of one
   are congruent to the corresponding parts of the other.
   b. If in a right triangle the altitude is drawn upon the hypotenuse, the
   length of each leg of the given triangle is the mean proportional between the length of the hypotenuse and the length of the segment of
   the hypotenuse adjacent to that leg.
   c. If two angles of one triangle are congruent to two angles of another
   triangle, the triangles are similar.
   d. The square of the length of the hypotenuse of a right triangle is equal
   to the sum of the squares of the lengths of the other two sides.

5. Indicate the order in which the following statements should be arranged
   so that they form a logical sequence. Tell whether each statement is a
   definition, a postulate, or a theorem.

a. The area of a triangle is equal to one-half the product of one side and the altitude drawn to that side.

b. The area of a rectangle is equal to the product of its base and its altitude.

c. The area of a parallelogram is equal to the product of one side and the altitude drawn to that side.

d. The area of a trapezoid is equal to one-half the product of the altitude and the sum of the bases.

e. The area of a polygonal region is the number of area units contained within the region.

4. Converses

Forming One Converse Statement

We have previously learned that the *converse* of a conditional statement in which the hypothesis and the conclusion each contain one piece of information is formed by interchanging the hypothesis and conclusion of the conditional statement. For example:

1. *Given Statement.*   If a triangle is equilateral, it is equiangular.
   Converse Statement. If a triangle is equiangular, it is equilateral.

2. *Given Statement*   If two angles are right angles, they are congruent.
   Converse Statement. If two angles are congruent, they are right angles.

3. *Given Statement.*   If p, then q.
   Converse Statement. If q, then p.

We have also learned that the converse of a true statement is not always a true statement, as is the case in example 2. There are times when the converse of a statement is true. There are other times when the converse of a statement is false. In fact, a statement which is false may have a converse statement which is true. For example:

Given Statement.   If an angle contains less than 180°, it is an acute angle.
Converse Statement. If an angle is an acute angle, it contains less than 180°.

NOTE. It is frequently easier to formulate the converse of a statement not written in the "if . . . , then . . ." form, by first rewriting the statement in the "if . . . , then . . ." form. For example, to write the converse of the statement "All right angles are congruent angles," we can rewrite this statement as: "If angles are right angles, they are congruent angles." The converse would then be written: "If angles are congruent angles, they are right angles."

Forming More Than One Converse Statement

When a statement has more than one condition in the hypothesis and more than one conclusion, more than one converse statement can be formed. Each converse is formed by interchanging any number of conditions of the hypothesis with an equal number of conclusions of the original statement. These converses are sometimes called *partial converses* or *multiple converses*.

Consider the following example:

Given Statement. If *p* is true and *q* is true, then *r* is true.

This statement will have two converses:

Converse Statement 1. If *r* is true and *q* is true, then *p* is true.
Converse Statement 2. If *p* is true and *r* is true, then *q* is true.

The number of converses that a statement has depends upon the number of conditions stated in the hypothesis and the number of conditions stated in the conclusion.

Converse of a Definition

We have learned that a good definition is reversible; that is, its subject and predicate can be interchanged. For example:

Statement 1. An isosceles triangle is a triangle in which two sides are congruent.
Statement 2. A triangle in which two sides are congruent is an isosceles triangle.

Observe that both statements are true and that statement 2 is the converse of statement 1. Therefore, when we say that a good definition is reversible, we are really saying that the converse of a good definition is always a true statement.

Reasoning From the Converse

Frequently, errors in everyday reasoning are made because, without realizing it, we assume that the converse of an accepted (true) statement is also true.

Mary told her mother that she believed that Nancy would become a movie star because she is a beautiful girl. Mary arrived at this conclusion because she believed that "If a girl becomes a movie star, she is beautiful." Mary assumed the truth of the converse statement, "If a girl is beautiful, she will become a movie star."

EXERCISES

In 1–16, write a converse for each of the statements. Determine whether each converse is true or false.

1. If I am not hungry, I do not eat.
2. If it is raining, a tennis match is not played.
3. If a man drives a Lincoln, he drives an American car.
4. If a baseball player hits a home run, he is credited with a hit.
5. If it is raining, the roads are wet.
6. Sisters are persons who have the same parents.
7. Peas are vegetables.
8. If an angle contains 90°, it is a right angle.
9. If a triangle has two congruent sides, it has two congruent angles.
10. If two lines are parallel, a transversal that intersects the lines makes a pair of alternate interior angles congruent.
11. If two triangles are congruent, they have three pairs of congruent angles.
12. If a quadrilateral is a parallelogram, its opposite sides are congruent.
13. If two chords of a circle are congruent, they have congruent arcs.
14. Two angles of an isosceles triangle are congruent.
15. If a quadrilateral is a parallelogram, its diagonals bisect each other.
16. In a circle, congruent chords are equidistant from the center.

In 17–19, write two converses for each of the statements. Determine whether each converse is true or false.

17. If a student is bright and conscientious, he will master his schoolwork.
18. If two triangles are congruent, three pairs of sides and three pairs of angles in the triangles are congruent.
19. If two opposite sides of a quadrilateral are both congruent and parallel, the figure is a parallelogram.

20. Converses of statements are (a) always true (b) sometimes true (c) never true.

In 21–25, is statement b a converse of statement a?

21. a. Base angles of an isosceles triangle are congruent.
    b. If a triangle is isosceles, its base angles are congruent.
22. a. Corresponding angles of parallel lines are congruent.
    b. If a transversal to two lines makes a pair of corresponding angles congruent, the lines are parallel.

23. *a.* The bisector of the vertex angle of an isosceles triangle is the median to the base.
   b. The median to the base of an isosceles triangle is the bisector of the vertex angle.

24. *a.* If a quadrilateral is a square, it is equilateral.
   b. If a quadrilateral is equilateral, it is a square.

25. *a.* In a circle, chords are congruent if they are equidistant from the center.
   b. In a circle, congruent chords are equidistant from the center.

26. Given the following theorem and one of its converses:
   Theorem. The line which bisects the vertex angle of an isosceles triangle is perpendicular to the base and bisects the base.
   Converse. The line from the vertex of an isosceles triangle which is perpendicular to the base bisects the base and also the vertex angle.
   Which is correct: *a, b,* or *c?* (*a*) Both the theorem and the converse are true. (*b*) The theorem is true and the converse is false. (*c*) Both the theorem and the converse are false.

27. Choose the converse of the following statement: "Pupils who are G. O. (General Organization) members get a discount at local stores." (*a*) Pupils who do not get a discount at local stores are not G. O. members. (*b*) Pupils get a discount at local stores if they are G. O. members. (*c*) Pupils who get a discount at local stores are G. O. members.

In 28–31, show that each of the exercises is an example of an error in reasoning caused by assuming the truth of a converse of a statement which is believed to be true.

28. Mr. Wells wrote to his mother that if it rains on Sunday he would not come to visit her. Mr. Wells did not visit his mother on Sunday. She therefore concluded that it had rained in her son's home town on Sunday.

29. Great musicians are very temperamental. Since Anne, who is studying the violin, is very temperamental, she should become a concert violinist.

30. Miss Glamour, a beautiful actress, uses CLEANRIGHT soap. Mary therefore uses CLEANRIGHT soap because she is looking forward to a career in the movies.

31. All native born citizens who meet the required qualifications may be elected to the United States Senate. Tom therefore believed that Senator Ralston of his state was a native-born citizen.

32. A good citizen votes at election time. Mr. Jones votes at election time. Therefore, Mr. Jones is a good citizen. This reasoning is (*a*) unsound and is an example of indirect reasoning (*b*) sound and is an example of direct reasoning (*c*) unsound and is an example of reasoning from a converse.

33. All residents of Los Angeles are residents of California. Mr. Brown is a resident of California and therefore is a resident of Los Angeles. This reasoning is *(a)* sound and is an example of indirect reasoning *(b)* unsound and is an example of indirect reasoning *(c)* unsound and is an example of reasoning from a converse.

5. Inverses

Forming One Inverse Statement

We have previously learned that the *inverse* of a conditional statement in which the hypothesis and the conclusion each contain one piece of information is formed by contradicting, or negating, both the hypothesis and the conclusion of the conditional statement. For example:

1. *Given Statement.*   If a triangle is equilateral, it is equiangular.
   Inverse Statement.   If a triangle is not equilateral, it is not equiangular.

2. *Given Statement.*   If a quadrilateral is a square, it is a parallelogram.
   Inverse Statement.   If a quadrilateral is not a square, it is not a parallelogram.

3. *Given Statement.*   If p, then q.
   Inverse Statement.   If not p, then not q. (If $\sim p$, then $\sim q$.)

Note, once again, that the inverse of a true statement may be a true statement, as is the case in example 1; also, that the inverse of a true statement may be a false statement, as is the case in example 2. In fact, a statement which is false may have an inverse statement which is true. For example:

Given Statement.   If it is not snowing, the ground is not wet.
Inverse Statement.   If it is snowing, the ground is wet.

Forming More Than One Inverse Statement

If a statement has more than one condition in the hypothesis and one conclusion, an inverse statement is formed by contradicting only one condition in the hypothesis and at the same time contradicting the conclusion. In such a case, more than one inverse statement may be formed.

Consider the following example:

Given Statement.   If p is true and q is true, then r is true. (If p and q, then r.)

This statement will have two inverses.

Inverse Statement 1.   If p is not true and q is true, then r is not true. (If $\sim p$ and q, then $\sim r$.)
Inverse Statement 2.   If p is true and q is not true, then r is not true. (If p and $\sim q$, then $\sim r$.)

To write the inverses of a statement that contains more than one conclusion, we first separate the statement into as many statements as there are
conclusions. Then we write the inverses of these separate statements.
Consider the following example:

Statement. If p is true, then q is true and r is true. (If p, then q and r.)

This statement may be separated into the following two statements:

1. If p is true, then q is true. (If p, then q.)
2. If p is true, then r is true. (If p, then r.)

The inverses of statements 1 and 2 can now be written in the usual way.

Reasoning From the Inverse

We have seen that if a statement is true, its inverse need not necessarily
be true. Frequently, errors in everyday reasoning are made because, without
realizing it, we assume that the inverse of an accepted (true) statement is also
true. For example, when an advertiser tells you, "Use 'Bright' toothpaste
for pearly white teeth," he would probably like you to assume, "If you do
not use 'Bright' toothpaste, you will not have pearly white teeth."

EXERCISES

In 1–9, write the inverse of each statement. Determine whether each
inverse is true or false.

1. If a man is stealing, he is breaking the law.
2. If you use "Charm" face powder, you will be beautiful.
3. The man who wears "Cutrite" clothes is well dressed.
4. Use "Cleanswell" for the smile of beauty.
5. If two chords are equidistant from the center of a circle, they are congruent.
6. The diagonals of a square are congruent.
7. A line which joins the midpoints of two sides of a triangle is parallel to
   the third side.
8. If two chords in a circle are parallel, they intercept congruent arcs between them.
9. If two lines cut by a transversal are not parallel, the alternate interior
   angles are not congruent.

10. The inverse of the statement "If two angles of a triangle are congruent,
    the opposite sides are congruent" is: (*a*) If two sides of a triangle are
    congruent, the opposite angles are congruent. (*b*) If two sides of a tri-

angle are not congruent, the opposite angles are not congruent. (c) If two angles of a triangle are not congruent, the opposite sides are not congruent.

In 11–14, write two inverses for each of the statements. Determine whether each inverse is true or false.

11. If a man is handy with tools and is conscientious, he makes a good mechanic.
12. If a driver does not maintain his car in good condition, and he does not exercise reasonable care in driving, he is likely to have an accident.
13. If two opposite sides of a quadrilateral are congruent and those two sides are parallel, the figure is a parallelogram.
14. In a circle, a line which passes through the midpoint of a chord, and also passes through the midpoint of the minor arc of the chord, must pass through the center of the circle.

In 15–19, show that each exercise is an example of an error in reasoning caused by assuming the truth of an inverse of a statement believed to be true.

15. Stars shine at night. Since the stars are not shining, it is not night.
16. Since Harry arrived at school late, he could not have left his home on time.
17. Since it is not raining, the ground is not wet.
18. Since the diagonals of a rhombus are perpendicular to each other, the diagonals of a quadrilateral in which all sides are not congruent cannot be perpendicular to each other.
19. Since a circle can be circumscribed about a regular polygon, a circle cannot be circumscribed about a trapezoid.

6. Contrapositives

Forming One Contrapositive Statement

The *contrapositive* of a conditional statement whose hypothesis has one part and whose conclusion has one part may be formed by first forming the converse of the conditional statement and then forming the inverse of this converse statement. For example:

1. *Given Statement.*   If two angles are right angles, they are congruent.

   Converse Statement.   If two angles are congruent, they are right angles.

   Contrapositive Statement   If two angles are not congruent, they are not
   (*Inverse of the Converse*).   right angles.

Another way of forming the contrapositive is first to form the inverse statement and then to form the converse of the inverse statement.

Given Statement.	If two angles are right angles, they are congruent.
Inverse Statement.	If two angles are not right angles, they are not congruent.
Contrapositive Statement (Converse of the Inverse).	If two angles are not congruent, they are not right angles.

In the preceding example, notice that both the given statement and the contrapositive are true.

2.

Given Statement.	If a person is a registered voter, then he has reached his 18th birthday.
Converse Statement.	If a person has reached his 18th birthday, then he is a registered voter.
Contrapositive Statement (Inverse of the Converse).	If a person has not reached his 18th birthday, then he is not a registered voter.

In the preceding example, notice that both the given statement and the contrapositive are true.

In general, for a given conditional statement we have the following:

Given Statement.	If p, then q.
Converse Statement.	If q, then p.
Contrapositive Statement (Inverse of the Converse).	If not q, then not p, or If $\sim q$, then $\sim p$.

Statements That Are Logical Equivalents

In the first two examples that were just given, both the given statement and the contrapositive statement are true. They illustrate that whenever a statement is true, its contrapositive statement is also true.

The statement "If an animal is an elephant, then it can fly" is a false statement. The contrapositive of this statement, "If an animal cannot fly, it is not an elephant," is also a false statement. This example illustrates that whenever a statement is false, its contrapositive statement is also false.

Postulate 62. If a statement is true, its contrapositive statement is true; if a statement is false, its contrapositive statement is false.

Because a statement and its contrapositive statement are both true or are both false, we say that a statement and its contrapositive are *logical equivalents*.

If we write the converse of a conditional statement and the inverse of that given statement, we will notice that one is the contrapositive of the other.

Given Statement.   If two angles are right angles, they are congruent.
Converse Statement. If two angles are congruent, they are right angles.
Inverse Statement.   If two angles are not right angles, they are not congruent.

Since the converse and inverse statements are contrapositives of each other, they must also be logical equivalents.

The relationships between a statement, its converse, its inverse, and its contrapositive are summarized pictorially in the rectangle shown in Fig. 12–2.

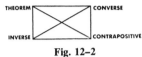

Fig. 12–2

Those statements which are at diagonally opposite vertices of the rectangle (for example, the inverse and the converse) are logically equivalent. When one is true, the other is also true; when one is false, the other is also false.

Those statements which are at consecutive vertices of the rectangle (for example, a theorem and its converse) are not logically equivalent. Therefore, the truth of one does not necessarily imply the truth of the other.

Using the Contrapositive in Indirect Proof

There are times when it is difficult to prove that a statement is true, whereas it may be easy to prove that its contrapositive is true. In such a case, we can first prove the contrapositive; then the truth of the original statement follows because a statement and its contrapositive are logical equivalents.

Forming More Than One Contrapositive Statement

If a statement has more than one condition in the hypothesis and one conclusion, the statement will have more than one converse statement. Each of these converse statements, in turn, will have inverse statements. In such a case, a statement will have more than one contrapositive statement. For example:

Given Statement.   In quadrilateral $ABCD$, if $\overline{AB} \parallel \overline{CD}$, and $\overline{AB} \cong \overline{CD}$, then $ABCD$ is a parallelogram.
Contrapositive Statement 1. If quadrilateral $ABCD$ is not a parallelogram and $\overline{AB} \cong \overline{CD}$, then $\overline{AB}$ is not parallel to $\overline{CD}$.
Contrapositive Statement 2. If quadrilateral $ABCD$ is not a parallelogram and $\overline{AB} \parallel \overline{CD}$, then $\overline{AB}$ is not congruent to $\overline{CD}$.

EXERCISES

In 1-7, write the converse, inverse, and contrapositive of each of the statements. Determine whether each statement you wrote is true or false.

1. If a person is honest, he does not steal.

2. If it is raining, the streets are wet.

3. If John has a fever, then he is sick.

4. If two sides of a triangle are congruent, the angles opposite them are congruent.

5. If two lines cut by a transversal are parallel, their alternate interior angles are congruent.

6. If a point is equidistant from the ends of a line segment, it is on the perpendicular bisector of the line segment.

7. If a point is on the line containing the bisector of an angle, it is equidistant from the sides of the angle.

8. If a triangle has two congruent altitudes, then the triangle is isosceles. Which of the following statements expresses a conclusion that logically follows from the given statement?   (*a*) If a triangle is isosceles, then the triangle has two congruent altitudes.   (*b*) If a triangle does not have two congruent altitudes, then the triangle is not isosceles.   (*c*) An isosceles triangle has two congruent altitudes.   (*d*) If a triangle is not isosceles, then the triangle does not have two congruent altitudes.

9. Given the statement "All rectangles are parallelograms." Which statement is a logical conclusion from the given statement?
   a. If *ABCD* is a parallelogram, then it is a rectangle.
   b. If *ABCD* is not a rectangle, then it is not a parallelogram.
   c. If *ABCD* is not a parallelogram, then it is not a rectangle.
   d. All parallelograms are rectangles.

10. All members of Arista are honor students. Which of the following statements expresses a conclusion that logically follows from the given statement?   (*a*) If John is an honor student, he is a member of Arista.   (*b*) If Mary is not a member of Arista, she is not an honor student.   (*c*) If Fred is not an honor student, he is not a member of Arista.

11. If a pupil in a certain school has room 125 as a homeroom, he is a senior. Which of the following statements expresses a conclusion that follows logically from the given statement?   (*a*) John is a senior in this school; therefore, he has room 125 as a homeroom.   (*b*) Tom is a junior in this school; therefore, he does not have room 125 as a homeroom.   (*c*) Paul has room 224 as a homeroom in this school; therefore, he is not a senior.

12. All members of the Science Club have completed biology. Which statement expresses a conclusion that follows from the given statement?   (*a*) If Harry has completed biology, he is a member of the Science Club.   (*b*) If Sarah has not completed biology, she is not a member of the Science Club.   (*c*) If Bill is not a member of the Science Club, he has not completed biology.   (*d*) If Martha is a member of the Science Club, she is an honor student in science.

7. Necessary and Sufficient Conditions

We will now learn how to discover whether a condition in the hypothesis of a statement is necessary and sufficient for the conclusion.

Proving That a Condition Is Sufficient

A *sufficient condition* is a fact or a set of facts which, when given in the hypothesis of a conditional statement, supplies enough information to make it possible to deduce the conclusion. For example:

"If a boy has a quarter, he can buy a ten-cent stamp."

From the condition in the hypothesis, "a boy has a quarter," we can deduce the conclusion, "he can buy a ten-cent stamp." Therefore, "a boy has a quarter" is a sufficient condition to deduce that "he can buy a ten-cent stamp."

"If a quadrilateral is a rectangle, its diagonals bisect each other."

From the condition in the hypothesis, "a quadrilateral is a rectangle," we can deduce the conclusion, "its diagonals bisect each other." Therefore, "a quadrilateral is a rectangle" is a sufficient condition to deduce that "its diagonals bisect each other."

To prove that a condition in the hypothesis of a conditional statement is sufficient for the conclusion, show that the conclusion can be deduced from the condition; that is, prove that the statement is true.

Proving That a Condition Is Necessary

A *necessary condition* is a fact or a set of facts which must be given in the hypothesis of a conditional statement to make it possible to deduce the conclusion.

In the statement "If a boy has a quarter, he can buy a ten-cent stamp," the hypothesis, "a boy has a quarter," is not necessary to deduce the conclusion, "he can buy a ten-cent stamp." The boy does not need as much as a quarter to buy a ten-cent stamp. "If a boy can buy a ten-cent stamp, he has a quarter," which is the converse of the given statement, is not true.

However, in the statement "If a boy has ten cents, he can buy a ten-cent stamp," the hypothesis, "a boy has ten cents," is necessary for the conclusion, "he can buy a ten-cent stamp." "If a boy can buy a ten-cent stamp, he has ten cents," which is the converse of the given statement, is true.

To prove that a condition in the hypothesis of a statement is necessary for the conclusion, show that the converse of the statement is true.

A condition may be both necessary and sufficient. Example: "If both pairs of opposite sides of a quadrilateral are congruent, the figure is a parallelogram." Both the converse of the statement and the statement are true. We can say, "A necessary and sufficient condition for a quadrilateral to be a parallelogram is that both pairs of its opposite sides are congruent."

The phrase "If and only if" is often used to indicate that the necessary and sufficient conditions are contained in the statement. For example, we would say, "A quadrilateral is a parallelogram if and only if both pairs of its opposite sides are congruent."

A condition may be necessary but may not be sufficient. Example: "If the diagonals of a parallelogram are congruent, it is a square." The converse of the statement is true, but the statement itself is false.

A condition may not be necessary but may be sufficient. Example: "If two angles are right angles, they are congruent." The converse of the statement is false, but the statement itself is true.

A condition may be neither necessary nor sufficient. Example: "If a quadrilateral is a trapezoid, its diagonals are congruent." Both the converse of the statement and the statement itself are false.

EXERCISES

In each of the following, state whether the condition in the hypothesis is both necessary and sufficient; necessary but not sufficient; not necessary but sufficient; neither necessary nor sufficient:

1. If a man is sick, he is in a hospital.
2. If a man is a Senator, he is a member of Congress.
3. If a girl is pretty, she will make a good wife.
4. A person with a smile has a pleasant personality.
5. Students who master their lessons pass their tests.
6. If the bases and the altitudes of two parallelograms are congruent, the parallelograms are congruent.
7. If two sides of a triangle are congruent, the angles opposite these sides are congruent.
8. Two lines are parallel if a transversal makes a pair of corresponding angles congruent.
9. If two angles are vertical angles, then they are congruent.
10. If a quadrilateral is a rhombus, the opposite angles are congruent.

8. Reasoning by Analogy

Reasoning by analogy consists of drawing the conclusion that if two situations or things are alike in some respects, they must be alike in other respects too. Because of the presence of similar elements, this conclusion may be true. However, the presence of dissimilar elements may cause the conclusion to be false. We see, therefore, that two situations are not necessarily alike in all respects because they are alike in some respects. Example: Orchids and gardenias are both beautiful flowers. Since orchids have no fragrance, gardenias have no fragrance. This conclusion is based upon the false reasoning that since gardenias and orchids have the similar element of beauty, they also possess the similar element of fragrance. Because of the fact that the fragrance-producing structures of the two flowers are not alike, the conclusion is false.

Thus, careless use of reasoning by analogy may lead to faulty conclusions. Although this method of reasoning is not a proof, it may be used for suggesting theories that may be proved by proper methods.

EXERCISES

In 1–7, state the similar elements and the dissimilar elements and indicate whether the conclusion is valid or invalid.

1. Mrs. Smith and Mrs. Arnold had skin rashes. Mrs. Smith's physician suggested that she stop eating tomatoes in order to improve the condition of her skin. Mrs. Arnold therefore also decided to stop eating tomatoes.

2. Both Tom Brady and Edgar Davis were the top ranking students in their college graduating class. Tom is very successful in business. Therefore Edgar must be successful too.

3. Alice and Eve are the two most beautiful girls in town. Alice has a charming personality. Therefore Eve has a charming personality too.

4. Sid was a champion sprinter at college. Since his brother Bob can run as fast as Sid, Bob too will be a champion sprinter at college.

5. A rhombus and a square are equilateral parallelograms whose diagonals are perpendicular to each other. Since the diagonals of a square are congruent, the diagonals of a rhombus are also congruent.

6. A rhombus and a parallelogram are quadrilaterals whose opposite sides are parallel. Since the diagonal of a rhombus bisects the angles through which it is drawn, the diagonal of a parallelogram also bisects the angles through which it is drawn.

7. A regular pentagon and a regular hexagon are equilateral and equiangular polygons. Since the diagonals of a regular pentagon are congruent, the diagonals of a regular hexagon are also congruent.

8. Give an example of a faulty conclusion which was made because of reasoning by analogy.

9. Reasoning by Generalization From Specific Cases

Generalization from specific cases, or *inductive reasoning,* consists of drawing a conclusion that something is generally true because it has been observed to be true in a limited number of specific cases.

Many scientific theories are the result of inductive reasoning based upon experimentation in specific situations. As the number of specific cases increases and the sampling of the set of situations about which a generalization is to be made is improved, the generalization itself tends to become more reasonable.

Jumping to a hasty conclusion may lead to an invalid conclusion. It is one of the frequent causes of poor reasoning. Example: In the past week, it rained every other day. Since it did not rain yesterday, it will rain today.

Let us study an example of poor reasoning from specific cases.

When we make a generalization from a study of specific cases, we make a statement about a set of objects which we found to be true for a subset of the set. For example, when Robert first entered Lincoln High School, the first three teachers he met were Mr. Jackson, Mr. Wells, and Mr. Parks. He therefore made the generalization that all his teachers would be men. He then made a broader generalization that all teachers in Lincoln High School are men. He went even further and generalized that all high school teachers in the city are men. Since Robert's observation was true only for the subset of teachers he had met, it is obvious that in making an assertion about the set of all teachers in the city, Robert became the victim of faulty reasoning.

EXERCISES

In 1–10, generalize the statement, and tell whether the generalization is true or false.

1. Some animals have four legs.
2. Some pretty girls are charming.
3. Some rich people are dishonest.
4. Some live trees have roots.

5. Some integers are even numbers.

6. Some angles are acute angles.

7. Some quadrilaterals are squares.

8. All right angles which an experimenter measured contained 90 degrees.

9. All the equilateral triangles in which Harry measured the angles were found to be equiangular.

10. In the case of all parallelograms in which Sarah measured the diagonals, she found the diagonals to be congruent.

In 11–19, explain why the exercise is an example of poor reasoning.

11. Since Allstate has beaten Fullbright in football for the last ten years, Allstate will win its football game with Fullbright this year.

12. Sam has made a hit in every game he has played this season. Sam will therefore make a hit in today's game.

13. Vitamin B has cured neuritis for four women that Mrs. Brill knows. Mrs. Brill therefore takes vitamin B to cure her pains.

14. Since the last three winners of the annual school mathematics award have been boys, a boy will win the award this year also.

15. Since there are at least two congruent angles in an isosceles triangle and also in an equilateral triangle, there are at least two congruent angles in a scalene triangle.

16. Since the diagonals of a square are congruent, the diagonals of a rhombus are also congruent.

17. Since the area of a rectangle and also the area of a square are equal to the product of two adjacent sides, the area of any parallelogram is equal to the product of two adjacent sides.

18. Since regular polygons of 3, 4, 5, and 6 sides can be constructed with compasses and straightedge, a regular polygon of any number of sides can also be constructed with compasses and straightedge.

19. Since a circle can be circumscribed about a rectangle and a square, a circle can be circumscribed about any parallelogram.

20. Give an example of a faulty conclusion which was made because of reasoning by generalization.

10. Circular Reasoning

Circular reasoning is a faulty method of reasoning in which the statement to be proved is assumed to be true and is then used in the proof of the statement.

Example: Mary stated that since Tom Spencer was the boy leader of Arista, he was the smartest boy in Stamford High School. Harriet asked

Mary how she knew that this was so. Mary replied, "If Tom Spencer were not the smartest boy in Stamford High School, he would not be the boy leader of Arista." Note that Mary's "proof" is actually the contrapositive, or logical equivalent, of her original statement. Therefore, in her "proof," Mary was only restating her assumption that Tom Spencer was the smartest boy in Stamford High School, a statement that might have been true or might have been false.

In geometry, circular reasoning occurs when, in the proof of a statement, we give the statement itself as a reason for one of the arguments in the proof.

Example: To prove "If two sides of a triangle are congruent, the angles opposite these sides are congruent," a pupil presented the following argument: "Since two sides of the triangle are given congruent, the triangle is isosceles. Since the triangle is isosceles, the two angles opposite the congruent sides are congruent because the base angles of an isosceles triangle are congruent."

Notice that the reason "the base angles of an isosceles triangle are congruent" is merely another way of stating the argument that it is supposed to support: "If a triangle is isosceles, the angles opposite the congruent sides are congruent."

Circular reasoning also occurs in geometry when in proving statement A we offer as a reason for one of the arguments a statement B whose proof presupposes the truth of statement A. If deducing the truth of statement B requires the use of statement A, then statement B cannot be used to deduce the truth of statement A. In order to avoid this type of circular reasoning, which violates proper logical sequence, we should be familiar with the sequence that is followed in the development of our theorems.

Example: In order to prove the theorem "If two sides of a triangle are congruent, the opposite angles are congruent" (theorem A), a pupil drew the altitude to the base and stated that the two triangles formed are congruent. He offered the following reason for this step: "Two right triangles are congruent if the hypotenuse and leg of one triangle are congruent respectively to the hypotenuse and leg of the other triangle" (theorem B). He was guilty of circular reasoning because, in his geometry course, in order to prove theorem B, theorem A was used as a reason for one of the arguments.

EXERCISES

In 1–9, explain why the exercise is an example of poor reasoning:

1. It is fortunate that New York City was founded where it is because it is important for a large city to have a good harbor.
2. We can celebrate Easter properly because it always falls on a holiday.
3. The catcher of our baseball team intends to stop wearing a mask because he has never been hit in the face by a ball.

4. Last year we put self-sealing tires on our car. It was a waste of money since we haven't had a flat tire during this whole year.

5. Carol said, "Mr. Walsh is a good teacher." "What makes you say that?" asked Sue. "Because all his pupils pass," responded Carol. "Why does that make him a good teacher?" inquired Sue. "That's obvious," said Carol. "If none of his pupils fail, he must be a good teacher."

6. In discussing the figure at the right, John claimed that $\angle 1 \cong \angle 2$. When Harold asked why, John replied, "Because $\overleftrightarrow{AB}$ is parallel to $\overleftrightarrow{CD}$." Harold then asked why $\overleftrightarrow{AB}$ is parallel to $\overleftrightarrow{CD}$. John replied, "Because the alternate interior angles, $\angle 1$ and $\angle 2$, are congruent."

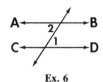

Ex. 6

7. In discussing the figure at the right, Sally claimed that $\angle 1$ and $\angle 2$ are right angles. Marion asked why this is true. Sally replied, "Because $\overleftrightarrow{CD}$ is perpendicular to $\overleftrightarrow{AB}$." Marion then asked why $\overleftrightarrow{CD}$ is perpendicular to $\overleftrightarrow{AB}$. Sally replied, "Because $\overleftrightarrow{CD}$ and $\overleftrightarrow{AB}$ form right angles when they intersect."

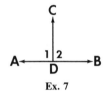

Ex. 7

8. Any point on the perpendicular bisector of a line segment is equidistant from the ends of the line segment.
Given: $\overleftrightarrow{DB} \perp \overline{AC}. \overline{AB} \cong \overline{BC}$. P is a point on $\overleftrightarrow{DB}$.
To prove: $PA = PC$.

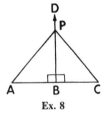

Ex. 8

Proof: *Statements*	*Reasons*
1. $\overleftrightarrow{DB} \perp \overline{AC}, \overline{AB} \cong \overline{BC}$.	1. Given.
2. $PA = PC$.	2. Any point on the perpendicular bisector of a line segment is equidistant from the ends of the line segment.

9. In a circle, congruent arcs have congruent chords.
Given: Circle O with $\overarc{AB} \cong \overarc{CD}$.
To prove: Chord $\overline{AB} \cong$ chord $\overline{CD}$.

Ex. 9

[The proof is given on the next page.]

Proof: Statements	*Reasons*
1. Circle O with $\overarc{AB} \cong \overarc{CD}$.	1. Given.
2. Chord $\overline{AB} \cong$ chord $\overline{CD}$.	2. In a circle, congruent arcs have congruent chords.

10. Give an example of a faulty conclusion which was made because of circular reasoning.

11. Sound or Unsound Reasoning

EXERCISES

In 1–21, read the exercise carefully. In each case, tell whether the reasoning is sound or unsound. If the reasoning is unsound, select from among the following the reason why it is unsound:

a. assuming the truth of a converse
b. assuming the truth of an inverse
c. using circular reasoning
d. using reasoning by generalization
e. using reasoning by analogy
f. using indirect reasoning incorrectly

1. In New York City, banks are closed on legal holidays. Therefore, in that city, banks are closed on July 4.

2. In the month of March, Boston has rainy weather. Therefore, if it is October, Boston has dry weather.

3. When it rains, the roads become wet. Since the roads are wet, it must have been raining.

4. When it is Sunday, the schools are closed. Therefore, when the schools are not closed, it is not Sunday.

5. Since the last two valedictorians in our school have been girls, the valedictorian of our class will also be a girl.

6. A man must be at least 18 years old to vote. Since Tom voted in the last election, he is at least 18 years old.

7. Since William is a dishonest boy, his sister Sally is also dishonest.

8. All men are mammals. If something is not a mammal, then it is not a man.

9. Woolen shirts are warm. Since my shirt is not woolen, it is not warm.

10. Diamond and graphite are both pure carbon. Since a diamond is very valuable, graphite must also be very valuable.

11. Wherever there is a high standard of living, there are excellent schools. Therefore, wherever there are excellent schools, there will be a high standard of living.

12. Mr. Smith finds that his car is overheating. Some of the causes of overheating are a faulty thermostat, a broken fan belt, a broken water pump, and a clogged radiator. With little difficulty, he has his thermostat, his fan belt, and his water pump checked and finds them to be all right. He concludes that his radiator must be clogged.

13. Since an equilateral triangle is also equiangular, an equilateral quadrilateral is also equiangular.

14. Since the median to the base of an isosceles triangle bisects the base, the median to the base of an equilateral triangle bisects the base.

15. Since the opposite angles of a parallelogram are congruent, the opposite angles of a rhombus are congruent.

16. Since the diagonals of a square are perpendicular to each other, it follows that if the diagonals of a quadrilateral are perpendicular to each other, the quadrilateral is a square.

17. Since it has been proved that congruent triangles have congruent bases and congruent altitudes, it follows that if two triangles are not congruent, they do not have congruent bases and congruent altitudes.

18. Since a circle can be circumscribed about a rectangle, if a quadrilateral is not a rectangle, a circle cannot be circumscribed about it.

19. Since a circle can be circumscribed about a regular polygon, if a circle can be circumscribed about a polygon, it is a regular polygon.

20. *Given:* $\triangle ABC$ in which $AC > CB$.

    Prove: $m\angle ABC > m\angle BAC$.

    Construct angle ABX congruent to angle BAC. Now $m\angle ABC$ is greater than $m\angle ABX$ because the whole is greater than any of its parts. Therefore, $m\angle ABC$ is greater than $m\angle BAC$ because a quantity may be substituted for its equal.

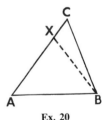

Ex. 20

21. John has learned that parallel chords intercept congruent arcs on a circle. In a diagram, chords $\overline{AB}$ and $\overline{CD}$ are intersecting chords. John therefore concludes that $\overset{\frown}{AC}$ cannot be congruent to $\overset{\frown}{BD}$.

CHAPTER XIII

Sequences and Proofs of Important Theorems

When we studied circular reasoning, we saw that we must be informed about the sequence in which we develop the theorems of geometry. The importance of this aspect of a course in deductive geometry is expressed in the following paragraph, which is an excerpt from the New York State Tenth Year Mathematics Syllabus:

The concepts of the nature of proof as well as the logical structure exhibited in a chain of propositions should be stressed in a course in formal geometry. To develop an understanding of sequential thinking, four areas have been selected for study. Each area of study includes the fundamental definitions and assumed theorems on which the sequence is based, and a set of theorems which are proved in logical order.

NOTE. The term "assumed theorem" means "postulate."

A study of the following four sequences can help to develop an understanding of sequential thinking.

Sequence A. Congruence and Parallelism

DEFINITION. *Parallel lines* are lines which lie in the same plane and do not intersect.

POSTULATE. Through a given point not on a given line, there exists one and only one line parallel to the given line.

THEOREM 1. When two parallel lines are cut by a transversal, the alternate interior (or corresponding) angles are congruent.

THEOREM 2. The sum of the measures of the angles of a triangle is 180.

THEOREM 3. Two triangles are congruent if two angles and a side opposite one of them in one triangle are congruent to the corresponding parts of the other.

THEOREM 4. Two right triangles are congruent if the hypotenuse and a leg of one triangle are congruent to the corresponding parts of the other.

THEOREM 5. A diameter perpendicular to a chord of a circle bisects the chord.

NOTE. If in the proof of 4, the hypotenuses are placed together, then include the theorems: If two sides of a triangle are congruent, the angles opposite these sides are congruent; and if two angles of a triangle are congruent, the sides opposite these angles are congruent.

Sequence B. Angle Measurement

DEFINITION. A *circle* is the set of points in a plane that are a fixed distance from a fixed point.

POSTULATE. The measure of a central angle is the measure of its intercepted arc.

THEOREM 1. If two sides of a triangle are congruent, the angles opposite these sides are congruent.

THEOREM 2. The measure of an exterior angle of a triangle is equal to the sum of the measures of two nonadjacent interior angles.

THEOREM 3. The measure of an angle inscribed in a circle is equal to one-half the measure of its intercepted arc.

a. Case I — where the center of the circle is on one side of the angle.
b. Cases II and III — where the center of the circle is in the interior of the angle and where it is in the exterior of the angle.

THEOREM 4*a.* The measure of an angle formed by two chords intersecting in the interior of a circle is equal to one-half the sum of the measures of the intercepted arcs.

THEOREM 4*b.* The measure of an angle formed by two secants drawn to a circle from an outside point is equal to one-half the difference of the measures of the intercepted arcs.

NOTE. This sequence may end with either of two different theorems, 4*a* or 4*b*.

Sequence C. Similarity

DEFINITION. *Similar polygons* are polygons which have   (1) their corresponding angles congruent and   (2) the ratios of the measures of all pairs of corresponding sides equal.

POSTULATE. A line parallel to one side of a triangle and intersecting the other two sides divides these sides proportionally.

THEOREM 1. If two angles of one triangle are congruent to two angles of another triangle, the triangles are similar.

THEOREM 2. If in a right triangle the altitude is drawn to the hypotenuse,

a. The two triangles thus formed are similar to the given triangle and are similar to each other.
b. The length of each leg of the given triangle is the mean proportional between the length of the hypotenuse and the length of the projection of that leg on the hypotenuse.

THEOREM 3. The square of the length of the hypotenuse of a right triangle is equal to the sum of the squares of the lengths of the legs.

Sequence D.   Area

DEFINITION. The *area of any polygonal region* is the number of area units contained within the region.

POSTULATE. The area of a rectangle is equal to the product of the length of its base and the length of its altitude.

THEOREM 1. The area of a parallelogram is equal to the product of the length of any base and the length of any corresponding altitude.

THEOREM 2. The area of a triangle is equal to one-half the product of the length of a side and the length of the altitude drawn to that side.

THEOREM 3a. The area of a regular polygon is equal to one-half the product of its perimeter and the length of its apothem.

THEOREM 3b. The area of a trapezoid is equal to one-half the product of the length of the altitude and the sum of the lengths of the bases.

THEOREM 4. The area of a circle is equal to one-half the product of its circumference and the length of its radius.

NOTE. This sequence may end with either 3a and 4, or 3b.

Pages 593–616 present complete proofs of important theorems. These theorems are also the required theorems in the New York State Tenth Year Mathematics Syllabus.

Theorem 9

If two sides of a triangle are congruent, the angles opposite these sides are congruent.

[The base angles of an isosceles triangle are congruent.]

Given: △*ACB* with $\overline{CA} \cong \overline{CB}$.

To prove: ∠*A* ≅ ∠*B*.

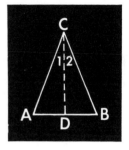

Plan: To prove that ∠*A* ≅ ∠*B*, show that ∠*A* and ∠*B* are corresponding angles of two congruent triangles. Two such triangles, △*ACD* and △*BCD*, are formed by drawing $\overline{CD}$, the bisector of vertex ∠*ACB*.

Proof: Statements	Reasons
1. Let $\overline{CD}$ be the bisector of vertex ∠*ACB*, *D* being the point at which the bisector intersects $\overline{AB}$.	1. Every angle has one and only one bisector.
2. ∠1 ≅ ∠2. (a. ≅ a.)	2. A bisector of an angle divides the angle into two congruent angles.
3. $\overline{CA} \cong \overline{CB}$. (s. ≅ s.)	3. Given.
4. $\overline{CD} \cong \overline{CD}$. (s. ≅ s.)	4. Reflexive property of congruence.
5. △*ACD* ≅ △*BCD*.	5. s.a.s. ≅ s.a.s.
6. ∠*A* ≅ ∠*B*.	6. Corresponding angles of congruent triangles are congruent.

Theorem 10 (Proof 1)*

If two angles of a triangle are congruent, the sides opposite these angles are congruent.

Given: $\triangle ACB$ with $\angle CAB \cong \angle CBA$.

To prove: $\overline{CA} \cong \overline{CB}$.

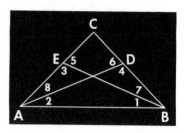

Plan: To prove that $\overline{CA} \cong \overline{CB}$, show that $\overline{CA}$ and $\overline{CB}$ are corresponding sides of two congruent triangles. Two such triangles, $\triangle ACD$ and $\triangle BCE$, can be formed by drawing $\overline{AD}$, the bisector of $\angle CAB$, and $\overline{BE}$, the bisector of $\angle CBA$. In order to prove $\triangle ACD \cong \triangle BCE$, we will first prove $\triangle ABE \cong \triangle BAD$. Then, we will use the congruence of corresponding parts of $\triangle ABE$ and $\triangle BAD$ in proving $\triangle ACD \cong \triangle BCE$.

Proof: *Statements* | *Reasons*
---

1. $\angle CAB \cong \angle CBA$.   (a. $\cong$ a.) | 1. Given.

2. Let $\overline{AD}$ be the bisector of $\angle CAB$, D being the point at which this bisector intersects $\overline{BC}$. Let $\overline{BE}$ be the bisector of $\angle CBA$, E being the point at which this bisector intersects $\overline{AC}$. | 2. Every angle has one and only one bisector.

3. $\angle 1 \cong \angle 2$.   (a. $\cong$ a.) | 3. Halves of congruent angles are congruent.

4. $\overline{AB} \cong \overline{AB}$.   (s. $\cong$ s.) | 4. Reflexive property of congruence.

5. $\triangle ABE \cong \triangle BAD$. | 5. a.s.a. $\cong$ a.s.a.

---

*This proof (proof 1) can be used if Theorem 10 is proved before the theorem "The sum of the measures of the angles of a triangle is 180" is proved.

6. $\overline{BE} \cong \overline{AD}$.   (s. $\cong$ s.)
   $\angle 3 \cong \angle 4$.

6. Corresponding parts of congruent triangles are congruent.

7. $\angle 5$ is supplementary to $\angle 3$.
   $\angle 6$ is supplementary to $\angle 4$.

7. Two angles are supplementary if the sum of their measures is 180.

8. $\angle 6 \cong \angle 5$.   (a. $\cong$ a.)

8. If two angles are supplementary to two congruent angles, then they are congruent.

9. $\angle 8 \cong \angle 7$.   (a. $\cong$ a.)

9. Halves of congruent angles are congruent.

10. $\triangle ACD \cong \triangle BCE$.

10. a.s.a. $\cong$ a.s.a.

11. $\overline{CA} \cong \overline{CB}$.

11. Corresponding parts of congruent triangles are congruent.

Theorem 24

The sum of the measures of the angles of a triangle is 180.

Given: △*ABC.*

To prove: $m\angle A + m\angle B + m\angle C = 180.$

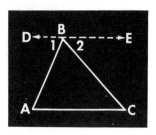

Plan: Let $\overleftrightarrow{DE}$ be the line through vertex B that is parallel to $\overleftrightarrow{AC}$. Since $\angle DBE$ is a straight angle, $m\angle DBE = 180$, or $m\angle 1 + m\angle B + m\angle 2 = 180$. We can prove that $m\angle A + m\angle B + m\angle C = 180$ by showing that $m\angle A + m\angle B + m\angle C = m\angle 1 + m\angle B + m\angle 2$.

Proof: *Statements*	*Reasons*
1. Let $\overleftrightarrow{DE}$ be the line through B that is parallel to $\overleftrightarrow{AC}$.	1. Through a given point, not on a given line, there exists one and only one line parallel to the given line.
2. $m\angle DBE = 180.$	2. A straight angle is an angle whose measure is 180.
3. $m\angle 1 + m\angle B + m\angle 2 = 180.$	3. The whole quantity is equal to the sum of all its parts.
4. $\angle A \cong \angle 1, \angle C \cong \angle 2,$ or $m\angle A = m\angle 1, m\angle C = m\angle 2.$	4. If two parallel lines are cut by a transversal, the alternate interior angles are congruent.
5. $m\angle A + m\angle B + m\angle C = 180.$	5. Substitution postulate.

Theorem 10 (Proof 2)*

If two angles of a triangle are congruent, the sides opposite these angles are congruent.

Given: $\triangle ACB$ with $\angle A \cong \angle B$.
To prove: $\overline{CA} \cong \overline{CB}$.

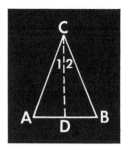

Plan: To prove that $\overline{CA} \cong \overline{CB}$, show that $\overline{CA}$ and $\overline{CB}$ are corresponding sides of two congruent triangles. Two such triangles, $\triangle ACD$ and $\triangle BCD$, can be formed by drawing $\overline{CD}$, the bisector of vertex $\angle ACB$.

Proof: *Statements*	*Reasons*
1. Let $\overline{CD}$ be the bisector of vertex $\angle ACB$, D being the point at which the bisector intersects $\overline{AB}$.	1. Every angle has one and only one bisector.
2. $\angle 1 \cong \angle 2$. (a. $\cong$ a.)	2. A bisector of an angle divides the angle into two congruent angles.
3. $\overline{CD} \cong \overline{CD}$. (s. $\cong$ s.)	3. Reflexive property of congruence.
4. $\angle A \cong \angle B$. (a. $\cong$ a.)	4. Given.
5. $\triangle ACD \cong \triangle BCD$.	5. s.a.a. $\cong$ s.a.a.
6. $\overline{CA} \cong \overline{CB}$.	6. Corresponding sides of congruent triangles are congruent.

* This proof (proof 2) can be used if Theorem 10 is proved after the theorem "The sum of the measures of the angles of a triangle is 180" is proved.

Theorem 26

Two right triangles are congruent if the hypotenuse and a leg of one triangle are congruent to the corresponding parts of the other. [hy. leg ≅ hy. leg]

Given: Rt. △*ABC* with ∠*B* a right angle, rt. △*DEF* with ∠*E* a right angle, hy. $\overline{AC}$ ≅ hy. $\overline{DF}$, and leg $\overline{BC}$ ≅ leg $\overline{EF}$.

To prove: Rt. △*ABC* ≅ rt. △*DEF*.

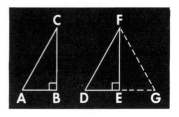

Plan: To prove that rt. △*ABC* ≅ rt. △*DEF*, show that both △*ABC* and △*DEF* are congruent to a third triangle.

Proof:

Statements	Reasons
1. Extend $\overline{DE}$ to *G* so that $\overline{EG}$ ≅ $\overline{AB}$. (s. ≅ s.)	1. A line segment may be extended any required length.
2. Draw $\overline{FG}$.	2. A line segment can be drawn joining two points.
3. $\overline{BC}$ ≅ $\overline{EF}$. (s. ≅ s.)	3. Given
4. ∠*DEG* is a straight angle.	4. A straight angle is an angle whose measure is 180.
5. ∠*B* and ∠*DEF* are right angles.	5. Given.
6. ∠*DEF* and ∠*GEF* are supplementary.	6. Supplementary angles are two angles the sum of whose measures is 180.
7. ∠*GEF* is a right angle.	7. The supplement of a right angle is a right angle.
8. ∠*B* = ∠*GEF*. (a. ≅ a.)	8. All right angles are congruent.
9. △*ABC* ≅ △*GEF*.	9. s.a.s. ≅ s.a.s.
10. $\overline{AC}$ ≅ $\overline{GF}$.	10. Corresponding sides of congruent triangles are congruent.
11. $\overline{AC}$ ≅ $\overline{DF}$.	11. Given.

12. $\overline{DF} \cong \overline{GF}$. (s. $\cong$ s.)	12. Transitive property of congruence.
13. $\angle D \cong \angle G$. (a. $\cong$ a.)	13. If two sides of a triangle are congruent, the angles opposite these sides are congruent.
14. $\angle DEF \cong \angle GEF$. (a. $\cong$ a.)	14. All right angles are congruent.
15. $\triangle DEF \cong \triangle GEF$.	15. s.a.a. $\cong$ s.a.a.
16. $\triangle ABC \cong \triangle DEF$.	16. Transitive property of congruence.

Theorem 60

A diameter perpendicular to a chord of a circle bisects the chord and its arcs.

Given: $\odot O$ with diameter $\overline{AB} \perp$ chord $\overline{CD}$.

To prove: $\overline{CE} \cong \overline{ED}$, $\overparen{CB} \cong \overparen{DB}$, $\overparen{CA} \cong \overparen{DA}$.

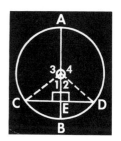

Plan: To prove that $\overline{CE} \cong \overline{ED}$, we can show that these line segments are corresponding sides of two congruent triangles. We can do this by drawing radii $\overline{OC}$ and $\overline{OD}$ and proving that rt. $\triangle OEC \cong$ rt. $\triangle OED$ by hy. leg $\cong$ hy. leg.

To prove that $\overparen{CB} \cong \overparen{DB}$, show that their central angles, $\angle 1$ and $\angle 2$, are congruent. To prove that $\overparen{CA} \cong \overparen{DA}$, show that their central angles, $\angle 3$ and $\angle 4$, are congruent.

[The proof is given on the next page.]

Proof: Statements

	Reasons

1. In ⊙O, diameter $\overline{AB}$ ⊥ chord $\overline{CD}$.
1. Given.

2. Draw radii $\overline{OC}$ and $\overline{OD}$.
2. A line segment may be drawn joining two points.

3. ∠OEC and ∠OED are rt. angles.
3. Perpendicular lines intersect forming right angles.

4. In △OEC and OED, $\overline{OC} \cong \overline{OD}$.
4. Radii of a circle are congruent.

5. $\overline{OE} \cong \overline{OE}$.
5. Reflexive property of congruence.

6. Rt. △OEC ≅ rt. △OED.
6. Hy. leg ≅ hy. leg.

7. $\overline{CE} \cong \overline{ED}$, ∠1 ≅ ∠2 or $m∠1 = m∠2$.
7. Corresponding parts of congruent triangles are congruent.

8. $\overparen{CB} = \overparen{DB}$.
8. In a circle, central angles whose measures are equal have equal arcs.

9. $\overparen{CB} \cong \overparen{DB}$.
9. In the same circle, equal arcs are congruent arcs.

10. $\overleftrightarrow{AOB}$ is a straight line.
10. A diameter of a circle is a line segment.

11. ∠3 is supp. to ∠1. ∠4 is supp. to ∠2.
11. If two adjacent angles have their non-common sides on the same straight line, they are supplementary.

12. ∠3 ≅ ∠4, or $m∠3 = m∠4$.
12. If two angles are congruent, their supplements are congruent.

13. $\overparen{CA} = \overparen{DA}$.
13. In a circle, central angles whose measures are equal have equal arcs.

14. $\overparen{CA} \cong \overparen{DA}$.
14. In the same circle, equal arcs are congruent arcs.

Theorem 71 (Case 1)

The measure of an angle inscribed in a circle is equal to one-half the measure of its intercepted arc.

Case 1. The center of the circle lies on one side of the angle.

Given: $\angle ABC$ is inscribed in $\odot O$. Side $\overline{BC}$ is
        a diameter of the circle.

To prove: $m\angle ABC = \frac{1}{2}m\widehat{AC}$.

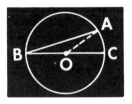

Plan: Show that $m\angle ABC$ equals one-half the measure of central angle
    AOC, which intercepts the same arc as $\angle ABC$. Since $m\angle AOC = m\widehat{AC}$, $m\angle ABC = \frac{1}{2}m\widehat{AC}$.

Proof: *Statements*	*Reasons*
1. Draw radius $\overline{OA}$.	1. A line segment may be drawn joining two points.
2. $\overline{OA} \cong \overline{OB}$.	2. Radii of a circle are congruent.
3. $\angle A \cong \angle B$.	3. If two sides of a triangle are congruent, the angles opposite these sides are congruent.
4. $m\angle A + m\angle B = m\angle AOC$.	4. The measure of an exterior angle of a triangle is equal to the sum of the measures of two non-adjacent interior angles.
5. $m\angle B + m\angle B = m\angle AOC$, or $2m\angle B = m\angle AOC$.	5. Substitution postulate.
6. $m\angle B = \frac{1}{2}m\angle AOC$.	6. Halves of equal quantities are equal.
7. $m\angle AOC = m\widehat{AC}$.	7. The measure of a central angle is equal to the measure of its intercepted arc.
8. $m\angle ABC = \frac{1}{2}m\widehat{AC}$.	8. Substitution postulate.

Theorem 71 (Case 2)

The measure of an angle inscribed in a circle is equal to one-half the measure of its intercepted arc.

Case 2. The center of the circle lies in the interior of the angle.

Given: $\angle ABC$ is inscribed in $\odot O$. The center of the circle, O, lies in the interior of the angle.

To prove: $m\angle ABC = \frac{1}{2}m\widehat{AC}$.

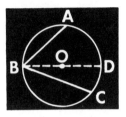

Plan: Through B, the vertex of $\angle ABC$, draw diameter $\overline{BD}$, forming $\angle ABD$ and $\angle CBD$, each of which is an inscribed angle one of whose sides is a diameter. The measure of $\angle ABC$ is the sum of the measures of $\angle ABD$ and $\angle CBD$.

Proof: Statements

1. Draw radius $\overline{BO}$.

2. Extend $\overline{BO}$ until it intersects the circle in point D, forming diameter $\overline{BD}$.

3. $m\angle ABD = \frac{1}{2}m\widehat{AD}$, $m\angle CBD = \frac{1}{2}m\widehat{CD}$.

4. $m\angle ABD + m\angle CBD = \frac{1}{2}m\widehat{AD} + \frac{1}{2}m\widehat{DC}$, or $m\angle ABC = \frac{1}{2}m\widehat{AD} + \frac{1}{2}m\widehat{DC}$.

5. $m\angle ABC = \frac{1}{2}(m\widehat{AD} + m\widehat{DC})$.

6. $m\angle ABC = \frac{1}{2}m\widehat{AC}$.

Reasons

1. A line segment may be drawn joining two points.

2. A line segment may be extended.

3. The measure of an inscribed angle in a circle, one of whose sides passes through the center of the circle, is equal to one-half the measure of its intercepted arc.

4. If equal quantities are added to equal quantities, the resulting quantities are equal.

5. Factoring (distributive property).

6. Substitution postulate.

Theorem 71 (Case 3)

The measure of an angle inscribed in a circle is equal to one-half the measure of its intercepted arc.

Case 3. The center of the circle lies in the exterior of the angle.

Given: $\angle ABC$ is inscribed in $\odot O$. The center of the circle, O, lies in the exterior of the angle.

To prove: $m\angle ABC = \frac{1}{2}m\widehat{AC}$.

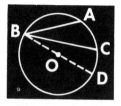

Plan: Through B, the vertex of $\angle ABC$, draw diameter $\overline{BD}$, forming $\angle ABD$ and $\angle CBD$, each of which is an inscribed angle one of whose sides is a diameter. The measure of $\angle ABC$ is the difference of the measures of $\angle ABD$ and $\angle CBD$.

Proof:

Statements	*Reasons*
1. Draw radius $\overline{BO}$.	1. A line segment may be drawn joining two points.
2. Extend $\overline{BO}$ until it intersects the circle in point D, forming diameter $\overline{BD}$.	2. A line segment may be extended.
3. $m\angle ABD = \frac{1}{2}m\widehat{AD}$, $m\angle CBD = \frac{1}{2}m\widehat{CD}$.	3. The measure of an inscribed angle in a circle, one of whose sides passes through the center of the circle, is equal to one-half the measure of its intercepted arc.
4. $m\angle ABD - m\angle CBD = \frac{1}{2}m\widehat{AD} - \frac{1}{2}m\widehat{CD}$, or $m\angle ABC = \frac{1}{2}m\widehat{AD} - \frac{1}{2}m\widehat{CD}$.	4. If equal quantities are subtracted from equal quantities, the resulting quantities are equal.
5. $m\angle ABC = \frac{1}{2}(m\widehat{AD} - m\widehat{CD})$.	5. Factoring (distributive property).
6. $m\angle ABC = \frac{1}{2}m\widehat{AC}$.	6. Substitution postulate.

Theorem 73

The measure of an angle formed by two chords intersecting in the interior of a circle is equal to one-half the sum of the measures of the intercepted arcs.

Given: $\angle 1$ is formed by chords $\overline{AB}$ and $\overline{CD}$ intersecting at E in the interior of the circle.

To prove: $m\angle 1 = \frac{1}{2}(m\widehat{DB} + m\widehat{AC})$.

Plan: Draw $\overline{AD}$, forming $\triangle ADE$, which has $\angle 1$ as an exterior angle. Show that the measure of $\angle 1$ is equal to the sum of the measures of inscribed angles A and D, or $m\angle 1 = m\angle A + m\angle D$.

Proof: *Statements*	*Reasons*
1. Chords $\overline{AB}$ and $\overline{CD}$ intersect at E.	1. Given.
2. Draw $\overline{AD}$.	2. A line segment may be drawn joining two points.
3. $\angle 1$ is an exterior angle of $\triangle ADE$.	3. An exterior angle of a triangle is formed by one side of the triangle and the extension of an adjacent side through the common vertex.
4. $m\angle 1 = m\angle A + m\angle D$.	4. The measure of an exterior angle of a triangle is equal to the sum of the measures of the two non-adjacent interior angles.
5. $m\angle A = \frac{1}{2}m\widehat{DB}$, $m\angle D = \frac{1}{2}m\widehat{AC}$.	5. The measure of an inscribed angle in a circle is equal to one-half the measure of its intercepted arc.
6. $m\angle 1 = \frac{1}{2}m\widehat{DB} + \frac{1}{2}m\widehat{AC}$.	6. Substitution postulate.
7. $m\angle 1 = \frac{1}{2}(m\widehat{DB} + m\widehat{AC})$.	7. Factoring (distributive property).

Theorem 74

The measure of an angle formed by two secants drawn to a circle from an outside point is equal to one-half the difference of the measures of the intercepted arcs.

Given: $\angle C$ is formed by secants $\overline{CDE}$ and $\overline{CBA}$ intersecting at point C outside the circle.

To prove: $m\angle C = \frac{1}{2}(m\widehat{AE} - m\widehat{BD})$.

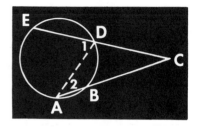

Plan: Draw chord $\overline{AD}$ to form inscribed angles 1 and 2. Show that $m\angle C = m\angle 1 - m\angle 2$.

Proof: *Statements*

1. $\overline{CDE}$ and $\overline{CBA}$ are secants.

2. Draw chord $\overline{AD}$.

3. $m\angle C + m\angle 2 = m\angle 1$.

4. $m\angle 2 = m\angle 2$.

5. $m\angle C = m\angle 1 - m\angle 2$.

6. $m\angle 1 = \frac{1}{2}m\widehat{AE}$, $m\angle 2 = \frac{1}{2}m\widehat{BD}$.

7. $m\angle C = \frac{1}{2}m\widehat{AE} - \frac{1}{2}m\widehat{BD}$.

8. $m\angle C = \frac{1}{2}(m\widehat{AE} - m\widehat{BD})$.

Reasons

1. Given.

2. A line segment may be drawn joining two points.

3. The measure of an exterior angle of a triangle is equal to the sum of the measures of the two non-adjacent interior angles.

4. Reflexive property of equality.

5. If equal quantities are subtracted from equal quantities, the resulting quantities are equal.

6. The measure of an inscribed angle is equal to one-half the measure of its intercepted arc.

7. Substitution postulate.

8. Factoring (distributive property).

Theorem 75

The measure of an angle formed by a tangent and a secant drawn to a circle from an outside point is equal to one-half the difference of the measures of the intercepted arcs.

Given: $\angle C$ is formed by secant $\overline{CDE}$ and tangent $\overline{CB}$ intersecting at point C outside the circle.

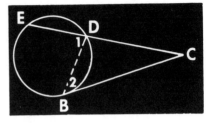

To prove: $m\angle C = \frac{1}{2}(m\widehat{EB} - m\widehat{BD})$.

Plan: Draw chord $\overline{BD}$, forming angles 1 and 2. Show that $m\angle C = m\angle 1 - m\angle 2$.

Proof: *Statements*	*Reasons*
1. $\overline{CDE}$ is a secant and $\overline{CB}$ is a tangent.	1. Given.
2. Draw chord $\overline{BD}$.	2. A line segment may be drawn joining two points.
3. $m\angle C + m\angle 2 = m\angle 1$.	3. The measure of an exterior angle of a triangle is equal to the sum of the measures of the two non-adjacent interior angles.
4. $m\angle 2 = m\angle 2$.	4. Reflexive property of equality.
5. $m\angle C = m\angle 1 - m\angle 2$.	5. If equal quantities are subtracted from equal quantities, the resulting quantities are equal.
6. $m\angle 1 = \frac{1}{2}m\widehat{EB}$.	6. The measure of an inscribed angle is equal to one-half the measure of its intercepted arc.
7. $m\angle 2 = \frac{1}{2}m\widehat{BD}$.	7. The measure of an angle formed by a tangent and a chord drawn from the point of contact is equal to one-half the measure of the intercepted arc.
8. $m\angle C = \frac{1}{2}m\widehat{EB} - \frac{1}{2}m\widehat{BD}$.	8. Substitution postulate.
9. $m\angle C = \frac{1}{2}(m\widehat{EB} - m\widehat{BD})$.	9. Factoring (distributive property).

Theorem 76

The measure of an angle formed by two tangents drawn to a circle from an outside point is equal to one-half the difference of the measures of the intercepted arcs.

Given: $\angle C$ is formed by tangents $\overleftrightarrow{CD}$ and $\overleftrightarrow{CB}$.

To prove: $m\angle C = \frac{1}{2}(m\overparen{BRD} - m\overparen{BSD})$.

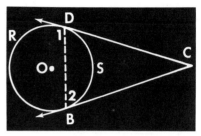

Plan: Draw chord $\overline{DB}$, forming angles 1 and 2. Show that $m\angle C = m\angle 1 - m\angle 2$.

Proof:

Statements	Reasons
1. $\overleftrightarrow{CB}$ and $\overleftrightarrow{CD}$ are tangents.	1. Given.
2. Draw chord $\overline{BD}$.	2. A line segment may be drawn joining two points.
3. $m\angle C + m\angle 2 = m\angle 1$.	3. The measure of an exterior angle of a triangle is equal to the sum of the measures of the two non-adjacent interior angles.
4. $m\angle 2 = m\angle 2$.	4. Reflexive property of equality.
5. $m\angle C = m\angle 1 - m\angle 2$.	5. If equal quantities are subtracted from equal quantities, the resulting quantities are equal.
6. $m\angle 1 = \frac{1}{2} m\overparen{BRD}$, $m\angle 2 = \frac{1}{2} m\overparen{BSD}$.	6. The measure of an angle formed by a tangent and a chord drawn from the point of contact is equal to one-half the measure of the intercepted arc.
7. $m\angle C = \frac{1}{2} m\overparen{BRD} - \frac{1}{2} m\overparen{BSD}$.	7. Substitution postulate.
8. $m\angle C = \frac{1}{2}(m\overparen{BRD} - m\overparen{BSD})$.	8. Factoring.

Theorem 88

Two triangles are similar if three angles of one triangle are congruent to three corresponding angles of the other. [a.a.a. ≅ a.a.a.]

Given: △*ABC* and *A'B'C'* in which
            ∠*A* ≅ ∠*A'*, ∠*B* ≅ ∠*B'*, and
            ∠*C* ≅ ∠*C'*.

To prove: △*ABC* ~ △*A'B'C'*.

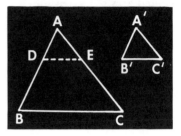

Plan: By definition, similar polygons are polygons whose correspond-
        ing angles are congruent and whose corresponding sides are in
        proportion. Since it is given that the angles of △*ABC* and △*A'B'C'*
        are congruent, in order to prove △*ABC* ~ △*A'B'C'*, we will
        prove that the corresponding sides of these triangles are in pro-
        portion; that is, $\dfrac{AB}{A'B'} = \dfrac{AC}{A'C'} = \dfrac{BC}{B'C'}$.

Proof: *Statements* | *Reasons*

1. Let *D* be a point on $\overline{AB}$, | 1. A line segment may be ex-
   extended through *B* if necessary, | tended as far as desired.
   such that $\overline{AD} \cong \overline{A'B'}$.
   (s. ≅ s.)

2. Let *E* be a point on $\overline{AC}$, ex- | 2. A line segment may be
   tended through *C* if necessary, | extended as far as desired.
   such that $\overline{AE} \cong \overline{A'C'}$.
   (s. ≅ s.)

3. Draw $\overline{DE}$. | 3. A line segment may be drawn
                                                           | joining two points.

4. ∠*A* ≅ ∠*A'*.   (a. ≅ a.) | 4. Given.

5. △*ADE* ≅ △*A'B'C'*. | 5. s.a.s. ≅ s.a.s.

6. ∠*ADE* ≅ ∠*B'*. | 6. Corresponding parts of con-
                                                           | gruent triangles are congruent.

7. ∠*B'* ≅ ∠*B*. | 7. Given.

8. $\angle ADE \cong \angle B$.	8. Transitive property of congruence.
9. $\overline{DE} \parallel \overline{BC}$.	9. If two lines are cut by a transversal making a pair of corresponding angles congruent, the lines are parallel.
10. $\dfrac{AB}{AD} = \dfrac{AC}{AE}$.	10. If a line is parallel to one side of a triangle and intersects the other two sides, the line divides those sides proportionally.
11. $AD = A'B'$, $AE = A'C'$.	11. Construction, step 1 and step 2.
12. $\dfrac{AB}{A'B'} = \dfrac{AC}{A'C'}$.	12. Substitution postulate.
13. Similarly, by cutting off lengths equal to $B'A'$ and $B'C'$ along $\overline{BA}$ and $\overline{BC}$ respectively (extended if necessary) we can prove that $C'A' \parallel CA$ and $\dfrac{BC}{B'C'} = \dfrac{AB}{A'B'}$.	13. Steps 1–12.
14. $\dfrac{AB}{A'B'} = \dfrac{AC}{A'C'} = \dfrac{BC}{B'C'}$.	14. Transitive property of equality.
15. $\triangle ABC \sim \triangle A'B'C'$.	15. Two polygons are similar if their corresponding angles are congruent and their corresponding sides are in proportion.

NOTE. We are not assuming that if $AB > A'B'$, then $AC > A'C'$, although the figure seems to suggest this.

Theorem 99

If the altitude is drawn to the hypotenuse of a right triangle,

a. **the two triangles thus formed are similar to the given triangle and similar to each other.**

b. **the length of each leg of the given triangle is the mean proportional between the length of the whole hypotenuse and the length of the projection of that leg on the hypotenuse.**

Given: $\triangle ABC$ with rt. $\angle ACB$, $\overline{CD} \perp \overline{AB}$.

To prove: (a) $\triangle ACD \sim \triangle ABC$,
                   $\triangle CBD \sim \triangle ABC$,
                   $\triangle ACD \sim \triangle CBD$.

       (b) $\dfrac{AB}{AC} = \dfrac{AC}{AD}$,

            $\dfrac{AB}{BC} = \dfrac{BC}{BD}$.

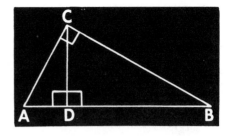

Plan: (a) $\triangle ACD$ can be proved similar to $\triangle CBD$ by showing that they are both similar to $\triangle ABC$.   (b) The proportions will follow from the similarities of triangles which were established in part (a).

Proof: *Statements*   *Reasons*

1. $\angle ACB$ is a rt. angle, $\overline{CD} \perp \overline{AB}$.	1. Given.
2. $\angle ADC$ is a rt. angle, $\angle BDC$ is a rt. angle.	2. Perpendicular lines intersect forming right angles.
3. In rt. $\triangle ACD$ and ABC, $\angle A \cong \angle A$.	3. Reflexive property of congruence.
4. $\angle ACB \cong \angle ADC$.	4. All right angles are congruent.
5. Rt. $\triangle ACD \sim$ rt. $\triangle ABC$.	5. a.a. $\cong$ a.a.
6. In rt. $\triangle CBD$ and ABC, $\angle B \cong \angle B$.	6. Reflexive property of congruence.
7. $\angle ACB \cong \angle BDC$.	7. All right angles are congruent.
8. Rt. $\triangle CBD \sim$ rt. $\triangle ABC$.	8. a.a. $\cong$ a.a.
9. $\triangle ACD \sim \triangle CBD$.	9. Transitive property of similarity.
10. $\dfrac{AB}{AC} = \dfrac{AC}{AD}, \dfrac{AB}{BC} = \dfrac{BC}{BD}$.	10. Corresponding sides of similar triangles are in proportion.

Theorem 100

In a right triangle, the square of the length of the hypotenuse is equal to the sum of the squares of the lengths of the legs.

Given: In $\triangle ABC$, $\angle ACB$ is a right angle, c is the length of the hypotenuse, and a and b are the lengths of the legs of the triangle.

To prove: $c^2 = a^2 + b^2$.

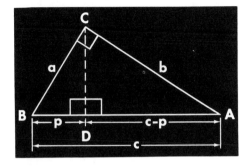

Plan: Draw $\overline{CD}$, the altitude to the hypotenuse $\overline{AB}$. Use the principle "In a right triangle, the length of each leg is the mean proportional between the length of the hypotenuse and the length of the projection of that leg on the hypotenuse" to find a^2 and b^2. Then add the results to show that $c^2 = a^2 + b^2$.

Proof: *Statements*	*Reasons*
1. In $\triangle ABC$, $\angle ACB$ is a right angle.	1. Given.
2. Draw $\overline{CD} \perp \overline{AB}$. Let $BD = p$, $AD = c - p$.	2. Through a point not on a given line, one and only one perpendicular can be constructed to the given line.
3. $\dfrac{c}{a} = \dfrac{a}{p}$ and $\dfrac{c}{b} = \dfrac{b}{c - p}$.	3. If the altitude is drawn to the hypotenuse of a right triangle, the length of each leg is the mean proportional between the length of the whole hypotenuse and the length of the projection of that leg on the hypotenuse.
4. $cp = a^2$ and $c^2 - cp = b^2$.	4. In a proportion, the product of the means is equal to the product of the extremes.
5. $c^2 = a^2 + b^2$.	5. If equal quantities are added to equal quantities, the resulting quantities are equal quantities.

Theorem 103

The area of a parallelogram is equal to the product of the length of any base and the length of any corresponding altitude.

[The area of a parallelogram is equal to the product of the length of one side and the length of the altitude drawn to that side.]

Given: $\square ABCD$ with the length of base $\overline{AB} = b$ and the length of altitude $\overline{DE} = h$, $\overline{DE} \perp \overline{AB}$.

To prove: Area of $\square ABCD = bh$.

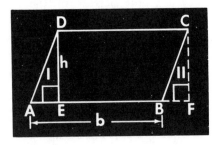

Plan: Construct $\overline{CF} \perp \overleftrightarrow{AB}$. Prove that the area of $\square ABCD$ is equal to the area of rectangle $CDEF$, which has the same base and altitude as $\square ABCD$.

Proof:

Statements	Reasons
1. $\square ABCD$ with the length of base $\overline{AB} = b$ and the length of altitude $\overline{DE} = h$, $\overline{DE} \perp \overleftrightarrow{AB}$.	1. Given.
2. $\overline{AB} \cong \overline{DC}$, or $AB = DC = b$.	2. Both pairs of opposite sides of a $\square$ are congruent.
3. Construct $\overline{CF} \perp \overleftrightarrow{AB}$, intersecting $\overleftrightarrow{AB}$ at F.	3. Through a point not on a given line, one and only one perpendicular may be constructed to the given line.
4. $\overline{DE} \parallel \overline{CF}$.	4. If two line segments are perpendicular to the same line, they are parallel.
5. $\overline{AB} \parallel \overline{DC}$.	5. Both pairs of opposite sides of a $\square$ are parallel.
6. $CDEF$ is a parallelogram.	6. If the opposite sides of a quadrilateral are parallel, it is a $\square$.
7. $\angle DEA$ and $\angle CFB$ are rt. angles.	7. If two lines are perpendicular, they intersect forming right angles.

8. *CDEF* is a rectangle with the length of base $\overline{CD} = b$ and the length of altitude $\overline{DE} = h$.

8. A $\square$ one of whose angles is a right angle is a rectangle.

9. In rt. $\triangle$I and II, $\overline{AD} \cong \overline{BC}$, $\overline{DE} \cong \overline{CF}$.

9. Both pairs of opposite sides of a $\square$ are congruent.

10. Rt. $\triangle$I $\cong$ rt. $\triangle$II.

10. Hy. leg $\cong$ hy. leg.

11. Area of $\triangle$I = area of $\triangle$II.

11. Congruent triangles are equal in area.

12. Area of quad. *CDEB* = area of quad. *CDEB*.

12. Reflexive property of equality.

13. Area of quad. *CDEB* + area of $\triangle$I = area of quad. *CDEB* + area of $\triangle$II, or area of $\square$ *ABCD* = area of rect. *CDEF*.

13. If equal quantities are added to equal quantities, the resulting quantities are equal.

14. Area of rect. *CDEF* = *bh*.

14. The area of a rectangle equals the product of its base and altitude.

15. Area of $\square ABCD = bh$.

15. Substitution postulate.

Theorem 104

The area of a triangle is equal to one-half the product of the length of a side and the length of the altitude drawn to that side.

Given: $\triangle ABC$ with the length of base $\overline{AC} = b$ and the length of altitude $\overline{BE} = h$.

To prove: Area of $\triangle ABC = \frac{1}{2}bh$.

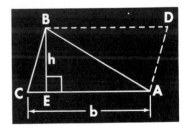

Plan: Through vertex *A*, construct a line $\parallel \overline{CB}$. Through vertex *B*, construct a line $\parallel \overline{CA}$. Let *D* be the point of intersection of the two lines that were constructed. Prove that the area of $\triangle ABC$ is equal to one-half the area of $\square CADB$, which has the same base and altitude as $\triangle ABC$.

[The proof is given on the next page.]

Proof: *Statements*

1. $\triangle ABC$ with base $\overline{AC}$, whose length is b and altitude $\overline{BE}$, whose length is h.	1. Given.
2. Through A, construct a line $\parallel$ $\overline{BC}$. Through B, construct a line $\parallel \overline{CA}$. These lines intersect at D.	2. Through a point not on a given line, one and only one line may be constructed parallel to the given line.
3. $CADB$ is a parallelogram with base of length b and altitude of length h.	3. If both pairs of opposite sides of a quadrilateral are parallel, it is a $\square$.
4. $\triangle ABC \cong \triangle BAD$, making the area of $\triangle ABC$ equal to the area of $\triangle BAD$, or area of $\triangle ABC = \frac{1}{2}$ area of $\square CADB$.	4. A diagonal divides a $\square$ into two congruent triangles.
5. Area of $\square CADB = bh$.	5. The area of a $\square$ is equal to the product of the length of any base and the length of any corresponding altitude.
6. Area of $\triangle ABC = \frac{1}{2}bh$.	6. Substitution postulate.

Theorem 107

The area of a trapezoid is equal to one-half the product of the length of its altitude and the sum of the lengths of its bases.

Given: Trapezoid $ABCD$ with $\overline{AB} \parallel \overline{DC}$, the length of base $\overline{AB} = b$, the length of base $\overline{DC} = b'$, and the length of altitude $\overline{DE} = h$.

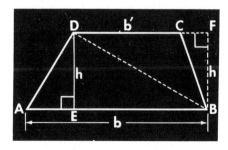

To prove: Area of trapezoid $ABCD = \frac{1}{2}h(b + b')$.

> *Plan:* Draw diagonal $\overline{BD}$, dividing the trapezoid into two triangles, $\triangle ABD$ and BCD. Find the area of each triangle. Add the results to obtain the area of the trapezoid.

Proof: *Statements*	*Reasons*
1. Trapezoid $ABCD$ with $\overline{AB} \parallel \overline{DC}$, bases of length b and b', and altitude of length h.	1. Given.
2. Draw diagonal $\overline{BD}$.	2. A line segment may be drawn joining two points.
3. Construct $\overline{BF} \perp \overleftrightarrow{DC}$, intersecting $\overleftrightarrow{DC}$ at F.	3. Through a point not on a given line, one and only one perpendicular may be constructed to the given line.
4. BF, the length of the altitude to side $\overline{CD}$ of $\triangle BCD$, $= DE$, the length of the altitude to side $\overline{AB}$ of $\triangle ABD = h$.	4. Parallel lines are everywhere equidistant.
5. Area of $\triangle ABD = \frac{1}{2}bh$, and area of $\triangle BCD = \frac{1}{2}b'h$.	5. The area of a triangle is equal to one-half the product of the length of a side and the length of the altitude drawn to that side.
6. Area of trapezoid $ABCD$ = area of $\triangle ABD$ + area of $\triangle BCD$.	6. Area-addition postulate.
7. Area of trapezoid $ABCD = \frac{1}{2}bh + \frac{1}{2}b'h$.	7. Substitution postulate.
8. Area of trapezoid $ABCD = \frac{1}{2}h(b + b')$.	8. Factoring (distributive property).

Theorem 120

The area of a regular polygon is equal to one-half the product of its perimeter and the length of its apothem.

Given: Regular polygon $ABCD \ldots$ with center O, perimeter $= p$, and length of apothem $= a$.

To prove: Area of regular polygon
$\qquad ABCD \ldots = \frac{1}{2}ap$.

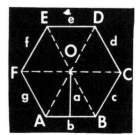

Plan: Divide the polygon into triangles by drawing radii. Find the areas of the triangles. Add the areas of the triangles to obtain the area of the regular polygon.

Proof: *Statements*   *Reasons*

1. From O, the center of the regular polygon, draw radii $\overline{OA}$, $\overline{OB}$, $\overline{OC}$, . . . , forming $\triangle AOB$, $\triangle BOC$, $\triangle COD$, ...

1. A line segment may be drawn joining two points.

2. In each of the triangles formed, an apothem of the regular polygon is the altitude drawn from vertex O to the opposite side.

2. Each apothem of a regular polygon is perpendicular to a side of the polygon.

3. The lengths of the altitudes of $\triangle AOB$, $\triangle BOC$, $\triangle COD$, . . . , constructed from vertex O, are equal to the length of any apothem, a.

3. In a regular polygon, the apothems are congruent.

4. Area of $\triangle AOB = \frac{1}{2}ab$, area of $\triangle BOC = \frac{1}{2}ac$, area of $\triangle COD = \frac{1}{2}ad$, ...

4. The area of a triangle is equal to one-half the product of the length of a side and the length of the altitude drawn to that side.

5. Area of reg. polygon $ABCD$ . . . = area of $\triangle AOB$ + area of $\triangle BOC$ + area of $\triangle COD$ + ...

5. Area-addition postulate.

6. Area of reg. polygon $ABCD$ . . . = $\frac{1}{2}ab + \frac{1}{2}ac + \frac{1}{2}ad + $ . . . .

6. Substitution postulate.

7. Area of polygon $ABCD$ . . . = $\frac{1}{2}a(b + c + d + $ . . .$)$.

7. Factoring.

8. $b + c + d + $ . . . $= p$.

8. The perimeter of a polygon is the sum of the lengths of its sides.

9. Area of regular polygon $ABCD$ . . . $= \frac{1}{2}ap$.

9. Substitution postulate.

CHAPTER XIV

Constructions

When a draftsman draws a scale drawing for a blueprint, he may use a ruler to measure lengths, a protractor to measure angles, and parallel rulers to draw parallel lines. In our work in geometry, when we *draw* a figure, we may also use these instruments. However, when we *construct* a figure in geometry, we may use only the two tools of geometry: the straightedge, which is an unmarked ruler, and the compasses.

In this chapter are presented important construction problems, the methods of performing these contructions, and plans for their proof. Those constructions that are marked with a star are the ones which the New York State Tenth Year Mathematics Syllabus lists as fundamental constructions.

Construction 1

To construct a line segment congruent (equal in length) to a given line segment.

Given: Line segment $\overline{AB}$.

Required: To construct a line segment $\overline{XY}$ congruent to segment $\overline{AB}$.

Construction:

1. Construct any line $\overleftrightarrow{CD}$ and mark a point X on it.

2. On line segment $\overline{AB}$, place the compasses so that the steel point is at A and the pencil point is at B.

3. Keeping the setting on your compasses, place the steel point at X and construct an arc intersecting line $\overleftrightarrow{CD}$ in Y.

4. Line segment $\overline{XY} \cong$ line segment $\overline{AB}$.

Plan for Proof: The construction makes $\overline{XY} \cong \overline{AB}$ because $\overline{XY}$ and $\overline{AB}$ are radii of congruent circles.

617

Construction 2

To construct a line segment whose length is equal to the sum of the lengths of two given line segments.

Given: Line segments of lengths
            a and b.

Required: To construct a line seg-
            ment whose length is
            equal to $a + b$.

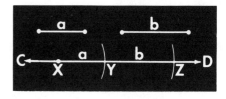

Construction:

1. Construct any line $\overleftrightarrow{CD}$ and mark a point X on it.
2. On $\overleftrightarrow{CD}$, construct segment $\overline{XY}$ whose length is a.
3. On $\overleftrightarrow{CD}$, construct segment $\overline{YZ}$ whose length is b.
4. $XZ = a + b$.

Plan for Proof: The construction makes $XZ = a + b$ because the length of the whole line segment $\overline{XZ}$ is equal to the sum of the lengths of its parts, $a + b$.

Construction 3

To construct an angle congruent to a given angle.

Given: $\angle ABC$ and point D.

Required: To construct at D
            an angle congruent
            to $\angle ABC$.

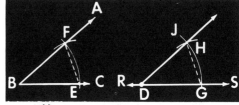

Construction:

1. Through point D construct any line $\overleftrightarrow{RS}$.

2. With B as a center and any convenient radius, construct an arc which intersects $\overrightarrow{BC}$ at E and $\overrightarrow{BA}$ at F.

3. With D as a center and using the same radius as in step 2, construct $\overparen{GJ}$ which intersects $\overrightarrow{DS}$ at G.

4. Construct $\overline{EF}$. With G as a center and a radius whose length is EF, construct an arc which intersects $\overparen{GJ}$ at H.

5. Construct $\overrightarrow{DH}$. $\angle HDS \cong \angle ABC$.

Plan for Proof: If $\overline{GH}$ is drawn, the construction makes $\overline{DH} \cong \overline{BF}$, $\overline{DG} \cong \overline{BE}$, $\overline{GH} \cong \overline{EF}$. Therefore, $\triangle DHG \cong \triangle BFE$ by s.s.s. $\cong$ s.s.s. Therefore, $\angle HDS \cong \angle ABC$.

Construction 4

To construct an angle whose measure is equal to the sum of the measures of two given angles.

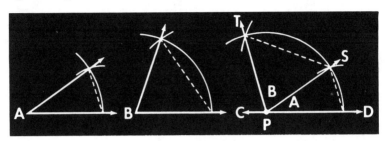

Given: ∠A and ∠B.

Required: To construct an angle whose measure is equal to $m\angle A + m\angle B$.

Construction:

1. Construct any line $\overleftrightarrow{CD}$ and mark a point P on it.

2. At P, construct $\angle DPS \cong \angle A$.

3. At P, construct $\angle SPT \cong \angle B$.

4. $m\angle DPT = m\angle A + m\angle B$.

Plan for Proof: The construction makes $m\angle DPT = m\angle A + m\angle B$ because the measure of the whole $\angle DPT$ is equal to the sum of $m\angle DPS$ (which equals $m\angle A$) and $m\angle SPT$ (which equals $m\angle B$).

★Construction 5

To bisect a given line segment.

[To construct the perpendicular bisector of a given line segment.]

Given: Line segment $\overline{AB}$.

Required: To bisect $\overline{AB}$.

Construction:

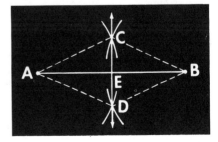

1. Open the compasses so that the distance between the steel point and the pencil point (this distance will be called the radius) is more than half of the length of $\overline{AB}$.

2. Using point A as a center, construct one arc above $\overline{AB}$ and one arc below $\overline{AB}$.

3. Using the same radius and point B as a center, construct another pair of arcs, one of which is above $\overline{AB}$ and the other below $\overline{AB}$. C and D are the points at which the arcs intersect.

4. Construct $\overleftrightarrow{CD}$. The construction makes $\overleftrightarrow{CD}$, the perpendicular bisector of $\overline{AB}$, intersect $\overline{AB}$ at E. Therefore, $\overline{AE} \cong \overline{EB}$.

Plan for Proof: If $\overline{CA}$, $\overline{CB}$, $\overline{DA}$, and $\overline{DB}$ are drawn, the construction makes $\overline{CA} \cong \overline{CB}$ and $\overline{DA} \cong \overline{DB}$ (radii of equal circles are congruent). Therefore, $\overleftrightarrow{CD}$ is the perpendicular bisector of $\overline{AB}$ because two points each equidistant from the ends of a line segment determine the perpendicular bisector of the line segment.

*Construction 6

To bisect a given angle.

[To construct the bisector of a given angle.]

Given: ∠ABC.

Required: To bisect ∠ABC.

Construction:

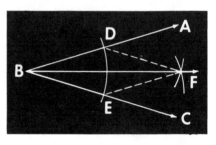

1. With B as a center and any convenient radius, construct an arc which intersects $\overrightarrow{BA}$ at D and $\overrightarrow{BC}$ at E.

2. With D and E as centers and with equal radii of sufficient length, construct arcs that intersect at F.

3. Construct $\overrightarrow{BF}$. Since ∠ABF ≅ ∠CBF, then $\overrightarrow{BF}$ bisects ∠ABC.

Plan for Proof: If $\overline{FD}$ and $\overline{FE}$ are drawn, the construction makes $\overline{BD} \cong \overline{BE}$ and $\overline{DF} \cong \overline{EF}$. Also, $\overline{BF} \cong \overline{BF}$. Therefore, △$BDF$ ≅ △BEF by s.s.s. ≅ s.s.s. Hence, ∠ABF ≅ ∠CBF.

*Construction 7

To construct a line perpendicular to a given line through a given point on the line.

Given: Point P is on line $\overleftrightarrow{AB}$.

Required: To construct a line through P perpendicular to $\overleftrightarrow{AB}$.

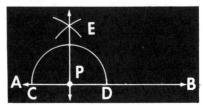

Construction:

1. With *P* as a center and any convenient radius, construct an arc which intersects $\overleftrightarrow{AB}$ at points *C* and *D*.

2. With *C* and *D* as centers and with a radius greater in length than the one used before, construct arcs that intersect at *E*.

3. Construct $\overleftrightarrow{EP}$, which is perpendicular to $\overleftrightarrow{AB}$ at *P*.

Plan for Proof: The construction bisects straight angle *APB*. Angle *APE* and angle *BPE* are right angles. Therefore, $\overleftrightarrow{EP}$ is perpendicular to $\overleftrightarrow{AB}$ because two straight lines which intersect at right angles are perpendicular to each other.

Construction 8

To construct a line perpendicular to a given line through a given point outside the line.

Given: Point *P* is outside
            line $\overleftrightarrow{AB}$.

Required: To construct a line
            through *P* perpen-
            dicular to $\overleftrightarrow{AB}$.

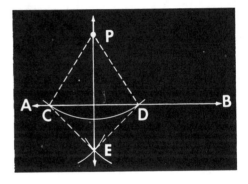

Construction:

1. With *P* as a center and any
   convenient radius, construct
   an arc which intersects $\overleftrightarrow{AB}$
   in *C* and *D*.

2. With *C* and *D* as centers and with a radius greater in length than one-half *CD*, construct arcs which intersect in *E*.

3. Construct $\overleftrightarrow{EP}$, which is perpendicular to $\overleftrightarrow{AB}$.

Plan for Proof: If $\overline{PC}$, $\overline{PD}$, $\overline{EC}$, and $\overline{ED}$ are drawn, the construction makes $\overline{PC} \cong \overline{PD}$ and $\overline{EC} \cong \overline{ED}$. Therefore, $\overleftrightarrow{PE}$ is the perpendicular bisector of $\overline{CD}$ because two points each equidistant from the ends of a line segment determine the perpendicular bisector of the line segment. Therefore, $\overleftrightarrow{PE}$ is perpendicular to $\overleftrightarrow{AB}$.

Construction 9

To construct the bisector of an angle of a given triangle.

Given: △*ABC*.

Required: To construct the bi-
          sector of ∠*A*.

Construction:

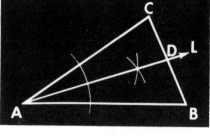

1. Construct $\overrightarrow{AL}$, the bisector of
   ∠*A*.

2. $\overrightarrow{AL}$ intersects $\overline{BC}$, the side opposite ∠*A*, at *D*.

3. Line segment $\overline{AD}$ is the bisector of ∠*A* in △*ABC*.

Plan for Proof: Since $\overrightarrow{AL}$ bisects ∠*A*, $\overline{AD}$ is the bisector of ∠*A* in △*ABC*
because a bisector of an angle of a triangle is the line segment, drawn from
a vertex, which bisects that angle and which terminates in the opposite
side.

NOTE. If the bisectors of the three angles of a triangle are constructed,
they will all intersect in the same point in the interior of the triangle. Hence,
we say that the three angle bisectors of a triangle are *concurrent*.

Construction 10

To construct a median of a given triangle.

Given: △*ABC*.

Required: To construct a median from
          vertex *A* to side $\overline{BC}$.

Construction:

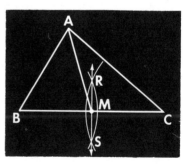

1. Construct $\overleftrightarrow{RS}$, the perpendicular bisector of $\overline{BC}$.

2. $\overleftrightarrow{RS}$ intersects $\overline{BC}$ at *M*.

3. Construct line segment $\overline{AM}$. This is
   the median from vertex *A* to side $\overline{BC}$.

Plan for Proof: Since $\overleftrightarrow{RS}$ is the perpendicular bisector of $\overline{BC}$, point *M* is
the midpoint of $\overline{BC}$. Therefore, $\overline{AM}$ is the median from vertex *A* to side
$\overline{BC}$ because a median of a triangle is the line segment which joins a vertex
and the midpoint of the opposite side.

NOTE. If the three medians of a triangle are constructed, they will all intersect in the same point in the interior of the triangle. Hence, we say that the three medians of a triangle are *concurrent*.

Construction 11

To construct an altitude of a given triangle.

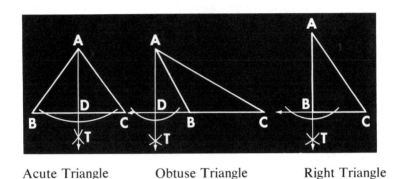

Acute Triangle   Obtuse Triangle   Right Triangle

Given: $\triangle ABC$.

Required: To construct an altitude from vertex A to side $\overline{CB}$.

Construction:

1. Through point A, construct $\overleftrightarrow{AT}$, a line perpendicular to $\overline{CB}$. Extend $\overline{CB}$ if necessary.

2. In acute triangle ABC, $\overleftrightarrow{AT}$ intersects $\overline{CB}$ at D. Line segment $\overline{AD}$ is the altitude from vertex A to side $\overline{CB}$.

3. In obtuse triangle ABC, $\overleftrightarrow{AT}$ intersects $\overline{CB}$ extended at D. Line segment $\overline{AD}$ is the altitude from vertex A to side $\overline{CB}$.

4. In right triangle ABC, $\overleftrightarrow{AT}$ intersects $\overline{CB}$ at B. Line segment $\overline{AB}$ is the altitude from vertex A to side $\overline{CB}$.

Plan for Proof: In acute triangle ABC, $\overleftrightarrow{AT}$ is perpendicular to $\overline{CB}$. Therefore, line segment $\overline{AD}$ is the altitude from vertex A to side $\overline{CB}$ because an altitude of a triangle is the line segment from a vertex perpendicular to the opposite side (or the line containing that side). Similarly, in obtuse triangle ABC, line segment $\overline{AD}$ is the altitude from vertex A to side $\overline{CB}$; in right triangle ABC, line segment $\overline{AB}$ is the altitude from vertex A to side $\overline{CB}$.

NOTE. If the three altitudes of a triangle are constructed, they will all intersect in the same point. In the case of the acute triangle, the three altitudes will intersect in the interior of the triangle; in the case of the obtuse triangle, in the exterior of the triangle; and in the case of the right triangle, at the vertex of the right angle. Hence, we say that the three altitudes of a triangle are *concurrent*.

★Construction 12

To construct a line parallel to a given line through a given external point.

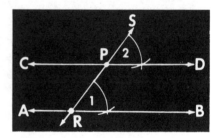

Given: Line $\overleftrightarrow{AB}$ and external point P.

Required: Through P, to construct a line parallel to $\overleftrightarrow{AB}$.

Construction:

1. Through P, construct any transversal, intersecting $\overleftrightarrow{AB}$ at R.

2. At P, construct $\angle SPD$ ($\angle 2$) $\cong \angle PRB$ ($\angle 1$). Make $\angle 2$ and $\angle 1$ a pair of corresponding angles.

3. $\overleftrightarrow{CD}$, which is also line $\overleftrightarrow{DP}$, passes through P and is parallel to $\overleftrightarrow{AB}$.

Plan for Proof: The construction makes $\angle 2 \cong \angle 1$. Therefore, $\overleftrightarrow{AB} \parallel \overleftrightarrow{CD}$ because if two lines are cut by a transversal making a pair of corresponding angles congruent, the lines are parallel.

★Construction 13

To divide a given line segment into any number of congruent parts.

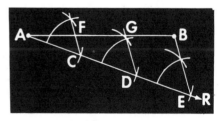

Given: Line segment $\overline{AB}$.

Required: To divide $\overline{AB}$ into any number of congruent parts [for example, three congruent parts].

Construction:

1. Construct $\overrightarrow{AR}$ making any convenient angle BAR.

2. On $\overrightarrow{AR}$, start at A and lay off any convenient length, AC, three times, so that $AC = CD = DE$.

3. Construct $\overleftrightarrow{EB}$.

4. Through D, construct $\overleftrightarrow{DG} \parallel \overleftrightarrow{EB}$. Through C, construct $\overleftrightarrow{CF} \parallel \overleftrightarrow{EB}$.

5. $\overline{AF}, \overline{FG}$, and $\overline{GB}$ are the three congruent parts of $\overline{AB}$.

Plan for Proof: The construction makes $\overline{AC} \cong \overline{CD} \cong \overline{DE}$ and $\overleftrightarrow{CF} \parallel \overleftrightarrow{DG} \parallel \overleftrightarrow{EB}$. Therefore, $\overline{AF} \cong \overline{FG} \cong \overline{GB}$ because if three or more parallel lines cut off segments of equal length on one transversal, they cut off segments of equal length on any transversal.

Construction 14

To construct a triangle when the three sides are given.

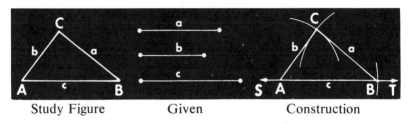

Study Figure   Given   Construction

Given: Line segments a, b, c, the sides of $\triangle ABC$.

Required: To construct $\triangle ABC$.

Construction:

1. On any line $\overleftrightarrow{ST}$, use a point A as a center and the length of c as a radius to construct segment $\overline{AB}$ so that AB is equal to the length of c.

2. With A as a center and the length of b as a radius, construct an arc.

3. With B as a center and the length of a as a radius, construct an arc which intersects the previous arc in C.

4. Construct $\overline{AC}$ and $\overline{BC}$. The required triangle is $\triangle ABC$.

Plan for Proof: The construction makes $\overline{AB} \cong$ segment c, $\overline{BC} \cong$ segment a, and $\overline{AC} \cong$ segment b. Therefore, $\triangle ABC$ is the required triangle.

Construction 15

To construct a triangle when two sides and the included angle are given.

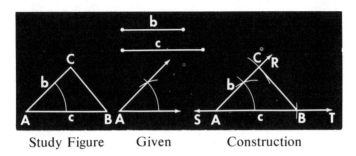

Study Figure   Given   Construction

Given: Line segments b and c and $\angle A$.

Required: To construct $\triangle ABC$ with sides b and c, and included $\angle A$.

Construction:

1. On any line $\overleftrightarrow{ST}$, use a point A as a center and the length of c as a radius to construct $\overline{AB} \cong$ segment c.

2. At A, construct $\angle BAR \cong \angle A$.

3. On $\overrightarrow{AR}$, with A as a center and the length of segment b as a radius, construct $\overline{AC} \cong$ segment b.

4. Construct $\overline{BC}$. The required triangle is $\triangle ABC$.

Plan for Proof: The construction makes $\overline{AB} \cong$ segment c, $\angle CAB \cong \angle A$, and $\overline{AC} \cong$ segment b. Therefore, $\triangle ABC$ is the required triangle.

Construction 16

To construct a triangle when two angles and the included side are given.

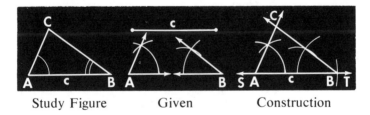

Study Figure   Given   Construction

Given: Line segment c, $\angle A$ and $\angle B$.

Required: To construct $\triangle ABC$ with $\angle A$, $\angle B$, and included side c.

Construction:

1. On any line $\overleftrightarrow{ST}$, use a point A as a center and the length of segment c as a radius to construct $\overline{AB} \cong$ segment c.

2. At A, construct an angle congruent to $\angle A$.

3. At B, construct an angle congruent to $\angle B$.

4. Extend the sides of $\angle A$ and $\angle B$, drawn in steps 2 and 3, until they intersect at C.

5. The required triangle is $\triangle ABC$.

Plan for Proof: The construction makes $\angle CAB \cong \angle A$, $\overline{AB} \cong$ segment c, and $\angle ABC \cong \angle B$. Therefore, $\triangle ABC$ is the required triangle.

Construction 17

To construct an angle containing 60° whose vertex is a given point.

Given: Point A.

Required: To construct an angle containing 60° whose vertex is A.

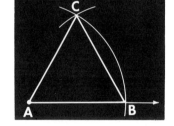

Construction:

1. Construct any line segment $\overline{AB}$.

2. Using A as the center and a radius whose length is equal to AB, construct an arc.

3. Using B as the center and a radius whose length is equal to AB, construct another arc which intersects the first arc in C.

4. Construct $\overline{CA}$ and $\overline{CB}$, forming equilateral triangle ABC.

5. $\angle CAB$ contains 60°.

Plan for Proof: The construction makes $\triangle ABC$ an equilateral triangle. Since an equilateral triangle is equiangular, $m\angle CAB = \frac{1}{3}$ of 180, or $m\angle CAB = 60$.

★Construction 18

To construct a line tangent to a given circle through a given point on the circle.

Given: Point P on circle O.

Required: To construct a tangent to circle O through P.

Construction:

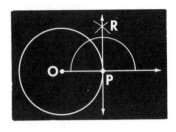

1. Construct radius $\overline{OP}$ and extend it outside the circle.

2. At P, construct $\overset{\leftrightarrow}{RP}$ perpendicular to $\overset{\leftrightarrow}{OP}$.

3. $\overset{\leftrightarrow}{RP}$ is the required tangent.

Plan for Proof: The construction makes $\overset{\leftrightarrow}{RP}$ perpendicular to $\overset{\leftrightarrow}{OP}$ at point P. Therefore, $\overset{\leftrightarrow}{RP}$ is a tangent to circle O because a line perpendicular to a radius of a circle at its outer extremity is a tangent to the circle.

★Construction 19

To construct a line tangent to a given circle through a given point outside the circle.

Given: Circle O and point P outside the circle.

Required: Through P, to construct a tangent to circle O.

Construction:

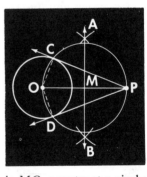

1. Construct $\overline{OP}$.

2. Construct $\overset{\leftrightarrow}{AB}$, the perpendicular bisector of $\overline{OP}$, to find M, the midpoint of $\overline{OP}$.

3. Using M as a center and a radius whose length is MO, construct a circle intersecting circle O in points C and D.

4. Construct $\overset{\leftrightarrow}{PC}$ and $\overset{\leftrightarrow}{PD}$. Each of the lines $\overset{\leftrightarrow}{PC}$ and $\overset{\leftrightarrow}{PD}$ is a tangent to circle O.

Plan for Proof: Construct $\overline{OC}$. Since $\overline{OP}$ is a diameter in circle M, $\angle OCP$ is a right angle because an angle inscribed in a semicircle is a right angle. Therefore, $\overset{\leftrightarrow}{PC}$ is a tangent to circle O because a line perpendicular to a radius of a circle at its outer extremity is a tangent to the circle. Similarly, $\overset{\leftrightarrow}{PD}$ is a tangent to circle O.

★Construction 20

To locate the center of a given circle.

Given: A circle.

Required: To locate the center of the circle.

Construction:

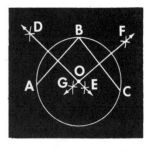

1. Construct any chord $\overline{AB}$.

2. Construct $\overleftrightarrow{DE}$, the perpendicular bisector of $\overline{AB}$.

3. Construct another chord $\overline{BC}$.

4. Construct $\overleftrightarrow{FG}$, the perpendicular bisector of $\overline{BC}$.

5. O, the point of intersection of lines $\overleftrightarrow{DE}$ and $\overleftrightarrow{FG}$, is the center of the given circle.

Plan for Proof: $\overleftrightarrow{DE}$ was constructed as the perpendicular bisector of chord $\overline{AB}$. Therefore, the center of the given circle is on $\overleftrightarrow{DE}$ because the perpendicular bisector of a chord passes through the center of the circle. Similarly, the center of the given circle is on $\overleftrightarrow{FG}$, the perpendicular bisector of chord $\overline{BC}$. Since O is the only point which is on both $\overleftrightarrow{DE}$ and $\overleftrightarrow{FG}$, it is the center of the given circle.

★Construction 21

To construct a circle circumscribed about a given triangle.

Given: $\triangle ABC$.

Required: To circumscribe a circle about $\triangle ABC$.

Construction:

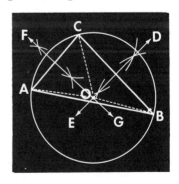

1. Construct $\overleftrightarrow{DE}$, the perpendicular bisector of $\overline{BC}$.

2. Construct $\overleftrightarrow{FG}$, the perpendicular bisector of $\overline{AC}$.

3. These perpendicular bisectors intersect at O.

4. Construct a circle using O as the center and a radius whose length is OA.

5. Circle O is the required circle.

Plan for Proof: Draw $\overline{OA}$, $\overline{OC}$, and $\overline{OB}$. Since $\overleftrightarrow{FG}$ is the perpendicular bisector of $\overline{AC}$, $OA = OC$ because any point on the perpendicular bisector of a line segment is equidistant from the ends of the segment. Similarly, since $\overleftrightarrow{DE}$ is the perpendicular bisector of $\overline{BC}$, $OC = OB$. Hence, $OA = OB = OC$. Therefore, a circle with O as its center and a radius whose length is OA passes through A, B, and C. That is, circle O circumscribes $\triangle ABC$.

*Construction 22

To construct a circle inscribed in a given triangle.

Given: $\triangle ABC$.

Required: To inscribe a circle in $\triangle ABC$.

Construction:

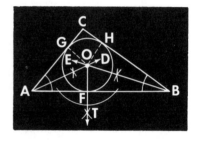

1. Construct $\overrightarrow{AD}$, the bisector of $\angle A$.

2. Construct $\overrightarrow{BE}$, the bisector of $\angle B$.

3. These angle bisectors intersect at O.

4. From O, construct $\overleftrightarrow{OT}$ perpendicular to $\overline{AB}$. $\overleftrightarrow{OT}$ intersects $\overline{AB}$ at F.

5. Construct a circle using O as the center and a radius whose length is the length of segment $\overline{OF}$.

6. Circle O is the required circle.

Plan for Proof: Since $\overrightarrow{AD}$ is the bisector of $\angle A$, O is equidistant from $\overrightarrow{AB}$ and $\overrightarrow{AC}$ because any point on the bisector of an angle is equidistant from the sides of the angle. Similarly, O is equidistant from $\overrightarrow{BA}$ and $\overrightarrow{BC}$. Hence, O is equidistant from $\overline{AB}$, $\overline{BC}$, and $\overline{AC}$. Since the length of the perpendicular $\overline{OF}$ measures the distance from O to $\overline{AB}$, a circle whose center is O with radius of length OF will be tangent to the sides of $\triangle ABC$. Therefore, circle O is inscribed in $\triangle ABC$.

Construction 23

To construct the fourth proportional to three given line segments.

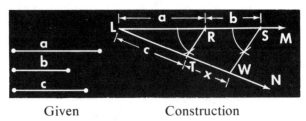

| Given | Construction |

Given: Line segments of lengths *a*, *b*, and *c*.

Required: To construct a line segment of length *x* so that *a*:*b* = *c*:*x*.

Construction:

1. Construct rays $\overrightarrow{LM}$ and $\overrightarrow{LN}$ to make a convenient angle.

2. On $\overrightarrow{LM}$, construct segment $\overline{LR}$ so that $LR = a$ and construct segment $\overline{RS}$ so that $RS = b$.

3. On $\overrightarrow{LN}$, construct segment $\overline{LT}$ so that $LT = c$.

4. Construct $\overleftrightarrow{RT}$.

5. Through *S*, construct $\overleftrightarrow{SW}$ parallel to $\overleftrightarrow{RT}$.

6. $\overline{TW}$ is the required line segment of length *x*.

Plan for Proof: The construction makes $\overleftrightarrow{SW}$ parallel to $\overleftrightarrow{RT}$. Therefore, *a*:*b* = *c*:*x* because a line parallel to one side of a triangle and intersecting the other two sides divides the other two sides proportionally.

Construction 24

To divide a given line segment into parts proportional to given line segments.

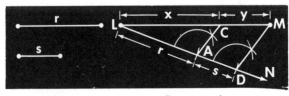

| Given | Construction |

Given: Line segment $\overline{LM}$ and line segments of lengths *r* and *s*.

Required: To divide $\overline{LM}$ into segments of lengths *x* and *y* proportional to *r* and *s*. (*x*:*y* = *r*:*s*)

[The construction is given on the next page.]

Construction:

1. Construct $\overleftrightarrow{LN}$ making any convenient angle *MLN*.

2. On $\overleftrightarrow{LN}$, construct $\overline{LA}$ so that *LA* = *r* and construct $\overline{AD}$ so that *AD* = *s*.

3. Construct $\overleftrightarrow{DM}$.

4. Through *A*, construct $\overleftrightarrow{AC}$ parallel to $\overleftrightarrow{DM}$.

5. $\overline{LC}$ and $\overline{CM}$ are the required segments of lengths *x* and *y*.

Plan for Proof: The construction makes $\overleftrightarrow{AC}$ parallel to $\overleftrightarrow{DM}$. Therefore, *x:y* = *r:s* because a line parallel to one side of a triangle and intersecting the other two sides divides the other two sides proportionally.

★Construction 25

To construct a triangle similar to a given triangle on a given line segment as a base.

Given: △*ABC* and line segment $\overline{RS}$.

Required: On line segment $\overline{RS}$, corresponding to side $\overline{AB}$ of △*ABC*, to construct a triangle similar to △*ABC*.

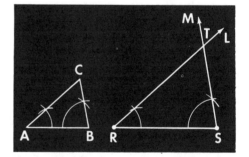

Construction:

1. At *R*, construct ∠*SRL* congruent to ∠*BAC*.

2. At *S*, construct ∠*RSM* congruent to ∠*ABC*.

3. Represent by *T* the point of intersection of rays $\overrightarrow{RL}$ and $\overrightarrow{SM}$.

4. The required triangle is △*RST*.

Plan for Proof: The construction makes ∠*R* ≅ ∠*A* and ∠*S* ≅ ∠*B*. Therefore, △*RST* ~ △*ABC* because two triangles are similar if two angles of one triangle are congruent respectively to two angles of the other triangle.

Construction 26

To construct the mean proportional between two given line segments.

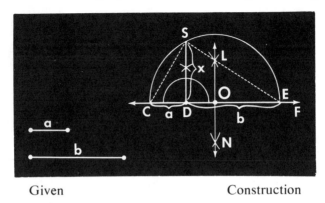

| Given | Construction |

Given: Line segments of lengths *a* and *b*.

Required: To construct a line segment of length *x* so that $a:x = x:b$.

Construction:

1. Construct line $\overleftrightarrow{CF}$. On line $\overleftrightarrow{CF}$, construct segment $\overline{CD}$ so that $CD = a$ and construct segment $\overline{DE}$ so that $DE = b$.

2. Construct $\overleftrightarrow{LN}$, the perpendicular bisector of line segment $\overline{CE}$, to find O, the midpoint of $\overline{CE}$.

3. Using O as a center and a radius whose length is OC, construct a semicircle whose diameter is $\overline{CE}$.

4. At D, the common endpoint of the segment whose length is *a* and the segment whose length is *b*, construct $\overleftrightarrow{DS}$ perpendicular to $\overleftrightarrow{CE}$, intersecting the semicircle at S.

5. $\overline{DS}$ is the required segment whose length is *x*, which is the mean proportional between the segments whose lengths are *a* and *b*; that is, $a:x = x:b$.

Plan for Proof: If line segments $\overline{CS}$ and $\overline{SE}$ are drawn, $\angle CSE$ is a right angle because an angle inscribed in a semicircle is a right angle. Since $\overline{SD}$ is perpendicular to $\overline{CE}$, $a:x = x:b$, because the length of the altitude drawn to the hypotenuse of a right triangle is the mean proportional between the lengths of the segments of the hypotenuse.

*Construction 27

To inscribe a square in a given circle.

Given: Circle O.

Required: To inscribe a square in circle O.

Construction:

1. Construct any diameter, $\overline{AC}$, in circle O.

2. At O, construct diameter $\overline{BD}$ perpendicular to diameter $\overline{AC}$.

3. Construct $\overline{AB}$, $\overline{BC}$, $\overline{CD}$, and $\overline{DA}$.

4. $ABCD$ is the required square.

Plan for Proof: Since central angles AOB, BOC, COD, and DOA are right angles, they are congruent. Hence, $\widehat{AB} \cong \widehat{BC} \cong \widehat{CD} \cong \widehat{DA}$. Therefore, $ABCD$ is a square because if a circle is divided into any number of congruent arcs, the chords of these arcs form a regular inscribed polygon.

*Construction 28

To inscribe a regular hexagon in a given circle.

Given: Circle O.

Required: To inscribe a regular hexagon in circle O.

Construction:

1. Construct any radius, $\overline{OA}$.

2. Using A as a center and a radius of length OA, construct an arc which intersects the circle at B.

3. Similarly, using B as a center and a radius of length OA, construct an arc which intersects the circle at C. In like manner, obtain points D, E, and F on the circle.

4. Draw $\overline{AB}$, $\overline{BC}$, $\overline{CD}$, $\overline{DE}$, $\overline{EF}$, and $\overline{FA}$.

5. $ABCDEF$ is the required regular hexagon.

Plan for Proof: If $\overline{OB}$ is drawn, the construction makes $\overline{AB} \cong \overline{OA} \cong \overline{OB}$. Since $\triangle AOB$ is an equilateral triangle, $m\angle AOB = 60$. Also, $m\widehat{AB} = 60$. The circle has been divided into 6 congruent arcs. Therefore, $ABCDEF$ is a regular hexagon because if a circle is divided into any number of congruent arcs, the chords of these arcs form a regular inscribed polygon.

⋆Construction 29

To inscribe an equilateral triangle in a given circle.

Given: Circle O.

Required: To inscribe an equilateral triangle in circle O.

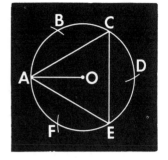

Construction:

1. Construct any radius $\overline{OA}$.

2. Using A as a center and a radius of length OA, construct an arc which intersects the circle at B.

3. Similarly, using B as a center and a radius of length OA, construct an arc which intersects the circle at C. In like manner, obtain points D, E, and F on the circle.

4. Construct $\overline{AC}$, $\overline{CE}$, and $\overline{EA}$, joining alternate points A, C, and E.

5. $\triangle ACE$ is the required equilateral triangle.

Plan for Proof: The construction makes $\overset{\frown}{AC} \cong \overset{\frown}{CE} \cong \overset{\frown}{EA}$. Therefore, $\triangle ACE$ is the required equilateral triangle because if a circle is divided into any number of congruent arcs, the chords of these arcs form a regular inscribed polygon.

Construction 30

To circumscribe a square about a given circle.

Given: Circle O.

Required: To   circumscribe   a   square about circle O.

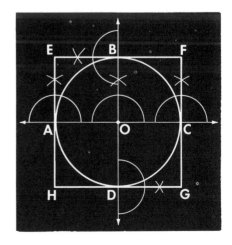

Construction:

1. Draw diameter $\overline{AC}$ in circle O.

2. At O, construct diameter $\overline{BD}$ perpendicular to diameter $\overline{AC}$.

3. At points A, B, C, and D, construct tangents to circle O which intersect at points E, F, G, and H.

4. $EFGH$ is the required square.

Plan for Proof: Since central angles *AOB*, *COB*, *DOC*, and *DOA* are right angles, they are congruent. Hence, $\overarc{AB} \cong \overarc{BC} \cong \overarc{CD} \cong \overarc{DA}$. Therefore, *EFGH* is a square circumscribed about circle *O* because if a circle is divided into any number of congruent arcs, the tangents drawn to the circle at the successive points of division form a regular circumscribed polygon.

Construction 31

To construct an isosceles triangle which has the same base as a given scalene triangle and which is equal in area to it.

Given: Scalene △*ABC* with base $\overline{AB}$.

Required: To construct an isosceles triangle whose base is $\overline{AB}$ and whose area is equal to the area of triangle *ABC*.

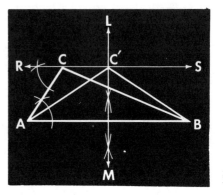

Construction:

1. Through vertex *C*, construct $\overleftrightarrow{RS}$ parallel to $\overline{AB}$.

2. Construct $\overleftrightarrow{LM}$, the perpendicular bisector of base $\overline{AB}$.

3. $\overleftrightarrow{RS}$ and $\overleftrightarrow{LM}$ intersect at *C'*.

4. Construct $\overline{AC'}$ and $\overline{BC'}$. Triangle *ABC'* is the required triangle.

Plan for Proof: Since $\overleftrightarrow{LM}$ is the perpendicular bisector of $\overline{AB}$, then $\overline{C'A} \cong \overline{C'B}$ because any point on the perpendicular bisector of a line segment is equally distant from the ends of the line segment. The construction makes $\overleftrightarrow{RS} \parallel \overleftrightarrow{AB}$. Therefore, △*ABC'* is equal in area to △*ABC* because the two triangles have a common base, $\overline{AB}$, and their vertices *C'* and *C* lie on a line parallel to the common base. Therefore, △*ABC'* is the required isosceles triangle.

Construction 32

To construct a triangle equal in area to a given pentagon.

Given: Pentagon $ABCDE$.

Required: To construct a triangle equal in area
                to pentagon $ABCDE$.

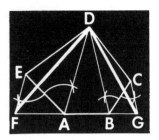

Construction:

1. Extend $\overline{AB}$ both to the right and to the left.

2. Construct diagonal $\overline{DB}$.

3. Through vertex C, construct $\overleftrightarrow{CG}$ parallel
   to $\overline{DB}$. $\overleftrightarrow{CG}$ intersects $\overline{AB}$ extended at G.

4. Construct $\overline{DG}$.

5. Construct diagonal $\overline{DA}$.

6. Through vertex E, construct $\overleftrightarrow{EF}$ parallel to $\overline{DA}$. $\overleftrightarrow{EF}$ intersects $\overline{BA}$ extended at F.

7. Construct $\overline{DF}$.

8. $\triangle FDG$ is the required triangle, which is equal in area to pentagon
   $ABCDE$.

Plan for Proof: The construction makes $\overleftrightarrow{EF} \parallel \overline{DA}$. Therefore, the area of
$\triangle AFD =$ the area of $\triangle AED$ because the two triangles have a common
base, $\overline{DA}$, and their vertices F and E lie on a line parallel to the base.
Similarly, since $\overleftrightarrow{CG} \parallel \overline{DB}$, the area of $\triangle BGD =$ the area of $\triangle BCD$. The
area of $\triangle ABD =$ the area of $\triangle ABD$ by the reflexive property of equality.
Therefore, the area of $\triangle AFD +$ the area of $\triangle ABD +$ the area of $\triangle BGD =$
the area of $\triangle AED +$ the area of $\triangle ABD +$ the area of $\triangle BCD$. Or, the area
of triangle $FDG =$ the area of pentagon $ABCDE$.

Construction 33

**To construct a rectangle that has a given base and is equal in area to a
given parallelogram.**

[The construction is given on the next page.]

Given   Analysis

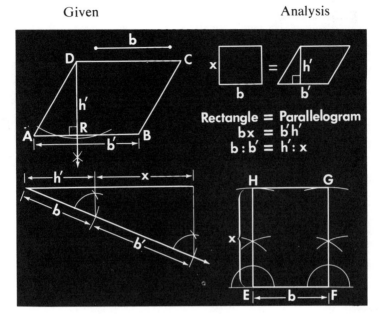

Construction

Given: $\square ABCD$ with base $\overline{AB}$ of length b' and altitude $\overline{DR}$ of length h'; b is the length of the base of the rectangle to be constructed.

Required: To construct a rectangle the length of whose base is b and whose area is equal to the area of $\square ABCD$.

Construction:

1. Construct $\overline{DR}$, the altitude of $\square ABCD$, whose length is represented by h'. (See the construction in the diagram of the given parallelogram.)

2. Construct the fourth proportional to b, b', and h' ($b:b' = h':x$).

3. The segment whose length is x is congruent to the altitude of the required rectangle.

4. Construct a rectangle $EFGH$ whose base is of length b and whose altitude is of length x.

5. $EFGH$ is the required rectangle, whose base is a segment of length b and whose area is equal to the area of $\square ABCD$.

Plan for Proof: Since the construction makes x the fourth proportional to b, b', and h', then $b:b' = h':x$ and $bx = b'h'$. Since the area of $\square ABCD = b'h'$ and the area of rectangle $EFGH = bx$, the area of rectangle $EFGH$ is equal to the area of $\square ABCD$.

Construction 34

To construct a square equal in area to a given triangle.

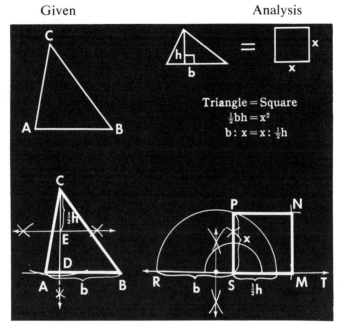

Given   Analysis

Triangle = Square
$\frac{1}{2}bh = x^2$
$b : x = x : \frac{1}{2}h$

Construction

Given: $\triangle ABC$.

Required: To construct a square equal in area to $\triangle ABC$.

Construction:

1. Construct altitude $\overline{CD}$ in $\triangle ABC$.

2. Bisect altitude $\overline{CD}$, whose length is h, so that $CE = \frac{1}{2}h$.

3. On work line $\overleftrightarrow{RT}$, construct x, the mean proportional between b and $\frac{1}{2}h$.

4. $\overline{SP}$, whose length is x, is the side of the required square.

5. On $\overleftrightarrow{ST}$, construct $\overline{SM}$ whose length is x. Using M and P as centers and a radius of length x, construct two arcs which intersect at N.

6. $SMNP$ is the required square, which is equal in area to $\triangle ABC$.

Plan for Proof: Since the construction makes x the mean proportional between b and $\frac{1}{2}h$, $b:x = x:\frac{1}{2}h$, or $x^2 = \frac{1}{2}bh$. Since the area of $\triangle ABC = \frac{1}{2}bh$ and the area of square $SMNP = x^2$, the area of square $SMNP$ is equal to the area of $\triangle ABC$.

CHAPTER XV

Summary of Methods of Proof

1. Proving Triangles Congruent

1. Two triangles are congruent if:
   a. two sides and the included angle of one triangle are congruent respectively to two sides and the included angle of the other. [s.a.s. $\cong$ s.a.s.]
   b. two angles and the included side of one triangle are congruent respectively to two angles and the included side of the other. [a.s.a. $\cong$ a.s.a.]
   c. the three sides of one triangle are congruent respectively to the three sides of the other. [s.s.s. $\cong$ s.s.s.]
   d. two angles and a side opposite one of them of one triangle are congruent to the two corresponding angles and the corresponding side of the other. [a.a.s. $\cong$ a.a.s.]
   e. they are congruent to a third triangle.
2. Two right triangles are congruent if:
   a. the hypotenuse and a leg of one triangle are congruent to the hypotenuse and a leg of the other. [hy. leg $\cong$ hy. leg]
   b. a side and an acute angle of one triangle are congruent respectively to a side and an acute angle of the other triangle.
   c. the legs of one right triangle are congruent to the legs of the other right triangle.
3. A diagonal divides a parallelogram into two congruent triangles.

2. Proving Line Segments Congruent

1. Line segments are congruent if they are congruent to the same line segment.
2. Line segments are congruent if they are congruent to congruent line segments.
3. Halves of congruent line segments are congruent.

640

4. Doubles of congruent line segments are congruent.
5. Corresponding sides of congruent polygons are congruent.
6. Legs of an isosceles triangle are congruent.
7. Sides opposite congruent angles in a triangle are congruent.
8. An equiangular triangle is equilateral.
9. Legs of an isosceles trapezoid are congruent.
10. Any point on the perpendicular bisector of a line segment is equidistant from the ends of the line segment.
11. Any point on the bisector of an angle is equidistant from the sides of the angle.
12. Segments of parallel lines cut off between parallel lines are congruent.
13. Segments of lines perpendicular to two parallel lines and intercepted between them are congruent.
14. If three or more parallel lines intercept congruent segments on one transversal, then they intercept congruent segments on any transversal.
15. If a line is parallel to one side of a triangle and bisects a second side, the line bisects the third side also.
16. The opposite sides of a parallelogram are congruent.
17. The diagonals of a parallelogram bisect each other.
18. In a circle or in congruent circles, radii or diameters are congruent.
19. In a circle or in congruent circles, congruent arcs have congruent chords.
20. In a circle or in congruent circles, chords equidistant from the center are congruent.
21. In a circle, a diameter perpendicular to a chord bisects the chord.
22. The tangents to a circle from an external point are congruent.
23. The midpoint of the hypotenuse of a right triangle is equidistant from all the vertices of the triangle.
24. Sides of an equilateral or regular polygon are congruent.
25. Radii of a regular polygon are congruent.
26. Apothems of a regular polygon are congruent.

3. Proving Angles Congruent

1. Angles are congruent if they are congruent to the same angle.
2. Angles are congruent if they are congruent to congruent angles.
3. Halves of congruent angles are congruent.
4. Doubles of congruent angles are congruent.
5. Corresponding angles of congruent polygons are congruent.
6. All right angles are congruent.
7. If two angles are vertical angles, they are congruent.
8. Complements of the same angle or congruent angles are congruent.

9. Supplements of the same angle or congruent angles are congruent.
10. Angles opposite congruent sides of a triangle are congruent.
11. An equilateral triangle is equiangular.
12. If two parallel lines are cut by a transversal, then the alternate interior angles are congruent.
13. If two parallel lines are cut by a transversal, then the corresponding angles are congruent.
14. If two angles of one triangle are congruent respectively to two angles of another triangle, then the third angles are congruent.
15. The opposite angles of a parallelogram are congruent.
16. The base angles of an isosceles triangle are congruent.
17. In a circle or in congruent circles, congruent arcs have congruent central angles.
18. In a circle or in congruent circles, if inscribed angles intercept the same arc or congruent arcs, then the inscribed angles are congruent.
19. In a circle, angles inscribed in the same arc are congruent.
20. Angles which have equal measures are congruent.
21. In similar polygons, corresponding angles are congruent.
22. Angles of an equiangular or regular polygon are congruent.

4. Proving a Triangle Isosceles

A triangle is an isosceles triangle if:
   a. two sides are congruent.
   b. two angles are congruent.

5. Proving Angles Complementary

Two angles are complementary if:
   a. the sum of their measures is 90.
   b. they are adjacent angles and their non-common sides are perpendicular to each other.
   c. they are the acute angles of a right triangle.

6. Proving Angles Supplementary

Two angles are supplementary if:
   a. the sum of their measures is 180.
   b. they are adjacent angles and their non-common sides are rays on the same straight line.

c. they are interior angles on the same side of a transversal which intersects two parallel lines.

d. they are exterior angles on the same side of a transversal which intersects two parallel lines.

e. they are consecutive angles of a parallelogram.

f. they are opposite angles in a quadrilateral which is inscribed in a circle.

7. Proving Lines Parallel

1. Two lines are parallel if the lines are cut by a transversal making:
    a. a pair of alternate interior angles congruent.
    b. a pair of corresponding angles congruent.
    c. a pair of interior angles on the same side of the transversal supplementary.
    d. a pair of exterior angles on the same side of the transversal supplementary.
2. Two lines parallel to the same line are parallel.
3. Two lines perpendicular to the same line are parallel.
4. The opposite sides of a parallelogram are parallel.
5. A line segment which joins the midpoints of two sides of a triangle is parallel to the third side.
6. A line which divides two sides of a triangle proportionally is parallel to the third side.
7. The median of a trapezoid is parallel to the bases.
8. Two lines are parallel if their slopes are equal or if they have no slopes.

8. Proving Lines Perpendicular

1. Two lines are perpendicular if they intersect, forming right angles.
2. Two lines are perpendicular if they intersect, forming congruent adjacent angles.
3. A line determined by two points each equidistant from the ends of a line segment is the perpendicular bisector of the line segment.
4. The diagonals of a rhombus are perpendicular to each other.
5. A line perpendicular to one of two parallel lines is perpendicular to the other.
6. An angle inscribed in a semicircle is a right angle whose sides are perpendicular to each other.
7. A tangent to a circle is perpendicular to a radius drawn to the point of contact.

8. In a circle, if a radius bisects a chord which is not a diameter, the radius is perpendicular to the chord.
9. If two circles intersect in two points, their line of centers is the perpendicular bisector of their common chord.
10. Two lines are perpendicular if the slope of one is the negative reciprocal of the slope of the other, or if one line has no slope and the slope of the other line is zero.

9. Proving a Quadrilateral a Parallelogram

A quadrilateral is a parallelogram if:
   a. both pairs of opposite sides are parallel.
   b. both pairs of opposite sides are congruent.
   c. two opposite sides are both congruent and parallel.
   d. the diagonals bisect each other.
   e. both pairs of opposite angles are congruent.

10. Proving a Quadrilateral a Rectangle

A quadrilateral is a rectangle if it is:
   a. equiangular.
   b. a parallelogram that contains one right angle.
   c. a parallelogram whose diagonals are congruent.

11. Proving a Quadrilateral a Rhombus

A quadrilateral is a rhombus if:
   a. it is equilateral.
   b. it is a parallelogram which has two congruent consecutive sides.
   c. its diagonals bisect each other at right angles.
   d. it is a parallelogram, and a diagonal bisects the angles whose vertices it joins.

12. Proving a Quadrilateral a Square

A quadrilateral is a square if it is:
   a. a rectangle which has two congruent consecutive sides.
   b. a rhombus which contains a right angle.

13. Proving Arcs Congruent

1. In a circle or in congruent circles, arcs are congruent if:
   a. they have congruent central angles.
   b. they have congruent chords.
   c. they are intercepted by congruent inscribed angles.
2. Parallel lines which intersect a circle intercept congruent arcs on the circle.
3. A diameter divides a circle into two congruent arcs.
4. A line which passes through the center of a circle and which is perpendicular to a chord bisects the arcs of the chord.

14. Proving Chords Congruent

In a circle or in congruent circles, chords are congruent if:
   a. they have congruent arcs.
   b. they are equidistant from the center.

15. Proving Triangles Similar

1. Two triangles are similar if:
   a. two angles of one triangle are congruent respectively to two angles of the other. [a.a. $\cong$ a.a.]
   b. an angle of one triangle is congruent to an angle of the other and the including sides are in proportion.
   c. their sides are respectively proportional.
   d. they are similar to the same triangle.
   e. one triangle is cut off by a line parallel to a side of the other.
   f. they are congruent triangles.
2. Two right triangles are similar if an acute angle of one triangle is congruent to an acute angle of the other.
3. If the altitude is drawn to the hypotenuse of a right triangle, the two triangles thus formed are similar to the given triangle and similar to each other.

16. Proving Line Segments in Proportion

1. In similar polygons, corresponding sides are in proportion.
2. A line parallel to one side of a triangle and intersecting the other two sides divides those sides proportionally.
3. Parallel lines intercept proportional segments on any two transversals.

4. If the altitude is drawn to the hypotenuse of a right triangle:
   a. the length of the altitude is the mean proportional between the lengths of the segments of the hypotenuse.
   b. the length of each leg is the mean proportional between the length of the whole hypotenuse and the length of the projection of that leg on the hypotenuse.
5. If from a point outside a circle a tangent and a secant are drawn to the circle, the length of the tangent is the mean proportional between the length of the secant and the length of its external segment.
6. In similar polygons, the ratio of the lengths of two corresponding sides is equal to the ratio of the lengths of any two corresponding line segments.

17. Proving Triangles Equal in Area (Equivalent)

1. Two triangles are equal in area if:
   a. they are congruent triangles.
   b. they have bases of equal length and altitudes of equal length.
   c. they have a common base and their vertices lie on a line parallel to the base.
2. A median drawn to a side of a triangle divides the triangle into two triangles equal in area.
3. A diagonal of a parallelogram divides the parallelogram into two triangles equal in area.

18. Proving Polygons Regular

1. A polygon is a regular polygon if:
   a. it is both equilateral and equiangular.
   b. it is an equilateral polygon inscribed in a circle.
2. If a circle is divided into three or more congruent arcs, the chords of these arcs form a regular inscribed polygon and the tangents at the points of division form a regular circumscribed polygon.

19. Proving Line Segments Unequal in Length

1. The length of a whole line segment is greater than the length of any of its parts.

2. The length of a line segment joining two given points is shorter than the length of any other path between the two points.
3. The sum of the lengths of two sides of a triangle is greater than the length of the third side.
4. If the measures of two angles of a triangle are unequal, the sides opposite these angles are unequal in length and the greater side lies opposite the greater angle.
5. The shortest line segment that can be drawn from a given point to a given line is the perpendicular from the point to the line.
6. If the first of three line segments is greater in length than the second and the second is greater in length than the third, then the first is greater in length than the third.
7. In the same circle or in congruent circles, the greater of two unequal minor arcs has the greater chord.
8. In the same circle or in congruent circles, the greater of two chords is nearer the center.
9. A diameter of a circle is longer than any chord which is not a diameter.

20. Proving Angles Unequal in Measure

1. The measure of an exterior angle of a triangle is greater than the measure of either nonadjacent interior angle.
2. If two sides of a triangle are unequal in length, the measures of the angles opposite these sides are unequal and the greater angle lies opposite the greater side.
3. If the measure of the first of three angles is greater than the measure of the second and the measure of the second is greater than the measure of the third, then the measure of the first is greater than the measure of the third.

CHAPTER XVI

Summary of Formulas and Numerical Relationships

1. Angle Relationships

1. The number of degrees contained in the supplement of an angle whose measure is a is represented by $(180 - a)$.
2. The number of degrees contained in the complement of an acute angle whose measure is a is represented by $(90 - a)$.
3. In a triangle ABC, $m\angle A + m\angle B + m\angle C = 180$.
4. The sum of the measures of the interior angles of a polygon of n sides is represented by $(n - 2)$ straight angles, or $180(n - 2)$ degrees.
5. The measure of each interior angle of an equiangular or regular polygon of n sides is represented by $\dfrac{180(n - 2)}{n}$ degrees.
6. The sum of the measures of the exterior angles of a polygon of n sides, taking one angle at each vertex, is 360 degrees.
7. The measure of each exterior angle of an equiangular or regular polygon of n sides is represented by $\dfrac{360}{n}$ degrees.

2. Midpoint Relationships

1. The length of a line segment which joins the midpoints of two sides of a triangle is equal to one-half the length of the third side.
2. The length of the median of a trapezoid $= \frac{1}{2}(b + b')$, where b and b' represent the lengths of the bases.
3. The medians of a triangle meet in a point whose distance from any vertex is two-thirds the distance from that vertex to the midpoint of the opposite side.
4. The length of the median drawn to the hypotenuse of a right triangle is equal to one-half the length of the hypotenuse.

3. Angle Measurement Relationships

1. In a circle, the measure of a central angle is equal to the measure of its intercepted arc.
2. In a circle, the measure of an inscribed angle is equal to one-half the measure of its intercepted arc.
3. In a circle, an angle inscribed in a semicircle is a right angle.
4. In a circle, the opposite angles of an inscribed quadrilateral are supplementary.
5. The measure of an angle formed by a tangent and a chord drawn at the point of contact is equal to one-half the measure of the intercepted arc.
6. The measure of an angle formed by two chords intersecting in the interior of a circle is equal to one-half the sum of the measures of the intercepted arcs.
7. The measure of an angle formed by two secants, a secant and a tangent, or two tangents drawn to a circle from an outside point is equal to one-half the difference of the measures of the intercepted arcs.

4. Proportion and Product Relationships

1. A line parallel to one side of a triangle divides the other two sides proportionally.
2. In similar triangles, corresponding altitudes of lengths h and h' have the same ratio as s and s', the lengths of any pair of corresponding sides. $h:h' = s:s'$.
3. In similar polygons, perimeters p and p' have the same ratio as s and s', the lengths of any pair of corresponding sides. $p:p' = s:s'$.
4. If the altitude is drawn to the hypotenuse of a right triangle:
   a. the length of the altitude is the mean proportional between the lengths of the segments of the hypotenuse.
   b. the length of each leg is the mean proportional between the length of the whole hypotenuse and the length of the projection of that leg on the hypotenuse.
5. If two chords intersect within a circle, the product of the lengths of the segments of one chord is equal to the product of the lengths of the segments of the other chord.
6. If from a point outside a circle a tangent and a secant are drawn to the circle, the length of the tangent is the mean proportional between the length of the secant and the length of its external segment.
7. If from a point outside a circle two secants are drawn, the product of the length of one secant and the length of its external segment equals the product of the length of the other secant and the length of its external segment.

5. Right Triangle Relationships

1. In a right triangle, $(\text{leg})^2 + (\text{leg})^2 = (\text{hypotenuse})^2$, or $a^2 + b^2 = c^2$, when a and b are the lengths of the legs and c is the length of the hypotenuse of the triangle.
2. In a 30°–60° right triangle:
    a. the length of the leg opposite the 30° angle equals one-half the length of the hypotenuse, h, or $\frac{1}{2}h$.
    b. the length of the leg opposite the 60° angle equals one-half the length of the hypotenuse, h, times $\sqrt{3}$, or $\frac{1}{2}h\sqrt{3}$.
    c. the ratio of the length of the shorter leg to the length of the hypotenuse is 1:2.
    d. the length of the larger leg equals the length of the shorter leg times $\sqrt{3}$.
3. In an equilateral triangle, the length of an altitude is equal to one-half the length of the side, s, times $\sqrt{3}$, or $\frac{1}{2}s\sqrt{3}$.
4. In a 45°–45° right triangle:
    a. the length of the hypotenuse is equal to the length of a leg, L, times $\sqrt{2}$, or $L\sqrt{2}$.
    b. the length of a leg is equal to one-half the length of the hypotenuse, h, times $\sqrt{2}$, or $\frac{1}{2}h\sqrt{2}$.
5. In a square:
    a. the length of a diagonal is equal to the length of a side, s, times $\sqrt{2}$, or $s\sqrt{2}$.
    b. the length of a side is equal to one-half the length of a diagonal, d, times $\sqrt{2}$, or $\frac{1}{2}d\sqrt{2}$.

6. Trigonometric Relationships

In rt. $\triangle ABC$:

a. $\sin A = \dfrac{\text{length of leg opposite } \angle A}{\text{length of hypotenuse}} = \dfrac{a}{c}$.

b. $\cos A = \dfrac{\text{length of leg adjacent to } \angle A}{\text{length of hypotenuse}} = \dfrac{b}{c}$.

c. $\tan A = \dfrac{\text{length of leg opposite } \angle A}{\text{length of leg adjacent to } \angle A} = \dfrac{a}{b}$.

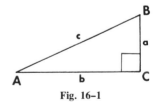

Fig. 16–1

7. Area Relationships

1. Area of a rectangle $= bh$, when b is the length of the base and h is the length of the altitude of the rectangle.

2. Area of a square $= s^2$, when s is the length of a side of the square.
3. Area of a parallelogram $= bh$, when b is the length of a base and h is the length of the altitude drawn to that base of the parallelogram.
4. Area of a parallelogram $= ab \sin C$, when a and b are the lengths of two consecutive sides of the parallelogram and C is the measure of the included angle.
5. Area of a triangle $= \frac{1}{2}bh$, when b is the length of a side of the triangle and h is the length of the altitude drawn to that side.
6. Area of a triangle $= \frac{1}{2}ab \sin C$, when a and b are the lengths of two consecutive sides of the triangle and C is the measure of the included angle.
7. Area of a right triangle $= \frac{1}{2}ab$, when a and b are the lengths of the legs of the right triangle.
8. Area of a triangle $= \sqrt{s(s-a)(s-b)(s-c)}$, when a, b, and c are the lengths of the sides of the triangle and s is $\frac{1}{2}(a+b+c)$, the semiperimeter of the triangle.
9. Area of an equilateral triangle $= \frac{s^2}{4}\sqrt{3}$, when s is the length of a side of the triangle.
10. Area of a trapezoid $= \frac{1}{2}h(b + b')$, when b and b' are the lengths of the bases and h is the length of the altitude of the trapezoid.
11. Area of a rhombus $= \frac{1}{2}d_1d_2$, when d_1 and d_2 are the lengths of the diagonals of the rhombus.
12. Area of a regular polygon $= \frac{1}{2}ap$, when a is the length of an apothem and p is the perimeter of the polygon.
13. The ratio of the areas A and A' of two similar triangles is equal to the ratio of the squares of the measures of any two corresponding line segments, l and l'. $A:A' = (l)^2:(l')^2$.

8. Polygon Relationships

1. The degree measure of each central angle of a regular polygon of n sides is represented by $\frac{360}{n}$.
2. The ratio of the perimeters p and p' of two similar polygons is equal to the ratio of the measures of any pair of corresponding sides s and s'. That is, $p:p' = s:s'$.
3. The ratio of the perimeters p and p' of regular polygons of the same number of sides is equal to the ratio of their sides s and s', their radii r and r', and their apothems a and a'. $p:p' = s:s'$, $p:p' = r:r'$, and $p:p' = a:a'$.
4. The ratio of the areas A and A' of two similar polygons is equal to the ratio of the squares of the measures of any two corresponding sides s and s'. $A:A' = (s)^2:(s')^2$.

9. Circle Relationships

1. The ratio of the circumferences C and C' of two circles is equal to the ratio of their radii r and r' and their diameters d and d'. $C:C' = r:r'$ and $C:C' = d:d'$.

2. In a circle, $\dfrac{C}{d} = \pi$, when C represents the circumference of the circle and d represents the length of its diameter.

3. Circumference of a circle $= \pi d$ or $2\pi r$, when d represents the length of a diameter and r represents the length of a radius of the circle.

4. Length of an arc $= \dfrac{n}{360} \times 2\pi r$, or $\dfrac{\text{length of an arc}}{\text{circumference}} = \dfrac{n}{360}$, when n represents the number of degrees contained in the arc or its central angle and r represents the length of a radius of the circle.

5. Area of a circle $= \pi r^2$, or $\frac{1}{4}\pi d^2$, when r represents the length of a radius and d represents the length of a diameter of the circle.

6. Area of a sector $= \dfrac{n}{360} \times \pi r^2$, or $\dfrac{\text{area of a sector}}{\text{area of a circle}} = \dfrac{n}{360}$, when n represents the number of degrees contained in the central angle or intercepted arc of the sector and r represents the length of a radius of the circle.

7. Area of a minor segment $=$ area of sector $-$ area of triangle.

8. In an equilateral triangle, the length of a radius, R, of the circumscribed circle is equal to two-thirds of h, the length of an altitude. $R = \frac{2}{3}h$.

9. In an equilateral triangle, the length of a radius, r, of the inscribed circle is equal to one-third of h, the length of an altitude. $r = \frac{1}{3}h$.

10. Coordinate Geometry Relationships

1. The coordinates of the midpoint $M(x_m, y_m)$ of the line segment which joins the points (x_1, y_1) and (x_2, y_2) are $x_m = \frac{1}{2}(x_1 + x_2)$ and $y_m = \frac{1}{2}(y_1 + y_2)$.

2. The distance, d, between two points (x_1, y_1) and (x_2, y_2) is given by the formula $d = \sqrt{(x_2 - x_1)^2 + (y_2 - y_1)^2}$.

3. An equation of a circle the length of whose radius is r and whose center is at the origin is $x^2 + y^2 = r^2$.

4. The slope, m, of a line passing through the points (x_1, y_1) and (x_2, y_2) as well as the slope of the line segment whose endpoints are these points, is given by the formula $m = \dfrac{y_2 - y_1}{x_2 - x_1}$ $(x_1 \neq x_2)$, or $m = \dfrac{\Delta y}{\Delta x}$.

5. If two lines are parallel, m_1, the slope of the first line, is equal to m_2, the slope of the second line $(m_1 = m_2)$ or both lines have no slope.

6. If two lines are perpendicular, then m_1, the slope of the first line, is the negative reciprocal of m_2, the slope of the second line $\left(m_1 = -\dfrac{1}{m_2}\right.$, or $m_1 m_2 = -1)$ or one line has no slope and the slope of the other line is zero.

7. An equation of a line parallel to the y-axis is $x = a$, when a is the abscissa of every point on the line.

8. An equation of a line parallel to the x-axis is $y = b$, when b is the ordinate of every point on the line.

9. An equation of a line whose slope is m and whose y-intercept is b is $y = mx + b$.

10. An equation of a line which passes through the point (x_1, y_1) and whose slope is m is $m(x - x_1) = y - y_1$.

CHAPTER XVII

Solid Geometry

In plane geometry, we study plane geometric figures which consist of points and lines lying in the same plane. In *solid geometry,* or *space geometry,* we study *solid figures,* or *space figures,* which consist of points and lines not all of which lie in the same plane.

We know that: In a plane, a figure such as a point has no dimensions. A figure such as a line has one dimension, length. And a figure such as a square has two dimensions, length and width.

In space, a figure may have three dimensions. For example, the cube shown in Fig. 17–1 has length, width, and height.

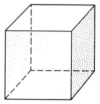

In solid geometry, we will study geometric figures in three-dimensional space. We will make use of the definitions, postulates, and theorems of plane geometry. Also, we will define new terms, accept additional postulates, and develop more theorems.

Fig. 17–1

1. Points, Lines, and Planes

A *plane,* which we have accepted as an undefined term, may be considered as a set of points that form a completely flat surface extending indefinitely in all directions. The top of a flat table is an example of a plane surface.

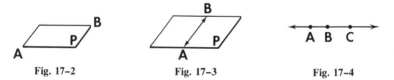

| Fig. 17–2 | Fig. 17–3 | Fig. 17–4 |

To represent a plane, we may use a quadrilateral or a parallelogram. The plane represented in Fig. 17–2 may be named "plane *P*" or "plane *AB*."

Definition. **A straight line in a plane separates the points of the plane which are not in the line into two regions each of which is called a *half-plane*.**

In Fig. 17–3, line $\overleftrightarrow{AB}$ divides plane P into two half-planes. $\overleftrightarrow{AB}$ is called the *edge* of each half-plane.

Definition. **Collinear points** **are a set of points all of which lie on the same straight line.**

In Fig. 17–4, points A, B, and C are collinear points, since they all lie on the same straight line $\overleftrightarrow{AC}$.

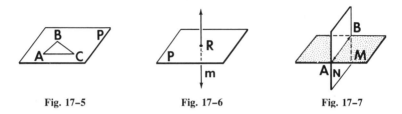

| Fig. 17–5 | Fig. 17–6 | Fig. 17–7 |

Definition. **Coplanar points** **are a set of points all of which lie in the same plane.**

In Fig. 17–5, points A, B, and C are coplanar points, since they all lie in the same plane P.

Definition. **The** *intersection of a line and a plane* **is the set of points that lie both on the line and in the plane.**

In Fig. 17–6, the intersection of line m and plane P is point R, the point that lies on line m and also lies in plane P. In drawing the figure, we represent the part of line m which cannot be seen by a broken line.

Definition. **The** *intersection of two planes* **is the set of points that lie in both planes.**

In Fig. 17–7, the intersection of plane M and plane N is the set of points that lie both in plane M and in plane N, that is, the set of points in line $\overleftrightarrow{AB}$. In drawing the figure, we represent the lines which cannot be seen by broken lines.

In order to learn how to visualize the relationships between lines and planes and to draw proper conclusions from these relationships, it is helpful to use pencils to represent lines and pieces of cardboard to represent planes.

EXERCISES

In 1–8, tell whether the object or figure is one-dimensional, two-dimensional, or three-dimensional.

1. line   **2.** triangle   **3.** rectangle   **4.** box

5. circle   **6.** tennis ball   **7.** rhombus   **8.** fishing rod

9. Draw two points A and B which are collinear.

10. Is it possible to draw two points which are not collinear? Why?
11. Draw three points A, B, and C which are collinear.
12. Draw three points D, E, and F which are not collinear.
13. Draw three points R, S, and T which are coplanar.
14. Is it possible to draw three points which are not coplanar?
15. Draw three points A, B, and C which are collinear and coplanar.
16. Draw three points D, E, and F which are coplanar but not collinear.
17. Draw three points A, B, and C which are coplanar but not collinear. Draw a fourth point P which is not in the same plane as points A, B, and C. (a) Find the number of lines that can be drawn joining all pairs of points. (b) Find the number of planes that can be passed through all sets of three points.

In 18–30, draw a figure representing a situation in which:

18. Plane R passes through point P.
19. Plane R passes through line $\overleftrightarrow{CD}$.
20. Plane R contains line $\overleftrightarrow{AB}$ and point P which is not on line $\overleftrightarrow{AB}$.
21. Plane R contains lines $\overleftrightarrow{AB}$ and $\overleftrightarrow{CD}$ which intersect at E.
22. Plane R contains points A, B, and C which are not collinear.
23. Line b intersects plane R in point P.
24. Planes M and N intersect in line $\overleftrightarrow{XY}$.
25. Line r and plane R do not intersect.
26. Planes R and S do not intersect.
27. Point P is not in plane X. Plane Q passes through P and intersects plane X in $\overleftrightarrow{CD}$.
28. Lines a and b intersect at W. Plane P contains line a but not line b.
29. Planes A and B do not intersect. Plane C intersects plane A in $\overleftrightarrow{PQ}$ and plane B in $\overleftrightarrow{RS}$.
30. Lines a and b do not intersect. Plane P passes through line a and intersects line b in point C.

31. How many lines can pass through a point (a) in a plane? (b) in space?
32. How many planes can be passed through a point in space?
33. How many lines can be passed through two points (a) in a plane? (b) in space?
34. How many planes can be passed through two points in space?
35. How many planes can contain line n in space?

36. *a.* Draw several examples of a line intersecting a plane when the line does not lie in the plane.
   b. What is the intersection in each case?

37. In how many points can a line intersect a plane when the line does not lie in the plane?

38. How many lines can intersect a plane *R* at a point *P?*

39. How many planes can intersect a line *m* at one of its points *P?*

40. *a.* Draw several examples of two planes intersecting.
   b. What is the intersection in each case?

41. In how many lines can two planes intersect?

42. Can three planes intersect in one line? If your answer is yes, illustrate with a drawing.

43. Can three planes intersect in one point? If your answer is yes, illustrate with a drawing.

44. How many positions can a flat metal plate take when it is placed at the (*a*) tip of one finger? (*b*) tips of two fingers? (*c*) tips of three fingers when the finger tips are not collinear?

45. How many planes can be passed through three points in space which are not collinear?

46. Can a plane always be passed through a line and a point not on that line? If your answer is yes, state the number of planes that can be passed through the line and the point.

47. Can a plane always be passed through two intersecting lines? If your answer is yes, state the number of planes that can be passed through the lines.

48. Can a plane always be passed through two parallel lines? If your answer is yes, state the number of planes that can be passed through the lines.

49. Can a plane always be passed through two lines that do not intersect? If your answer is no, give an illustration.

50. If a line lies in a plane, where does every point on the line lie?

2. Properties of Planes

The exercises in the preceding unit include specific illustrations of the following general properties of planes:

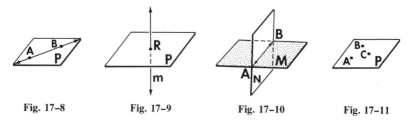

Fig. 17–8   Fig. 17–9   Fig. 17–10   Fig. 17–11

Postulate S1. **If a straight line passes through two points in a plane, the line lies entirely in the plane.**

In Fig. 17–8, if line $\overleftrightarrow{AB}$ passes through points A and B which lie in plane P, then the entire line $\overleftrightarrow{AB}$ lies in plane P.

Postulate S2. **A plane and a line which does not lie in the plane can intersect in one and only one point.**

In Fig. 17–9, if line m does not lie in plane P, then line m can intersect plane P in one and only one point R.

Postulate S3. **If two planes intersect, their intersection is one and only one straight line.**

In Fig. 17–10, if plane M intersects plane N, their intersection is the one and only one straight line $\overleftrightarrow{AB}$.

Definition. **A figure is *determined* when there is one and only one such figure that meets a set of given conditions.**

For example, since one and only one, or exactly one, straight line can be drawn which passes through two points, we say that two points determine a line.

Postulate S4. **A plane is determined by three points which are not on the same straight line.**

In Fig. 17–11, if points A, B, and C are not on the same straight line, there is one and only one plane P which contains points A, B, and C.

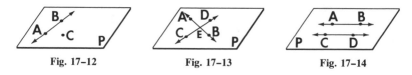

Fig. 17–12   Fig. 17–13   Fig. 17–14

Theorem S1. **A plane is determined by a line and a point not on that line.**

In Fig. 17–12, if $\overleftrightarrow{AB}$ is a line and C is a point which is not on $\overleftrightarrow{AB}$, there is one and only one plane P which contains line $\overleftrightarrow{AB}$ and point C.

***Theorem S2*. A plane is determined by two intersecting lines.**

In Fig. 17–13, if lines $\overleftrightarrow{AB}$ and $\overleftrightarrow{CD}$ intersect at E, there is one and only one plane P which contains both line $\overleftrightarrow{AB}$ and line $\overleftrightarrow{CD}$.

***Theorem S3*. A plane is determined by two parallel lines.**

In Fig. 17–14, if line $\overleftrightarrow{AB}$ is parallel to line $\overleftrightarrow{CD}$, there is one and only one plane P which contains both line $\overleftrightarrow{AB}$ and line $\overleftrightarrow{CD}$.

MODEL PROBLEM

Prove that a plane is determined by a line and a point not on that line.

Given: Straight line l and point C not on line l.

To prove: There is one and only one plane P that
contains both line l and point C.

Plan: Prove that there are two points A and B
on line l which, together with the given point C, determine a
plane. Then prove that this plane, which contains point C, also
contains line l.

Proof: *Statements*	*Reasons*
1. Line l is a straight line.	1. Given.
2. A and B are two points on line l.	2. Every straight line contains at least two points.
3. Point C is not on line l.	3. Given.
4. There is one and only one plane P that contains points A, B, and C.	4. A plane is determined by three points which are not on the same line.
5. Plane P contains line l.	5. If a straight line passes through two points in a plane, the line lies entirely in the plane.

EXERCISES

1. What do two points always determine?

2. *a.* Give an example of two intersecting planes in your mathematics classroom.

   b. Name the geometric figure which is the intersection of these planes.

3. Why is a tripod used to support a camera or a surveyor's transit?
4. How many noncollinear points determine a plane?
5. Why can a four-legged table which stands on a level floor rock?
6. Must every triangle be a plane figure? Why?
7. Must every geometric figure that has four vertices be a plane figure? Why?
8. How many planes are determined by three straight lines which are not coplanar and all of which pass through one point?
9. Must two parallel lines be coplanar? Why?
10. Must three parallel lines be coplanar? Why?
11. How many planes are determined by three parallel lines which are not coplanar?
12. Must two perpendicular lines always be coplanar? Why?

In 13–18, write a postulate or a theorem which supports the given statement.

13. Line $\overleftrightarrow{RS}$ intersects plane M in one and only one point.
14. Line $\overleftrightarrow{CD}$ which passes through points C and D in plane N lies entirely in plane N.
15. Three noncollinear points D, E, and F determine plane T.
16. Parallel lines $\overleftrightarrow{LM}$ and $\overleftrightarrow{RS}$ determine plane P.
17. If planes R and S intersect, their intersection is a straight line.
18. Line $\overleftrightarrow{PQ}$ and point S which is not on $\overleftrightarrow{PQ}$ determine plane Y.

19. Place four points A, B, C, and D in plane P so that when they are joined in pairs they will determine six lines.
20. Place four points A, B, C, and D in plane P so that when they are joined in pairs they will determine one line.
21. Place four points A, B, C, and D in space so that they will determine one plane. Draw the figure.
22. Place four points A, B, C, and D in space so that they will determine four planes. Draw the figure.

In 23–29, write a formal proof.

23. *Given:* Point P lies in plane X, and point Q lies in plane X.
    Prove: Line $\overleftrightarrow{PQ}$ lies in plane X.
24. *Given:* Line l intersects plane P which does not contain line l.
    Prove: The intersection of line l and plane P is a point.
25. *Given:* R, S, and T, the vertices of triangle RST, lie in plane P.
    Prove: The sides of triangle RST lie in plane P.

26. *Given:* Plane X and plane Y intersect in $\overleftrightarrow{AB}$, point P lies in both plane X and plane Y.
   Prove: Point P lies on line $\overleftrightarrow{AB}$.

27. Prove that a plane is determined by two intersecting lines.

28. Prove that a plane is determined by two parallel lines.

29. Prove that the sides of a parallelogram are coplanar.

3. Lines Perpendicular to Planes

We have learned that in a plane there can be one and only one line perpendicular to a given line at a given point on the line. In Fig. 17–15, $\overleftrightarrow{RP}$ is the one and only one line which is perpendicular to line $\overleftrightarrow{AB}$ at point P.

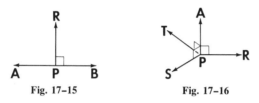

Fig. 17–15   Fig. 17–16

However, in space there are many lines that are perpendicular to a given line at a given point on the line. Fig. 17–16 shows three lines, $\overleftrightarrow{PR}$, $\overleftrightarrow{PS}$, and $\overleftrightarrow{PT}$, each of which is perpendicular to line $\overleftrightarrow{AP}$ at point P.

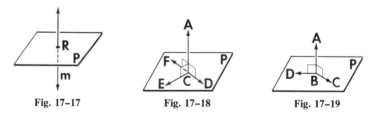

Fig. 17–17   Fig. 17–18   Fig. 17–19

Definition. **The point of intersection of a straight line and a plane is called the** *foot of the line.*

In Fig. 17–17, if point R is the point of intersection of line m and plane P, point R is the foot of line m.

Definition. **A** *line is perpendicular to a plane* **if it is perpendicular to every line in the plane which passes through its foot.**

In Fig. 17–18, line $\overleftrightarrow{AC}$ is perpendicular to plane P if line $\overleftrightarrow{AC}$ is perpendicular to every line in plane P ($\overleftrightarrow{DC}$, $\overleftrightarrow{EC}$, $\overleftrightarrow{FC}$, etc.) which passes through C, the foot of $\overleftrightarrow{AC}$.

Postulate S5. **If a line is perpendicular to each of two intersecting lines at their point of intersection, the line is perpendicular to the plane determined by these two intersecting lines.**

In Fig. 17–19, if $\overleftrightarrow{AB}$ is perpendicular to each of the intersecting lines $\overleftrightarrow{CB}$ and $\overleftrightarrow{DB}$ at their point of intersection, B, then $\overleftrightarrow{AB}$ is perpendicular to plane P, which is determined by intersecting lines $\overleftrightarrow{CB}$ and $\overleftrightarrow{DB}$.

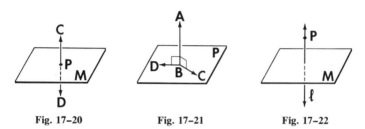

| Fig. 17–20 | Fig. 17–21 | Fig. 17–22 |

Postulate S6. **There is one and only one line perpendicular to a plane at a point in the plane.**

In Fig. 17–20, if point P is in plane M, there is one and only one line $\overleftrightarrow{CD}$ which is perpendicular to plane M at point P.

Postulate S7. **All the perpendiculars to a line, at a point on the line, lie in a plane which is perpendicular to the line at that point.**

In Fig. 17–21, if $\overleftrightarrow{CB}$ and $\overleftrightarrow{DB}$ are two lines which are perpendicular to line $\overleftrightarrow{AB}$ at point B, they lie in plane P, which is perpendicular to $\overleftrightarrow{AB}$ at point B.

Postulate S8. **There is one and only one line perpendicular to a plane passing through a point not in the plane.**

In Fig. 17–22, if P is a point which is not in plane M, then from P there is one and only one line, line l, which is perpendicular to plane M.

MODEL PROBLEMS

1. *Given:* $\overleftrightarrow{AB} \perp$ plane P.
$\overleftrightarrow{BC}$ and $\overleftrightarrow{BD}$ lie in plane P.
$\overline{BC} \cong \overline{BD}$.

To prove: $\overline{AC} \cong \overline{AD}$.

Plan: To prove that $\overline{AC} \cong \overline{AD}$, prove that the triangles in which these lines are corresponding sides, $\triangle ABC$ and $\triangle ABD$, are congruent.

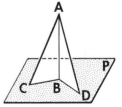

Proof: *Statements*	*Reasons*
1. $\overleftrightarrow{AB} \perp$ plane P.	1. Given.
2. $\overleftrightarrow{BC}$ and $\overleftrightarrow{BD}$ lie in plane P.	2. Given.
3. $\overleftrightarrow{AB} \perp \overleftrightarrow{BC}, \overleftrightarrow{AB} \perp \overleftrightarrow{BD}$.	3. If a line is perpendicular to a plane, the line is perpendicular to every line in the plane passing through its foot.
4. $\angle ABC$ and $\angle ABD$ are right angles.	4. Perpendicular lines intersect forming right angles.
5. $\angle ABC \cong \angle ABD$. (a. $\cong$ a.)	5. All right angles are congruent.
6. $\overline{BC} \cong \overline{BD}$. (s. $\cong$ s.)	6. Given.
7. $\overline{AB} \cong \overline{AB}$. (s. $\cong$ s.)	7. Reflexive property of congruence.
8. $\triangle ABC \cong \triangle ABD$.	8. s.a.s. $\cong$ s.a.s.
9. $\overline{AC} \cong \overline{AD}$.	9. Corresponding sides of congruent triangles are congruent.

2. *Given:* $ABCD$ is a square.
            $AFED$ is a square.
            $\overleftrightarrow{AF}$ and $\overleftrightarrow{AB}$ lie in plane P.

To prove: $\overleftrightarrow{DA} \perp$ plane P.

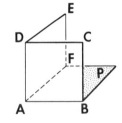

Plan: To prove that $\overleftrightarrow{DA}$ is perpendicular to plane P, prove that $\overleftrightarrow{DA}$ is perpendicular to both lines $\overleftrightarrow{AB}$ and $\overleftrightarrow{AF}$ at their point of intersection, A.

Proof: *Statements*	*Reasons*
1. $ABCD$ is a square.	1. Given.
2. $\overleftrightarrow{DA} \perp \overleftrightarrow{AB}$.	2. Two consecutive sides of a square are perpendicular to each other.
3. $AFED$ is a square.	3. Given.
4. $\overleftrightarrow{DA} \perp \overleftrightarrow{AF}$.	4. Same as reason 2.
5. $\overleftrightarrow{AF}$ and $\overleftrightarrow{AB}$ lie in plane P.	5. Given.

[The proof continues on the next page.]

Proof: *Statements*

6. $\overleftrightarrow{DA} \perp$ plane P.

Reasons

6. If a line is perpendicular to each of two intersecting lines at their point of intersection, the line is perpendicular to the plane determined by these two intersecting lines.

EXERCISES

1. In a plane, how many lines can be drawn perpendicular to a given line at a given point on the line?

2. In space, how many lines can be drawn perpendicular to a given line at a given point on the line?

3. If a line is perpendicular to a plane, must it be perpendicular to every line in the plane passing through its foot?

4. If a line is perpendicular to a line in a plane, must it also be perpendicular to the plane?

5. If a line is perpendicular to each of two lines that lie in a plane, must it also be perpendicular to the plane?

6. If a line is perpendicular to each of two intersecting lines at their point of intersection, must it also be perpendicular to the plane determined by the intersecting lines?

7. How many lines can be drawn perpendicular to a plane at a point on the plane?

8. Where do all the perpendiculars that can be drawn to a line at a point on the line lie?

9. Through a point outside a plane, how many lines can be drawn perpendicular to the plane?

10. If $\overleftrightarrow{AE}$ is perpendicular to plane P, name the lines that are perpendicular to $\overleftrightarrow{AE}$.

11. How can a carpenter make certain that a column which he is installing in a room will be perpendicular to the level floor of the room?

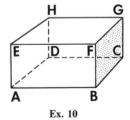

Ex. 10

In 12–17, write a formal proof.

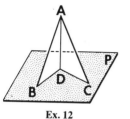

Ex. 12

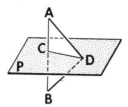

Ex. 13

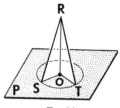

Ex. 14

12. *Given:* $\overleftrightarrow{AD} \perp$ plane P, $\overleftrightarrow{DB}$ and $\overleftrightarrow{DC}$ lie in plane P, $\overline{AB} \cong \overline{AC}$.
Prove: $\angle ABD \cong \angle ACD$.

13. *Given:* $\overleftrightarrow{AB} \perp$ plane P, points C and D lie in plane P, C is the midpoint of $\overline{AB}$.
Prove: $\overline{DA} \cong \overline{DB}$.

14. *Given:* O is the center of a circle which lies in plane P, $\overleftrightarrow{RO} \perp$ plane P, S and T lie on circle O.
Prove: $\overline{RS} \cong \overline{RT}$.

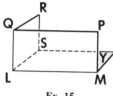

Ex. 15

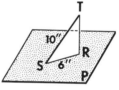

Ex. 18

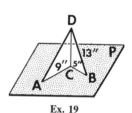

Ex. 19

15. *Given:* $LMPQ$ and $LSRQ$ are rectangles, $\overleftrightarrow{LM}$ and $\overleftrightarrow{LS}$ lie in plane Y.
Prove: Plane $Y \perp \overleftrightarrow{LQ}$.

16. Prove that if a plane is perpendicular to a line segment at its midpoint, the distances from any point in the plane to the ends of the line segment are equal.

17. Prove that if each of three lines is perpendicular to the other two, then each of these lines is perpendicular to the plane of the other two.

18. $\overleftrightarrow{TR} \perp$ plane P, $RS = 6$ in., and $TS = 10$ in. Find the length of $\overline{TR}$.

19. $\overleftrightarrow{DC} \perp$ plane P, $DB = 13$ in., $BC = 5$ in., $AC = 9$ in. Find the length of $\overline{AD}$.

4. Parallel Lines and Planes

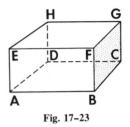

Fig. 17–23 represents a rectangular solid. The top, the bottom, and the four sides of the solid figure, that is, its six faces, are rectangles. Because they are opposite sides of a rectangle, segments $\overline{AB}$ and $\overline{EF}$ will not meet no matter how far they are extended. Since they lie in the same plane, they are parts of parallel lines. It is apparent from the figure that segments $\overline{EF}$ and $\overline{GC}$ also will not meet no matter how far they are extended. However, they are not parts of parallel lines because they do not lie in the same plane. Segments $\overline{EF}$ and $\overline{GC}$ are parts of *skew lines*.

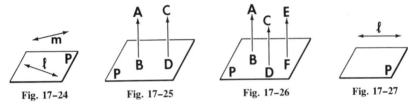

| Fig. 17–24 | Fig. 17–25 | Fig. 17–26 | Fig. 17–27 |

*Definition. **Skew lines** are lines that do not lie in the same plane.*

In Fig. 17–24, line l, which lies in plane p, and line m, which does not lie in plane p, are skew lines, since they do not lie in the same plane.

Theorem S4. Two or more lines perpendicular to the same plane are parallel.

In Fig. 17–25, if $\overleftrightarrow{AB} \perp$ plane P and $\overleftrightarrow{CD} \perp$ plane P, then $\overleftrightarrow{AB} \parallel \overleftrightarrow{CD}$.

Theorem S5. If each of two lines is parallel to a third line, then the lines are parallel to each other.

In Fig. 17–26, if both $\overleftrightarrow{AB}$ and $\overleftrightarrow{EF}$ are parallel to $\overleftrightarrow{CD}$, then $\overleftrightarrow{AB}$ and $\overleftrightarrow{EF}$ are parallel to each other. If $\overleftrightarrow{AB} \parallel \overleftrightarrow{CD}$ and $\overleftrightarrow{EF} \parallel \overleftrightarrow{CD}$, then $\overleftrightarrow{AB} \parallel \overleftrightarrow{EF}$.

*Definition. A **line and a plane are parallel** if they do not intersect.*

In Fig. 17–27, line l and plane P are parallel if they do not intersect.

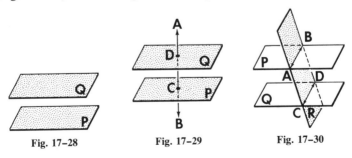

| Fig. 17–28 | Fig. 17–29 | Fig. 17–30 |

Definition. Two planes are parallel if they do not intersect.

In Fig. 17–28, plane P and plane Q are parallel if they do not intersect.

Theorem S6. **Two planes which are perpendicular to the same line are parallel.**

In Fig. 17–29, if plane P is perpendicular to $\overleftrightarrow{AB}$ at C and plane Q is perpendicular to $\overleftrightarrow{AB}$ at D, then plane $P \parallel$ plane Q.

Theorem S7. **If two parallel planes are cut by a third plane, the lines of intersection are parallel.**

In Fig. 17–30, if plane P is parallel to plane Q, and plane R intersects plane P in $\overleftrightarrow{AB}$ and plane Q in $\overleftrightarrow{CD}$, then intersections $\overleftrightarrow{AB}$ and $\overleftrightarrow{CD}$ are parallel.

Let us write a formal proof for the preceding theorem.

MODEL PROBLEM

Given: Plane $P \parallel$ plane Q. Plane R intersects plane P in $\overleftrightarrow{AB}$ and plane Q in $\overleftrightarrow{CD}$.

To prove: $\overleftrightarrow{AB} \parallel \overleftrightarrow{CD}$.

Plan: To prove that $\overleftrightarrow{AB}$ is parallel to $\overleftrightarrow{CD}$, prove that $\overleftrightarrow{AB}$ and $\overleftrightarrow{CD}$ are lines that lie in the same plane and will not intersect.

Proof: *Statements*	*Reasons*
1. Plane R intersects plane P in $\overleftrightarrow{AB}$ and plane Q in $\overleftrightarrow{CD}$, or $\overleftrightarrow{AB}$ and $\overleftrightarrow{CD}$ lie in the same plane.	1. Given.
2. $\overleftrightarrow{AB}$ and $\overleftrightarrow{CD}$ are lines.	2. If two planes intersect, their intersection is one and only one straight line.
3. Plane $P \parallel$ plane Q.	3. Given.
4. $\overleftrightarrow{AB}$, which is in plane P, cannot intersect $\overleftrightarrow{CD}$, which is in plane Q.	4. If two planes are parallel, they do not intersect.
5. $\overleftrightarrow{AB} \parallel \overleftrightarrow{CD}$.	5. Two lines are parallel if they lie in the same plane and do not intersect.

EXERCISES

In 1–20, tell whether each statement is *always true, sometimes true,* or *never true.*

1. Two lines which do not intersect are parallel.
2. Two skew lines intersect in a point.
3. Two planes that are not parallel intersect in a line.
4. A line which intersects one of two parallel planes intersects the other also.
5. If a line is parallel to one of two parallel planes, it is also parallel to the other plane.
6. If a line is perpendicular to one of two parallel planes, it is also perpendicular to the other plane.
7. Two planes which are perpendicular to the same line are parallel to each other.
8. Two planes which are parallel to a line are parallel to each other.
9. Two planes which are parallel to the same plane are parallel to each other.
10. A plane can be drawn parallel to a given plane through a point outside the given plane.
11. A plane can be drawn parallel to a given plane through a line which does not lie in the given plane.
12. A line which intersects one of two parallel lines also intersects the other.
13. Two lines perpendicular to the same line are parallel to each other.
14. Two lines perpendicular to the same plane are parallel to each other.
15. If each of two lines is parallel to a plane, the lines lie in a plane.
16. If two lines are perpendicular to the same plane, they are perpendicular to each other.
17. If two lines are skew to the same line, they are skew to each other.
18. Two lines which lie in two parallel planes can intersect.
19. Through either of two skew lines, a plane can be passed parallel to the other line.
20. If two lines are parallel, then two planes, each containing one and only one of these lines, are parallel to each other.

In 21–25, give a word or expression that, when inserted in the blank, makes the resulting statement true.

21. Two planes that are _____ to the same line are parallel to each other.
22. Two lines perpendicular to the same plane are _____ .

23. If each of two lines is _____ to a third line, the lines are parallel to each other.

24. If a line outside a plane is parallel to a line in the plane, the line is _____ to the plane.

25. A straight line perpendicular to one of two parallel planes is _____ to the other.

26. If point A lies outside plane P, how many lines parallel to plane P can be drawn through point A?

27. If $\overleftrightarrow{AB}$ and $\overleftrightarrow{CD}$ are parallel lines and plane P is perpendicular to $\overleftrightarrow{AB}$, must plane P be perpendicular to $\overleftrightarrow{CD}$?

28. If $\overleftrightarrow{AB}$ intersects plane P, how many planes containing $\overleftrightarrow{AB}$ can be drawn parallel to plane P?

29. Lines $\overleftrightarrow{AB}$ and $\overleftrightarrow{CD}$ which intersect at E are both parallel to plane P. What relation exists between plane P and the plane determined by lines $\overleftrightarrow{AB}$ and $\overleftrightarrow{CD}$?

30. If line $\overleftrightarrow{AB}$ is parallel to plane P, how many planes which contain $\overleftrightarrow{AB}$ can be drawn parallel to plane P?

In 31–33, write a formal proof.

31. Prove that an edge of a rectangular solid is parallel to each of two faces of the solid. [Assume that the opposite faces of the solid lie in parallel planes.]

32. Prove that two lines which are perpendicular to the same plane are coplanar.

33. Prove that parallel segments which are intercepted by parallel planes are congruent.

5. Dihedral Angles and Perpendicular Planes

Dihedral Angles

For many relationships in plane geometry, there are similar relationships in space geometry. We know that in a plane two lines may coincide, or they may never intersect, or they may intersect, forming an angle. Similarly, in space, two planes may coincide, or they may never intersect, or they may intersect, forming a *dihedral angle*.

Definition. **A *dihedral angle* is a set of points consisting of the union of two intersecting half-planes and their common edge.**

The half-planes that form the dihedral angle are called the *faces* of the dihedral angle. The line of intersection of the faces of the angle is called the *edge* of the dihedral angle.

A dihedral angle may be named by using four points, two on the common edge and one in each of the two half-planes. The dihedral angle shown in Fig. 17–31 is named ∠*C-AB-D* or ∠*D-AB-C*.

Definition. A *plane angle of a dihedral angle* is an angle formed by two rays, one in each face of the dihedral angle, drawn perpendicular to the edge of the dihedral angle at the same point.

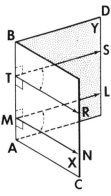

Fig. 17–31

Angle *STR* in Fig. 17–31 is the plane angle of dihedral angle *C-AB-D* because $\overrightarrow{TS}$ in face *Y* is perpendicular to $\overleftrightarrow{AB}$ at *T*, and $\overrightarrow{TR}$ in face *X* is also perpendicular to $\overleftrightarrow{AB}$ at *T*.

Theorem S8. The plane angles of a dihedral angle are congruent.

In Fig. 17–31, if ∠*STR* and ∠*LMN* are plane angles of dihedral angle *C-AB-D*, then ∠*STR* ≅ ∠*LMN*.

Definition. The *measure of a dihedral angle* is the measure of its plane angle.

In Fig. 17–31, the number of degrees contained in dihedral angle *C-AB-D* is the same as the number of degrees contained in its plane angle *STR*.

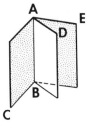

Fig. 17–32

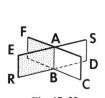

Fig. 17–33

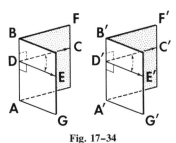

Fig. 17–34

Definition. *Adjacent dihedral angles* are two dihedral angles which have the same edge and a common face between them.

In this definition, we took the liberty of using an undefined phrase, "a common face between them." However, in actual practice this should present no difficulty. In Fig. 17–32, dihedral angles *E-AB-D* and *C-AB-D* are adjacent dihedral angles. The plane determined by points *A*, *B*, and *D* is the common face between the dihedral angles.

Definition. Vertical dihedral angles are two dihedral angles that have a common edge and whose faces are opposite half-planes.

In Fig. 17–33, dihedral angles *E-BA-F* and *C-BA-D* are a pair of vertical dihedral angles.

Definition. Congruent dihedral angles are dihedral angles that have the same measure.

In Fig. 17–34, if dihedral angle *F-BA-G* and dihedral angle *F'-B'A'-G'* have the same measure, then angle *F-BA-G* and angle *F'-B'A'-G'* are congruent.

Theorem S9. Two dihedral angles are congruent if their plane angles are congruent.

In Fig. 17–34, dihedral angles *G-AB-F* and *G'-A'B'-F'* are congruent if their plane angles *EDC* and *E'D'C'* are congruent.

Theorem S10. If two dihedral angles are congruent, their plane angles are congruent.

In Fig. 17–34, if dihedral angles *G-AB-F* and *G'-A'B'-F'* are congruent, their plane angles *EDC* and *E'D'C'* are congruent.

Definition. A *dihedral angle is called acute, right, obtuse, or straight* if its plane angle is acute, right, obtuse, or straight.

Definition. Two dihedral angles are complementary if their plane angles are complementary.

Definition. Two dihedral angles are supplementary if their plane angles are supplementary.

Theorem S11. Two dihedral angles which are complementary to the same or congruent dihedral angles are congruent.

Theorem S12. Two dihedral angles which are supplementary to the same or congruent dihedral angles are congruent.

Theorem S13. If two planes intersect, the vertical dihedral angles are congruent.

In Fig. 17–33 (page 670), the vertical dihedral angles *F-AB-R* and *S-AB-C* are congruent.

Perpendicular Planes

Definition. Two planes are perpendicular if they intersect and form right dihedral angles.

In Fig. 17–35, if dihedral angle *S-AB-R* and dihedral angle *T-AB-R* are right dihedral angles, then plane *Y* is perpendicular to plane *X*.

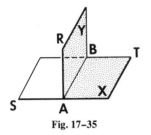

Fig. 17–35

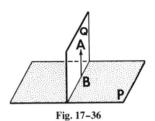

Fig. 17–36

Theorem S14. **If a straight line is perpendicular to a plane, every plane which contains the line is perpendicular to the plane.**

In Fig. 17–36, if $\overleftrightarrow{AB}$ is perpendicular to plane *P* and plane *Q* contains $\overleftrightarrow{AB}$, then plane *Q* is perpendicular to plane *P*.

EXERCISES

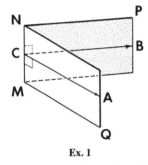

Ex. 1

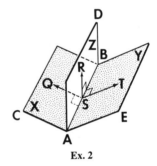

Ex. 2

1. *a.* Name the dihedral angle.
   b. Name the plane angle of the dihedral angle.
2. Plane *Z* bisects dihedral angle *C-AB-E.* (*a*) Name the congruent dihedral angles. (*b*) Name the congruent plane angles.
3. Draw two planes that are perpendicular to each other.

In 4–11, give the definition of the term.

4. acute dihedral angle
5. right dihedral angle
6. obtuse dihedral angle
7. straight dihedral angle
8. adjacent dihedral angles
9. supplementary dihedral angles
10. complementary dihedral angles
11. vertical dihedral angles

In 12–19, tell whether or not the statement is *always true, sometimes true*, or *never true*.

12. Two planes which are perpendicular to the same plane are parallel.

13. Through a point outside a plane, one and only one plane can be drawn perpendicular to the plane.

14. If one of two parallel planes is perpendicular to a third plane, the second of the parallel planes is also perpendicular to the third plane.

15. Two dihedral angles which have a common edge are adjacent dihedral angles.

16. If two adjacent dihedral angles are supplementary, they are congruent.

17. If each of two parallel lines is parallel to a given plane, the plane determined by the parallel lines is perpendicular to the given plane.

18. All plane angles of a dihedral angle are congruent.

19. A plane perpendicular to the edge of a dihedral angle intersects the faces in rays which form a plane angle of the dihedral angle.

20. If a line is perpendicular to a plane, how many planes containing this line are parallel to the plane?

21. If a line is perpendicular to a plane, how many planes containing this line are perpendicular to the plane?

22. If a line which is not perpendicular to a plane intersects the plane, how many planes containing this line are perpendicular to the plane?

23. If a line is parallel to a plane, how many planes containing this line are perpendicular to the plane?

24. If a line lies in a plane, how many planes containing this line are perpendicular to the plane?

25. If two rays form a plane angle of a dihedral angle, do these rays lie in the same plane? Give the reason for your answer.

26. Can a line be perpendicular to both faces of a dihedral angle? Explain your answer.

27. Prove that if two dihedral angles are complementary to the same dihedral angle, they are congruent.

28. Prove that if two dihedral angles are supplementary to congruent dihedral angles, they are congruent.

29. Prove that if two planes intersect, vertical dihedral angles are congruent. [*Hint:* Draw a plane perpendicular to the common edge of the dihedral angles.]

6. Measuring Distances in Space

In general, the *distance from a point to a figure* is the length of the short-est of the segments that can be drawn from the given point to points of the figure.

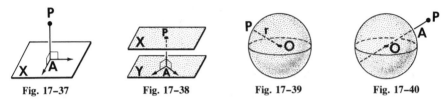

Fig. 17–37   Fig. 17–38   Fig. 17–39   Fig. 17–40

Definition. The *distance from a point to a plane* is the length of the segment **whose endpoints are the given point and the foot of the perpendicular drawn from the point to the plane.**

In Fig. 17–37, if $\overleftrightarrow{PA} \perp$ plane X, the length of $\overline{PA}$ is the distance from point P to plane X.

Definition. The *distance between two parallel planes* is the distance from any **point in one plane to the other plane.**

In parallel planes X and Y (Fig. 17–38), if P is any point in plane X and $\overleftrightarrow{PA}$ is perpendicular to plane Y, the length of segment $\overline{PA}$ is the distance be-tween planes X and Y.

It may appear that this definition is not valid at this point. However, it may be justified in light of theorem S15, whose proof does not depend upon this definition.

Definition. A *sphere* is the set of all points in space at a given distance from **a given point called the center.**

The sphere shown in Fig. 17–39 is the set of points at a given distance r from point O. The line segment joining P, a point on the sphere, and O, the center of the sphere, that is, $\overline{OP}$, is a radius of the sphere whose length is represented by r.

Definition. The *distance from a point to a sphere* is the length of the segment **whose endpoints are the given point and the point of intersection of the sphere with the line that passes through the center of the sphere and the given point.**

In Fig. 17–40, the distance from point P to sphere O is the length of seg-ment $\overline{PA}$.

Equidistance in Space

Theorem S15. **Parallel planes are everywhere equidistant.**

In Fig. 17–41, if plane X is parallel to plane Y and if AB represents the distance from point A to plane Y, and CD represents the distance from point C to plane Y, then $AB = CD$.

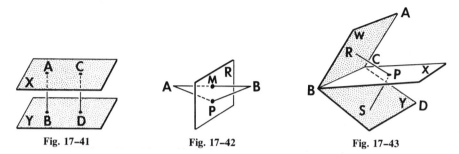

Fig. 17–41   Fig. 17–42   Fig. 17–43

Theorem S16. Every point in the plane which is perpendicular to a line segment at its midpoint is equidistant from the ends of the segment.

In Fig. 17–42, if plane R is perpendicular to segment $\overline{AB}$ at its midpoint M, then point P in plane R is equidistant from A and B, or $PA = PB$.

Theorem S17. Every point in the plane which bisects a dihedral angle is equidistant from the faces of the dihedral angle.

In Fig. 17–43, if P is a point in plane X which bisects dihedral angle A-BC-D, then PR, the distance from P to plane W, is equal to PS, the distance from P to plane Y, or $PR = PS$.

EXERCISES

1. In Fig. 17–41, if the length of $\overline{AB}$ is represented by $3x - 1$ and the length of $\overline{CD}$ is represented by $x + 9$, find the distance between plane X and plane Y.

2. In Fig. 17–42, if the distance from P to M is 12, the length of $\overline{AM}$ is represented by $5x - 1$, and the length of $\overline{MB}$ is represented by $2x + 5$, find the length of $\overline{AP}$.

3. In Fig. 17–43, $m\angle RPS = 60$ and $PR = 8$. If $\overline{RS}$ is drawn, find the perimeter of triangle RPS.

4. In Fig. 17–43, $m\angle RPS = 90$ and $PR = 6$. If $\overline{RS}$ is drawn, find its length in radical form.

7. Polyhedrons

A *geometric solid* is a region of space enclosed by planes and curved surfaces. Examples of geometric solids are prisms, cubes, pyramids, spheres, cylinders, and cones.

Definition. A *polyhedron* is a solid enclosed by polygons.

The figure shown (Fig. 17–44) is a polyhedron because the solid is enclosed only by polygons, which are called *faces*. The line segment which is the intersection of any two faces of a polyhedron is called an *edge*. The point of intersection of three or more edges is called a *vertex*.

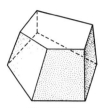

Fig. 17–44

The sphere, the cylinder, and the cone are not polyhedrons because they are not bounded by polygons.

Regular Polyhedrons

Definition. A *regular polyhedron* is a polyhedron whose faces are congruent regular polygons and which has the same number of faces intersecting at each vertex.

There are only five regular polyhedrons. They are shown in Fig. 17–45. Notice that the faces of these regular polyhedrons are equilateral triangles, squares, or regular pentagons:

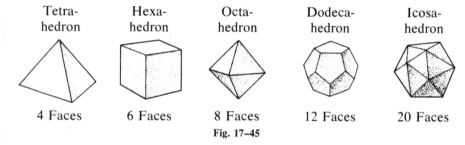

Tetra-hedron	Hexa-hedron	Octa-hedron	Dodeca-hedron	Icosa-hedron
4 Faces	6 Faces	8 Faces	12 Faces	20 Faces

Fig. 17–45

Prisms

Definition. A *prism* is a polyhedron two of whose faces are congruent polygons which lie in parallel planes and whose other faces are parallelograms.

In the prism shown (Fig. 17–46), $\triangle ABC$ and $\triangle DEF$ are called the *bases;* $\square ABED$, $\square ACFD$, and $\square BCFE$ are called the *lateral faces;* and $\overline{AD}$, $\overline{CF}$, and $\overline{BE}$ are called the *lateral edges.* The line segment whose length measures the distance between the parallel bases, $\overline{RS}$, is called the *altitude of the prism.*

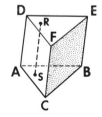

Fig. 17–46

Definition. A *right prism* is a prism whose lateral edges are perpendicular to the bases. (See Fig. 17–47.)

Definition. An *oblique prism* is a prism whose lateral edges are not perpendicular to the bases. (See Fig. 17–48.)

Definition. A *regular prism* is a prism whose bases are regular polygons. (See Fig. 17–49.)

Right Prism   Oblique Prism   Regular Prism

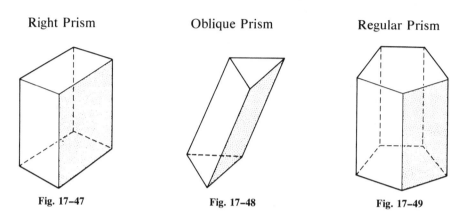

Fig. 17–47   Fig. 17–48   Fig. 17–49

Prisms are further classified according to their bases. The right prism shown is a *quadrangular prism* because its bases are quadrilaterals. The oblique prism shown is *triangular* because its bases are triangles. The regular prism shown is *pentagonal* because its bases are pentagons.

Definition. A *parallelepiped* is a prism whose bases are parallelograms. (See Fig. 17–50.)

Definition. A *rectangular parallelepiped,* also called a *rectangular solid,* is a parallelepiped whose lateral faces and bases are rectangles. (See Fig. 17–51.)

Definition. A *cube* is a rectangular parallelepiped whose lateral faces and bases are squares. (See Fig. 17–52.)

Parallelepiped   Rectangular   Cube
       Parallelepiped

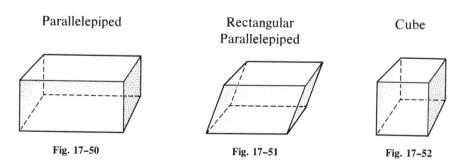

Fig. 17–50   Fig. 17–51   Fig. 17–52

EXERCISES

1. Draw each of the following figures and tell how many vertices, how many faces, and how many edges it has:
   a. a parallelepiped   *b.* a right triangular prism   *c.* a cube

2. Name two objects which are examples of rectangular solids.

3. What is the smallest number of faces a polyhedron can have?

4. What is the smallest number of faces a prism can have?

5. Can a prism have lateral faces which are triangles?

6. Can a prism have bases which are pentagons?

7. Can an oblique prism have regular polygons as bases?

8. If the bases of a parallelepiped are rectangles, must the lateral faces be rectangles?

9. What type of polygon is (*a*) a lateral face of a cube?   (*b*) a base of a cube?

10. What type of polygon is a lateral face of a prism?

11. Prove that the lateral edges of a prism are congruent.

12. Prove that the bases of a triangular prism are congruent.

13. Prove that the lateral edges of a rectangular prism are perpendicular to the bases of the prism.

14. $\overline{AC}$ and $\overline{DB}$ are diagonals of a cube.
   a. Prove that $\overline{AC} \cong \overline{DB}$.
   b. Prove that $\overline{AC}$ and $\overline{DB}$ bisect each other.
       NOTE. $\overline{AC}$ and $\overline{DB}$, segments whose endpoints are vertices not in the same face of the cube, are called *diagonals of the cube*. *ABCD* is called the *section of the cube* made by a plane that is passed through the lateral edges $\overline{AB}$ and $\overline{CD}$.

Ex. 14

15. In a prism, a plane is passed through two nonconsecutive lateral edges. Prove that the section of the prism made by the plane is a parallelogram.

8. Pyramids

Fig. 17–53 represents a polyhedron which is called a *pyramid.* It is formed by joining the vertices of polygon *ABCDE*, called the *base*, to a point *V*, called the *vertex*, which is not in the plane of the base.

The triangular faces of the pyramid, for example, triangles *VAB* and *VBC*, are called *lateral faces*. They are formed by joining the vertex to the ends of a side of the base. The intersections of the lateral faces, for example $\overline{VA}$ and $\overline{VB}$, are called the *lateral edges*. The *altitude*

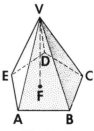

Fig. 17–53

of the pyramid, $\overline{VF}$, is the line segment which joins the vertex of the pyramid and the foot of the perpendicular drawn from the vertex to the base of the pyramid.

Pyramids are called triangular, quadrangular, pentagonal, etc. when their bases are triangles, quadrilaterals, pentagons, etc.

Fig. 17–54 represents a *regular pyramid*, which is a pyramid whose base is a regular polygon and whose lateral edges are congruent. The altitude drawn from the vertex to the base of any of the lateral faces, for example, $\overline{VE}$, is the *slant height* of the regular pyramid.

Fig. 17–54

EXERCISES

1. Can the base of a pyramid be a rhombus?

2. Can the base of a regular pyramid be a rhombus?

3. Can the lateral faces of a pyramid be squares?

4. What type of polygon must each lateral face of a regular pyramid be?

5. How many lateral faces does a pyramid have if its base has n sides?

In 6–10, tell whether each statement is *always true, sometimes true,* or *never true.*

6. The lateral faces of a pyramid are isosceles triangles.

7. If a pyramid has an equilateral triangle as its base, the pyramid is a regular pyramid.

8. The foot of the altitude of a regular pyramid is equidistant from the vertices of the base of the pyramid.

9. The slant height of a regular pyramid bisects the side of the base to which it is drawn.

10. In a regular pyramid, the slant height is longer than a lateral edge.

11. Prove that the lateral faces of a regular pyramid are congruent isosceles triangles.

12. Prove that the foot of the altitude of a regular pyramid is the center of the circle which circumscribes the base of the pyramid.

9. Cylinders and Cones

Cylinders

Fig. 17–55 represents a *right circular cylinder,* also called a *cylinder of revolution* because it may be generated by revolving a rectangle, such as rectangle *ABO'O,* about one of its sides as an axis.

The *bases* of the cylinder are congruent circles which lie in parallel planes. The *axis* $\overline{OO'}$, which is the line segment joining the centers of the bases, is perpendicular to the planes of the bases. The *altitude of the cylinder* is the distance between the bases. An *element of the cylinder,* for example, $\overline{AB}$, is a segment which joins points on the circles of the two bases and is perpendicular to the bases.

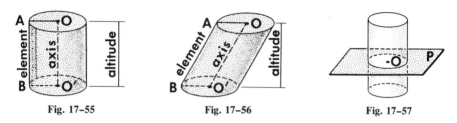

| Fig. 17–55 | Fig. 17–56 | Fig. 17–57 |

Fig. 17–56 represents an *oblique circular cylinder.* The bases of this cylinder are congruent circles which lie in parallel planes. However, the axis of this cylinder, OO', is not perpendicular to the planes of the bases. Line segment $\overline{AB}$ is an *element of the cylinder.*

Theorem S18. **The intersection of the elements of a right circular cylinder and a plane parallel to the bases is a circle.**

If plane P is parallel to the bases of the right circular cylinder shown in Fig. 17–57, the intersection of plane P and the elements of the cylinder is circle O.

Cones

Fig. 17–58 represents a *right circular cone,* also called a *cone of revolution* because it may be generated by revolving a right triangle, such as triangle AOV, about one of its legs as an axis.

The *vertex, V,* is a point lying outside the plane of the *base,* which is a circle. The *axis,* $\overline{VO}$, which is the line segment joining the vertex and the center of the base, is perpendicular to the plane of the base. The *altitude of the cone* is the line segment from the vertex perpendicular to the base. An *element of the cone,* for example, $\overline{VA}$, is a line segment which joins the vertex of the cone and any point on the circle which is the base. In a right circular cone, a line segment such as $\overline{VA}$ is also called the *slant height.*

Fig. 17–59 represents an *oblique circular cone.* The base of this cone is a circle. However, the axis of this cone, $\overline{VO}$, is not perpendicular to the plane of the base. Line segment $\overline{VA}$ is an *element of the cone.*

Theorem S19. **The intersection of the elements of a right circular cone and a plane parallel to the base, when the plane does not contain the vertex of the cone, is a circle.**

In Fig. 17–60, if plane *P*, which does not contain the vertex of the right circular cone, is parallel to the base of the cone, then the intersection of plane *P* and the elements of the cone is circle *O*.

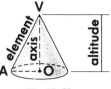

Fig. 17–58

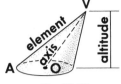

Fig. 17–59

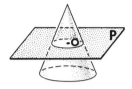

Fig. 17–60

EXERCISES

1. What type of figure is the base of an oblique circular cone?
2. How many bases does a circular cylinder have?
3. How many bases does a right circular cone have?
4. What solid is generated when a right triangle is revolved about one of its legs as an axis?
5. What solid is generated when a rectangle is revolved about one of its sides as an axis?
6. Describe the intersection of a right circular cylinder and a plane passed perpendicular to the axis of the cylinder.
7. Describe the intersection of a right circular cone and a plane passed parallel to the base of the cone when the plane does not contain the vertex of the cone.

In 8–20, tell whether each statement is *always*, *sometimes*, or *never true*.

8. The bases of a circular cylinder are congruent.
9. The axis of an oblique cylinder is perpendicular to the base.
10. The axis of a right circular cone is perpendicular to the base.
11. The length of the altitude of a cone is greater than the length of an element of the cone.
12. The axis of a cylinder joins the centers of its bases.
13. The intersection of a plane and the elements of a cylinder is a circle.
14. The intersection of a plane and the elements of a cylinder is a rectangle.
15. The intersection of a plane and the elements of a cone is a triangle.
16. All the elements of a right circular cylinder are congruent.
17. The length of the axis of a right circular cone is equal to the length of the altitude.
18. The axis of a cylinder intersects an element of the cylinder.
19. The axis of a cone intersects an element of the cone.
20. All the elements of a right circular cone are congruent.

10. Spheres

We have already defined a sphere as the set of
all points in space at a given distance from a given
point called the center.

In the sphere shown (Fig. 17–61), point O is the
center of the sphere. A line segment, such as $\overline{OC}$,
which joins the center of the sphere to a point on the
sphere, is called a *radius of the sphere.* A line segment, such as $\overline{AB}$, which joins two points of the
sphere and passes through its center, is called a
diameter of the sphere.

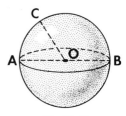

Fig. 17–61

Definition. Congruent spheres **are spheres whose radii are congruent.**

Theorem S20. **If a plane intersects a sphere in more than one point, the
intersection is a circle.**

In Fig. 17–62, the intersection of plane P
and sphere O is circle $O;$ the intersection of
plane Q and sphere O is circle O'. The intersection of a sphere with a plane that passes
through its center is called a *great circle of the
sphere.* Circle O is a great circle of the sphere.
The intersection of a sphere with a plane that
does not pass through its center is called a *small
circle of the sphere.* Circle O' is a small circle
of the sphere.

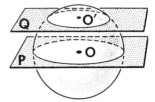

Fig. 17–62

If a plane intersects a sphere in one point,
the plane is tangent to the sphere. In Fig.
17–63, plane T, which intersects sphere O in
only one point, P, is tangent to sphere O. When
a plane is tangent to a sphere, the plane is perpendicular to a radius of the sphere (drawn to
the point of contact) at the outer extremity of
the radius. Plane T is perpendicular to radius
$\overline{OP}$ at P.

Any line, such as $\overleftrightarrow{PR}$, which is perpendicular to a radius of a sphere at the outer ex-
tremity of the radius, is called a *tangent to the
sphere.*

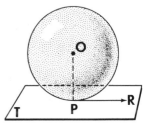

Fig. 17–63

EXERCISES

1. What is the relationship between two radii of a sphere?

2. What is the relationship between a radius of a sphere and a diameter of the sphere?

3. What is the greatest number of points in which a line can intersect a sphere?

4. If a nontangent plane intersects a sphere, describe the intersection.

5. How many planes can be drawn tangent to a sphere at a point on the sphere?

6. How many lines can be drawn tangent to a sphere at a point on the sphere?

7. How many lines can be drawn tangent to a sphere from a point outside the sphere?

8. How many planes can be drawn tangent to a sphere through a point outside the sphere?

9. If $\overline{AB}$ is a diameter of a sphere, how many great circles of the sphere have $\overline{AB}$ as their diameter?

10. If A and B are two points on a sphere which are not the ends of a diameter, how many great circles of the sphere pass through A and B?

11. What is the relationship between two great circles of the same sphere?

12. What is the intersection of two great circles of a sphere?

13. Prove that all great circles of a sphere are congruent.

14. Prove that one and only one great circle can be passed through two points on a sphere which are not the ends of a diameter.

15. Prove that if two planes are tangent to a sphere at the ends of a diameter, the planes are parallel.

11. Using the Pythagorean Theorem in Solid Geometry

Although the Pythagorean Theorem holds true only in plane figures which are right triangles, we shall soon see that it also has many applications in solid geometry.

Definition. A diagonal of a rectangular solid is a line segment joining two vertices of the solid which do not lie in the same face of the solid.

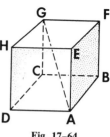

In the rectangular solid shown in Fig. 17–64, line segment $\overline{GA}$ is a diagonal because it joins vertices G and A which do not lie in the same face of the solid. Other diagonals would be $\overline{FD}$, $\overline{HB}$, and $\overline{EC}$.

Fig. 17–64

MODEL PROBLEMS

1. In the rectangular solid shown, $DA = 4$ in., $DC = 3$ in., and $GC = 12$ in.

 a. Find the length of $\overline{CA}$, a diagonal of the base $ABCD$.

 b. Using the result found in part *a*, find the length of $\overline{GA}$, a diagonal of the solid.

 c. If $DA = l$, $DC = w$, and $GC = h$, represent the length of $\overline{GA}$ in terms of l, w, and h.

 Solution:

 a. *ABCD* is a rectangle because the base of a rectangular solid is a rectangle. Therefore, $\triangle CDA$ is a right triangle in which $\angle CDA$ is a right angle.

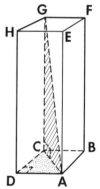

 1. In rt. $\triangle CDA$, $(CA)^2 = (DA)^2 + (DC)^2$

 2. $\qquad (CA)^2 = (4)^2 + (3)^2$

 3. $\qquad (CA)^2 = 16 + 9 = 25$

 4. $\qquad\quad CA = 5$

 Answer: $CA = 5$ in.

 b. Since an edge of a rectangular solid is perpendicular to the base of the solid, the edge is perpendicular to any line in the base passing through its foot. Therefore, $\overleftrightarrow{GC} \perp \overleftrightarrow{CA}$, and $\triangle GCA$ is a right triangle in which $\angle GCA$ is a right angle.

 1. In rt. $\triangle GCA$, $(GA)^2 = (CA)^2 + (GC)^2$

 2. $\qquad (GA)^2 = (5)^2 + (12)^2$

 3. $\qquad (GA)^2 = 25 + 144 = 169$

 4. $\qquad\quad GA = 13$

 Answer: $GA = 13$ in.

c. 1. In rt. $\triangle CDA$, $(CA)^2 = (DA)^2 + (DC)^2$ $\qquad DA = l, DC = w.$

2. $\qquad\qquad (CA)^2 = l^2 + w^2$

3. In rt. $\triangle GCA$, $(GA)^2 = (CA)^2 + (GC)^2$ $\qquad GC = h.$

4. $\qquad\qquad (GA)^2 = (CA)^2 + h^2$ $\qquad (CA)^2 = l^2 + w^2.$

5. Therefore, $\quad (GA)^2 = l^2 + w^2 + h^2$

6. $\qquad\qquad GA = \sqrt{l^2 + w^2 + h^2}$

Answer: $GA = \sqrt{l^2 + w^2 + h^2}.$

NOTE. If the length of the diagonal of a rectangular solid is represented by d and its dimensions are represented by l, w, and h, then

$$d = \sqrt{l^2 + w^2 + h^2}$$

2. In a regular square pyramid, the length of each side of the square base is 12 in. and the length of the altitude is 8 in.

a. Find the length of the slant height of the pyramid.

b. Find, in radical form, the length of the lateral edge of the pyramid.

Solution:

a. Altitude of the pyramid, $\overline{EF}$, is perpendicular to the plane of the base $ABCD$ and is therefore perpendicular to $\overleftrightarrow{FG}$. FG equals one-half of the length of a side of the base. Therefore, $FG = \frac{1}{2}(12 \text{ in.})$, or 6 in.

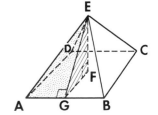

1. In rt. $\triangle EFG$, $(EG)^2 = (EF)^2 + (FG)^2$

2. Since $EF = 8$, $(EG)^2 = (8)^2 + (6)^2$

3. $\qquad\qquad (EG)^2 = 64 + 36 = 100$

4. $\qquad\qquad EG = 10$

Answer: Length of slant height $= 10$ in.

b. Since slant height $\overline{EG}$ is an altitude of isosceles triangle AEB, G is the midpoint of $\overline{AB}$. AG equals one-half of the length of a side of the base. Therefore, $AG = \frac{1}{2}(12 \text{ in.})$, or 6 in.

1. In rt. $\triangle EGA$, $(EA)^2 = (EG)^2 + (AG)^2$

2. $\qquad\qquad (EA)^2 = (10)^2 + (6)^2 = 100 + 36 = 136$

3. $\qquad\qquad EA = \sqrt{136} = \sqrt{4\cdot 34} = 2\sqrt{34}$

Answer: Length of lateral edge $= 2\sqrt{34}$ in.

3. In a sphere whose radius is 13 in., find the length of a radius of a small circle of the sphere if the plane of the small circle is 5 in. from the center of the sphere.

Solution: If O is the center of the sphere and $\overline{OA}$ is perpendicular to the plane of the small circle of the sphere, then $OA = 5$ in. and A is the center of the small circle. If $\overline{OA}$ is perpendicular to the plane of the small circle, then $\overleftrightarrow{OA} \perp \overleftrightarrow{AP}$, forming right triangle OAP.

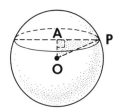

1. In rt. $\triangle OAP$, $(AP)^2 + (OA)^2 = (OP)^2$
   Since $OA = 5$ and $OP = 13$,

2. $(AP)^2 + (5)^2 = (13)^2$

3. $(AP)^2 + 25 = 169$

4. $(AP)^2 = 144$

5. $AP = 12$

Answer: Length of a radius of the small circle of the sphere is 12 in.

EXERCISES

In this set of exercises, all answers may be left in radical form unless otherwise indicated.

Exercises 1–4 refer to the rectangular solid shown.

1. If $AB = 8$ in., $BC = 6$ in., and $BF = 24$ in., find:
   a. AE   *b. EF*   *c. FG*   *d. DB*
   e. FC   *f. AF*   *g. HB*

2. If $AB = 5$ in., $AD = 3$ in., and $HD = 6$ in., find:
   a. BD   *b. AC*   *c. HB*   *d. GA*

3. If $HB = 13$ in., $HD = 12$ in., and $AB = 4$ in., find BC.

4. If $HB = 10$ in., $FB = 5$ in., and $AD = 4$ in., find AB.

Ex. 1–4

5. Find the length of a diagonal of each of the faces of a cube and the length of each of the diagonals of a cube if the length of each edge of the cube is:
   a. 1 in.   *b.* 2 in.   *c.* 4 in.   *d.* 5 in.   *e.* 10 in.

6. The length of each edge of a cube is represented by e. (*a*) Represent the length of a diagonal of each face of the cube in terms of e. (*b*) Represent the length of a diagonal of the cube in terms of e.

7. The length of each side of the base of a regular square pyramid is 8 in. and the length of the altitude of the pyramid is 3 in. (*a*) Find the length of the slant height of the pyramid. (*b*) Find the length of a lateral edge of the pyramid.

8. The length of each side of the base of a regular square pyramid is 10 in. and the length of the altitude of the pyramid is 12 in. (*a*) Find the length of the slant height of the pyramid. (*b*) Find, correct to the *nearest inch*, the length of a lateral edge of the pyramid.

9. Find the measure of a diagonal of a rectangular solid whose length is 5 inches, width is 3 inches, and height is 8 inches.

10. The length of a diagonal of the base of a rectangular solid is $\sqrt{91}$ inches. If the height of the solid is 3 inches, find the measure of a diagonal of the solid.

11. The length of a diagonal of a base of a cube is $5\sqrt{2}$ inches. Find the length of a diagonal of the cube.

12. The length of each edge of a regular square pyramid is 8 in. (*a*) Find the length of the slant height of the pyramid. (*b*) Find the length of the altitude of the pyramid.

13. In a rectangular solid, the measures of the length, width, and height are in the ratio 3:4:12. If the measure of a diagonal of the solid is 26 in., find the measures of the length, width, and height of the solid.

14. The length of a radius of a sphere is 10 inches. Find the length of a radius of a small circle of the sphere if the distance of the plane of the small circle from the center of the sphere is:
    a. 6 in.   *b.* 8 in.   *c.* 5 in.   *d.* 7 in.   *e.* $\sqrt{19}$ in.   *f.* $5\sqrt{3}$ in.

15. The length of a radius of a small circle of a sphere is 24 in. The distance from the center of the sphere to the plane of the small circle is 10 inches. Find the length of a radius of the sphere.

16. The length of a radius of a sphere is 25 in. The length of a radius of a small circle of the sphere is 15 in. Find the distance from the center of the sphere to the plane of the small circle of the sphere.

17. In a sphere, the plane of a small circle whose radius is 12 in. long is 9 in. from the center of the sphere. In this sphere, find the length of a radius of a small circle if its plane is 12 inches from the center of the sphere.

18. The length of a radius of a sphere is represented by R. The length of a radius of a small circle of the sphere is represented by r. Represent, in terms of R and r, the distance from the center of the sphere to the plane of the small circle of the sphere.

19. The length of a radius of the base of a right circular cone is 9 in. The length of the altitude of the cone is 12 in. Find the length of an element of the cone.

20. The length of the altitude of a right circular cone is 15 in. The length of an element of the cone is 25 in. Find the length of a radius of the base of the cone.

21. The length of a radius of the base of a right circular cone is 5 in. The length of an element of the cone is 10 in. Find, correct to the *nearest inch*, the length of the altitude of the cone.

12. Loci in Space

We have learned how to determine in a plane the locus of points which satisfy given conditions. We have seen that in a plane loci may consist of points and lines. Now we will determine in space the locus of points which satisfy given conditions. We will see that in space loci may consist of surfaces as well as points and lines.

In space geometry, we cannot actually construct on a flat sheet of paper the locus of points which satisfy given conditions. Therefore, we will visualize and sketch each locus informally. Also, because of our informal and limited treatment of space geometry, we will postulate the locus theorems rather than prove them.

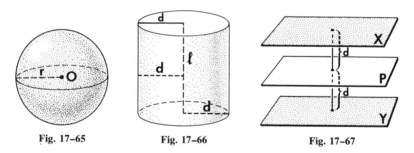

Fig. 17–65   Fig. 17–66   Fig. 17–67

Postulate S9. **In space, the locus of points a given distance from a given point is a sphere whose center is the given point and whose radius is the given distance.**

In Fig. 17–65, if the given point is O and the given distance is r, the sphere (spherical surface) shown is the locus of points whose distance from O is r.

Postulate S10. **In space, the locus of points at a given distance from a given line is a cylindrical surface.**

In Fig. 17–66, if the given line is l and the given distance is d, then the cylindrical surface shown is the locus of points whose distance from line l is d.

Postulate S11. **In space, the locus of points at a given distance from a given plane is a pair of planes parallel to the given plane and at the given distance from it.**

In Fig. 17–67, if the given plane is P and the given distance is d, then planes X and Y, which are both parallel to plane P, as shown, are the locus of points whose distance from plane P is d.

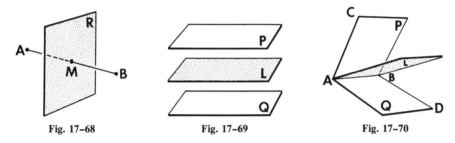

Fig. 17–68   Fig. 17–69   Fig. 17–70

Postulate S12. **In space, the locus of points equidistant from two given points is the plane perpendicular to the segment which joins the given points at its midpoint.**

In Fig. 17–68, if A and B are the given points, then plane R, which is perpendicular to $\overline{AB}$ at its midpoint M, as shown, is the locus of points equidistant from points A and B.

Postulate S13. **In space, the locus of points equidistant from two parallel planes is a third plane parallel to each of the given planes and midway between them.**

In Fig. 17–69, if planes P and Q are the given parallel planes, then plane L, which is parallel to both planes P and Q and is midway between them, as shown, is the locus of points equidistant from planes P and Q.

Postulate S14. **In space, the locus of points equidistant from the faces of a dihedral angle is the plane which bisects the dihedral angle.**

In Fig. 17–70, if planes P and Q are the faces of dihedral angle C-AB-D, then plane L, which bisects the dihedral angle, as shown, is the locus of points equidistant from planes P and Q.

MODEL PROBLEMS

1. Describe the locus of points equidistant from two concentric spheres the lengths of whose radii are 2 in. and 6 in.

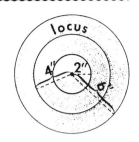

   Solution: The locus is a sphere (spherical surface) which has the same center as the given spheres and the length of whose radius is 4 in.

2. *Given:* Plane *R* and points *A* and *B* which are not in plane *R*. Line segment $\overline{AB}$ is not perpendicular to plane *R*.

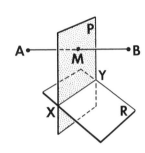

   a. Describe the locus of points equidistant from *A* and *B*.

   b. Describe the locus of points in plane *R* equidistant from *A* and *B*.

   Solution:

   a. The locus of points equidistant from *A* and *B* is a plane *P* perpendicular to $\overline{AB}$, the segment which joins *A* and *B*, at its midpoint *M*.

   b. The locus of points in plane *R* equidistant from *A* and *B* is a line $\overleftrightarrow{XY}$ which is the intersection of plane *P* and plane *R*.

3. *Given:* Planes *R* and *S* are parallel planes and the distance between them is 8 in. Point *P* is 2 in. from plane *R* and 6 in. from plane *S*.

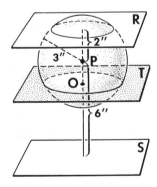

   a. Describe the locus of points equidistant from plane *R* and plane *S*.

   b. Describe the locus of points 3 in. from point *P*.

   c. Describe the locus of points which are equidistant from planes *R* and *S* and 3 in. from point *P*.

Solution:

a. The locus of points equidistant from parallel planes *R* and *S* is plane *T*, which is parallel to both planes *R* and *S* and midway between them.

b. The locus of points 3 in. from point *P* is a sphere (spherical surface) whose center is point *P* and the length of whose radius is 3 in.

c. The locus of points which are equidistant from planes *R* and *S* and 3 in. from *P* is the intersection of plane *T* with the sphere (spherical surface) whose center is *P*. This intersection is circle *O*, which is a small circle of sphere *P*.

EXERCISES

1. Describe the locus of points equidistant from two opposite faces of a rectangular solid.

2. Describe the locus of points equidistant from two parallel faces of a rectangular solid.

3. Describe the locus of points equidistant from two adjacent faces of a rectangular solid.

4. Describe the locus of points in space equidistant from two points *M* and *N* which are 10 inches apart.

5. Describe the locus of points in space 10 inches from a given point *P*.

6. Describe the locus of points in space 10 inches from a given line *l*.

7. Describe the locus of points in space 10 inches from a given plane *P*.

8. Describe the locus of points in space which are 5 inches from a sphere whose radius is 3 inches long.

9. Describe the locus of points in space which are equidistant from two concentric spheres whose radii are 4 inches and 12 inches long.

10. Planes *R* and *S* are parallel, and plane *T* is not parallel to planes *R* and *S*. (*a*) Describe the locus of points in space equidistant from planes *R* and *S*. (*b*) Describe the locus of points in space 5 inches from plane *T*. (*c*) Describe the locus of points in space which are equidistant from planes *R* and *S* and which are also 5 inches from plane *T*.

11. *P-AB-R* is a dihedral angle. Point *C* is in plane *P* but not in plane *R*. Point *D* is in plane *R* but not in plane *P*. (*a*) Describe the locus of points in space equidistant from the faces of dihedral angle *P-AB-R*. (*b*) Describe the locus of points in space equidistant from points *C* and *D*. (*c*) Describe the locus of points that satisfy the conditions stated in both part *a* and part *b*.

12. Plane R intersects plane S. (*a*) Describe the locus of points in space at a given distance d from plane R. (*b*) Describe the locus of points in space at the given distance d from plane S. (*c*) Describe the locus of points in space that satisfy the conditions stated in both part *a* and part *b*.

13. Planes M and N are parallel planes and the distance between them is 20 in. Point P is 4 in. from plane M and 16 in. from plane N.

    a. Describe the locus of points in space equidistant from plane M and plane N.

    b. Describe the locus of points in space d inches from point P.

    c. Describe the locus of points which satisfy the conditions stated in both part *a* and part *b* when:

    (1) $d > 6$ in.   (2) $d = 6$ in.   (3) $d < 6$ in.

14. Describe the locus of points in space which are a given distance d from a given plane and equidistant from two points in the plane.

15. A line is perpendicular to a plane. Describe the locus of points in space which are a given distance d from the line and equidistant from two points on the line.

16. A line is perpendicular to a plane. Describe the locus of points in space that are a given distance d from the line and the given distance d from a point on the line.

17. *a*. Describe the locus of points in a plane that are equidistant from the vertices of a square.

    b. Describe the locus of points in space that are equidistant from the vertices of a square.

18. Describe the locus of points in space that are the centers of spheres tangent to the faces of a dihedral angle.

19. The distance between two points A and B is represented by d. Describe the locus of points in space equidistant from A and B and whose distance from A is a constant (*a*) greater than $\frac{d}{2}$. (*b*) equal to $\frac{d}{2}$. (*c*) less than $\frac{d}{2}$.

13. Measuring Surface Areas of Solid Figures

Although it is possible to prove the theorems dealing with the measurement of the surface areas of solid figures, we will postulate some of these theorems because of our informal and limited treatment of solid geometry.

The Right Prism

Definition. **The *lateral area of a prism* is the sum of the areas of its lateral faces.**

Definition. **The *total area of a prism* is the sum of its lateral area and the areas of its two bases.**

In our work, we will consider only the right prism.

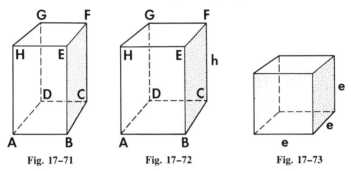

Fig. 17–71   Fig. 17–72   Fig. 17–73

In the right prism shown in Fig. 17–71:

1. The lateral area is equal to the sum of the areas of the four rectangular faces, or

   area of $ABEH$ + area of $BCFE$ + area of $CDGF$ + area of $DAHG$

2. The total area is equal to the sum of the lateral area and the areas of the two bases, or the sum of the following areas of rectangles:

   (area of $ABEH$ + area of $BCFE$ + area of $CDGF$ + area of $DAHG$) + (area of $ABCD$ + area of $HEFG$)

Postulate S15. **The lateral area of a right prism is equal to the product of the perimeter of its base and the measure of its altitude.**

In Fig. 17–72, if the lateral area of a right prism is represented by S, the perimeter of the base is represented by p, and the measure of the altitude of the prism is represented by h, then

$$S = ph$$

If the total area of a right prism is represented by T, its lateral area is represented by S, and the area of its base is represented by B, then

$$T = S + 2B$$

Theorem S21. **In a cube the length of whose edge is represented by e, whose lateral area is represented by S, and whose total area is represented by T, (a) $S = 4e^2$ and (b) $T = 6e^2$.**

We can derive these formulas in the following manner:

In Fig. 17–73, where the right prism shown pictures a cube the length of whose edge is represented by e, we have:

(a) $S = ph = 4e \cdot e = 4e^2$,   or $S = 4e^2$

(b) $T = S + 2B = 4e^2 + 2e^2 = 6e^2$,   or $T = 6e^2$

MODEL PROBLEMS

1. Find the lateral area and total area of a rectangular solid in which the dimensions of the base are 5 in. and 4 in. and the length of the altitude is 3 in.

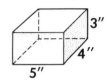

Solution:

1. Perimeter of the base, $p = 5 + 4 + 5 + 4 = 18$.

2. Altitude of the solid, $h = 3$.

3. Lateral area of the solid, $S = ph$

4. $\qquad\qquad\qquad\qquad S = (18)(3) = 54$

5. Area of the base, $B = (5)(4) = 20$.

6. Total area of the solid, $T = S + 2B$

7. $\qquad\qquad T = 54 + 2(20) = 54 + 40 = 94$

Answer: Lateral area $= 54$ sq. in., total area $= 94$ sq. in.

2. If the total area of a cube is 150 sq. in., find the length of an edge of the cube.

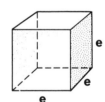

Solution:

1. Total area of the cube, $T = 6e^2$

2. $\qquad\qquad\qquad 150 = 6e^2$

3. $\qquad\qquad\qquad 25 = e^2$

4. $\qquad\qquad\qquad 5 = e$

Answer: The length of an edge of the cube is 5 in.

EXERCISES

1. Find the lateral area and the total area of a rectangular solid with the following dimensions:

   a. $l = 6$ in., $w = 3$ in., $h = 7$ in.   b. $l = 8$ ft., $w = 3$ ft., $h = 6$ ft.

   c. $l = 9$ ft., $w = 8$ ft., $h = \frac{1}{3}$ ft.   d. $l = 10$ ft., $w = 4$ ft., $h = 6$ in.

2. Find the lateral area and the total area of a cube if the measure of an edge of the cube is:
   a. 3 ft.   *b.* 8 in.   *c.* 10 in.   *d.* $\frac{1}{4}$ yd.   *e.* 1.5 in.

3. Find the lateral area and the total area of a right triangular prism if the base of the prism is an equilateral triangle whose side measures 10 in. and the altitude of the prism measures 8 in.

4. Find the lateral area and the total area of a right hexagonal prism if the base of the prism is a regular hexagon whose side measures 5 in. and the altitude of the prism measures 4 in.

5. Find the lateral area and the total area of a right triangular prism if the base of the prism is a right triangle whose legs measure 5 in. and 12 in. and the altitude of the prism measures 8 in.

6. If the lateral area of a cube is 36 square inches, find the length of an edge of the cube.

7. If the total area of a cube is 36 square inches, find the length of an edge.

8. The base of a right prism is a rhombus whose diagonals measure 10 in. and 2 ft. The altitude of the prism measures 6 in. Find the lateral area and the total area of the prism.

9. A room is 15 ft. long, 12 ft. wide, and 8 ft. high. Find the number of square feet of wallpaper that would be needed to paper the four walls.

10. Find the number of square inches of sheet metal needed to make a closed box 12 in. long, 9 in. wide, and 6 in. deep.

11. An open-top aquarium in the form of a rectangular solid is made of plate glass. If the width, length, and height of the tank measure respectively 24 in., 48 in., and 18 in., find the number of square feet of plate glass required to make the tank.

12. If the diagonal of the base of a cube measures 6 inches, find the lateral area and the total area of the cube.

13. Prove that the ratio of the total area of a cube to the lateral area of the cube is 3:2.

14. Prove that if the edge of a cube measures twice the edge of a smaller cube, the total area of the large cube is four times the total area of the small cube.

15. Prove that the lateral area of a right prism is equal to the perimeter of its base multiplied by the measure of its altitude.

The Regular Pyramid

Definition. The *lateral area of a pyramid* is the sum of the areas of its lateral faces.

Definition. The *total area of a pyramid* is the sum of its lateral area and the area of its base.

In our work, we will consider only the regular pyramid. In the regular square pyramid shown in Fig. 17–74:

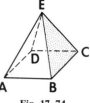

1. The lateral area is equal to the sum of the areas of the four lateral triangular faces, or area of $\triangle ABE$ + area of $\triangle BCE$ + area of $\triangle CDE$ + area of $\triangle DAE$.

Fig. 17–74

2. The total area is the sum of the lateral area and the area of the base, which is a square, or

(area of $\triangle ABE$ + area of $\triangle BCE$ + area of $\triangle CDE$ + area of $\triangle DAE$) + area of square $ABCD$

Postulate S16. The lateral area of a regular pyramid is equal to one-half the product of the perimeter of its base and the measure of its slant height.

In Fig. 17–75, if the lateral area of a regular pyramid is represented by S, the perimeter of the base is represented by p, and the measure of the slant height of the pyramid is represented by l, then

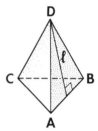

$$S = \frac{1}{2}pl$$

If the total area of a regular pyramid is represented by T, its lateral area is represented by S, and the area of its base is represented by B, then

Fig. 17–75

$$T = S + B$$

MODEL PROBLEM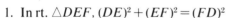

Find the lateral area and the total area of a regular triangular pyramid if each edge of the base measures 6 in. and each lateral edge of the pyramid measures 5 in. [Answers may be left in radical form.]

Solution: Since the given pyramid is a regular pyramid, $\triangle HDF$ is an isosceles triangle. Slant height $\overline{DE} \perp \overline{HF}$ and $\overline{DE}$ bisects $\overline{HF}$. Therefore, $EF = 3$.

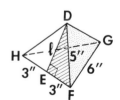

1. In rt. $\triangle DEF$, $(DE)^2 + (EF)^2 = (FD)^2$

2. $\qquad\qquad l^2 + (3)^2 = (5)^2$

3. $\qquad\qquad l^2 + 9 = 25$

4. $\qquad\qquad l^2 = 16$

5. $\qquad\qquad l = 4$

6. The perimeter of equilateral triangle FGH, the base of the pyramid, is 18 in.

7. Lateral area of the pyramid, $S = \frac{1}{2}pl$
$$S = \frac{1}{2}(18)(4) = (9)(4) = 36$$

8. Area of equilateral triangle $FGH = \frac{s^2}{4}\sqrt{3} = \frac{(6)^2}{4}\sqrt{3} = \frac{36}{4}\sqrt{3} = 9\sqrt{3}.$

9. Total area of the pyramid, $T = S + B$
$$T = 36 + 9\sqrt{3}$$

Answer: Lateral area $= 36$ sq. in., total area $= (36 + 9\sqrt{3})$ sq. in.

EXERCISES

In the following exercises, answers may be left in radical form:

1. Find the lateral area of a regular pyramid if the perimeter of its base is 20 in. and its slant height measures 8 in.

2. Find the lateral area and the total area of a regular square pyramid if each side of the square base measures 12 in. and the slant height measures 20 in.

3. The base of a regular pyramid is a pentagon. If the lateral area of the pyramid is 100 sq. in. and the slant height measures 4 in., find the measure of a side of the pentagon.

4. Find the lateral area and the total area of a regular triangular pyramid if each edge of the base measures 10 in. and each lateral edge of the pyramid measures 13 in.

5. The base of a regular pyramid is a hexagon each of whose sides measures 12 in. The lateral edge of the pyramid measures 10 in. Find the lateral area and the total area of the pyramid.

6. Each side of the base of a regular square pyramid measures 24 in. The altitude of the pyramid measures 5 in. Find the lateral area and the total area of the pyramid.

7. Each side of the base of a regular square pyramid measures 6 in. and the lateral edge of the pyramid measures 5 in. Find the lateral area and the total area of the pyramid.

8. Each of the six edges of a triangular pyramid measures 4 ft. Find the total area of the pyramid.

9. Find the lateral area and the total area of a regular hexagonal pyramid which has an altitude of 8 in. and a lateral edge of 10 in.

10. Prove that the lateral area of a regular pyramid is equal to one-half its perimeter multiplied by the measure of its slant height.

The Right Circular Cylinder

Definition. **The** *lateral area of a cylinder* **is equal to the area of its curved cylindrical surface.**

Definition. **The** *total area of a cylinder* **is equal to the sum of its lateral area and the areas of its two circular bases.**

In our work, we will consider only the right circular cylinder. (See Fig. 17–76.)

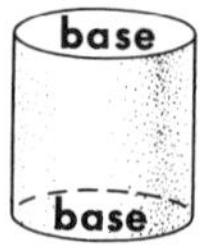

Postulate S17. **The lateral area of a right circular cylinder is equal to the product of the circumference of its base and the measure of its altitude.**

Fig. 17–76

If the lateral area of a right circular cylinder is represented by S, the circumference of its base by C, the length of the radius of the base by r, and the length of its altitude by h (Fig. 17–77), then

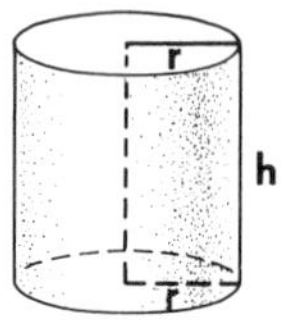

$$S = Ch, \quad \text{or} \quad S = 2\pi rh$$

Fig. 17–77

If the total area of a right circular cylinder is represented by T, the area of its base is represented by B, the length of the radius of the base is represented by r, and the length of the altitude of the cylinder is represented by h, then

$$T = S + 2B, \quad \text{or} \quad T = 2\pi rh + 2\pi r^2$$

MODEL PROBLEM

Find, in terms of π, the lateral area and the total area of a right circular cylinder if the radius of its base measures 5 in. and its altitude measures 8 in.

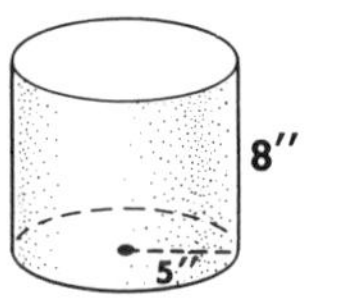

Solution:

1. Lateral area of the cylinder, $S = 2\pi rh$

2. $S = 2\pi(5)(8) = 80\pi$

3. Total area of the cylinder, $T = 2\pi rh + 2\pi r^2$

4. $T = 2\pi(5)(8) + 2\pi(5)^2$

5. $T = 80\pi + 50\pi = 130\pi$

Answer: Lateral area $= 80\pi$ sq. in., total area $= 130\pi$ sq. in.

EXERCISES

1. Find, in terms of π, the lateral area and the total area of a right circular cylinder in which: (*a*) $r = 4$ ft., $h = 12$ ft. (*b*) $r = 7$ in., $h = 6$ in. (*c*) $r = 6.5$ in., $h = 10$ in.

2. The lateral area of a right circular cylinder is 64π sq. in. If the radius of the base of the cylinder measures 4 in., find the measure of the altitude of the cylinder.

3. The lateral area of a right circular cylinder is 100π sq. ft. If the altitude of the cylinder measures 10 ft., find the measure of the radius of the base of the cylinder.

4. Find how many square inches of sheet metal are needed to make a closed right cylindrical can if the radius of the base measures 7 in. and the height of the can measures 10 in. [Use $\pi = \frac{22}{7}$.]

5. Find the number of square feet of steel required to make an open-top cylindrical tank if the radius of its base measures 10 ft. and its height measures 15 ft. [Use $\pi = 3.14$.]

6. A manufacturer makes a closed right cylindrical can whose base has a radius of 7 in. and whose height measures 14 in. He also makes a can whose base has a radius of 14 in. and whose height measures 7 in. (*a*) Which can requires more metal? (*b*) How much more metal does it require? [Use $\pi = \frac{22}{7}$.]

7. In a right circular cylinder, the radius of the base measures 21 in. and the height measures 10 in. In a second right circular cylinder, the radius of the base measures 42 in. and the height measures 10 in.
   a. Find the ratio of the lateral area of the large cylinder to the lateral area of the small cylinder.
   b. If the measure of the radius of the base of a cylinder is doubled and the measure of the height is unchanged, what is the ratio of the lateral area of the large cylinder to the lateral area of the small cylinder? Prove your answer.

8. The sides of a rectangle measure 8 in. and 5 in.
   a. Find the lateral area and the total area of the cylinder which is generated by revolving the rectangle about the 8-inch side as an axis.
   b. Find the lateral area and the total area of the cylinder which is generated by revolving the rectangle about the 5-inch side as an axis.

9. The lateral area of a right circular cylinder is represented by S, the measure of the radius of its base is represented by r, and the measure of its altitude is represented by h. Represent r in terms of S and h.

The Right Circular Cone

Definition. The *lateral area of a cone* is equal to the area of its curved conical surface.

Definition. The *total area of a cone* is equal to the sum of its lateral area and the area of its base.

In our work, we will consider only the right circular cone. (See Fig. 17–78.)

Postulate S18. The lateral area of a right circular cone is equal to one-half the product of the circumference of its base and the measure of its slant height.

Fig. 17–78

If the lateral area of a right circular cone is represented by S, the circumference of the base is represented by C, the measure of the radius of the base is represented by r, and the measure of the slant height is represented by l (Fig. 17–79), then

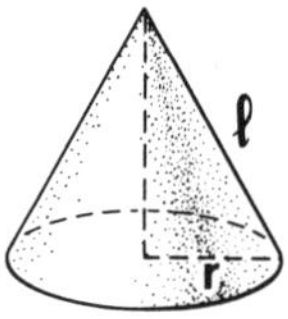

Fig. 17–79

$$S = \frac{1}{2}Cl, \quad \text{or} \quad S = \pi rl \quad (C = 2\pi r)$$

If the total area of a right circular cone is represented by T, the area of its base is represented by B, the measure of the radius of its base is represented by r, and the measure of its slant height is represented by l, then

$$T = S + B, \quad \text{or} \quad T = \pi rl + \pi r^2$$

MODEL PROBLEM

Find the lateral area and the total area of a right circular cone in which the radius of the base measures 14 in. and the slant height measures 20 in. [Use $\pi = \frac{22}{7}$.]

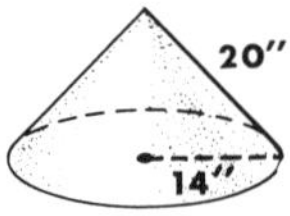

Solution:

1. Lateral area of the cone, $S = \pi rl$

2. $\qquad\qquad S = (\frac{22}{7})(14)(20) = 880$

3. Total area of the cone, $T = \pi rl + \pi r^2$

4. $\qquad\qquad T = (\frac{22}{7})(14)(20) + (\frac{22}{7})(14)(14)$

5. $\qquad\qquad T = 880 + 616 = 1496$

Answer: Lateral area = 880 sq. in., total area = 1496 sq. in.

EXERCISES

1. Find, in terms of π, the lateral area and the total area of a right circular cone in which: (a) $r = 8$ in., $l = 12$ in. (b) $r = 5$ in., the length of the altitude $= 12$ in. (c) the length of the altitude $= 8$ in., $l = 10$ in.

2. If the lateral area of a right circular cone is 36π sq. in. and the radius of its base measures 3 in., find the measures of the slant height and the altitude of the cone.

3. A large canvas tent is in the form of a right circular cone. Find the number of square feet of material it has if the measure of the radius of the base of the tent is 42 ft. and the measure of the altitude of the cone is 28 ft. [Use $\pi = \frac{22}{7}$.]

4. The legs of a right triangle measure 6 in. and 8 in.
   a. Find the lateral area of the right circular cone that is generated when the triangle is rotated about the 6-inch side as an axis.
   b. Find the lateral area of the right circular cone that is generated when the triangle is rotated about the 8-inch side as an axis.

5. The lateral area of a cone is 70% of its total area. Find the ratio of the measure of the slant height of the cone to the measure of the radius of the cone.

6. The measure of the radius of the base of a cone is equal to the measure of the slant height of a second cone, and the measure of the slant height of the first cone is equal to the measure of the radius of the base of the second cone. What is the relationship between the lateral areas of the two cones?

7. If the measure of the radius of a cone and the measure of the slant height of a cone are each doubled, by what number is the lateral area of the cone multiplied?

The Sphere

Definition. **The *area of a sphere* is equal to the area of its curved spherical surface.**

Postulate S19. **The area of a sphere is equal to four times the area of one of its great circles.**

If the area of a sphere is represented by S, the area of one of its great circles is represented by A, and the measure of the radius of the sphere is represented by r (Fig. 17–80), then

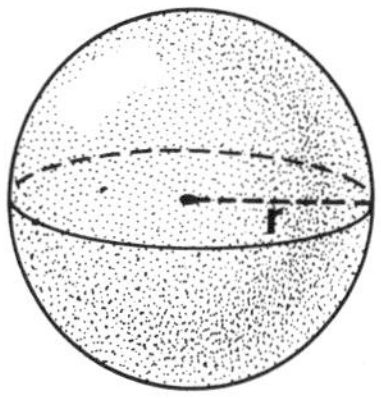

$$S = 4A, \quad \text{or} \quad S = 4\pi r^2 \qquad (A = \pi r^2)$$

Fig. 17–80

MODEL PROBLEM

Find the area of a sphere whose radius measures 14 in.
  [Use $\pi = \frac{22}{7}$.]

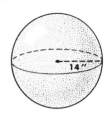

Solution:

1. Area of the sphere, $S = 4\pi r^2$

2. $\qquad\qquad\qquad S = 4(\frac{22}{7})(14)(14)$

3. $\qquad\qquad\qquad S = 2464$

Answer: Area of the sphere = 2464 sq. in.

EXERCISES

1. Express, in terms of π, the area of a sphere whose radius measures:
   a. 2 in.   *b.* 5 in.   *c.* $\frac{1}{2}$ ft.   *d.* $\sqrt{5}$ yd.   *e.* $3\sqrt{2}$ in.
2. Express, in terms of π, the area of a sphere whose diameter measures:
   a. 4 in.   *b.* 7 ft.   *c.* 1 yd.   *d.* $\sqrt{8}$ yd.   *e.* $4\sqrt{3}$ in.
3. The area of a sphere is 100π sq. in. Find the measure of the radius of the sphere.
4. The area of a sphere is 12π sq. ft. Find the measure of the diameter of the sphere.
5. The ratio of the measures of the radii of two spheres is 1:3. Find the ratio of the areas of the two spheres.
6. The ratio of the areas of two spheres is 25:1. Find the ratio of the measures of the radii of the two spheres.
7. A sphere is inscribed in a cylinder as shown.
   a. Prove that the lateral area of the cylinder is equal to the area of the sphere.
   b. Prove that the ratio of the total area of the cylinder to the area of the sphere is 3:2.

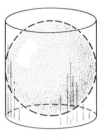

Ex. 7

14. Measuring Volumes of Solid Figures

We will assume that with every closed solid figure there is associated a unique positive number called the *volume* of the figure.

Definition. A *unit of volume* is the space contained in a cube that measures one unit on a side.

A *cubic inch* (cu. in.) is the space contained in a cube whose length, width, and height each measures one inch, as shown in Fig. 17–81. Other cubic units are the *cubic foot* (cu. ft.), the *cubic yard* (cu. yd.), and the *cubic centimeter* (cu. cm.).

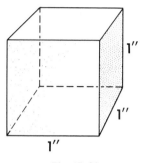

Fig. 17–81

Definition. The *volume of a solid* is the number of units of volume contained in the interior of the solid.

Although it is possible to prove the theorems dealing with the measurement of volumes of solid figures, we will postulate some of these theorems because of our informal and limited treatment of solid geometry.

The Right Prism

In our work, we will consider only the right prism.

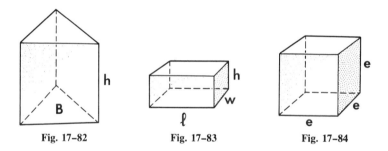

Fig. 17–82   Fig. 17–83   Fig. 17–84

Postulate S20. The volume of a right prism is equal to the product of the area of its base and the measure of its altitude.

In Fig. 17–82, if the volume of a right prism is represented by V, the area of the base of the prism is represented by B, and the measure of the altitude of the prism is represented by h, then

$$V = Bh$$

Theorem S22. The volume of a rectangular solid is the product of the measures of its length, width, and height.

In Fig. 17–83, if the volume of a rectangular solid is represented by V, and the measures of the length, width, and height of the solid are represented by l, w, and h respectively, then $V = Bh$ becomes

$$V = lwh \qquad (B = lw)$$

Theorem S23. The volume of a cube is equal to the cube of the measure of an edge.

In Fig. 17–84, if the volume of a cube is represented by V and the measure of an edge of the cube is represented by e, then $V = lwh$ becomes

$$V = e \cdot e \cdot e, \quad \text{or} \quad V = e^3 \qquad (l = e, w = e, h = e)$$

MODEL PROBLEMS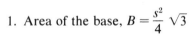

1. The base of a right prism is an equilateral triangle each of whose sides measures 4 in. The altitude of the prism measures 5 in. Find the volume of the prism. [Answer may be left in radical form.]

   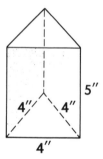

   Solution: The base of the prism is an equilateral triangle.

   1. Area of the base, $B = \dfrac{s^2}{4} \sqrt{3}$

   2. $\qquad B = \dfrac{(4)^2}{4} \sqrt{3} = \dfrac{16}{4} \sqrt{3} = 4\sqrt{3}$

   3. Volume of the prism, $V = Bh$

   4. $\qquad V = (4\sqrt{3})(5) = 20\sqrt{3}$

   Answer: Volume of prism $= 20\sqrt{3}$ cu. in.

2. How many cubic feet are contained in a packing case which is a rectangular solid 4 ft. long, 3 ft. wide, and $3\frac{1}{2}$ ft. high?

   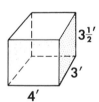

   Solution: The packing case is a rectangular solid.

   1. Volume of the solid, $V = lwh$

   2. $\qquad V = (4)(3)(3\frac{1}{2}) = 42$

   Answer: The packing case contains 42 cu. ft.

3. Find the volume of a cube whose total area is 54 sq. in.

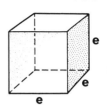

Solution:

1. Total area of the cube, $T = 6e^2$

2. $\qquad\qquad\qquad 54 = 6e^2$

3. $\qquad\qquad\qquad 9 = e^2$

4. $\qquad\qquad\qquad 3 = e$

5. Volume of the cube, $V = e^3$

6. $\qquad\qquad\qquad V = (3)^3 = 27$

Answer: Volume of cube = 27 cu. in.

EXERCISES

In the following exercises, answers may be left in radical form:

1. Find the volume of a right prism if the area of its base is 20 sq. in. and its altitude measures 8 in.

2. The base of a right prism is a right triangle in which the legs measure 6 in. and 8 in. The altitude of the prism measures 5.5 in. Find the volume of the prism.

3. Find the volume of a rectangular solid with the following dimensions:
   a. $l = 5$ in., $w = 4$ in., $h = 7$ in.   *b.* $l = 10$ ft., $w = 3$ ft., $h = 6$ ft.
   c. $l = 12$ ft., $w = 8$ ft., $h = \frac{1}{3}$ ft.   *d.* $l = 14$ ft., $w = 4$ ft., $h = 6$ in.

4. Find the volume of a cube if an edge of the cube measures:
   a. 5 ft.   *b.* 10 in.   *c.* 7 cm.   *d.* $\frac{1}{3}$ yd.   *e.* 2.5 in.

5. The base of a right triangular prism is an equilateral triangle whose side measures 6 in. The altitude of the prism measures 12 in. Find the volume of the prism.

6. The base of a right prism is a regular hexagon whose side measures 8 in. The altitude of the prism measures 5 in. Find the volume of the prism.

7. If the volume of a cube is 150 cu. in., find the length of an edge.

8. Find the volume of a cube whose lateral area is 64 sq. in.

9. The base of a right prism is a rhombus whose diagonals measure 6 in. and 8 in. The altitude of the prism measures 9 in. Find the volume of the prism.

10. Over a rectangular driveway 60 feet long and 9 feet wide, a layer of crushed rock is to be spread to an average depth of 4 inches. Find the number of cubic feet of crushed rock that must be used.

11. One gallon contains 231 cubic inches. How many gallons will a tank which is a rectangular solid hold if it is 22 in. long, 14 in. wide, and 12 in. high?

12. The excavation for the foundation of a house is to be 48 ft. long, 30 ft. wide, and 6 ft. deep. How many cubic yards of earth must be removed?

13. A diagonal of the base of a cube measures $6\sqrt{2}$ in. Find the volume of the cube.

14. The volume of a cube is equal to the volume of a rectangular solid which has a length of 20 in., a width of 5 in., and a height of 10 in. Find the length of an edge of the cube.

15. The measure of the length of the base of a rectangular solid is 3 in. more than the measure of the width. The height of the solid measures 5 in. If the volume of the solid is 140 cu. in., find the measure of the sides of the base.

The Pyramid

Postulate S21. The volume of a pyramid is equal to one-third the product of the area of its base and the measure of its altitude.

If the volume of a pyramid is represented by V, the area of its base is represented by B, and the measure of its altitude is represented by h (Fig. 17–85), then

$$V = \frac{1}{3}Bh$$

Fig. 17–85

MODEL PROBLEM

Find the volume of a regular square pyramid if each edge of the base measures 10 in. and the slant height of the pyramid measures 13 in.

Solution:

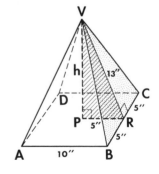

1. In rt. $\triangle VPR$, $(VP)^2 + (PR)^2 = (VR)^2$

2. $\qquad\qquad h^2 + (5)^2 = (13)^2$

3. $\qquad\qquad h^2 + 25 = 169$

4. $\qquad\qquad h^2 = 144$

5. $\qquad\qquad h = 12$

6. Area of the base of the pyramid,
$$B = s^2 = (10)^2 = 100$$

7. Volume of pyramid, $V = \frac{1}{3}Bh$

8. $\qquad\qquad V = \frac{1}{3}(100)(12) = 400$

Answer: Volume of pyramid = 400 cu. in.

EXERCISES

In the following exercises, answers may be left in radical form:

1. The area of the base of a pyramid is 35 sq. in. If the measure of the altitude of the pyramid is 4 in., find its volume.

2. The volume of a pyramid is 144 cu. in. If the measure of the altitude of the pyramid is 8 in., find the area of its base.

3. The area of the base of a pyramid is 36 sq. in. If the volume of the pyramid is 180 cu. in., find the measure of its altitude.

4. Find the volume of a regular square pyramid if each edge of its base measures 8 in. and its altitude measures 10 in.

5. Find the volume of a regular triangular pyramid whose base edge measures 12 in. and whose altitude measures 8 in.

6. Each edge of the base of a regular hexagonal pyramid measures 6 in. If the altitude of the pyramid measures 4 in., find its volume.

7. The base of a pyramid is a right triangle whose legs measure 12 in. and 16 in. The altitude of the pyramid measures 9 in. Find the volume of the pyramid.

8. The base edge of a regular square pyramid measures 12 in. The slant height of the pyramid measures 10 in. Find the volume of the pyramid.

9. Find the volume of a regular square pyramid if each edge of its base measures 6 in. and each lateral edge measures 12 in.

10. Each base edge of a regular hexagonal pyramid measures 6 in. The altitude of the pyramid measures 8 in. Find: (a) the measure of a lateral edge of the pyramid   (b) the measure of the slant height of the pyramid   (c) the lateral area of the pyramid   (d) the total area of the pyramid   (e) the volume of the pyramid.

11. If the measure of each base edge of a regular pyramid is represented by e and the measure of the altitude of the pyramid is represented by h, represent, in terms of e and h, the volume of the pyramid if its base is: (a) a square   (b) an equilateral triangle   (c) a regular hexagon.

The Right Circular Cylinder

In our work, we will consider only the right circular cylinder.

Postulate S22. **The volume of a right circular cylinder is equal to the product of the area of its base and the measure of its altitude.**

If the volume of a right circular cylinder is represented by V, the area of its base is represented by B, the measure of the radius of the base is represented by r, and the measure of the altitude is represented by h (Fig. 17–86), then

$$V = Bh, \quad \text{or} \quad V = \pi r^2 h \qquad (B = \pi r^2)$$

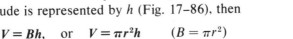

Fig. 17–86

MODEL PROBLEM

Find, in terms of π, the volume of a right circular cylinder if the radius of its base measures 4 in. and its altitude measures 5 in.

Solution:

1. Volume of the cylinder, $V = \pi r^2 h$

2. $\qquad V = \pi(4)^2(5) = \pi(16)(5)$

3. $\qquad V = 80\pi$

Answer: Volume of cylinder $= 80\pi$ cu. in.

EXERCISES

In the following exercises, answers may be left in terms of π unless otherwise indicated:

1. Find the volume of a right circular cylinder if the area of its base is 154 sq. in. and its altitude measures 8 in.

2. Find the volume of a right circular cylinder if the radius of its base measures 6 in. and its altitude measures 12 in.

3. Find the volume of a right circular cylinder if the diameter of its base measures 14 in. and its altitude measures 10 in.

4. The circumference of the base of a right circular cylinder is 18π in. The altitude of the cylinder measures 7 in. Find the volume of the cylinder.

5. The radius of a cylindrical can measures $3\frac{1}{2}$ in. Its height measures 8 in. Find the capacity of the can in cubic inches. [Use $\pi = \frac{22}{7}$.]

6. Find the volume of a cylindrical oil tank if the diameter of the base measures 70 ft. and the height measures 40 ft. [Use $\pi = \frac{22}{7}$.]

7. A cylindrical tank used for storing water has a diameter of 12 feet and a height of 14 feet. How many gallons of water will the tank hold? [One cubic foot contains 7.5 gallons.]

8. The sides of a rectangle measure 6 in. and 3 in.
   a. Find the volume of a cylinder which is generated by revolving the rectangle about the 6-inch side as an axis.
   b. Find the volume of a cylinder which is generated by revolving the rectangle about the 3-inch side as an axis.

9. Two cylinders have congruent bases. The measure of the altitude of one cylinder is twice the measure of the altitude of the other cylinder. Compare the volumes of the cylinders.

10. Two cylinders have congruent altitudes. The ratio of the measures of the radii of their bases is 3:1. Find the ratio of their volumes.

11. The figure shows a right circular cylinder inscribed in a cube the measure of whose edge is represented by e. Express the volume of the cylinder in terms of e.

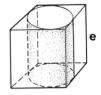

The Right Circular Cone

In our work, we will consider only the right circular cone.

Postulate S23. **The volume of a right circular cone is equal to one-third the product of the area of its base and the measure of its altitude.**

If the volume of a right circular cone is represented by V, the area of its base is represented by B, the measure of the radius of its base is represented by r, and the measure of its altitude is represented by h (Fig. 17–87), then

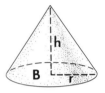

$$V = \frac{1}{3}Bh, \quad \text{or} \quad V = \frac{1}{3}\pi r^2 h \quad (B = \pi r^2)$$

Fig. 17–87

MODEL PROBLEM

Find, in terms of π, the volume of a right circular cone if the radius of its base measures 6 in. and its altitude measures 8 in.

Solution:

1. Volume of cone, $V = \frac{1}{3}\pi r^2 h$

2. $\qquad\qquad V = \frac{1}{3}\pi(6)^2(8)$

3. $\qquad\qquad V = \frac{1}{3}\pi(36)(8)$

4. $\qquad\qquad V = 96\pi$ cu. in.

Answer: Volume of cone $= 96\pi$ cu. in.

EXERCISES

In exercises 1–6, answers may be left in terms of π.

1. The area of the base of a right circular cone is 64π sq. in. The altitude of the cone measures 6 in. Find the volume of the cone.

2. Find the volume of a right circular cone if the radius of its base measures 10 in. and its altitude measures 9 in.

3. The diameter of the base of a right circular cone measures 7 in. The altitude of the cone measures 12 in. Find the volume of the cone.

4. The circumference of the base of a right circular cone is 6π in. The altitude of the cone measures 14 in. Find the volume of the cone.

5. The slant height of a right circular cone measures 13 in. The altitude of the cone measures 5 in. Find the volume of the cone.

6. A cone is generated by revolving a right triangle whose legs measure 5 in. and 7 in. about the 7-inch side as an axis. Find the volume of the cone.

7. Find to the *nearest cubic inch* the volume of an ice cream cone if the diameter of the base of the cone measures 2 in. and the height of the cone measures 4.5 in. [Use $\pi = 3.14$.]

8. In a right circular cylinder and a right circular cone, the radii of the bases are congruent and the altitudes are congruent. Compare the volumes of the two figures.

9. In two right circular cones, the altitudes are congruent and the ratio of the measures of the radii of their bases is 2:1. Find the ratio of the volumes of the two cones.

10. In two right circular cones, the radii of the bases are congruent and the ratio of the measures of the altitudes is 2:1. Find the ratio of the volumes of the two cones.

The Sphere

Postulate S24. **The volume of a sphere is equal to one-third the product of its area and the measure of its radius.**

If the volume of a sphere is represented by V, its area is represented by S, and the measure of its radius is represented by r (Fig. 17–88), then

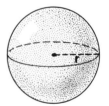

$$V = \frac{1}{3}Sr, \quad \text{or} \quad V = \frac{4}{3}\pi r^3 \qquad (S = 4\pi r^2)$$

Fig. 17–88

MODEL PROBLEM

Find to the *nearest cubic inch* the volume of a sphere whose radius measures 7 in. [Use $\pi = \frac{22}{7}$.]

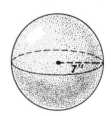

Solution:

1. Volume of sphere, $V = \frac{4}{3}\pi r^3$

2. $\qquad\qquad V = (\frac{4}{3})(\frac{22}{7})(7)(7)(7)$

3. $\qquad\qquad V = \frac{4}{3}(22)(49)$

4. $\qquad\qquad V = \frac{4312}{3} = 1437\frac{1}{3}$

Answer: Volume of sphere = 1437 cu. in.

EXERCISES

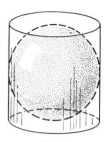

Ex. 6

1. Express, in terms of π, the volume of a sphere whose radius measures:
   a. 3 in.   *b.* 4 in.   *c.* $\frac{2}{3}$ ft.   *d.* 3.5 cm.   *e.* 1.4 ft.

2. Find, in terms of π, the volume of a sphere whose diameter measures 42 in.

3. Find, in terms of π, the volume of a sphere whose area is 144π sq. in.

4. The volume of a sphere is 36π cu. in. Find, in terms of π, the area of the sphere.

5. The ratio of the measures of the radii of two spheres is 2:1. Find the ratio of the volumes of the spheres.

6. A sphere is inscribed in a cylinder. Find the ratio of the volume of the cylinder to the volume of the sphere.

CHAPTER XVIII
Review of Algebra

1. Adding Signed Numbers

The Absolute Value of a Signed Number

The *absolute value* of a signed number represents the distance between the graph of the number and the zero point, or origin, on the real number line (see Fig. 18–1).

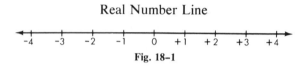

Real Number Line

Fig. 18-1

For example, the absolute value of +3 is 3, written $|+3| = 3$; the absolute value of -3 is 3, written $|-3| = 3$; the absolute value of +4 is 4, written $|+4| = 4$; the absolute value of -4 is 4, written $|-4| = 4$. Also, the absolute value of 0 is 0, written $|0| = 0$.

Note that since +3 and 3 represent the same number, $|3| = 3$. Similarly, $|4| = 4$.

The Opposite of a Signed Number

Because of the manner in which the above number line is constructed, we can see that each number on the number line can be paired with another number on the number line on the opposite side of 0 and at an equal distance from 0. For example, +3 can be paired with -3 because +3 and -3 are on opposite sides of 0, with each number being 3 units from 0. We say that -3 is the *opposite* of +3. Similarly +4 is the opposite of -4. We also say that the opposite of 0 is 0.

Adding Signed Numbers With Like Signs

PROCEDURE. To add signed numbers with like signs, add the absolute values of the numbers and place the common sign before the sum.

MODEL PROBLEMS

Add:

1. $+ 3$	2. $+15$	3. $- 4$	4. -15
$+10$	$+ 9$	-12	-14
$+13$	$+24$	-16	-29

Adding Signed Numbers With Unlike Signs

PROCEDURE. To add signed numbers with unlike signs, find the difference of the absolute values of the numbers and place the sign of the number which has the greater absolute value before the difference.

MODEL PROBLEMS

Add:

1. +8	**2.** −9	**3.** −6	**4.** +12
−3	+2	+8	−36
+5	−7	+2	−24

Adding Signed Numbers Which Are Opposites

The sum of two numbers which are opposites is 0. Thus $(+5) + (−5) = 0$.

When the sum of two numbers is 0, we call one of the numbers the *additive inverse* of the other number. Thus, $+5$ is the additive inverse of $−5$; $−5$ is the additive inverse of $+5$; $+9$ is the additive inverse of $−9$; $−9$ is the additive inverse of $+9$; 0 is the additive inverse of 0.

EXERCISES

In 1–16, add the signed numbers.

1. +15	**2.** −20	**3.** +12	**4.** +20	**5.** −50	**6.** +30
+ 9	−15	− 8	−60	+70	−30

7. $(+15) + (+19)$ **8.** $(+13) + (−32)$ **9.** $(−41) + (−9)$

10. $(−12) + (+37)$ **11.** $(−28) + (+19)$ **12.** $(−20) + (+20)$

13. $(+20) + (−15) + (+9)$ **14.** $(+30) + (−18) + (−12)$

15. $(−19) + (+8) + (−15)$ **16.** $(−17) + (−19) + (+40)$

2. Subtracting Signed Numbers

In the subtraction example $28 − 12 = 16$, the *subtrahend*, 12, is the number being subtracted. The *minuend*, 28, is the number from which the subtrahend is subtracted. The *difference*, 16, is the result of the subtraction.

Subtraction

28 minuend
12 subtrahend
16 difference

PROCEDURE 1. To subtract a signed number, add the opposite (the additive inverse) of the subtrahend to the minuend.

OR

PROCEDURE 2. To subtract a signed number, mentally change the sign of the subtrahend and add the result to the minuend.

MODEL PROBLEMS ~~~~~~~~~~~~~~~

Subtract:

1. $+30$	**2.** $+45$	**3.** -19	**4.** -19	**5.** -7
$\underline{+12}$	$\underline{-20}$	$\underline{+17}$	$\underline{-\ 7}$	$\underline{-7}$
$+18$	$+65$	-36	-12	0

EXERCISES

In 1–15, subtract.

1. $+50$	**2.** $+18$	**3.** $+15$	**4.** $+36$	**5.** -27	**6.** $+19$
$\underline{+30}$	$\underline{+29}$	$\underline{+15}$	$\underline{-15}$	$\underline{-\ 8}$	$\underline{-19}$

7. -39	**8.** -45	**9.** -26	**10.** -15	**11.** -20	**12.** -6
$\underline{+15}$	$\underline{+17}$	$\underline{-18}$	$\underline{-31}$	$\underline{-20}$	$\underline{+6}$

13. $(+19) - (+30)$ **14.** $(-12) - (-25)$ **15.** $(+22) - (-8)$

3. Multiplying Signed Numbers

PROCEDURE. To multiply two signed numbers:

1. When two signed numbers have like signs, find the product of the absolute values of the numbers and place a plus sign before the product.
2. When two signed numbers have unlike signs, find the product of the absolute values of the numbers and place a minus sign before the product.

The product of any signed number and 0 is 0. For example, $(+5)(0) = 0$; also, $(0)(-3) = 0$.

MODEL PROBLEMS ~~~~~~~~~~~~~~

Multiply:

1. $+12$	**2.** -13	**3.** $+18$	**4.** -15	**5.** $\ \ 0$
$\underline{+\ 4}$	$\underline{-\ 5}$	$\underline{-\ 3}$	$\underline{+\ 6}$	$\underline{-8}$
$+48$	$+65$	-54	-90	0

EXERCISES

In 1–12, multiply.

1. $+9$	**2.** $+20$	**3.** -11	**4.** -17	**5.** $+16$	**6.** $+9$
$\underline{+8}$	$\underline{+\ 4}$	$\underline{-\ 7}$	$\underline{+\ 3}$	$\underline{-\ 4}$	$\underline{\quad 0}$

7. $(+20)$ by $(+5)$ **8.** (-12) by (-5) **9.** $(+11)$ by (-7)

10. $(+8)$ by $(+\frac{3}{4})$ **11.** $(-\frac{3}{5})$ by (-20) **12.** $(+\frac{1}{2})$ by $(-\frac{2}{3})$

In 13–18, find the value of the given number expression.

13. $(+4)^2$ **14.** $(+10)^2$ **15.** $(-5)^2$ **16.** $(+\frac{1}{2})^2$ **17.** $(+\frac{3}{5})^2$ **18.** $(-\frac{1}{3})^2$

4. Dividing Signed Numbers

In the division example $36 \div 9 = 4$, or $\frac{36}{9} = 4$, the *dividend*, 36, is the number which is being divided. The *divisor*, 9, is the number by which we divide. The *quotient*, 4, is the result of the division.

Division

$$\frac{\text{dividend}}{\text{divisor}} \ \frac{36}{9} = 4 \text{ quotient}$$

PROCEDURE. To divide signed numbers:

1. When two signed numbers have like signs, find the quotient of the absolute values of the numbers and place a plus sign before the quotient.
2. When two signed numbers have unlike signs, find the quotient of the absolute values of the numbers and place a minus sign before the quotient.

Zero divided by any number other than zero gives a quotient of zero. For example, $0 \div 6 = 0$.

It is meaningless to divide a number by zero. For example, $6 \div 0$ has no answer because there is no number which, when multiplied by 0, gives 6 as the result.

MODEL PROBLEMS

Divide:

1. $(+60) \div (+15) = +4$ **2.** $(-27) \div (-3) = +9$

3. $(+90) \div (-10) = -9$ **4.** $(-45) \div (+9) = -5$

EXERCISES

In 1–18, divide.

1. $(+18)$ by $(+6)$ **2.** (-36) by (-3) **3.** $(+52)$ by (-4)

4. $(+84)$ by (-12) **5.** (-30) by (-6) **6.** $(+100)$ by (-25)

7. $(+55) \div (-11)$ **8.** $(0) \div (+7)$ **9.** $(-144) \div (+9)$

10. $(+4) \div (-8)$ **11.** $(-6) \div (-9)$ **12.** $(-15) \div (-12)$

13. $(-5) \div (-9)$ **14.** $(+3) \div (-7)$ **15.** $(+20) \div (-8)$

16. $\begin{array}{r} +24 \\ +\ 6 \\ \hline \end{array}$ **17.** $\begin{array}{r} -45 \\ -\ 9 \\ \hline \end{array}$ **18.** $\begin{array}{r} +24 \\ -16 \\ \hline \end{array}$

5. Adding Algebraic Expressions

Like terms are terms having the same variables as factors, with corresponding variables having the same exponent. Examples of like terms are: $3a$ and $4a$, $8x^2$ and $5x^2$, $2ab$ and $-7ab$.

Adding Monomials

To add like terms, we can use the commutative and distributive principles of multiplication. For example, $3 \cdot a + 4 \cdot a = (3 + 4)a = 7a$. Therefore, $3a + 4a = 7a$.

PROCEDURE. To add like monomials, find the sum of the coefficients and multiply this sum by the common literal factors.

MODEL PROBLEMS

Add:

1. $\begin{array}{r} +6x \\ +3x \\ \hline +9x \end{array}$ **2.** $\begin{array}{r} -5y \\ -\ y \\ \hline -6y \end{array}$ **3.** $\begin{array}{r} +7x^2 \\ -2x^2 \\ \hline +5x^2 \end{array}$ **4.** $\begin{array}{r} -12y^2 \\ +\ 4y^2 \\ \hline -\ 8y^2 \end{array}$ **5.** $\begin{array}{r} +8x \\ -8x \\ \hline 0 \end{array}$

Adding Polynomials

PROCEDURE. To add polynomials:

1. Write the polynomials so that the like terms are arranged in separate vertical columns. For convenience, arrange the polynomials in descending or ascending powers of a particular variable.
2. Add the like terms in each column separately.

MODEL PROBLEMS

Add:

1. $\begin{array}{r} 4x + 3y - 5z \\ 3x - 5y - 6z \\ -2x -\ y + 3z \\ \hline 5x - 3y - 8z \end{array}$ **2.** $\begin{array}{r} 3x^2 + 2x - 3 \\ -2x^2 - 5x + 7 \\ -\ x^2 + 8x - 6 \\ \hline 5x - 2 \end{array}$

3. Represent the perimeter of a triangle the measures of whose sides are represented by $5x + 8$, $6x - 5$, $2x - 3$.

Solution: To represent the perimeter of the triangle, find the sum of the measures of all its sides.

Method 1	*Method 2*
$5x + 8$	$P = (5x + 8) + (6x - 5) + (2x - 3)$
$6x - 5$	$P = 5x + 8 + 6x - 5 + 2x - 3$
$\underline{2x - 3}$	$P = 13x$
$13x$	

Answer: $P = 13x$.

EXERCISES

In 1–12, add.

1. $+8x$ **2.** $-6x$ **3.** $+12x^2$ **4.** $-18y^2$ **5.** $-3bh$ **6.** $+6x$
    $\underline{+3x}$ $\underline{+9x}$ $\underline{-\ 5x^2}$ $\underline{+13y^2}$ $\underline{-5bh}$ $\underline{-6x}$

7. $(+6x) + (-4x) + (-5x) + (+10x)$ **8.** $-5y + 7y + 8y - 6y$

9. $8r - 3t$ **10.** $y + 8z$ **11.** $9x^2 + 5$ **12.** $x^2 + 3x + 5$
    $-2r + 3t$ $5y -\ z$ $-2x^2 - 8$ $2x^2 - 4x - 1$
    $\underline{-6r + 5t}$ $\underline{-8y - 5z}$ $\underline{+\ x^2 - 3}$ $\underline{-5x^2 + 2x + 4}$

In 13–16, represent the perimeter of a figure the measures of whose sides are represented by:

13. $3x - 2$, $5x - 5$, $8x + 3$
14. $x + 2y$, $3x + 4y$, $x - 6y$
15. $4x - 6$, $2x + 10$, $5x - 15$, $x + 30$
16. $6x - 5$, $2x$, $3x - 2$, $x + 4$

In 17–21, represent the perimeter of a rectangle the measure of whose width is represented by x and the measure of whose length is represented by:

17. $2x + 1$ **18.** $3x - 1$ **19.** $4x + 5$ **20.** $6x - 4$ **21.** $5 - 2x$

In 22–25, represent the sum of the measures of the arcs whose measures are represented by:

22. $4x$, $2x - 20$, $6x + 40$, $x - 10$ **23.** x, $5x - 6$, $4x + 5$, $x + 1$
24. $x + 20$, $3x - 60$, $2x + 10$, $4x + 30$ **25.** $3x$, $4x$, $5x - 30$, $2x - 60$

6. Removing Parentheses by Multiplication

By using the distributive principle of multiplication, we obtain

$$7(x + 5) = 7 \cdot x + 7 \cdot 5 = 7x + 35$$

PROCEDURE. To remove parentheses when they are immediately preceded by a monomial, multiply each term in the parentheses by the monomial; that is, use the distributive principle of multiplication.

Note that if the parentheses are preceded by a plus or a minus sign without an indicated coefficient, the coefficient is understood to be 1.

Thus, $5 + (2x - 3)$ means $5 + 1(2x - 3)$
and $5y - (2 - 7y)$ means $5y - 1(2 - 7y)$.

MODEL PROBLEMS

Remove parentheses and collect like terms:

1. $6x - 3(5 + x)$
    $= 6x - 15 - 3x$
    $= 3x - 15$

2. $2c + (7c - 4)$
    $= 2c + 1(7c - 4)$
    $= 2c + 7c - 4$
    $= 9c - 4$

3. $(9 - 2x) - (6 - 2x)$
    $= 1(9 - 2x) - 1(6 - 2x)$
    $= 9 - 2x - 6 + 2x$
    $= 3$

EXERCISES

In 1–15, remove parentheses and collect like terms when possible.

1. $2(5x + 6)$
2. $5(2x - 10)$
3. $10(4x + 3)$
4. $5(d + 3) - 10$
5. $5 - 4(3x - 5)$
6. $8 - (4x - 2)$
7. $x + (90 - x)$
8. $(180 - x) + x$
9. $(180 - x) - (90 - x)$
10. $\frac{1}{2}(4x + 60)$
11. $\frac{1}{2}(2x - 36)$
12. $\frac{1}{2}(x - 50)$
13. $x(x + 2)$
14. $x(x - 4)$
15. $2x(x + 4)$

7. Evaluating Formulas

PROCEDURE. To evaluate a formula:

1. Replace the variables with their given values.
2. Do the indicated arithmetic. If no parentheses (or other grouping symbols) appear, perform the multiplication and division operations first, and then the addition and subtraction operations. When parentheses do appear, replace each expression within parentheses by its value in the form of a single number.

MODEL PROBLEMS

1. If $A = \frac{1}{2}bh$, find A when $b = 5$ and $h = 12$.

Solution:

1. $A = \frac{1}{2}bh$

2. $A = \frac{1}{2}(5)(12)$

3. $A = \frac{1}{2}(60)$

4. $A = 30$

Answer: 30.

2. If $A = \pi r^2$, find A when $r = 14$ and $\pi = \frac{22}{7}$.

Solution:

1. $A = \pi r^2$

2. $A = \frac{22}{7}(14)(14)$

3. $A = 22(2)(14)$

4. $A = 616$

Answer: 616.

3. If $A = \frac{h}{2}(b+c)$, find A when $h = 5$, $b = 2$, $c = 14$.

Solution:

1. $A = \frac{h}{2}(b + c)$

2. $A = \frac{5}{2}(2 + 14)$

3. $A = \frac{5}{2}(16)$

4. $A = 5(8) = 40$

Answer: 40.

4. If $D = \frac{1}{2}(x - y)$, find D when $x = 120$ and $y = 80$.

Solution:

1. $D = \frac{1}{2}(x - y)$

2. $D = \frac{1}{2}(120 - 80)$

3. $D = \frac{1}{2}(40)$

4. $D = 20$

Answer: 20.

EXERCISES

1. The formula for the area of a rectangle is $A = bh$. Find A when:
   a. $b = 10$ in., $h = 8$ in.
   b. $b = 7.5$ yd., $h = 3.4$ yd.
   c. $b = 8\frac{1}{2}$ ft., $h = 6$ ft.
   d. $b = 4$ ft., $h = 10$ in.

2. The formula for the area of a triangle is $A = \frac{1}{2}bh$. Find A when:
   a. $b = 6$ in., $h = 10$ in.
   b. $b = 7$ in., $h = 14$ in.
   c. $b = 3$ yd., $h = 5$ yd.
   d. $b = 10.5$ yd., $h = 7.6$ yd.

3. The formula for the area of a circle is $A = \pi r^2$. Find A when $\pi = \frac{22}{7}$ and $r =$:
   a. 7 ft.   b. 21 in.   c. 5.6 ft.   d. $3\frac{1}{2}$ yd.   e. 10 in.

4. If $x = \frac{1}{2}(y + z)$, find x when:
   a. $y = 40$, $z = 60$
   b. $y = 120$, $z = 80$
   c. $y = 50$, $z = 130$
   d. $y = 45$, $z = 30$

5. If $x = \frac{1}{2}(y - z)$, find x when:

    a. $y = 180$, $z = 40$ *b.* $y = 135$, $z = 45$

    c. $y = 65$, $z = 40$ *d.* $y = 120$, $z = 75$

6. The formula for the area of a trapezoid is $A = \frac{1}{2}h(b + b')$. Find A when:

    a. $h = 10$, $b = 8$, $b' = 6$ *b.* $h = 8$, $b = 12$, $b' = 5$

    c. $h = 9$, $b = 14$, $b' = 8$ *d.* $h = 7$, $b = 9$, $b' = 4$

7. If $c = \sqrt{a^2 + b^2}$, find c when:

    a. $a = 3$, $b = 4$ *b.* $a = 6$, $b = 8$ *c.* $a = 5$, $b = 12$

    d. $a = 15$, $b = 20$ *e.* $a = 4$, $b = 4$ *f.* $a = 5$, $b = 6$

8. If $m = \dfrac{r - s}{p - q}$, find m when:

    a. $r = 10$, $s = 2$, $p = 5$, $q = 3$

    b. $r = 12$, $s = 6$, $p = 8$, $q = 4$

    c. $r = 8$, $s = 2$, $p = 16$, $q = 4$

8. Solving Simple Equations Involving One Variable

To *solve an equation* means to find the set of all numbers which can replace the variable in the equation and make the resulting equation a true statement. Each number which makes the equation a true statement is called a *root* of the equation. The set of numbers whose members are the roots of the equation is called the *solution set* of the equation. For example, among all the numbers we know, 9 is the only number that can replace the variable x in the equation $x - 5 = 4$ and make the resulting statement, $9 - 5 = 4$, a true statement. Therefore, 9 is the root of the equation $x - 5 = 4$. Also, $\{9\}$ is the solution set of the equation $x - 5 = 4$.

Equivalent Equations

Equations which have exactly the same roots, or which have the same solution sets, are called *equivalent equations*. For example, the equations $x - 5 = 4$ and $x = 9$ are equivalent equations because the root of each equation is 9, or the solution set is $\{9\}$.

When we solve an equation, we transform it into an equivalent equation whose roots and solution set are easily determined. To do this, we make use of the following principles:

1. If the same number is added to or subtracted from both members of an equation, the resulting equation is an equivalent equation.
2. If both members of an equation are multiplied or divided by the same non-zero number, the resulting equation is an equivalent equation.

Now we will see how these principles can be used in solving equations.

Solving Equations by Using Addition

Solve: $x - 5 = 4$

Solution: In the equation $x - 5 = 4$, the x and the 5 are related by the operation of subtraction. Hence, we use the inverse operation, addition, to solve the equation.

1. $x - 5 = 4$
2. $x - 5 + 5 = 4 + 5$ A_5 (Add 5 to both members of the preceding
3. $x = 9$ equation.)

$$Check: x - 5 = 4$$
$$9 - 5 \overset{?}{=} 4$$
$$4 = 4$$

Answer: $x = 9$, or solution set is $\{9\}$.

Solving Equations by Using Subtraction

Solve: $x + 7 = 9$

Solution: In the equation $x + 7 = 9$, the x and the 7 are related by the operation of addition. Hence, we use the inverse operation, subtraction, to solve the equation.

1. $x + 7 = 9$
2. $x + 7 - 7 = 9 - 7$ S_7 (Subtract 7 from both members of the preceding
3. $x = 2$ equation.)

$$Check: x + 7 = 9$$
$$2 + 7 \overset{?}{=} 9$$
$$9 = 9$$

Answer: $x = 2$, or solution set is $\{2\}$.

Solving Equations by Using the Additive Inverse

The equations $x - 5 = 4$ and $x + 7 = 9$, which were previously solved by using addition and subtraction, can also be solved by making use of the additive inverse of a number.

a. Solve: $x - 5 = 4$

Solution: We know that the sum of -5 and its additive inverse, $+5$, is 0. Therefore, we add $+5$ to both members of the equation.

1. $x - 5 = 4$
2. $x - 5 + (+5) = 4 + (+5)$ A_{+5}
3. $x + 0 = 9$
4. $x = 9$

b. Solve: $x + 7 = 9$

Solution: **We** add -7, the additive inverse of $+7$, to both members of the
equation.

1. $x + 7 = 9$
2. $x + 7 + (-7) = 9 + (-7)$ A_{-7}
3. $x + 0 = 2$
4. $x = 2$

Solving Equations by Using Division

Solve: $7x = 35$

Solution: In the equation $7x = 35$, the 7 and the x are related by the operation
of multiplication. Hence, we use the inverse operation, division, to solve
the equation.

1. $7x = 35$
2. $\dfrac{7x}{7} = \dfrac{35}{7}$ D_7 (Divide both members of the preceding equation by 7.)
3. $x = 5$ *Check:* $7x = 35$
$$7 \times 5 \overset{?}{=} 35$$
$$35 = 35$$

Answer: $x = 5$, or solution set is $\{5\}$.

Solving Equations by Using Multiplication

Solve: $\dfrac{x}{4} = 5$

Solution: In the equation $\dfrac{x}{4} = 5$, the x and the 4 are related by the operation
of division. Hence, we use the inverse operation, multiplication, to solve
the equation.

1. $\dfrac{x}{4} = 5$

2. $4 \times \dfrac{x}{4} = 4 \times 5$ M_4 (Multiply both members of the preceding equation
by 4.)

3. $x = 20$ *Check:* $\dfrac{x}{4} = 5$

$$\dfrac{20}{4} \overset{?}{=} 5$$

$$5 = 5$$

Answer: $x = 20$, or solution set is $\{20\}$.

Solving Equations by Using the Multiplicative Inverse

The equations $7x = 35$ and $\frac{x}{4} = 5$, which were previously solved by using division and multiplication, can also be solved by making use of the multiplicative inverse of a number.

When the product of two numbers is 1, we say that one number is the *multiplicative inverse,* or the *reciprocal,* of the other. Since $(7)(\frac{1}{7}) = 1$, we say that $\frac{1}{7}$ is the multiplicative inverse of 7. Likewise, since $(\frac{2}{5})(\frac{5}{2}) = 1$, we say that $\frac{5}{2}$ is the multiplicative inverse of $\frac{2}{5}$.

a. Solve: $7x = 35$

> *Solution:* We know that the product of 7 and its multiplicative inverse, $\frac{1}{7}$, is 1. Therefore, we multiply both members of the equation by $\frac{1}{7}$.
>
> 1. $\qquad 7x = 35$
> 2. $\quad \frac{1}{7}(7x) = \frac{1}{7}(35) \qquad M\frac{1}{7}$
> 3. $\quad (\frac{1}{7} \cdot 7)x = 5$
> 4. $\qquad 1 \cdot x = 5$
> 5. $\qquad\quad x = 5$

b. Solve: $\frac{x}{4} = 5$

> *Solution:* $\frac{x}{4}$ may be represented as $\frac{1}{4}x$. Therefore, we multiply both members of the equation by 4, the multiplicative inverse of $\frac{1}{4}$.
>
> 1. $\qquad \frac{x}{4} = 5$
> 2. $\quad 4\left(\frac{1}{4}x\right) = 4(5) \qquad M_4$
> 3. $\quad \left(4 \cdot \frac{1}{4}\right)x = 20$
> 4. $\qquad 1 \cdot x = 20$
> 5. $\qquad\quad x = 20$

Solving Equations by Using Several Operations

Solve: $2x + 3 = 15$

Method 1

Solution: In the equation $2x + 3 = 15$, there are two operations, multiplication and addition, involving the variable x. We therefore use the inverse operations, division and subtraction, to solve the equation. First we will use subtraction, then division. [The solution continues on the next page.]

1. $2x + 3 = 15$ *Check:* $2x + 3 = 15$

2. $2x + 3 - 3 = 15 - 3$ S_3 $2 \times 6 + 3 \overset{?}{=} 15$

3. $2x = 12$ $12 + 3 \overset{?}{=} 15$

4. $x = 6$ D_2 $15 = 15$

Answer: $x = 6$, or solution set is $\{6\}$.

Method 2

Solution: In solving the equation $2x + 3 = 15$, we will first use the additive
inverse of $+3$, which is -3, then the multiplicative inverse of 2, which is $\frac{1}{2}$.

1. $2x + 3 = 15$
2. $2x + 3 + (-3) = 15 + (-3)$ A_{-3}
3. $2x + 0 = 12$
4. $2x = 12$
5. $\frac{1}{2}(2x) = \frac{1}{2}(12)$ $M_{\frac{1}{2}}$
6. $1 \cdot x = 6$
7. $x = 6$

EXERCISES

In 1–40, solve and check the equation.

1. $5x = 50$ **2.** $8x = 64$ **3.** $10y = 5$ **4.** $16z = 12$

5. $\frac{x}{7} = 5$ **6.** $\frac{y}{9} = 18$ **7.** $\frac{1}{2}x = 4$ **8.** $12 = \frac{y}{3}$

9. $x - 2 = 8$ **10.** $t - 8 = 0$ **11.** $60 = y - 15$ **12.** $x - 7 = 7$

13. $x + 5 = 17$ **14.** $y + 1 = 12$ **15.** $4 + x = 4$ **16.** $25 = y + 11$

17. $3x + 5 = 35$ **18.** $55 = 6x + 7$ **19.** $14 = 12y + 8$

20. $4x - 1 = 15$ **21.** $3y - 5 = 16$ **22.** $11 = 16d - 1$

23. $2x + 3x = 50$ **24.** $5x - 2x = 33$ **25.** $18 = 7x - x$

26. $8x - 3x + 7 = 87$ **27.** $6x + 12 - x = 52$ **28.** $95 = 8c - 3c + 15$

29. $39 = x + 5x$ **30.** $45 = 6x - 3$ **31.** $5n - 5 + 2n = 30$

32. $\frac{1}{3}x + 5 = 19$ **33.** $\frac{1}{2}x + \frac{1}{4}x = 12$ **34.** $41 = \frac{3x}{2} - 10$

35. $2x + 3x = 90$

37. $x + 9x + 5x = 360$

39. $x + x + x - 30 = 180$

36. $3x + 4x + 5x = 180$

38. $x + x + 40 = 90$

40. $5x + 3x - 40 + 2x = 360$

9. Solving Equations Which Have the Variable in Both Members

Using Addition or Subtraction

PROCEDURE. To solve an equation which has the variable in both members:

1. Transform the equation into an equivalent equation in which the variable appears in only one member.
2. Solve the resulting equation.

MODEL PROBLEMS

1. Solve: $8x = 30 + 5x$

Solution:

Method 1	*Method 2*
Subtract $5x$ from both members of the equation (S_{5x}).	Add $-5x$, the additive inverse of $+5x$, to both members (A_{-5x}).
1. $\qquad 8x = 30 + 5x$	1. $\qquad 8x = 30 + 5x$
2. $8x - 5x = 30 + 5x - 5x$	2. $8x + (-5x) = 30 + 5x + (-5x)$
3. $\qquad 3x = 30$	3. $\qquad 3x = 30 + 0$
4. $\qquad x = 10 \qquad D_3$	4. $\qquad 3x = 30$
	5. $\qquad x = 10 \qquad M_{\frac{1}{3}}$

$$\textit{Check: } 8x = 30 + 5x$$
$$8(10) \overset{?}{=} 30 + 5(10)$$
$$80 \overset{?}{=} 30 + 50$$
$$80 = 80$$

Answer: $x = 10$, or solution set is $\{10\}$.

2. Solve: $7x - 3 = 12 + 2x$

Solution:

Method 1	*Method 2*
Subtract $2x$ from both members of the equation (S_{2x}).	Add $-2x$, the additive inverse of $+2x$, to both members (A_{-2x}).

Method 1		*Method 2*	
1. $\quad 7x - 3 = 12 + 2x$		1. $\quad\quad 7x - 3 = 12 + 2x$	
2. $7x - 3 - 2x = 12 + 2x - 2x$		2. $7x - 3 + (-2x) = 12 + 2x + (-2x)$	
3. $\quad 5x - 3 = 12$		3. $\quad\quad 5x - 3 = 12 + 0$	
4. $5x - 3 + 3 = 12 + 3$	A_3	4. $\quad\quad 5x - 3 = 12$	
5. $\quad 5x = 15$		5. $5x - 3 + (+3) = 12 + (+3)$	A_{+3}
6. $\quad x = 3$	D_5	6. $\quad\quad 5x + 0 = 15$	
		7. $\quad\quad 5x = 15$	
		8. $\quad\quad x = 3$	$M_{\frac{1}{5}}$

$$Check: 7x - 3 = 12 + 2x$$
$$7(3) - 3 \overset{?}{=} 12 + 2(3)$$
$$21 - 3 \overset{?}{=} 12 + 6$$
$$18 = 18$$

Answer: $x = 3$, or solution set is $\{3\}$.

Using Transposition

If $5x - 3 = 10$, then $5x - 3 + 3 = 10 + 3$, or $5x = 10 + 3$. Notice that the -3 disappeared from the left member of the equation $5x - 3 = 10$ and it now appears with its sign changed in the right member of the equation $5x = 10 + 3$. Similarly, if $4y = 20 + 2y$, then $4y - 2y = 20$, which is obtained by adding $-2y$ to each member of the given equation.

We see that a term may be transferred from one member of an equation to the other member if the sign of the term is changed. This procedure is called *transposition*. Observe that transposition is merely a shortened way of adding the same number to, or subtracting the same number from, both members of an equation.

PROCEDURE. To solve a first-degree equation using transposition:

1. Transpose all terms containing the variable to one member of the equation; transpose all other terms to the other member of the equation.
2. Collect the terms in each member of the equation separately.
3. Divide both members of the equation by the coefficient of the variable.

MODEL PROBLEM

Solve: $7x - 8 = 10 + 4x$

Solution:

1. $7x - 8 = 10 + 4x$

2. $7x - 4x = 10 + 8$ Transposing.

3. $3x = 18$ Collecting like terms.

4. $x = 6$ $\mathbf{D}_3$

$$Check: 7x - 8 = 10 + 4x$$
$$7(6) - 8 \overset{?}{=} 10 + 4(6)$$
$$42 - 8 \overset{?}{=} 10 + 24$$
$$34 = 34$$

Answer: $x = 6$, or solution set is $\{6\}$.

EXERCISES

In 1–24, solve and check the equation.

1. $7x = 10 + 2x$ **2.** $9x = 44 - 2x$ **3.** $12y = 3y + 27$

4. $8x = 90 - 2x$ **5.** $4 - 2y = 6y$ **6.** $3 - y = 8y$

7. $8x = 5x + 90$ **8.** $180 - 3x = 6x$ **9.** $160 = 360 - 2x$

10. $y = 9y - 56$ **11.** $x = 9x - 72$ **12.** $2y = 5y - 81$

13. $5x - 7 = 2x + 8$ **14.** $10x + 8 = 32 - 2x$

15. $90 - 2x = 45 + 3x$ **16.** $3x + 11 = 18 - 4x$

17. $9y - 5 = 7 + 8y$ **18.** $5x - 13 = 43 - 2x$

19. $15x = 5(x + 6)$ **20.** $7(x - 2) = 5x$

21. $30x = 4(5x + 20)$ **22.** $2(x + 30) = 180 - x$

23. $70 - 2x = 2(x + 5)$ **24.** $2(5x - 1) = 3(3x + 7)$

10. Solving Equations Containing Fractions

PROCEDURE. To solve an equation containing fractions:

1. Transform the equation into a simpler equation that does not contain fractions. Do this by multiplying both members of the equation by the lowest common denominator (L.C.D.) for the fractions in the equation.
2. Solve the resulting equation.

MODEL PROBLEM

Solve: $\frac{1}{2}(x - 40) = 50$

Solution:

1.　　　$\frac{1}{2}(x - 40) = 50$

2. $2 \cdot \frac{1}{2}(x - 40) = 2 \cdot 50$　　M₂ (Multiply both members of the preceding equation by the L.C.D., 2.)

3.　　　$x - 40 = 100$　　*Check:* $\frac{1}{2}(x - 40) = 50$

4.　　　　$x = 140$　　　　$\frac{1}{2}(140 - 40) \overset{?}{=} 50$

　　　　　　　　　　　　　$\frac{1}{2}(100) \overset{?}{=} 50$

　　　　　　　　　　　　　　　$50 = 50$

Answer: $x = 140$, or solution set is $\{140\}$.

EXERCISES

In 1–23, solve the equation.

1. $\frac{1}{2}x = 90$ **2.** $\frac{2}{3}x = 180$ **3.** $44 = \frac{22}{7}D$ **4.** $\frac{4}{7}R = 88$

5. $\frac{1}{2}(5x) = 30$ **6.** $\frac{1}{3}(3x) = 60$ **7.** $72 = \dfrac{9x}{2}$ **8.** $39 = \frac{1}{2}(13x)$

9. $\frac{1}{2}(x + 20) = 60$ **10.** $\frac{1}{2}(x + 70) = 50$ **11.** $90 = \frac{1}{2}(120 + x)$

12. $110 = \frac{1}{2}(80 + x)$ **13.** $\frac{1}{2}(x - 40) = 10$ **14.** $\frac{1}{2}(x - 40) = 40$

15. $35 = \frac{1}{2}(100 - x)$ **16.** $90 = \frac{1}{2}(200 - x)$ **17.** $\frac{1}{2}(6)(x + 10) = 60$

18. $\frac{1}{2}(5)(x + 30) = 150$ **19.** $270 = \frac{9}{2}(40 + x)$ **20.** $3x = \frac{1}{2}(4)(x + 8)$

21. $\dfrac{5}{2}(3 + x) = 75$ **22.** $\dfrac{7x}{2} = \dfrac{3}{2}(x + 12)$ **23.** $\dfrac{x}{6} = \dfrac{1}{2}(360 - x)$

11. Transforming Formulas

A formula may be expressed in more than one form. When a formula is to be solved for a particular variable, the formula may have to be transformed.

PROCEDURE. To transform a formula:

1. Consider the formula as an equation with several variables which is to be solved for the indicated variable.
2. Solve the formula for the indicated variable in terms of the other variables by applying the principles of solving equations.

MODEL PROBLEMS

1. Solve the formula $V = \frac{1}{3}Bh$ for h.

Solution:

1. $V = \frac{1}{3}Bh$

2. $3(V) = 3(\frac{1}{3}Bh)$ M_3

3. $3V = Bh$

4. $\dfrac{3V}{B} = h$ D_B

Answer: $h = \dfrac{3V}{B}$.

2. Solve the formula $P = 2(l + w)$ for w.

Solution:

1. $P = 2(l + w)$

2. $P = 2l + 2w$

3. $P - 2l = 2w$ S_{2l}

4. $\dfrac{P - 2l}{2} = w$ D_2

Answer: $w = \dfrac{P - 2l}{2}$.

EXERCISES

In 1–15, solve the formula for the indicated variable or constant.

1. $A = bh$ for h **2.** $C = \pi d$ for π **3.** $A = lw$ for l

4. $cx = ab$ for x **5.** $rs = ny$ for y **6.** $bx = c^2$ for x

7. $\frac{1}{2}x = y$ for x **8.** $z = \frac{1}{2}x$ for x **9.** $A = \frac{1}{2}bh$ for h

10. $K = \dfrac{ap}{2}$ for a **11.** $\dfrac{C}{2\pi} = R$ for C **12.** $C = \dfrac{360}{N}$ for N

13. $P = 2B + 2H$ for H **14.** $P = 2(a + b)$ for b **15.** $A = \dfrac{h}{2}(b + c)$ for h

12. Solving a System of Simultaneous Linear Equations by Addition or Subtraction

MODEL PROBLEMS

1. Solve the system of equations and check: $x + 3y = 13$
$$x + y = 5$$

How to proceed	*Solution*
1. Since the coefficients of one of the variables, x, are the same in both equations, subtracting the corresponding members of the two equations will eliminate the variable x.	$\begin{aligned} x + 3y &= 13 \\ \underline{x + y} &= \underline{5} \\ 2y &= 8 \end{aligned}$
2. Solve the resulting equation for the variable y.	$y = 4 \qquad D_2$
3. Substitute the value of y in either equation involving both variables.	$\begin{aligned} x + y &= 5 \\ x + 4 &= 5 \end{aligned}$
4. Solve the resulting equation for the variable x.	$x = 1 \qquad S_4$

Check: Substitute the x-value and the y-value of the common solution in each of the given equations.

$$x + 3y = 13 \qquad x + y = 5$$
$$1 + 3(4) \overset{?}{=} 13 \qquad 1 + 4 \overset{?}{=} 5$$
$$13 = 13 \qquad 5 = 5$$

Answer: Since $x = 1$, $y = 4$, the solution is $(1, 4)$, or the solution set is $\{(1, 4)\}$.

2. Solve the system of equations and check: $5a + 2b = 11$
$4a - 3b = 18$

How to proceed	*Solution*
1. Multiply both members of the first equation by 3 and both members of the second equation by 2 so that the absolute value of the coefficient of b will be the same in both equations.	$5a + 2b = 11$ $4a - 3b = 18$ $15a + 6b = 33$ $\underline{8a - 6b = 36}$
2. Add the corresponding members of the two equations to eliminate the variable b.	$23a = 69$
3. Solve for the variable a.	$a = 3$ $\mathbf{D}_{23}$
4. Substitute the value of a in either equation involving both variables.	$5a + 2b = 11$ $5(3) + 2b = 11$
5. Solve the resulting equation for the variable b.	$15 + 2b = 11$ $2b = 11 - 15$ $2b = -4$ $b = -2$ $\mathbf{D}_2$

Check: Substitute the a-value and the b-value of the common solution in each of the given equations.

$$5a + 2b = 11 \qquad\qquad 4a - 3b = 18$$
$$5(3) + 2(-2) \overset{?}{=} 11 \qquad 4(3) - 3(-2) \overset{?}{=} 18$$
$$15 - 4 \overset{?}{=} 11 \qquad\qquad 12 + 6 \overset{?}{=} 18$$
$$11 = 11 \qquad\qquad 18 = 18$$

Answer: Since $a = 3$, $b = -2$, the solution is $(3, -2)$, or the solution set is $\{(3, -2)\}$.

EXERCISES

In 1–15, solve the set of equations and check.

1. $x + y = 12$
$x - y = 4$

2. $m + 3n = 18$
$m + 2n = 14$

3. $x + 2y = 8$
$x - 2y = 4$

4. $5x + 4y = 27$
$x - 2y = 11$

5. $2m + n = 12$
$m + 2n = 9$

6. $3a - b = 13$
$2a + 3b = 16$

7. $2x + 3y = 6$
   $3x + 5y = 15$

8. $5a + 3b = 17$
   $4a - 5b = 21$

9. $4x - 6y = 15$
   $6x - 4y = 10$

10. $2x + y = 17$
    $5x = 25 + y$

11. $x - 2y = 8$
    $2y = 3x - 16$

12. $6y = x$
    $5y = 2x - 14$

13. $\dfrac{y-5}{x-3} = 9$

    $\dfrac{y-9}{x-1} = \dfrac{5}{3}$

14. $\dfrac{y-2}{x-1} = -1$

    $\dfrac{y-11}{x-4} = \dfrac{1}{2}$

15. $51 = \dfrac{1}{2}(22y - 12x)$

    $92 = \dfrac{1}{2}(24y - 4x)$

13. Factoring Polynomials Whose Terms Have a Common Monomial Factor

A monomial which divides into each term of a polynomial is called a *common monomial factor* of the polynomial. Thus, since a divides into each term of the polynomial $ax + ay + az$, a is a common monomial factor of $ax + ay + az$. To find the other factor, we divide $ax + ay + az$ by a, obtaining $x + y + z$. Therefore, we may write $ax + ay + az = a(x + y + z)$. Notice that $a(x + y + z) = ax + ay + az$ is an example of the distributive principle of multiplication.

PROCEDURE. To factor a polynomial whose terms have a common monomial factor:

1. Find the highest monomial that will divide exactly into each term of the polynomial. This monomial is one factor of the polynomial.
2. Divide the polynomial by the monomial factor. The quotient is the other factor.
3. Write the answer by placing the second factor inside parentheses and the common monomial factor in front of the parentheses.

MODEL PROBLEMS

1. Factor: $5x + 5y$

Solution:

1. 5 is the highest monomial factor of both $5x$ and $5y$.

2. Divide $5x + 5y$ by 5 to find the other factor.
   $(5x + 5y) \div 5 = x + y$

3. $5x + 5y = 5(x + y)$

Answer: $5(x + y)$.

2. Factor: $\frac{1}{2}ra + \frac{1}{2}rb$

Solution:

1. $\frac{1}{2}r$ is the highest monomial factor of both $\frac{1}{2}ra$ and $\frac{1}{2}rb$.

2. Divide $\frac{1}{2}ra + \frac{1}{2}rb$ by $\frac{1}{2}r$.
   $(\frac{1}{2}ra + \frac{1}{2}rb) \div \frac{1}{2}r = a + b$

3. $\frac{1}{2}ra + \frac{1}{2}rb = \frac{1}{2}r(a + b)$

Answer: $\frac{1}{2}r(a + b)$.

EXERCISES

In 1–20, factor the expression.

1. $2a + 2b$	**2.** $8m + 8n$	**3.** $4x - 4y$
4. $6R - 6r$	**5.** $6x + 18y$	**6.** $10r - 20t$
7. $12m + 18n$	**8.** $20a - 25b$	**9.** $bx + by$
10. $cm + cn$	**11.** $sr - st$	**12.** $xc - dx$
13. $p + prt$	**14.** $\frac{1}{2}hb + \frac{1}{2}hc$	**15.** $\frac{1}{2}ab + \frac{1}{2}ac + \frac{1}{2}ad$
16. $\pi r^2 + \pi R^2$	**17.** $x^2 - 4x$	**18.** $a^2 - 9a$
19. $y^2 + 3y$	**20.** $z^2 + 6z$	

14. Factoring the Difference of Two Squares

Since the product of $x + y$ and $x - y$ is $x^2 - y^2$, the factors of $x^2 - y^2$ are $(x + y)$ and $(x - y)$. Therefore, $x^2 - y^2 = (x + y)(x - y)$.

PROCEDURE. To factor an expression which is the difference of two squares:

1. For each of the square terms, find the square root which has a positive numerical coefficient.
2. Write two factors: one is the *sum* of the two square roots; the other is the *difference* of the two square roots.

MODEL PROBLEM

Factor: $x^2 - 9$

Solution: $\sqrt{x^2} = x,\ \sqrt{9} = 3$
$$x^2 - 9 = (x + 3)(x - 3)$$

Answer: $(x + 3)(x - 3)$.

EXERCISES

In 1–12, factor the expression.

1. $x^2 - 4$	**2.** $x^2 - 25$	**3.** $x^2 - 100$	**4.** $c^2 - 16$
5. $s^2 - 49$	**6.** $t^2 - 100$	**7.** $16a^2 - b^2$	**8.** $25n^2 - m^2$
9. $4x^2 - 49y^2$	**10.** $81c^2 - .04$	**11.** $49x^2 - \frac{1}{9}$	**12.** $\frac{1}{9}r^2 - \frac{64}{49}s^2$

15. Factoring Trinomials of the Form $x^2 + bx + c$

PROCEDURE. To factor a trinomial of the form $x^2 + bx + c$, we must find two binomials which have the following characteristics:

1. The product of the first terms of both binomials must be equal to the first term in the trinomial.
2. The product of the last terms of both binomials must be equal to the last term of the trinomial.
3. The algebraic sum of the last terms of the binomials must be equal to the coefficient of the middle term of the trinomial.

MODEL PROBLEMS

1. Factor: $x^2 + 7x + 10$

   Solution: Since the last term of $x^2 + 7x + 10$ is $+10$ and the coefficient of x is $+7$, we are looking for two numbers whose product is $+10$ and whose algebraic sum is $+7$. These two numbers are $+5$ and $+2$. Therefore, $x^2 + 7x + 10 = (x + 5)(x + 2)$.

   Answer: $(x + 5)(x + 2)$.

2. Factor: $y^2 - 8y + 15$

   Solution: Since the last term of $y^2 - 8y + 15$ is $+15$ and the coefficient of y is -8, we are looking for two numbers whose product is $+15$ and whose algebraic sum is -8. These two numbers are -5 and -3. Therefore, $y^2 - 8y + 15 = (y - 5)(y - 3)$.

   Answer: $(y - 5)(y - 3)$.

3. Factor: $a^2 + 5a - 6$

   Solution: Since the last term of $a^2 + 5a - 6$ is -6 and the coefficient of a is $+5$, we are looking for two numbers whose product is -6 and whose algebraic sum is $+5$. These two numbers are $+6$ and -1. Therefore, $a^2 + 5a - 6 = (a + 6)(a - 1)$.

   Answer: $(a + 6)(a - 1)$.

4. Factor: $s^2 - 4s - 12$

   Solution: Since the last term of $s^2 - 4s - 12$ is -12 and the coefficient of s is -4, we are looking for two numbers whose product is -12 and whose algebraic sum is -4. These two numbers are -6 and $+2$. Therefore, $s^2 - 4s - 12 = (s - 6)(s + 2)$.

   Answer: $(s - 6)(s + 2)$.

EXERCISES

In 1–18, factor the expression.

1. $a^2 + 3a + 2$ 2. $c^2 + 6c + 5$ 3. $y^2 + 10y + 9$
4. $x^2 + 11x + 24$ 5. $b^2 + 13b + 30$ 6. $z^2 + 10z + 25$
7. $x^2 - 8x + 7$ 8. $x^2 - 9x + 8$ 9. $x^2 - 6x + 8$
10. $x^2 - 13x + 36$ 11. $c^2 - 14c + 40$ 12. $x^2 - 20x + 64$
13. $y^2 + 4y - 5$ 14. $x^2 - 8x - 9$ 15. $y^2 - 5y - 6$
16. $x^2 - 7x - 18$ 17. $x^2 + 3x - 40$ 18. $x^2 + 13x - 48$

16. Finding the Square Root of a Number

MODEL PROBLEMS

1. Find $\sqrt{1369}$.

Solution:

$$\begin{array}{r} 3\ \ 7.\ \\ \sqrt{13\ 69.} \\ \hline 9 \\ 67\ \overline{\big|\ 469} \\ 469 \end{array}$$

1. Starting at the decimal point, separate 1369 into groups of two digits each.

2. The largest perfect square less than 13 is 9, which is 3 squared. Write the 3 over the 13 and 9 under the 13. Subtract 9 from 13. Bring down the next group, 69.

3. Form the trial divisor by multiplying the answer 3 by 2, giving 6. Annex a 0, giving 60 as the trial divisor.

4. Divide the remainder, 469, by 60. The quotient is 7.

5. Place the 7 above the 69 and to the right of the 6.

6. $67 \times 7 = 469$. Subtract: $469 - 469 = 0$.

Answer: 37.

2. Find to the *nearest tenth* the square root of 42.

Method 1

Solution:

1. Place two groups each containing two zeros after the decimal point in order to find the square root to two decimal places.

2. Follow the procedure outlined in problem 1.

3. Round off the answer, correct to the nearest tenth.

$$
\begin{array}{r}
6.\ 4\ \ 8 \\
\sqrt{42.\ \overline{00}\ \overline{00}} \\
36 \\
\hline
124\ \ |\ 600 \\
496 \\
\hline
1288\ \ |\ 10400 \\
10304 \\
\hline
96
\end{array}
$$

Answer: 6.5.

Method 2

Solution: $\sqrt{42}$ is not a whole number because $6^2 = 36$ and $7^2 = 49$. Since 42 is between 36 and 49, $\sqrt{42}$ is between 6 and 7. Since 42 is a little closer to 36 than it is to 49, let us estimate that $\sqrt{42}$ is 6.4 to the nearest tenth.

If this estimate is correct, then when 42 is divided by 6.4 the quotient should also be 6.4. At the right, we see the division in which the quotient found to two decimal places is 6.56. Therefore, 6.4 is too small for $\sqrt{42}$ and 6.56 is too large.

$$
\begin{array}{r}
6.56 \\
6.4_\wedge)\overline{42.0_\wedge 00} \\
384 \\
\hline
360 \\
320 \\
\hline
400 \\
384 \\
\hline
16
\end{array}
$$

Let us take the average of 6.4 and 6.56 as our next estimate for $\sqrt{42}$. The average of 6.4 and 6.56 is $\dfrac{6.4 + 6.56}{2} = \dfrac{12.96}{2} = 6.48$. When we divide 42 by 6.48, the quotient is 6.48. Since both the quotient and the divisor are 6.5, correct to the nearest tenth, $\sqrt{42}$, correct to the nearest tenth, is 6.5.

$$
\begin{array}{r}
6.48 \\
6.48_\wedge)\overline{42.00_\wedge 00} \\
3888 \\
\hline
3120 \\
2592 \\
\hline
5280 \\
5184 \\
\hline
96
\end{array}
$$

EXERCISES

In 1–20, find the square root of the number.

1. 225	**2.** 625	**3.** 256	**4.** 289	**5.** 576
6. 676	**7.** 1,521	**8.** 1,296	**9.** 2,601	**10.** 7,225
11. 9,801	**12.** 15,376	**13.** 16,900	**14.** 17,689	**15.** 161,604
16. 9.61	**17.** 56.25	**18.** 42.25	**19.** 161.29	**20.** 1.1025

In 21–35, find to the *nearest tenth* the square root of the number.

21. 2	**22.** 3	**23.** 5	**24.** 8	**25.** 12
26. 18	**27.** 27	**28.** 32	**29.** 50	**30.** 75
31. 18.25	**32.** 73.61	**33.** 205.78	**34.** 8.5	**35.** 61.7

In 36–40, find to the *nearest tenth* the value of the number.

36. $4\sqrt{2}$	**37.** $7\sqrt{2}$	**38.** $4\sqrt{3}$	**39.** $6\sqrt{3}$	**40.** $\frac{7}{2}\sqrt{3}$

17. Simplifying a Radical Whose Radicand Is a Product

A *radical* is any indicated root of a number. For example, $\sqrt{42}$ is a radical. The symbol $\sqrt{}$ is called a *radical sign*; and 42, the number written under the radical sign, is called the *radicand*.

The square root of the product of positive factors is equal to the product of the square roots of the factors, or $\sqrt{ab} = \sqrt{a} \cdot \sqrt{b}$ when $a > 0$ and $b > 0$.

Thus, $\sqrt{100} = \sqrt{25 \times 4} = \sqrt{25} \cdot \sqrt{4} = 5 \cdot 2 = 10$

$$\sqrt{4 \times 5} = \sqrt{4} \cdot \sqrt{5} = 2\sqrt{5}$$
$$\sqrt{x^2 \cdot x} = \sqrt{x^2} \cdot \sqrt{x} = x\sqrt{x}$$

NOTE. In the previous example, the variable x represents a positive number. In sections 17–22 (pages 737–745), all variables under a radical sign represent positive numbers.

PROCEDURE. To simplify the square root of a product:

1. Find two factors of the radicand, one of which is the largest perfect square which is a factor of the radicand.
2. Express the square root of the product as the product of the square roots of the factors.
3. Find the square root of the factor which is a perfect square.

MODEL PROBLEMS

Simplify:

1. $\sqrt{18} = \sqrt{9 \times 2} = \sqrt{9} \cdot \sqrt{2} = 3\sqrt{2}.$

2. $4\sqrt{50} = 4\sqrt{25 \times 2} = 4\sqrt{25} \cdot \sqrt{2} = 4 \cdot 5\sqrt{2} = 20\sqrt{2}.$

3. $\frac{1}{2}\sqrt{48} = \frac{1}{2}\sqrt{16 \times 3} = \frac{1}{2}\sqrt{16} \cdot \sqrt{3} = \frac{1}{2} \cdot 4\sqrt{3} = 2\sqrt{3}.$

4. $\sqrt{2x^2} = \sqrt{x^2 \cdot 2} = \sqrt{x^2} \cdot \sqrt{2} = x\sqrt{2}.$

EXERCISES

In 1–30, simplify the radical.

1. $\sqrt{8}$	**2.** $\sqrt{12}$	**3.** $\sqrt{18}$	**4.** $\sqrt{27}$	**5.** $\sqrt{32}$
6. $\sqrt{48}$	**7.** $\sqrt{50}$	**8.** $\sqrt{72}$	**9.** $\sqrt{75}$	**10.** $\sqrt{98}$
11. $\sqrt{162}$	**12.** $\sqrt{192}$	**13.** $\sqrt{200}$	**14.** $\sqrt{300}$	**15.** $\sqrt{500}$
16. $2\sqrt{8}$	**17.** $3\sqrt{12}$	**18.** $2\sqrt{32}$	**19.** $5\sqrt{75}$	**20.** $10\sqrt{18}$
21. $\frac{1}{2}\sqrt{48}$	**22.** $\frac{1}{2}\sqrt{72}$	**23.** $\frac{1}{4}\sqrt{32}$	**24.** $\frac{1}{3}\sqrt{27}$	**25.** $\frac{1}{3}\sqrt{108}$
26. $\sqrt{2s^2}$	**27.** $\sqrt{3s^2}$	**28.** $\sqrt{5s^2}$	**29.** $\sqrt{4s^3}$	**30.** $\sqrt{9s^3}$

In 31–38, use the table of square roots on page 747 to find the value of the radical, correct to the *nearest tenth*.

31. $\sqrt{200}$	**32.** $\sqrt{180}$	**33.** $\sqrt{300}$	**34.** $\sqrt{640}$
35. $2\sqrt{288}$	**36.** $\frac{1}{2}\sqrt{192}$	**37.** $\frac{3}{4}\sqrt{1.76}$	**38.** $\frac{2}{3}\sqrt{175}$

18. Simplifying a Radical Whose Radicand Is a Fraction

The square root of a fraction in which both the numerator and the denominator are positive numbers is equal to the square root of the numerator divided by the square root of the denominator, or $\sqrt{\dfrac{a}{b}} = \dfrac{\sqrt{a}}{\sqrt{b}}$ when $a > 0$ and $b > 0$.

Thus, $\sqrt{\dfrac{4}{9}} = \dfrac{\sqrt{4}}{\sqrt{9}} = \dfrac{2}{3}$ and $\sqrt{\dfrac{14}{4}} = \dfrac{\sqrt{14}}{\sqrt{4}} = \dfrac{\sqrt{14}}{2}.$

PROCEDURE. To simplify the square root of a fraction:

1. If the denominator of the radicand is not a perfect square, multiply the radicand by 1 represented as a fraction whose numerator and denominator are the least positive integer which will make the denominator of the product a perfect square.
2. Express the square root of the fraction as the square root of its numerator divided by the square root of its denominator.
3. If possible, simplify the result.

MODEL PROBLEMS

Simplify:

1. $\sqrt{\dfrac{3}{4}} = \dfrac{\sqrt{3}}{\sqrt{4}} = \dfrac{\sqrt{3}}{2}$ or $\dfrac{1}{2}\sqrt{3}.$

2. $6\sqrt{\dfrac{1}{3}} = 6\sqrt{\dfrac{1}{3}\cdot\dfrac{3}{3}} = 6\sqrt{\dfrac{3}{9}} = \dfrac{6\sqrt{3}}{\sqrt{9}} = \dfrac{6\sqrt{3}}{3} = 2\sqrt{3}.$ $\qquad \dfrac{3}{3} = 1$

3. $\sqrt{\dfrac{9}{5}} = \sqrt{\dfrac{9}{5}\cdot\dfrac{5}{5}} = \sqrt{\dfrac{45}{25}} = \dfrac{\sqrt{45}}{\sqrt{25}} = \dfrac{\sqrt{9}\cdot\sqrt{5}}{5} = \dfrac{3\sqrt{5}}{5}$ or $\dfrac{3}{5}\sqrt{5}.$ $\quad \dfrac{5}{5} = 1$

4. $\sqrt{\dfrac{c}{d}} = \sqrt{\dfrac{c}{d}\cdot\dfrac{d}{d}} = \sqrt{\dfrac{cd}{d^2}} = \dfrac{\sqrt{cd}}{\sqrt{d^2}} = \dfrac{\sqrt{cd}}{d}$ or $\dfrac{1}{d}\sqrt{cd}.$ $\qquad \dfrac{d}{d} = 1$

EXERCISES

In 1–20, simplify the radical.

1. $\sqrt{\frac{1}{4}}$ **2.** $\sqrt{\frac{1}{9}}$ **3.** $\sqrt{\frac{25}{36}}$ **4.** $20\sqrt{\frac{81}{100}}$ **5.** $6\sqrt{\frac{49}{144}}$

6. $\sqrt{\frac{3}{4}}$ **7.** $\sqrt{\frac{5}{9}}$ **8.** $\sqrt{\frac{3}{49}}$ **9.** $14\sqrt{\frac{8}{49}}$ **10.** $10\sqrt{\frac{24}{25}}$

11. $\sqrt{\frac{1}{2}}$ **12.** $\sqrt{\frac{1}{3}}$ **13.** $\sqrt{\frac{1}{5}}$ **14.** $4\sqrt{\frac{5}{2}}$ **15.** $6\sqrt{\frac{2}{9}}$

16. $\sqrt{\dfrac{x}{2}}$ **17.** $\sqrt{\dfrac{s}{3}}$ **18.** $\sqrt{\dfrac{A}{6}}$ **19.** $\sqrt{\dfrac{s^2}{2}}$ **20.** $\sqrt{\dfrac{3s^2}{4}}$

In 21–25, use the table of square roots on page 747 to find the value of the radical, correct to the *nearest tenth*.

21. $\sqrt{\frac{5}{9}}$ **22.** $\sqrt{\frac{13}{81}}$ **23.** $\sqrt{\frac{1}{2}}$ **24.** $12\sqrt{\frac{1}{3}}$ **25.** $\frac{5}{3}\sqrt{\frac{9}{50}}$

19. Multiplying Monomials Containing Radicals

The product of the square roots of two positive numbers is equal to the square root of the product of the numbers, or $\sqrt{a} \cdot \sqrt{b} = \sqrt{ab}$ when $a > 0$ and $b > 0$.

Thus, $\sqrt{3} \cdot \sqrt{5} = \sqrt{15}$ and $2\sqrt{x} \cdot 3\sqrt{y} = 2 \cdot 3 \cdot \sqrt{x} \cdot \sqrt{y} = 6\sqrt{xy}$.

PROCEDURE. To multiply two monomial square roots:

1. Multiply the coefficients to find the coefficient of the product.
2. Multiply the radicands to find the radicand of the product.
3. If possible, simplify the result.

MODEL PROBLEMS

Multiply:

1. $\sqrt{8} \cdot \sqrt{2} = \sqrt{16} = 4$.

2. $3\sqrt{6} \cdot 5\sqrt{2} = 15\sqrt{12} = 15\sqrt{4} \cdot \sqrt{3} = 15 \cdot 2\sqrt{3} = 30\sqrt{3}$.

3. $(2\sqrt{3})^2 = 2\sqrt{3} \cdot 2\sqrt{3} = 4\sqrt{9} = 4 \cdot 3 = 12$.

4. $\sqrt{3x} \cdot \sqrt{6x} = \sqrt{18x^2} = \sqrt{9x^2} \cdot \sqrt{2} = 3x\sqrt{2}$.

EXERCISES

In 1–27, multiply the radicals or square the radical as indicated in the exercise.

1. $\sqrt{12} \cdot \sqrt{3}$	**2.** $\sqrt{32} \cdot \sqrt{2}$	**3.** $2\sqrt{18} \cdot 3\sqrt{8}$
4. $\sqrt{2} \cdot \sqrt{3}$	**5.** $2\sqrt{2} \cdot 4\sqrt{3}$	**6.** $3\sqrt{3} \cdot \sqrt{6}$
7. $(\sqrt{2})^2$	**8.** $(\sqrt{3})^2$	**9.** $(\sqrt{8})^2$
10. $(\sqrt{5})^2$	**11.** $(\sqrt{7})^2$	**12.** $(\sqrt{11})^2$
13. $(4\sqrt{2})^2$	**14.** $(7\sqrt{2})^2$	**15.** $(\frac{1}{2}\sqrt{2})^2$
16. $(3\sqrt{3})^2$	**17.** $(5\sqrt{3})^2$	**18.** $(\frac{1}{3}\sqrt{3})^2$
19. $(\sqrt{x})^2$	**20.** $(\sqrt{2x})^2$	**21.** $\left(\sqrt{\frac{x}{2}}\right)^2$
22. $(\sqrt{ab})^2$	**23.** $(\sqrt{2cd})^2$	**24.** $(\sqrt{3xy})^2$
25. $(s\sqrt{2})^2$	**26.** $\left(\frac{s}{2}\sqrt{2}\right)^2$	**27.** $\left(\frac{s}{2}\sqrt{3}\right)^2$

20. Rationalizing a Monomial Radical Denominator Which Is Irrational

When the denominator of a fraction is a radical which is an irrational number, changing the fraction to an equivalent fraction whose denominator is a rational number is called *rationalizing the denominator* of the fraction.

PROCEDURE. To rationalize a monomial radical denominator, transform the fraction into an equivalent fraction which has a rational denominator by multiplying both the numerator and the denominator of the given fraction by the least radical which will make its denominator a rational number.

MODEL PROBLEMS

Rationalize the denominator:

1. $\dfrac{12}{\sqrt{2}} = \dfrac{12}{\sqrt{2}} \cdot \dfrac{\sqrt{2}}{\sqrt{2}} = \dfrac{12\sqrt{2}}{\sqrt{4}} = \dfrac{12\sqrt{2}}{2} = 6\sqrt{2}.$ $\dfrac{\sqrt{2}}{\sqrt{2}} = 1$

2. $\dfrac{4}{\sqrt{12}} = \dfrac{4}{\sqrt{12}} \cdot \dfrac{\sqrt{3}}{\sqrt{3}} = \dfrac{4\sqrt{3}}{\sqrt{36}} = \dfrac{4\sqrt{3}}{6} = \dfrac{2\sqrt{3}}{3}$ or $\dfrac{2}{3}\sqrt{3}.$ $\dfrac{\sqrt{3}}{\sqrt{3}} = 1$

EXERCISES

In 1–15, rationalize the denominator and simplify the resulting fraction.

1. $\dfrac{1}{\sqrt{2}}$ **2.** $\dfrac{1}{\sqrt{3}}$ **3.** $\dfrac{1}{\sqrt{5}}$ **4.** $\dfrac{3}{\sqrt{2}}$ **5.** $\dfrac{2}{\sqrt{3}}$

6. $\dfrac{4}{\sqrt{2}}$ **7.** $\dfrac{9}{\sqrt{3}}$ **8.** $\dfrac{10}{\sqrt{5}}$ **9.** $\dfrac{12}{\sqrt{8}}$ **10.** $\dfrac{36}{\sqrt{12}}$

11. $\dfrac{1}{\sqrt{x}}$ **12.** $\dfrac{ab}{\sqrt{b}}$ **13.** $\dfrac{\sqrt{s}}{\sqrt{2}}$ **14.** $\dfrac{9}{\sqrt{3h}}$ **15.** $\dfrac{\sqrt{2s}}{\sqrt{g}}$

In 16–20, find the value of the fraction correct to the *nearest tenth*.

16. $\dfrac{12}{\sqrt{3}}$ **17.** $\dfrac{4}{\sqrt{2}}$ **18.** $\dfrac{5}{\sqrt{3}}$ **19.** $\dfrac{3}{\sqrt{2}}$ **20.** $\dfrac{8}{\sqrt{8}}$

21. Solving Quadratic Equations Using Factoring

A polynomial equation in which the highest exponent of the variable that appears is 2 is called a *quadratic equation*. $x^2 + 5x + 4 = 0$ is a quadratic equation. Such an equation is of the *second degree*.

When all the terms of a quadratic equation in one variable have been collected on one side of the equation and 0 appears on the other side, the quadratic equation is in *standard form*. For example, $x^2 - 2x - 3 = 0$ is in standard form. The equation $x^2 + 3x = 40$ is not in standard form. However, it can be transformed into an equivalent equation, $x^2 + 3x - 40 = 0$, which is in standard form.

In general, the standard form of a quadratic equation in one variable is

$$ax^2 + bx + c = 0$$

where a, b, and c are constants and a is not zero.

If the product of two factors is zero, then at least one of the factors is zero.

Thus, if $(x - 5)(x - 2) = 0$, then $x - 5 = 0$ or $x - 2 = 0$.

PROCEDURE. To solve a quadratic equation using factoring:

1. If necessary, transform the equation into standard form by removing parentheses, clearing fractions and combining like terms in the left member, and making the right member zero.
2. Factor the left member of the equation.
3. Set each factor containing the variable equal to zero.
4. Solve each of the resulting equations.
5. Check by substituting each value of the variable in the original equation.

NOTE. Every quadratic equation has two roots which may be equal or may be unequal.

MODEL PROBLEMS

1. Solve: $x^2 - 2x - 15 = 0$.

Solution:

1. $x^2 - 2x - 15 = 0$
2. $(x - 5)(x + 3) = 0$
3. $x - 5 = 0$ | $x + 3 = 0$
4. $x = 5$ $x = -3$

Answer: $x = 5$ and $x = -3$, or solution set is $\{5, -3\}$.

The check is left to the student. Note that the value $x = 5$ and the value $x = -3$ must be checked individually.

2. Solve: $x(x + 2) = 24$.

Solution:

1. $x(x + 2) = 24$
2. $x^2 + 2x = 24$
3. $x^2 + 2x - 24 = 0$
4. $(x - 4)(x + 6) = 0$
5. $x - 4 = 0$ | $x + 6 = 0$
6. $x = 4$ $x = -6$

Answer: $x = 4$ and $x = -6$, or solution set is $\{4, -6\}$.

The check is left to the student.

EXERCISES

In 1–33, solve and check the equation.

1. $x^2 - 3x + 2 = 0$	**2.** $y^2 - 7y + 6 = 0$	**3.** $z^2 - 5z + 4 = 0$
4. $x^2 - 8x + 16 = 0$	**5.** $p^2 - 8p + 12 = 0$	**6.** $r^2 - 12r + 35 = 0$
7. $x^2 - 4x - 5 = 0$	**8.** $x^2 - x - 12 = 0$	**9.** $y^2 - 3y - 10 = 0$
10. $x^2 - 49 = 0$	**11.** $x^2 - 81 = 0$	**12.** $3x^2 - 12 = 0$
13. $x^2 - 2x = 0$	**14.** $y^2 - 5y = 0$	**15.** $x^2 - x = 0$
16. $x^2 - x = 6$	**17.** $y^2 - 12 = 4y$	**18.** $x^2 = 14 - 5x$
19. $r^2 = 4$	**20.** $x^2 = 25$	**21.** $3x^2 = 27$
22. $x^2 + 9 = 25$	**23.** $x^2 + 64 = 100$	**24.** $144 + y^2 = 169$
25. $x^2 = 9x - 20$	**26.** $30 + x = x^2$	**27.** $6 + x = x^2$
28. $x^2 + 3x - 4 = 50$	**29.** $x^2 - 8x + 28 = 3x$	**30.** $x^2 + 5x - 15 = 3x$
31. $\dfrac{16}{y} = \dfrac{y}{4}$	**32.** $x = \dfrac{40}{x - 3}$	**33.** $\dfrac{x}{3} = \dfrac{8}{x + 2}$

22. Solving Incomplete Quadratic Equations

An *incomplete quadratic equation,* or *pure quadratic equation,* is a quadratic equation which contains the second power of the variable, but not the first power. Thus, $x^2 - 49 = 0$ is an incomplete, or pure, quadratic equation.

PROCEDURE. To solve an incomplete quadratic equation:

1. If necessary, clear fractions and remove parentheses.
2. Collect all terms containing the square of the variable (x^2) on one side of the equation; collect all other terms (the constants) on the other side of the equation.
3. Divide both members of the equation by the coefficient of the square of the variable (the coefficient of x^2).
4. Take the square root of both members of the equation. Since every positive number has both a positive square root and a negative square root, place a $\pm$ sign in front of the square root of the constant (the known number).
5. Check the resulting values by substituting them in the original equation.

MODEL PROBLEMS

1. Solve: $x^2 + 64 = 100$

2. Solve for x, correct to the *nearest tenth:* $4x^2 = x^2 + 36$

Solution:

1. $x^2 + 64 = 100$
2. $\quad\quad x^2 = 100 - 64$
3. $\quad\quad x^2 = 36$
4. $\quad\quad x = \pm 6$

Solution:

1. $\quad\quad 4x^2 = x^2 + 36$
2. $4x^2 - x^2 = 36$
3. $\quad\quad 3x^2 = 36$
4. $\quad\quad x^2 = 12$
5. $x = \pm\sqrt{12}$
6. $x = \pm 2\sqrt{3} = \pm 2(1.73) = \pm 3.46$
7. $x = \pm 3.5$ to the nearest tenth

Answer: $x = +6$, $x = -6$, or solution set is $\{+6, -6\}$.

The check is left to the student.

Answer: $x = +3.5$, $x = -3.5$, or solution set is $\{+3.5, -3.5\}$.

The check is left to the student. Since 3.5 and −3.5 are round numbers, the check will be approximate.

EXERCISES

In 1–15, solve the equation.

1. $x^2 = 4$ **2.** $y^2 = 49$ **3.** $z^2 = 100$

4. $x^2 - 64 = 0$ **5.** $a^2 - 25 = 0$ **6.** $b^2 - 36 = 0$

7. $3x^2 = 12$ **8.** $5y^2 = 45$ **9.** $3m^2 = 243$

10. $x^2 + 9 = 25$ **11.** $x^2 + 25 = 169$ **12.** $x^2 + 576 = 625$

13. $100 - x^2 = 64$ **14.** $169 - x^2 = 144$ **15.** $225 - x^2 = 81$

In 16–27, solve for x. Give answer in simplest radical form.

16. $x^2 = 3$ **17.** $x^2 = 10$ **18.** $x^2 = 12$

19. $x^2 = 72$ **20.** $3x^2 = 6$ **21.** $3x^2 = 81$

22. $4x^2 - x^2 = 36$ **23.** $4x^2 = x^2 + 144$ **24.** $4x^2 = 16 + x^2$

25. $\dfrac{x}{5} = \dfrac{4}{x}$ **26.** $\dfrac{x}{8} = \dfrac{6}{2x}$ **27.** $\dfrac{x+2}{4} = \dfrac{2}{x-2}$

In 28–39, solve for the positive value of x, correct to the *nearest tenth*.

28. $x^2 = 18$ **29.** $x^2 = 32$ **30.** $x^2 = 27$

31. $3x^2 = 36$ **32.** $2x^2 = 16$ **33.** $2x^2 = 100$

34. $x^2 + x^2 = 64$ **35.** $4x^2 - x^2 = 81$ **36.** $4x^2 = x^2 + 144$

37. $x^2 + 9 = 36$ **38.** $x^2 + 16 = 64$ **39.** $x^2 - 16 = 16$

In 40–45, solve for x.

40. $x^2 = b^2$ **41.** $x^2 = 25a^2$ **42.** $9x^2 = r^2$

43. $4x^2 - a^2 = 15a^2$ **44.** $x^2 + a^2 = c^2 \ (c > a)$ **45.** $x^2 + b^2 = c^2 \ (c > b)$

46. Solve for s: $s^2 = A \ (A > 0)$

47. Solve for r: $A = \pi r^2 \ (A > 0)$

23. Solving Quadratic Equations by Formula

Every quadratic equation can be written in the form $ax^2 + bx + c = 0$, a not being zero.

The roots of this equation can be represented by the following formulas:

$$\text{root } 1 = \frac{-b + \sqrt{b^2 - 4ac}}{2a} \qquad \text{root } 2 = \frac{-b - \sqrt{b^2 - 4ac}}{2a}$$

These formulas may be written together in the following form, which is often called the *quadratic formula:*

$$x = \frac{-b \pm \sqrt{b^2 - 4ac}}{2a}$$

PROCEDURE. To solve a quadratic equation by the quadratic formula:

1. Transform the given equation into an equivalent equation of the form $ax^2 + bx + c = 0$ by collecting all terms in the left member and making the right member zero.

2. Compare the resulting equation with the general equation

$$ax^2 + bx + c = 0,$$

to determine the values of a, b, and c.

3. Substitute these values in the quadratic formula:

$$x = \frac{-b \pm \sqrt{b^2 - 4ac}}{2a}$$

4. Perform the necessary arithmetic to find the values of x.

MODEL PROBLEM

Solve for x, correct to the *nearest tenth*: $2x^2 - 3x = 4$

Solution:

1. $2x^2 - 3x = 4$

2. Transforming the equation into standard form: $2x^2 - 3x - 4 = 0$

3. Comparing with $ax^2 + bx + c = 0$: $a = 2$, $b = -3$, $c = -4$

4. Quadratic formula is $x = \dfrac{-b \pm \sqrt{b^2 - 4ac}}{2a}$

5. Substituting: $x = \dfrac{-(-3) \pm \sqrt{(-3)^2 - 4(2)(-4)}}{2(2)}$

6. $\qquad\qquad x = \dfrac{3 \pm \sqrt{9 + 32}}{4}$

7. $\qquad\qquad x = \dfrac{3 \pm \sqrt{41}}{4}$

8. $\qquad\qquad x = \dfrac{3 \pm 6.40}{4}$

9. $x = \dfrac{3 + 6.40}{4}$ $\qquad$ $x = \dfrac{3 - 6.40}{4}$

10. $x = \dfrac{9.40}{4} = 2.35$ $\qquad$ $x = \dfrac{-3.40}{4} = -.85$

11. $x = 2.4$ $\qquad\qquad$ $x = -.9$

Answer: $x = 2.4$, $x = -.9$, or solution set is $\{2.4, -.9\}$.

```
              6. 4  0
        √ 41. 00 00
          36
   124  | 500
        | 496
  1280  | 400
        |   0
        | 400
```

EXERCISES

In 1–12, solve the equation by using the quadratic formula. Express irrational roots in simplest radical form.

1. $x^2 + 2x - 24 = 0$ $\qquad$ **2.** $x^2 - 9x + 20 = 0$ $\qquad$ **3.** $x^2 - 6x + 9 = 0$

4. $x^2 + 12 = 7x$ $\qquad$ **5.** $x^2 - 30 = x$ $\qquad$ **6.** $x^2 = 5x + 14$

7. $2x^2 - 5x + 2 = 0$ $\qquad$ **8.** $3x^2 - 10x + 3 = 0$ $\qquad$ **9.** $5x^2 = 3x + 2$

10. $x^2 - 4x + 1 = 0$ $\qquad$ **11.** $x^2 + 5x = 2$ $\qquad$ **12.** $2x^2 = 6x - 1$

In 13–24, find, correct to the *nearest tenth*, the roots of the equation.

13. $x^2 + 3x - 3 = 0$ $\qquad$ **14.** $y^2 - 4y + 2 = 0$ $\qquad$ **15.** $2c^2 - 7c + 1 = 0$

16. $x^2 + 2x - 4 = 0$ $\qquad$ **17.** $3x^2 - 2x - 6 = 0$ $\qquad$ **18.** $2x^2 - 8x + 1 = 0$

19. $3x^2 + 5x - 1 = 0$ $\qquad$ **20.** $2x^2 + 4x = 3$ $\qquad$ **21.** $2x^2 - 10x = 9$

22. $2x^2 - 2x = 3$ $\qquad$ **23.** $x^2 = 20x + 10$ $\qquad$ **24.** $x^2 = 12 - 9x$

Squares and Square Roots

No.	Square	Square Root	No.	Square	Square Root	No.	Square	Square Root
1	1	1.000	51	2,601	7.141	101	10,201	10.050
2	4	1.414	52	2,704	7.211	102	10,404	10.100
3	9	1.732	53	2,809	7.280	103	10,609	10.149
4	16	2.000	54	2,916	7.348	104	10,816	10.198
5	25	2.236	55	3,025	7.416	105	11,025	10.247
6	36	2.449	56	3,136	7.483	106	11,236	10.296
7	49	2.646	57	3,249	7.550	107	11,449	10.344
8	64	2.828	58	3,364	7.616	108	11,664	10.392
9	81	3.000	59	3,481	7.681	109	11,881	10.440
10	100	3.162	60	3,600	7.746	110	12,100	10.488
11	121	3.317	61	3,721	7.810	111	12,321	10.536
12	144	3.464	62	3,844	7.874	112	12,544	10.583
13	169	3.606	63	3,969	7.937	113	12,769	10.630
14	196	3.742	64	4,096	8.000	114	12,996	10.677
15	225	3.873	65	4,225	8.062	115	13,225	10.724
16	256	4.000	66	4,356	8.124	116	13,456	10.770
17	289	4.123	67	4,489	8.185	117	13,689	10.817
18	324	4.243	68	4,624	8.246	118	13,924	10.863
19	361	4.359	69	4,761	8.307	119	14,161	10.909
20	400	4.472	70	4,900	8.367	120	14,400	10.954
21	441	4.583	71	5,041	8.426	121	14,641	11.000
22	484	4.690	72	5,184	8.485	122	14,884	11.045
23	529	4.796	73	5,329	8.544	123	15,129	11.091
24	576	4.899	74	5,476	8.602	124	15,376	11.136
25	625	5.000	75	5,625	8.660	125	15,625	11.180
26	676	5.099	76	5,776	8.718	126	15,876	11.225
27	729	5.196	77	5,929	8.775	127	16,129	11.269
28	784	5.292	78	6,084	8.832	128	16,384	11.314
29	841	5.385	79	6,241	8.888	129	16,641	11.358
30	900	5.477	80	6,400	8.944	130	16,900	11.402
31	961	5.568	81	6,561	9.000	131	17,161	11.446
32	1,024	5.657	82	6,724	9.055	132	17,424	11.489
33	1,089	5.745	83	6,889	9.110	133	17,689	11.533
34	1,156	5.831	84	7,056	9.165	134	17,956	11.576
35	1,225	5.916	85	7,225	9.220	135	18,225	11.619
36	1,296	6.000	86	7,396	9.274	136	18,496	11.662
37	1,369	6.083	87	7,569	9.327	137	18,769	11.705
38	1,444	6.164	88	7,744	9.381	138	19,044	11.747
39	1,521	6.245	89	7,921	9.434	139	19,321	11.790
40	1,600	6.325	90	8,100	9.487	140	19,600	11.832
41	1,681	6.403	91	8,281	9.539	141	19,881	11.874
42	1,764	6.481	92	8,464	9.592	142	20,164	11.916
43	1,849	6.557	93	8,649	9.644	143	20,449	11.958
44	1,936	6.633	94	8,836	9.695	144	20,736	12.000
45	2,025	6.708	95	9,025	9.747	145	21,025	12.042
46	2,116	6.782	96	9,216	9.798	146	21,316	12.083
47	2,209	6.856	97	9,409	9.849	147	21,609	12.124
48	2,304	6.928	98	9,604	9.899	148	21,904	12.166
49	2,401	7.000	99	9,801	9.950	149	22,201	12.207
50	2,500	7.071	100	10,000	10.000	150	22,500	12.247

Values of the Trigonometric Functions

Angle	Sine	Cosine	Tangent	Angle	Sine	Cosine	Tangent
1°	.0175	.9998	.0175	46°	.7193	.6947	1.0355
2°	.0349	.9994	.0349	47°	.7314	.6820	1.0724
3°	.0523	.9986	.0524	48°	.7431	.6691	1.1106
4°	.0698	.9976	.0699	49°	.7547	.6561	1.1504
5°	.0872	.9962	.0875	50°	.7660	.6428	1.1918
6°	.1045	.9945	.1051	51°	.7771	.6293	1.2349
7°	.1219	.9925	.1228	52°	.7880	.6157	1.2799
8°	.1392	.9903	.1405	53°	.7986	.6018	1.3270
9°	.1564	.9877	.1584	54°	.8090	.5878	1.3764
10°	.1736	.9848	.1763	55°	.8192	.5736	1.4281
11°	.1908	.9816	.1944	56°	.8290	.5592	1.4826
12°	.2079	.9781	.2126	57°	.8387	.5446	1.5399
13°	.2250	.9744	.2309	58°	.8480	.5299	1.6003
14°	.2419	.9703	.2493	59°	.8572	.5150	1.6643
15°	.2588	.9659	.2679	60°	.8660	.5000	1.7321
16°	.2756	.9613	.2867	61°	.8746	.4848	1.8040
17°	.2924	.9563	.3057	62°	.8829	.4695	1.8807
18°	.3090	.9511	.3249	63°	.8910	.4540	1.9626
19°	.3256	.9455	.3443	64°	.8988	.4384	2.0503
20°	.3420	.9397	.3640	65°	.9063	.4226	2.1445
21°	.3584	.9336	.3839	66°	.9135	.4067	2.2460
22°	.3746	.9272	.4040	67°	.9205	.3907	2.3559
23°	.3907	.9205	.4245	68°	.9272	.3746	2.4751
24°	.4067	.9135	.4452	69°	.9336	.3584	2.6051
25°	.4226	.9063	.4663	70°	.9397	.3420	2.7475
26°	.4384	.8988	.4877	71°	.9455	.3256	2.9042
27°	.4540	.8910	.5095	72°	.9511	.3090	3.0777
28°	.4695	.8829	.5317	73°	.9563	.2924	3.2709
29°	.4848	.8746	.5543	74°	.9613	.2756	3.4874
30°	.5000	.8660	.5774	75°	.9659	.2588	3.7321
31°	.5150	.8572	.6009	76°	.9703	.2419	4.0108
32°	.5299	.8480	.6249	77°	.9744	.2250	4.3315
33°	.5446	.8387	.6494	78°	.9781	.2079	4.7046
34°	.5592	.8290	.6745	79°	.9816	.1908	5.1446
35°	.5736	.8192	.7002	80°	.9848	.1736	5.6713
36°	.5878	.8090	.7265	81°	.9877	.1564	6.3138
37°	.6018	.7986	.7536	82°	.9903	.1392	7.1154
38°	.6157	.7880	.7813	83°	.9925	.1219	8.1443
39°	.6293	.7771	.8098	84°	.9945	.1045	9.5144
40°	.6428	.7660	.8391	85°	.9962	.0872	11.4301
41°	.6561	.7547	.8693	86°	.9976	.0698	14.3007
42°	.6691	.7431	.9004	87°	.9986	.0523	19.0811
43°	.6820	.7314	.9325	88°	.9994	.0349	28.6363
44°	.6947	.7193	.9657	89°	.9998	.0175	57.2900
45°	.7071	.7071	1.0000	90°	1.0000	.0000	

INDEX

Index